DIGITAL SPECTRAL ANALYSIS

PRENTICE-HALL SIGNAL PROCESSING SERIES

Alan V. Oppenheim, Editor

DIGITAL
SPECTRAL
ANALYSIS

WITH APPLICATIONS

S. Lawrence Marple Jr.

Martin Marietta Aerospace
Baltimore, Maryland

PRENTICE–HALL, INC., Englewood Cliffs, New Jersey 07632

Library of Congress Cataloging-in-Publication Data

MARPLE, S. LAWRENCE, JR.
    Digital spectral analysis.

    Bibliography:
    Includes index.
    1. Spectral theory (Mathematics)   2. Signal
processing—Digital techniques.   I. Title.
QA280.M38   1987   519.5′5   86-9391
ISBN 0-13-214149-3

Cover design: 20/20 Services, Inc.
Manufacturing buyer: Gordon Osbourne

If your diskette is defective or damaged in transit, return it directly to Prentice-Hall at the address below for a no-charge replacement within 90 days of the date of purchase. Mail the defective diskette together with your name and address.

Prentice-Hall, Inc.
Attention: Ryan Colby
College Operations
Englewood Cliffs, NJ 07632

LIMITS OF LIABILITY AND DISCLAIMER OF WARRANTY:

The author and publisher of this book have used their best efforts in preparing this book and software. These efforts include the development, research, and testing of the theories and programs to determine their effectiveness. The author and publisher make no warranty of any kind, expressed or implied, with regard to these programs or the documentation contained in this book. The author and publisher shall not be liable in any event for incidental or consequential damages in connection with, or arising out of, the furnishing, performance, or use of these programs.

PRENTICE-HALL INTERNATIONAL (UK) LIMITED, *London*
PRENTICE-HALL OF AUSTRALIA PTY. LIMITED, *Sydney*
EDITORA PRENTICE-HALL DO BRASIL LTDA., *Rio de Janeiro*
PRENTICE-HALL CANADA INC., *Toronto*
PRENTICE-HALL HISPANOAMERICANA, S.A., *Mexico*
PRENTICE-HALL OF INDIA PRIVATE LIMITED, *New Delhi*
PRENTICE-HALL OF JAPAN, INC., *Toyko*
PRENTICE-HALL OF SOUTHEAST ASIA PTE. LTD., *Singapore*

To Susi, Darci, Rebecca, and Matthew
For their love and patience during the past six years.

CONTENTS

4 REVIEW OF RANDOM PROCESS THEORY   111

5 CLASSICAL SPECTRAL ESTIMATION   130

6 PARAMETRIC MODELS OF RANDOM PROCESSES   172

7 AUTOREGRESSIVE PROCESS AND SPECTRUM PROPERTIES   189

8 AUTOREGRESSIVE SPECTRAL ESTIMATION: BLOCK DATA ALGORITHMS   206

9 AUTOREGRESSIVE SPECTRAL ESTIMATION: SEQUENTIAL DATA ALGORITHMS   261

10 AUTOREGRESSIVE–MOVING AVERAGE SPECTRAL ESTIMATION
285

11 PRONY'S METHOD
303

12 MINIMUM VARIANCE SPECTRAL ESTIMATION
350

13 EIGENANALYSIS-BASED FREQUENCY ESTIMATION 361

14 SUMMARY OF SPECTRAL ESTIMATORS 379

15 MULTICHANNEL SPECTRAL ESTIMATION 386

NOTATIONAL CONVENTIONS

- Parentheses enclose the argument of a continuous function.

  Examples: $x(t)$

- Brackets enclose the argument of a discrete function.

  Examples: $y[n]$

- Scalar variables and scalar functions are denoted by lowercase Latin and Greek letters.

  Examples: $\alpha \quad r_{xx}(\tau)$

- Transforms (Fourier, z) are denoted by uppercase Latin and Greek letters. Transforms of scalar functions will use the corresponding uppercase letter for its transform.

Time Function	Transform
$x(t)$	$X(f)$
$y[n]$	$Y(z)$

  Exceptions: F—Frequency sampling interval (scalar)
  N—Number of samples (scalar)
  T—Time sampling interval (scalar)

- Vectors are denoted by lowercase bold Latin and Greek letters.

  Examples: $\mathbf{d} \quad \boldsymbol{\gamma}$

- Block vectors are denoted by underlined lowercase bold Latin and Greek letters.

  Examples: $\underline{\mathbf{c}} \quad \underline{\boldsymbol{\delta}}$

- Matrices are denoted by uppercase bold Latin and Greek letters.

  Examples: $\mathbf{A} \quad \boldsymbol{\Phi}$

- Block matrices are denoted by underlined uppercase bold Latin and Greek letters.

  Examples: $\underline{\mathbf{B}} \quad \underline{\boldsymbol{\Gamma}}$

- Special notation:
    - T Vector and matrix tranposition
    - H Vector and matrix complex conjugate transposition
    - $*$ Scalar, vector, and matrix complex conjugation
    - $\star$ Convolution operator
    - $\hat{x}$ Hat denotes an estimate (of x in this case)

GLOSSARY OF KEY SYMBOLS

$a_p[k]$	Parameter of pth-order autoregression at time index k
$a_p^b[k]$	Coefficient of pth-order backward linear prediction at time index k
$a_p^f[k]$	Coefficient of pth-order forward linear prediction at time index k
ACS	Autocorrelation sequence
AIC	Akaike information criterion
AR	Autoregressive
ARMA	Autoregressive–moving average
B_e	Equivalent bandwidth in hertz
B_s	Effective statistical bandwidth in hertz
$b_q[k]$	Parameter of qth-order moving average at time index k
$c_{xx}[m]$	Autocovariance of discrete process $x[n]$ at lag m
$c_{xy}[m]$	Crosscovariance of discrete processes $x[n]$ and $y[n]$ at lag m
CCS	Cross correlation sequence
$\mathrm{cov}\{xy\}$	Covariance between random variables x and y
CTFS	Continuous-time Fourier series
CTFT	Continuous-time Fourier transform
$\det \mathbf{A}$	Determinant of matrix $\mathbf{A}$
DTFS	Discrete-time Fourier series
DTFT	Discrete-time Fourier transform
E	Signal energy or squared error energy
$\mathcal{E}\{x[n]\}$	Expectation operation on random process $x[n]$
$\mathbf{e}(f)$	Complex sinusoid vector
$e_p^b[k]$	Backward linear prediction error at pth order
$e_p^f[k]$	Forward linear prediction error at pth order
ESD	Energy spectral density
$\mathcal{F}\{x(t)\} = X(f)$	Continuous Fourier transform of continuous-time signal $x(t)$
$\mathcal{F}^{-1}\{X(f)\} = x(t)$	Inverse continuous Fourier transform of $X(f)$
f	Frequency in hertz
F	Frequency sampling interval in hertz
FFT	Fast Fourier transform
h	Entropy rate
$\mathbf{I}$	Identity matrix
$\mathrm{Im}\{x\}$	Imaginary part of complex variable x
j	Imaginary constant, $\sqrt{-1}$
$\mathbf{J}$	Reflection (exchange) matrix
$k_p = a_p[p]$	Reflection coefficient at order p
MA	Moving average
MEM	Maximum entropy method
MLE	Maximum likelihood estimate
MV	Minimum variance (spectrum)
$\mathrm{mse}\{x\}$	Mean square error of random variable x

n	Discrete time or space index
N	Number of data samples
p	Autoregressive model order
$p(x)$	Probability density function of random variable x
$P_{xx}(f)$	Power spectral density
$P_{xy}(f)$	Cross power spectral density
$P_{xx}[m]$	Discrete power spectral density
PDF	Probability density function
PSD	Power spectral density
q	Moving average model order
Q	Statistical quality ratio of var/mean^2
$r_{xx}[m]$	Autocorrelation sequence at lag m
$r_{xy}[m]$	Cross correlation sequence at lag m
$\mathbf{R}_p$	Autocorrelation matrix composed of $r_{xx}[0]$ to $r_{xx}[p]$
$\mathrm{Re}\{x\}$	Real part of complex variable x
s	Continuous space variable (units of ft, m, km, etc.)
S	Spatial sampling interval
$S_{xx}(f)$	Energy spectral density
$S_{xx}[m]$	Discrete energy spectral density
SVD	Singular value decomposition
t	Continuous time variable (units of seconds)
$\mathrm{tr}\,\mathbf{A}$	Trace of matrix $\mathbf{A}$
T	Temporal sampling interval in seconds
$\mathbf{T}$	Toeplitz matrix
T_e	Equivalent time width in seconds
TBP	Time-bandwidth product
$\mathbf{v}_i$	Eigenvector i
$\mathrm{var}\{x\}$	Variance of random variable x
$x[n]$	Discrete time (or space) function
$x(t)$	Continuous time (or space) function
$u[n]$	Driving noise random process
WSS	Wide-sense stationary
z	Complex variable
$\mathcal{Z}\{h[n]\} = \mathsf{H}(z)$	z-transform of $h[n]$
$\mathcal{Z}^{-1}\{\mathsf{H}(z)\} = h[n]$	Inverse z-transform of $\mathsf{H}(z)$
$\mathbf{0}_m$	Vector of m zero elements
$\delta(t)$	Continuous delta function
$\delta[n]$	Discrete delta function
λ_i	Eigenvalue i
ρ^b	Backward linear prediction squared error (variance)
ρ^f	Forward linear prediction squared error (variance)
ρ^{fb}	Forward plus backward linear prediction squared error (variance)
ρ_w	Variance of white noise process $w[n]$
$\mathrm{III}\,(t)$	Sampling function

PREFACE

The idea for a text on digital spectral estimation evolved from discussions during the 1979 IEEE International Conference on Acoustics, Speech, and Signal Processing in Washington, D.C. It was clear to the author at that time that a unifying treatment of both old and new methods of spectral estimation was needed for a variety of reasons. Nearly two decades have passed since the last classic text on spectral estimation was written by Jenkins and Watts in 1968. Newer spectral estimation approaches have since been developed independently in various application fields, leading to a diversity of terminology to often describe similar concepts. There has been a dramatic increase in spectral estimation research activity for a decade prior to this text within the digital signal processing community. The primary motivation has apparently been the development of techniques for enhanced spectral resolution, particularly for short data sequences. The casual reader of the recent technical literature is confronted with a bewildering assortment of performance claims. It seems, therefore, timely to clear away the smoke and take a more objective perspective of the current state of spectral estimation. The first attempt at unification appeared as a tutorial coauthored with S. M. Kay in the November 1981 issue of the *IEEE Proceedings*.

This author has received numerous requests since the publication of the tutorial paper in the *Proceedings* for computer programs of various spectral estimation methods. This response has led to the inclusion of numerous program listings in the text. This text not only permits an opportunity to provide greater depth of detail than can be written for a journal paper, but it also allows the inclusion of more advanced topics which could not be included in the *Proceedings* tutorial.

Spectral estimation has for several decades been a traditional research area for statisticians. The introduction of the digital fast Fourier transform (FFT) algorithm two decades ago, however, has expanded the role of spectral estimation from one of research novelty to one of practical utility. The digital signal processing community has, as a result, taken an ever-increasing interest in spectral estimation research and applications.

The goal of this book is to provide a broad perspective of spectral estimation techniques and their implementation. As a result, the reader will not encounter as much statistical depth as commonly found in more theoretical treatments of spectral estimation. The practice of spectral estimation with finite data sets is not an exact science; a great deal of experimentation and subjective trade-off is usually required. There is little statistical guidance on which to rely; most statistical analyses make very restrictive assumptions about the nature of the data (e.g., the noise component of the signal is white and Gaussian) and usually apply only to the asymptotic case; that is, the data set is permitted to grow to infinite size. The practice of spectral estimation, therefore, has more of an empirical basis and less of a solid theoretical basis. It is not surprising that new spectral estimation methods are often promoted in the literature with subjective evaluation based on limited test cases, appealing more to spectral estimators that make a good visual impression when plotted and less to spectral estimators that demonstrate good statistical behavior. No position has been taken in this text on the relative superiority of any of the techniques. What has been done is to provide the algorithms necessary for calculation of various spectral estimators and to highlight the trade-offs that should be considered for each method. Readers may then decide for themselves whether one method or another is better for their application. Further insight and a more thorough statistical treatment of many of the methods of this book may be found in *Modern Spectral Estimation* by S. M. Kay (Prentice-Hall, 1987).

A motivation for the interest in several of the methods presented in this text is the apparent high-resolution performance that can be achieved for data sequences of very limited number of samples. A major emphasis, therefore, is the behavior of each spectral estimator for short data sets. A short data sequence is one in which the spectral resolution required is of the same order as the reciprocal sequence length. Another emphasis area of this text is that of fast algorithms. A fast algorithm is a nonobvious computational procedure that is more computationally efficient than the obvious procedure. Just as the fast Fourier transform (FFT) algorithm made classical spectral analysis practical, fast algorithms have also been developed to reduce the computational burden for many of the alternative spectral estimation methods. Without fast algorithms, more exotic methods of spectral estimation might not be considered for practical applications because of the high computational overhead.

This text is primarily concerned with spectral estimation of discrete-time or discrete-space sequences derived by sampling continuous-time or continuous-space signals. Uniform sampling is normally assumed. The spectral analysis is assumed performed by a digital computer or by digital circuitry. A strict distinction between digital signals and discrete signals is usually made in the literature. Discrete signals are signals represented as sequences of numbers, whose amplitudes are continuous. Digital signals are those for which both time (space) and amplitude are discrete. The title *Digital Spectral Analysis* was selected only to indicate that *digital* means of processing are to be used to compute the spectral estimates of *discrete* data sequences.

Prerequisites for this text include course material in discrete-time linear system and transform theory, such as that found in *Signals and Systems* by Oppenheim and Willsky (Prentice-Hall, 1983), introductory probability and statistics, such as that found in *Probability, Random Variables, and Stochastic Processes* by Papoulis (McGraw-Hill, 1984), and linear algebra, such as that found in *Applied Linear Algebra* by Noble and Daniel (Prentice-Hall, 1977). Although the text has been written with problems so that it can be used in a first-year graduate-level course, the chapters have been organized to facilitate the implementation of any spectral estimation technique. Concise summaries are provided at the beginning of each chapter for each spectral estimation technique, together with computer programs where appropriate. The intent is to enable minimal implementation effort for those interested only in application of a method. Theoretical details follow each summary for those interested and may be read after the reader has tried out the computer programs to gain some familiarity with a selected spectral estimator.

After a historical introduction in Chap. 1, Chaps. 2–4 provide the necessary theoretical background and review material in linear systems, Fourier transforms, matrix algebra, random processes, and statistics. Chapter 5 summarizes classical spectral estimation as it is practiced today. Chapter 6 provides the overview for parametric modeling approaches to spectral estimation. Specific parametric methods may be found in Chaps. 7–10 on autoregressive (AR), moving average (MA), and autoregressive–moving average (ARMA) spectral estimation. Prony's method, a close relative of the AR approach, is presented in Chap. 11. Nonparametric approaches to spectral estimation include the minimum variance method of Chap. 12 and the estimators based on eigenanalysis of Chap. 13. Chapter 14, which summarizes all of the methods in Chaps. 5–13, may serve as a starting place for those readers interested in selecting a spectral estimation technique for their application. A summary table in Chap. 14 will assist readers to focus on specific methods that may be appropriate for their application. Extensions of many of the methods presented in Chaps. 5–13 to multichannel and two-dimensional spectral estimation are developed in Chaps. 15 and 16, respectively.

The complex-valued data case is encountered frequently in digital signal processing. The output of fast Fourier transforms (FFT), complex demodulation processes, and inphase-quadrature processing are three examples of sources for complex-valued data. It is for this reason that the computer programs of this text have been developed to process complex-valued data. Readers with only real-valued data can convert any of the complex data algorithms to handle real-valued data by appropriate modifications to the programs. See Appendix IV for details of this conversion.

Great care has been taken to ensure that all spectral estimator expressions have the proper scaling factors to yield power spectral density in units of power per hertz. The dependence on the sample interval and the number of samples is particularly emphasized. Some books choose normalized definitions for spectral estimators that omit these important dependencies in order to simplify the mathematical descriptions.

Many of the references cited at the end of each chapter are available in the two IEEE Press reprint volumes *Modern Spectrum Analysis I*, edited by D. G. Childers [1978], and *Modern Spectrum Analysis II*, edited by S. Kesler [1986]. These two volumes provide supplementary details for many techniques that appear in this text.

This author wishes to acknowledge the very significant contributions and collaborations provided by my colleague Steven M. Kay of the University of Rhode Island. Very helpful reviews of the book manuscript were provided by Albert H. Nuttall, Steven W. Lang, Thomas W. Parks, Chrysostomos Nikias, Mos Kaveh, James H. McClellan, David Scheibner, Marc P. Mignolet, and Robert G. Currie. The author also wishes to thank Schlumberger Well Services and Martin Marietta Aerospace for use of the TEX computer typesetting facilities available on each company's VAX computer to prepare the entire manuscript.

S.L.M.   Baltimore, MD

COMMENTS ON THE ENCLOSED FLOPPY DISK

A floppy disk has been included with this text. It contains source codes of all 35 computer programs in the book, as listed in Appendix V. Filenames on the disk contain only the first eight letters of the subroutine names used in the book; for example, subroutine PERIODOGRAM has filename PERIODOG.FOR on the disk. One additional file, TESTDATA.LIS, is an ASCII listing of the 64 complex test data samples given in Appendix II. The disk has a double-sided 360 kB format readable by any personal computer with an MS-DOS 2 or 3 operating system, such as the IBM XT or AT. Questions regarding the software may be directed to the author's corporate address:

Martin Marietta Aerospace
Baltimore Division
103 Chesapeake Park Plaza
Baltimore, Maryland 21220

The same software is also available on 9-track tape for a fee; contact the author for availability.

1

INTRODUCTION

Spectral analysis is any signal processing method that characterizes the frequency content of a measured signal. The Fourier transform is the mathematical foundation for relating a time or space signal, or a model of this signal, to its frequency-domain representation. Statistics play a significant role in spectral analysis because most signals have a noisy or random aspect. If the underlying statistical attributes of a signal were known exactly or could be determined without error from a finite interval of the signal, then spectral analysis would be an exact science. The practical reality, however, is that only an *estimate* of the spectrum can be made from a single finite segment of the signal. As a result, the practice of spectral analysis since the 1880s has tended to be a subjective craft, using mostly science but requiring a degree of empirical art.

The difficulty of the spectral estimation problem is illustrated by Fig. 1.1. Two typical spectral estimates are shown in this figure, obtained by processing the same finite sample sequence by two different spectral estimation techniques. Each spectral plot represents the distribution of signal strength with frequency. A precise meaning of signal "strength" in terms of energy or energy per unit time (power) will be provided in Chaps. 2 and 4. The units of frequency, as adopted in this text, are either cycles per second (hertz) for temporal signals or cycles per meter (wavenumber) for spatial signals. Signal strength $P(f)$ at frequency f is typically plotted in units of decibels (dB) relative to the maximum spectral strength P_{max} over all frequencies, computed as $10\log_{10}[P(f)/P_{max}]$. The maximum strength plotted, therefore, will be 0 dB. The significant differences between the two spectral estimates may be attributed to differing assumptions made concerning the nature

Figure 1.1   Two different spectral estimates produced from the same measured data.

of the data and to the type of averaging used to account for the statistical impact of noise in the data. In a situation where no *a priori* knowledge of signal characteristics is available, one would find it difficult to select which of the two spectral estimates, if either, has represented the true underlying spectrum with better fidelity. It appears that estimate 1.1(b) has higher resolution than estimate 1.1(a), but this could be an artifact of the processing used to generate estimate 1.1(b), rather than actual detail that exists in the spectrum. This is the kind of uncertainty that arises in practice and that illustrates the subjective nature of spectral analysis.

Classical methods of spectral estimation have been well documented by several texts; the books by Blackman and Tukey [1958] and Jenkins and Watts [1968] are probably the two best known. Since the publication of these and related texts, there has been a growing interest in devising alternative spectral estimation methods that perform better for limited data sequences. In particular, new methods of spectral estimation have been promoted that yield apparent improvements in frequency resolution over that achievable with classical spectral estimates. Limited data sequences occur frequently in practice. For example, to study intrapulse modulation characteristics of a radar, only a few time samples may be taken from a single very short radar pulse. In sonar, many data samples are available, but target motion necessitates that the analysis interval be short in order to assume that the target statistics are effectively unchanging within the analysis interval. The emphasis in this book is on the new, or "modern," methods of spectral estimation that have evolved in the 15 years prior to this text. In this sense, this text supplements the classical spectral estimation material covered in earlier texts. All methods described in this text assume sampled digital data, in contrast to some earlier texts that considered only continuous data.

The intent of each chapter is to provide the reader with an understanding of the assumptions that are made concerning the method or methods. The beginning of each chapter summarizes the technique, or techniques, covered in that chapter, enabling scientists and engineers to implement readily a spectral estimator without being immersed in the theoretical details of the chapter. Some guidelines for applications are also provided. No attempt has been made to rank the spectral estimation methods with respect to each other. This text provides a variety of spectral estimation computer programs; users should probably apply several of the techniques to their experimental data. It may then be possible to extract a better understanding of the measured process from features common in all of the selected spectral estimates. For generality, complex-valued signals are assumed. The use of complex-valued signals is becoming more commonplace in digital signal processing systems. Appendix 2.B describes two common sources of complex-valued signals.

An illuminating perspective of spectral analysis may be obtained by studying its historical roots. Further insight may be developed by examining some of the issues of spectral estimation. Both topics are covered in the remaining sections of this chapter. A brief description of how to use this text concludes the chapter.

1.1 HISTORICAL PERSPECTIVE

Cyclic, or recurring, processes observed in natural phenomena have instilled in humans, since the earliest times, the basic concepts that are embedded to this day in modern spectral estimation. Without performing an explicit mathematical analysis, ancient civilizations were able to devise calendars and time measures from their observations of the *periodicities* in the length of the day, the length of the year, the seasonal changes, the phases of the moon, and the motion of other heavenly bodies such as planets. In the sixth century B.C., Pythagoras developed a relationship between the periodicity of pure sine vibrations of musical notes produced by a string of fixed tension and a number representing the length of the string. He believed that the essence of harmony was inherent in numbers. Pythagoras extended this empirical relationship to describe the *harmonic* motion of heavenly bodies, describing it as the "music of the spheres."

The mathematical basis for modern spectral estimation has its origins in the seventeenth-century work of the scientist Sir Isaac Newton. He observed that sunlight passing through a glass prism was expanded into a band of many colors. Thus, he discovered that each color represented a particular wavelength of light and that the white light of the sun contained all wavelengths. It was also Newton who introduced [1671] the word *spectrum* as a scientific term to describe this band of light colors. Spectrum is a variant of the Latin word "specter," meaning image or ghostly apparition. The adjective associated with spectrum is *spectral*. Thus, *spectral* estimation, rather than *spectrum* estimation, is the preferred terminology. Newton presented the first mathematical treatment in *Principia* [1687] of the periodicity of wave motion that Pythagoras had empirically observed.

The solution to the wave equation for the vibrating musical string was developed by Daniel Bernoulli [1738], a mathematician who discovered the general solution for the displacement $u(x,t)$ of the string at time t and position x (the endpoints of the string are at $x = 0$ and $x = \pi$) in the wave equation to be

$$u(x,t) = \sum_{k=1}^{\infty} \sin kx \left(A_k \cos kct + B_k \sin kct\right) \quad , \tag{1.1}$$

where c is a physical quantity characteristic of the material of the string, representing the velocity of the traveling waves on the string. The mathematician L. Euler [1755] demonstrated that the coefficients A_k and B_k in the series given by Eq. (1.1), which would later be called the *Fourier series*, were found as solutions to

$$A_k = \frac{2}{\pi} \int_0^{\pi} u(x,0) \sin kx \, dx$$

$$B_k = \frac{2}{\pi} \int_0^{\pi} u(x,0) \cos kx \, dx \quad . \tag{1.2}$$

The French engineer Jean Baptiste Joseph Fourier in his thesis *Analytical Theory of Heat* [1822] extended the wave equation results by asserting that any arbitrary function $u(x)$, even one with a finite number of discontinuities, could be represented as an infinite summation of sine and cosine terms,

$$u(x) = \sum_{k=1}^{\infty} (A_k \cos k\alpha x + B_k \sin k\alpha x) \quad . \tag{1.3}$$

The mathematics of taking a function $u(x)$, or its samples, and determining its A_k and B_k coefficients has become known as *harmonic analysis*, due to the harmonic relationship between the sine and cosine terms.

Beginning in the mid-nineteenth century, practical scientific applications using harmonic analysis to study phenomenologic data such as sound, weather, sunspot activity, magnetic deviations, river flow, and tidal variations were being made. In many of these applications, the fundamental period was either obscured by measurement error noise or was not visually evident. In addition, secondary periodic components that bore no harmonic relationship to the fundamental periodicity were often present. This yielded some problems with the estimates of the various periodicities. Manual computation of the Fourier series coefficients by direct computational techniques or by graphic-aided methods proved to be extremely tedious and were limited to very small data sets. Mechanical harmonic analyzers were developed to assist in the analysis. These calculating machines were basically mechanical integrators, or planimeters, because they found the area under the curves $u(x) \sin kx$ and $u(x) \cos kx$ over the interval $0 \leq x \leq \pi$, thereby providing a calculation of the Fourier series coefficients A_k and B_k. The British physicist Sir William Thomson (Lord Kelvin, of the temperature scale fame) developed the first mechanical harmonic analyzer based on a dual-function-product planimeter, $\int u(\theta)\phi(\theta)\,d\theta$, invented by his brother James Thomson and modified to evaluate cosine and sine functions [1876, 1878]. Figure 1.2(a) and (e) illustrates versions of this device. A tracing point was guided manually along the plotted curve to be analyzed; the coefficients were then read from the integrating cylinders. A different integrating cylinder was required to evaluate the coefficients up to only the third harmonic. It was used by the British Meteorological Office to analyze graphical records of daily changes in atmospheric temperature and pressure. Observers said of this device that, due to its size and weight, it was practically a permanent fixture in the room where it was used. Improvements in harmonic analyzers were subsequently made by O. Henrici [1894] [see Fig. 1.2(b)], A. Sharp [1894], G. U. Yule [1895], and the American physicists Albert A. Michelson (of the measurement of the speed of light fame) and S. W. Stratton [1898]. The Michelson-Stratton harmonic analyzer [Fig. 1.2(c)], designed using spiral springs, was particularly impressive in that it not only could process 80 harmonic coefficients simultaneously, but it also could work as a synthesizer (inverse Fourier transform) to construct the superposition of the Fourier series components. Michelson used the machine in his Nobel Prize-winning optical studies. As a synthesizer, the machine could add interference fringes represented by simple harmonic curves. As an analyzer, it decomposed a visibility curve into harmonic components representing the distribution of light in a source.

The results from a harmonic analysis in this era were sometimes used to synthesize a periodic waveform from the harmonic components for purposes of prediction (a Fourier series model of a data sequence). One of the earliest uses was for tidal prediction. Using direct manual calculation, Sir William Thomson performed harmonic analyses of tidal gauge observations from British ports starting in 1866; by 1872 he had developed a tide-predicting machine that utilized the coefficients determined from his harmonic analysis. Later versions of this machine [see Fig. 1.2(d)] could combine up to 10 harmonic tidal constituents that were initialized by crank and pulley settings, as a function of the port where tides were to be predicted. Thomson's tide predictor was a rather large machine, with a base 3 feet by 6 feet. It took approximately 4 hours to draw one year of tidal curves for one harbor. A tide predictor built by William Ferrel in 1882, now on display in the Smithsonian Museum in Washington, D.C., was used by the U.S. Coast and Geodetic Survey to prepare tide tables from 1883 to 1910.

Although the mechanical harmonic analyzers were useful for evaluating time series with *obvious* periodicities (smoothly varying time sequence with little or no noise), numerical methods of harmonic analysis (fitting a Fourier series) were still required when evaluating very noisy data (described in the early literature as data with "irregular fluctuations") for possible *hidden* periodicities (nonobvious periodic signals), or evaluating signals with nonharmonically related periods. Of the many scientists who used harmonic analysis, Schuster [1897, 1898, 1900, 1905, 1906] made the most profound impact on what has become the classic spectral estimation

Figure 1.2 Nineteenth-century mechanical harmonic analyzers and synthesizers (forward and inverse Fourier transformers). (a) Kelvin's original harmonic analyzer model (1876). (b) Michelson-Stratton harmonic analyzer and synthesizer (1898). (c) Henrici-Coradi harmonic analyzer (1894). (d) Kelvin's harmonic synthesizer for tidal prediction (circa 1890). (e) Kelvin's first operational 7-disk harmonic analyzer (mean and 6 harmonics) (1878). Photos courtesy The Science Museum, London.

technique. He suggested that a plot of the squared envelope $S_k = A_k^2 + B_k^2$ of the Fourier transform coefficients (first proposed by Stokes [1879])

$$A_k = \frac{2}{nT_0} \int_\tau^{\tau+nT_0} u(t) \cos kt \, dt$$

$$B_k = \frac{2}{nT_0} \int_\tau^{\tau+nT_0} u(t) \sin kt \, dt$$

(1.4)

be computed over a range of n integral periods of T_0, where the setting $k = 2\pi/T_0$ should be made. Schuster's notation has been used here. Schuster termed his method the *periodogram* [1898]. The periodogram, in concept, could be evaluated over a continuum of periods (inverse frequencies). In his papers, Schuster recognized many of the problems and peculiarities of the periodogram. Depending on the choice of starting time τ, he observed that irregular and different patterns were obtained, sometimes producing spurious peaks (he called them "accidental periodicities") where no periodicity truly existed. Schuster [1894,1904] knew from his understanding of Fourier analysis of optical spectra that averaging of S_k, obtained by evaluation of different data segments (with the period T_0 fixed), was necessary to smooth the periodogram (obtain the "mean periodogram" in Schuster's jargon) and remove the spurious parts of the spectrum. Although he recognized the need to average, the implementation required computational means beyond the resources available in Schuster's era. Quoting Schuster [1898, p. 25],

> The periodogram as defined by the equations [1.4] will in general show an irregular outline, and also depend on the value of τ. In the optical analysis of light we are helped by the fact that the eye only receives the impression of the average of a great number of adjacent periods, and also the average, as regards time, of the intensity of radiation of any particular period .... If we were to follow the optical analogy we should have to vary the time τ ... continuously and take the average value of $r = \sqrt{A^2 + B^2}$ obtained in this way for *each* value of k ... but this would involve an almost prohibitive labor.

A thorough theoretical understanding of the statistical basis for averaging was still thirty years away in the work of Wiener, and fifty years from practical implementation of spectral averaging methods based on fast Fourier transform algorithms and digital computers to significantly reduce the "prohibitive" computational burden.

Schuster was also aware of the sidelobes (he called them "spurious periodicities") around mainlobe responses in the periodogram that are inherent in all Fourier analysis of finite record lengths. His cognizance of sidelobes was due to his ability to make an analogy with the diffraction patterns of the optical spectroscope caused by its limited spatial aperture ("limited resolving power"). Schuster pointed out that many researchers in his day were incorrectly asserting that all maxima in the periodogram were hidden periodicities when, in fact, many were sidelobes rather than true periodicities. In addition to the spurious periodicities in the periodogram,

Schuster was also aware of the estimation bias introduced into the periodogram estimate when the measurement interval was not an exact integer multiple of the period under analysis. Many scientists in Schuster's day thought that white light might be a close grouping of monochromatic line components (analogous to white noise being a grouping of sinusoidal frequencies), but Schuster was able to show empirically that white light was a continuum of frequencies. Wiener was later able to extend this white light analogy to a statistical white noise process.

Schuster applied the periodogram to find hidden periodicites in meteorological, magnetic declination, and sunspot number data. The periodogram analysis of the sunspot numbers [Schuster, 1906] is of particular interest as these numbers will be used as a test case throughout the book. See the next section for more information on sunspot numbers. Schuster performed preprocessing of the monthly sunspot numbers for the years 1749 to 1894, followed by a periodogram analysis. The periodogram analysis yielded an estimate of 11.125 years for the sunspot cycle. This is the basis for the classic 11-year sunspot cycle referenced in astronomical literature.

Conceptually, a time series consisting of a sinusoid of frequency f_0 Hz with "superposed irregular fluctuations" (additive noise) should show a peak in the periodogram at a period $T_0 = 1/f_0$. However, many researchers in the early part of this century found that periodograms computed using noisy data were very erratic and did not show any dominant peaks that might be considered periodicities in the data. This was true even if the data length were increased. Examples of such periodograms are illustrated in Fig. 1.3. As more and more data samples are used, the periodogram fluctuates more and more. This behavior led to a certain amount of disenchantment with the periodogram for several decades, which is unfortunate because most users were ignorant of the averaging considerations suggested by Schuster. Slutsky [1927], and later Daniell [1946], both independently observed that the fluctuations in periodograms of white noise were of the same magnitude as the mean value of the periodogram itself. The fluctuations tended to be uncorrelated from frequency to frequency (see Appendix 4.A for an analysis), irrespective of the length of the time-series interval available for analysis. Both also suggested that the periodogram fluctuations could be reduced by averaging the periodogram over neighboring frequencies. This concept is the basis of one method of smoothing the periodogram that is discussed in Chap. 5.

The disenchantment with the periodogram led the British statistican G. Yule to introduce in 1927 a notable alternative analysis method. Yule's idea was to model a time series with linear regression analysis in order to find one or two periodicities in data [Yule, 1927]. His main interest was to obtain a more accurate determination of the primary periodicity in sunspot numbers, and to search for additional periodicities in the data. Yule felt that the "superposed irregular fluctuations" (additive noise) hypothesis of the Schuster periodogram might not hold in the case of sunspot numbers. Yule suggested that sunspot numbers might better be described by a different time-series model of the physical phenomenon, namely a recursive harmonic process driven by a noise process, or "disturbances"

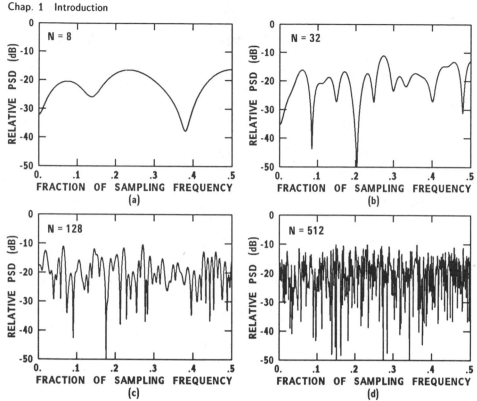

Figure 1.3   Periodograms of white Gaussian noise for record lengths. The term PSD stands for power spectral density. (a) $N = 8$. (b) $N = 32$. (c) $N = 128$. (d) $N = 512$. An increase in spectral fluctuations, rather than a tendency to a flat spectrum, results when the record length is increased.

as Yule called the individual noise samples. Using a simple trigonometric identity

$$\sin(kx) = 2\cos(x)\sin([k-1]x) - \sin([k-2]x)$$

with the substitution $x = 2\pi fT$, a symmetric homogeneous difference equation that describes a single discrete time harmonic variation may be written

$$u(k) - au(k-1) + u(k-2) = 0 \quad .$$

Here $u(k) = \sin(2\pi fkT)$ is the harmonic component, T is the sample interval, f is the frequency of the harmonic variation, and $a = 2\cos(2\pi fT)$ is a coefficient that characterizes the harmonic. Yule conjectured that if the sunspot numbers had only one periodic component, then the sunspot number sequence could be generated by the process

$$u(k) = au(k-1) - u(k-2) + \epsilon(k) \quad , \tag{1.5}$$

where $\epsilon(k)$ was some small random impulsive "disturbance" at each time index k. Yule called this the "harmonic curve equation." Thus, Yule devised the basis of what has become known as the parametric approach to spectral analysis: characterizing the data measurements as the output of some time-series model. Yule determined the parameter a via a least squares analysis using the 1749–1924 yearly mean sunspot numbers with the sample mean removed. He esimated that $a = 1.62374$, from which, for $T = 1$ year, he estimated a period $1/f = 10.08$ years per sunspot cycle. Not being satisfied with this number, he then filtered the sunspot numbers by taking a 3-year moving average over the data; a second least squares analysis of this filtered sunspot number sequence yielded a period of $1/f = 11.43$ years per cycle. Yule then tried to find if there might be two periodicities in the sunspot numbers by least squares fitting of a fifth-order symmetric difference equation to the data. This yielded periods of 11.95 and 1.42 years per sunspot cycle. However, he discounted a two-period model because the squared error went up, rather than down, for the two-period model.

Still not satisfied with his estimates, Yule took a cue from the structure of the "harmonic curve equation" and decided to generalize the difference equation approach and use least squares regression analysis of the model

$$u(k) = b(1)u(k - 1) + b(2)u(k - 2) + \epsilon(k) \tag{1.6}$$

for arbitrary $b(1)$ and $b(2)$. This is strictly an autoregression (u regressed on itself), and marks the first time that a least squares autoregression was performed for the purpose of spectral analysis. The least squares solution to the regression equation (1.6) is a damped sinusoid. Yule found, using Eq. (1.6), a damped sinusoidal period of 10.60 years for the unfiltered sunspot numbers, and 11.164 years for the filtered data. Although Yule could not conjecture what, if any, physical meaning to attach to the damping, he felt that the period estimates were still reasonable. Walker [1931] also used the technique of Yule to investigate a damped sinusoidal time series. The normal equations arising out of the least squares analysis have been called the *Yule-Walker equations*, in honor of these pioneers of regression modeling. It is interesting to note that Walker, as well as Alter [1927], also anticipated the empirical spectral estimation techniques later espoused by Tukey. In his 1931 paper (p. 524), Walker states:

> Some light is thrown by this [regression] analysis on the utility of a series of values of the serial correlation coefficients, a "correlation-periodogram," as a substitute for the ordinary Fourier-Schuster periodogram when there is no question of damped oscillations.

The methods used by Yule are reminiscent of another, much older data-fitting procedure by Baron de Prony [1795]. Prony discovered a method of fitting an exponential model to a set of data representing pressure and volume relationships of gases. Prony's procedure involved an exact, rather than least squares, regression fit to the data. The regression coefficients are used as coefficients of a polynomial, whose roots are the model exponents. The amplitude of each exponential component is then found by a second pass through the data.

The year 1930 marked a major turning point for spectral analysis. Norbert Wiener published his classic paper *Generalized Harmonic Analysis* [1930]. This paper placed spectral analysis on a firm statistical foundation in its treatment of random processes. Several significant contributions were made. Precise statistical definitions of *autocorrelation* and *power spectral density* (PSD) were given for stationary random processes. These two functions of a random process were shown to be related via a continuous Fourier transform, which is the basis of what is known today as the Wiener-Khintchine theorem (Khintchine [1934], who made related contributions, is also honored). The use of the Fourier transform, rather than the Fourier series of traditional harmonic analysis, enabled Wiener to define spectra in terms of a *continuum* of frequencies, rather than as *discrete* harmonic frequencies. White noise was shown by Wiener to have a uniform PSD, that is, to be composed of all frequencies equally, a result he deduced from his studies of Brownian motion and from Schuster's optical analogies. Other early contributions to the statistical characterization of spectral analysis include Bartlett [1946, 1948, 1950] and Kendall [1945].

The regression equation of Yule may be regarded as a prediction of the signal by a linear combination of past samples of that signal plus a noise contribution, thereby constituting a so-called *linear prediction* problem. Building on the probabilistic framework for time series developed by Khintchine and Slutsky, Wold [1938] developed a unified stochastic linear difference equation model for discrete-time series. Wold introduced the terms *moving average* for time-series models originally described by Slutsky (who used the term "moving summation"), and *linear autoregression* for time-series models originally described by Yule. He was also the first to describe the relationship between the autoregressive parameters and the autocorrelation sequence as the "Yule-Walker equations." In his 1938 monograph, Wold also introduced a very important decomposition theorem (Theorem 7) for stationary time series. This theorem asserted that any stationary random process could be expressed as the sum of a deterministic component and a one-sided moving average process driven by white noise. This theorem led Kolmogoroff [1939] to the formulation and solution of the linear prediction problem. Computing a spectrum from the autoregressive coefficients was suggested as early as 1948 by Bartlett [1948, p. 686], who used a second-order autoregressive power spectral density. The equations of the linear prediction problem and the Yule-Walker equations have a special structure first studied by the German mathematician O. Toeplitz [1911]. This structure was exploited by a colleague of Wiener, N. Levinson, to develop a very efficient computational procedure to solve the Yule-Walker equations [Levinson, 1947]. Extensions of the linear prediction concept to digital seismic data was promoted by the Geophysical Analysis Group (GAG) at MIT during the 1950s. This work, particularly that of Enders Robinson [1954], made significant contributions to the modern digital methods of spectral analysis and signal processing.

Whereas Wiener might be considered the pioneer of modern *theoretical* spectral analysis, John Tukey might be considered the pioneer of modern *empirical* spectral analysis. In a paper at Woods Hole, Massachusetts, in June 1949, Tukey laid out an empirical foundation for spectral estimation using correlation estimates produced from finite time sequences. His procedure also included the proper design for data collection and an approximate statistical distribution of the spectral estimate. A classic treatise describing this procedure in detail was published with Blackman in 1958. Many of the terms of modern spectral estimation (such as "aliasing," "windowing," "prewhitening," "tapering," "smoothing," "decimation," and so forth) can be attributed to Tukey.

The next key contribution to digital spectral analysis came in the form of a very efficient computational algorithm to solve the discrete Fourier transform, a version of the Fourier transform applicable to digital data processing. While there is evidence of contributions by many researchers to the development of a fast Fourier transform (FFT) [Heideman et al., 1984], a concise paper by Jim Cooley and John Tukey [1965] focused the attention of the digital processing community on the practicality of efficient Fourier transform computation. The FFT, perhaps more than any other contribution, has led to an increased usage of digital spectral analysis as a signal processing tool.

The prime motivator for the current interest in high-resolution spectral estimation from limited time or space sequences may be attributed to the work of John Burg [1967]. His high-resolution spectral estimate, which he described in the context of a maximum entropy mathematical formalism, has been instrumental in the development of parametric, or modeling, approaches to high-resolution spectral estimation. The maximum entropy spectrum is very closely related to autoregressive spectral analysis. Both Bartlett [1948] and Parzen [1957] had suggested the use of autoregressive spectral estimation, but not until Burg's work did interest in this method receive significant attention.

The development of fast computational algorithms continues to have an impact on newer methods of spectral estimation, much as the FFT has had with classical spectral estimates. Fast algorithms make real-time implementation feasible for many of the newer spectral estimation methods. Fast algorithms for fitting least squares linear parametric models to data samples have been a topic of research for approximately the last decade. The work of Morf and Kailath at Stanford University has been prominent in early contributions to this area.

Additional historical material on spectral estimation may be found in a survey paper by Robinson [1982].

1.2 SUNSPOT NUMBERS

Due to their historic interest for spectral estimation, the sunspot number series will be used as a test example for the spectral estimation methods presented in this text. Some discussion of their origin is therefore appropriate. Sunspots have been observed with the naked eye since at least 300 A.D., as they are mentioned in old Chinese records of this era. Telescopic observations of sunspots have been made in Europe since 1610 A.D. Modern systematic measurements of sunspots began in 1835. By 1843, Hofrat Heinrich Schwabe had discovered the basic cyclic nature between minimum and maximum numbers of spots on the sun's surface.

In order to quantify the results of the observations, the *relative* sunspot number R was introduced by Rudolf Wolf in 1848 as a measure of sunspot activity. The value of R attempts to account for the fact that sunspots tend to appear in groups. The determination of R is strictly by manual observation on a daily basis. Two separate measurements are actually taken. The first is a count s of the total number of individual spots, regardless of their size. The second is a count g of the numbers of sunspot groups. The original Wolf relative sunspot number was simply a weighted combination $R = 10g + s$. This arbitrary weighting of the two counts reflected the relative importance of a new sunspot. A greater increase in activity is observed when a new spot appears in a region which had been spotless before (thus forming a new group) than in a region which already had an existing group. Note that no measurement of sunspot *area* is made, which would seem to be a more sensitive measure. This is a reflection of the limitations in instrumentation in Wolf's day. However, later analysis has shown that the *yearly* means of R are almost linearly proportional to the *yearly* spot area means.

Because 10–50 observers are typically used to obtain a single daily *average* relative sunspot number, some adjustment for the type of observation equipment (for example, magnification power), geographic location, locale (for example, typical atmospheric and weather conditions), and observer (his counting method and personal judgment) must be made. Thus, each observer's R value is weighted by $k(10g + s)$, where k is an observer scaling factor specific to the observatory's locale and equipment. The Wolf baseline instrument and location gives $k = 1$. It may be seen that the relative sunspot numbers are somewhat subjective. The factor k is a variable that must be determined empirically for each observer. The daily value of R is a function of the number of observers actually reporting. Weather conditions and days off taken by the observers may cause fluctuations in the daily sunspot numbers.

Although initiated in 1848, Wolf [1868] researched archives to find estimates for the relative sunspot numbers for years prior to 1848. Daily records are now available back to the year 1818, estimates of monthly means have been made back to 1749, estimates of annual means have been made back to 1700, and the epochs of maximum and minimum points in sunspot activity have been noted in recorded observations since 1610. Wolf assumed an 11.1-year cycle to guide his backdated estimates of sunspot numbers. Current research has produced estimates of annual sunspot numbers back to 1500 A.D. based on correlation of sunspot activity with terrestrial meterological data, climate variations (droughts and famines), radiocarbon chronology, dendrochronology (tree-ring studies), and paleomagnetic investigations [Schove, 1983]. Variations in mean annual temperatures and mean annual magnetic declinations have been found, for example, to have an approximate 19- to 22-year cycle, roughly twice that of the basic sunspot cycle.

Appendix I contains the monthly means and yearly means of R from 1700 to 1984. These are plotted in Fig. 1.4. The Swiss Federal Observatory in Zurich has continued Wolf's numbers to the present and is the international source for R.

Figure 1.4   Annual mean relative sunspot numbers since 1700.

Figure 1.5   Daily relative sunspot numbers for January 1982 (solid line for international numbers and dashed line for AAVSO numbers).

Figure 1.6   Monthly mean relative sunspot numbers for 1961–1983 (solid line for international numbers and dashed line for AAVSO numbers).

The key to reasonable and meaningful sunspot numbers is averaging. A large number of observers from a variety of geographical locations are used to obtain a daily average. The daily average is probably not sufficient averaging, as Fig. 1.5 illustrates. This figure plots the daily numbers for a typical month, comparing the international relative sunspot numbers (R_I) prepared in Zurich with the American Association of Variable Star Observers (AAVSO) relative sunspot numbers (R_A). One can see that the sunspot activity may vary greatly over a 1-month interval. Although the two curves generally track each other, there are slight differences between the two curves. This is partly explained by the rotation period of the sun. The sun does not have a single rotation period; it rotates faster at the equator than at other solar latitudes. The mean rotation period at the equator is estimated to be in a range from 25 to 27 days, while at 60° latitude the mean rotation period is about 31 days. Sunspots themselves vary in duration from a few hours to several months. Figure 1.6 illustrates the differences between the two sunspot number sources using monthly averaging. The monthly mean is probably the minimum averaging interval in which sunspot numbers start becoming stable, with yearly means proving to be the most stable numbers.

1.3 A TEST CASE

Although the sunspot number data are a classical time series, there is no way to ascertain the true spectrum from such a relatively short data sequence. A synthetic test data sequence has also been devised in order to characterize the short data record behavior of each spectral estimator with a known signal scenario. The data consists of 64 samples of a complex-valued process consisting of four complex sinusoids and a complex additive colored noise process. Figure 1.7 plots the real and imaginary components of the sequence in a way that emphasizes the discrete nature of the data. Appendix II provides a tabular listing of the sample values. This test data set is also used to provide the reader with a mechanism to verify the implementation of each spectral estimator for which a computer program has been supplied. A listing of appropriate output parameters, using the test data as input, is provided with each program. Readers may also compare their spectral plots with the ones provided in the summary section of each chapter.

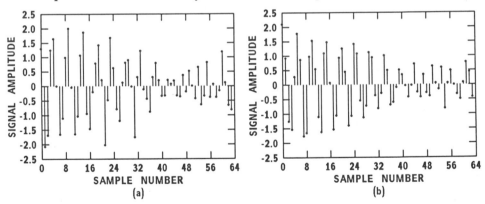

Figure 1.7   Complex test data sequence. (a) Real part. (b) Imaginary part.

The true spectrum, calculated by analytical means, is illustrated in Fig. 1.8. The frequency axis represents the frequency as a fraction of the sampling frequency, that is, the actual frequency f in Hz normalized by dividing by the sampling frequency $f_s = 1/T$, where T is the data sample interval. Due to the sampling theorem for signals (see Chap. 2), the fractional frequencies must lie between $-.5$ and $.5$. Two of the sinusoids in the spectrum have been placed very closely together at fractional frequencies .2 and .21 in order to test the resolution capability of a spectral estimator. Two weaker complex sinusoidal signals of 20 dB less power than the stronger sinusoids were placed at fractional frequencies .1 and −.15. These sinusoidal signals were selected to test a spectral estimator's capability to pick out weaker signal components among stronger signals. The colored noise process was generated by passing two independently generated zero-mean real white noise processes through identical moving average filters (see Chaps. 6 and 10) to separately generate the real and imaginary components of the test data noise process. Each filter had the identical raised cosine spectral response, as seen in Fig. 1.8 between fractional frequencies .2 to .5 centered at .35 or between −.2 to −.5 centered at −.35. Although the shape of the colored noise process is identical for both positive and negative frequencies in the exact spectrum shown in Fig. 1.8, this symmetry will not be seen in the spectral estimates shown in this book because the real and imaginary parts of the colored noise process were generated independently, i.e., the real and imaginary parts are uncorrelated. The height of the lines representing the sinusoidal components of the spectrum are adjusted to reflect the power of each sinusoid relative to the *total* power in the colored noise process. Thus, the two stronger sinusoids have more power than the noise, while the two weaker sinusoids have less power than the noise.

Figure 1.8   Analytically determined spectrum of test data process.

1.4 ISSUES IN SPECTRAL ESTIMATION

The interest in alternative spectral analysis methods has been promoted by the promise of improved performance, such as better frequency resolution, increased signal detectability, or retention of spectral shape "fidelity" with fewer parameters. It has been difficult to characterize analytically the performance of most methods in the limited time (short data record) case; only very limited empirical results may

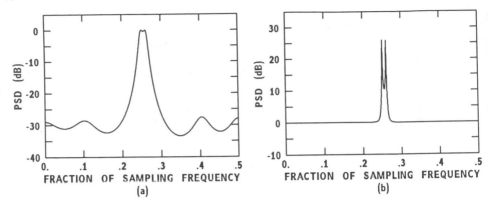

Figure 1.9 Visual enhancement of spectral resolution. (a) Original spectrum. (b) Enhanced spectrum obtained by $1/(1-x)$ mapping.

be found in the literature. This has led to a number of issues in modern spectral estimation. Some of these key issues are now highlighted.

1.4.1 Resolution

Spectral resolution is high on the list of key issues in contemporary spectral estimation, especially in regard to limited data sequences. Just what constitutes resolution is a subjective area. One of the earliest definitions was provided by Lord Rayleigh [1879, p. 269], who provided this working definition for the resolution of telescopes with finite spatial aperture:

> As the power of a telescope is measured by the closeness of the double stars which it can resolve, so the power of a spectroscope ought to be measured by the closeness of the closest double lines in the spectrum which it is competent to resolve.

Analogous definitions for resolution of finite-time aperture signals have been proposed. Formal definitions of resolution are presented in Chaps. 2 and 5. A common practice in the literature is to convey the relative resolutions of two spectral estimators based on visual impressions. Consider in Fig. 1.9 two spectral estimates. The spectral estimate shown in Fig. 1.9(a) has a unit normalized peak that barely yields two distinguishable peaks to indicate the presence of two spectral components. If one simply forms the new spectral function

$$P_B(f) = \frac{1}{1 - P_A(f)} \quad ,$$

which is plotted in Fig. 1.9(b), then the appearance is a spectrum with "higher" resolution. The truth is that both spectra contain the same information. Visual comparisons alone are, therefore, not sufficient to judge resolution performance [Kay and Demeure, 1984].

1.4.2 Signal Detectability

The use of spectral estimation to detect the presence of signals brings up another issue. Consider the periodograms illustrated in Fig. 1.10. Both periodograms are based on the same 1024-point realization of a process consisting of a single sinusoid in additive white noise at −17-dB signal-to-noise ratio (SNR). Figure 1.10(a) is a single periodogram based on the entire 1024 samples. The sinusoid located at fractional frequency .2 is detectable above the noise level in the spectral estimate. Figure 1.10(b) is a smoothed periodogram obtained by segmenting the data into intervals of 32 data samples and averaging the periodograms of the resulting 32 segments. The flat characteristic of white noise is more evident in this spectral estimate, but the response due to the presence of the sinusoid is not detectable. In fact, it may be shown that the unsmoothed periodogram yields an improved detectability over that of the smoothed periodogram by roughly the square root of the number of segments, or $10 \log \sqrt{32} \approx 7.5$ dB in this case. In terms of characterizing the entire spectrum, the smoothed spectral estimate of Fig. 1.10(b) is better; in terms of detectability, however, the unsmoothed estimate is better. Thus, the motivation for the type of spectral estimate selected will depend on whether one is interested in a smooth estimate over the entire range of frequencies, or better detectability over selected portions of the spectral frequency range. Spectral estimation algorithms are, therefore, not necessarily good detection algorithms.

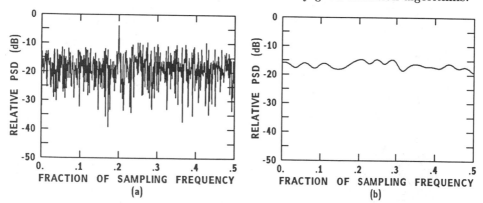

Figure 1.10   (a) Unsmoothed periodogram with one sinusoid detectable. (b) Smoothed periodogram with no sinusoids detectable.

1.4.3 Confusing Parameter Estimation With Spectral Estimation

The spectral estimation problem involves the estimation of a *function* of frequency. The performance of a spectral estimator is judged by how well it matches the known spectrum of a test signal over a continuous range of frequencies. There are applications where only the behavior of the spectral estimator local to specific frequency regions is of interest. Estimating the frequency of a sinusoid in white noise, the example used in Fig. 1.10, is one such application. As a *spectral estimator*, the estimate of Fig. 1.10(b) is better because it more closely resembles the flat spectrum of white noise. As a *sinusoidal frequency estimator*, the estimate of Fig. 1.10(a) is better because the sinusoidal frequency may be more accurately determined. There is some confusion in the literature because many *parameter estimation* problems are presented in spectral estimation contexts, even though the spectral estimator function is not the ultimate quantity sought.

The parameter estimation problem and the spectral estimation problem require separate statistical treatments, although the two estimation problems often overlap for specific cases. The performance of a *spectral* estimator should, therefore, not entirely be judged in terms of its performance as a *parameter* estimator. The comparison made in Fig. 1.10 shows, for example, that the smoothed periodogram is a good *spectral* estimator, but a poor *parameter* estimator, the parameter in this case being the sinusoidal frequency.

1.4.4 One Estimate Is Not Enough

A spectral estimate produced from a finite data record represents a guess as to the true spectral function had an infinite statistical record been available. The behavior and performance of spectral estimators must, therefore, be characterized in statistical terms. The bias and variance are common statistical measures of estimator performance. As analytical determination of bias and variance is usually not mathematically tractable, a practical scheme is to overlap the plots of several spectral estimate realizations and visually examine the bias and variance among the estimates as a function of frequency. Areas in the overlapped spectral plots where the experimental variance is great would indicate that the spectral features seen in the spectrum of a single realization may not be statistically significant. On the other hand, features in the overlapped spectra where the variance is small are more confidently attributed to actual frequency components in the signal. However, the application of spectral estimation to short data records often does not permit multiple spectral estimates to be made. Statistical analysis of single spectral estimates made from short data records is a difficult problem in general. For these reasons, the reader is cautioned not to draw any statistical conclusions when comparing the various spectral estimates made using the test case of Sec. 1.3.

1.4.5 The Whole Picture

The formal definition of the spectrum, to be found in Chap. 4, will show that it is a function strictly of the second-order statistics. The second-order statistics are also assumed to remain unchanged, or *stationary*, over time. Thus, the spectrum is not a complete statistical picture of a random process that may have other information in third- and higher-order statistics. Many common signals analyzed in practice are also not stationary, so that the methods of this text could not be applied to a whole data record. In practice, though, short data segments from the longer data record may be considered to be locally stationary, permitting spectral estimation methods in this text to be used. The time-varying statistics may then be treated by examining the variations in spectral estimates from segment to segment.

1.5   HOW TO USE THIS TEXT

This text has been structured to permit easy implementation of many of the spectral estimators described. Each chapter that concerns spectral estimators begins with a summary section that highlights specific estimator algorithms implemented in that chapter, including step-by-step algorithm flowcharts. FORTRAN subroutines of algorithms in a chapter are appended to that chapter. Readers may stop with the summary in order to first get "hands-on" experience with one or more algorithms cited in the chapter, before proceeding deeper into a chapter to get the theoretical and mathematical details. The subroutine listings are keyed to the equation numbers in the text in order to assist readers in their understanding of the program code. Each subroutine assumes the data to be processed is complex-valued. The descriptions that accompany each subroutine will indicate a means for converting the program to process real-valued data.

Those readers desiring assistance in the selection of a spectral estimation technique may find the summary table in Chap. 14 helpful. All key spectral estimation algorithms are listed in this table, including location within the text where the algorithm is discussed.

The chapters of the book have been organized into four major components: background material, spectral estimators for one-dimensional single-channel data sequences, summary of the one-dimensional single-channel spectral estimators, and spectral estimators for multichannel or two-dimensional data sequences. The background material (Chaps. 2–4) provides the mathematical foundation for the balance of the text, including the definition of the power spectral density. Spectral estimators are grouped according to three classes: classical spectral estimators (Chap. 5), parametric spectral estimators (Chaps. 6–11), and nonparametric spectral estimators (Chaps. 12–13). Multichannel and two-dimensional spectral estimators are presented in Chaps. 15 and 16, respectively. Multichannel refers to the spectral analysis of vector data (e.g., data from an array of sensors) that is a function of a scalar (e.g., time). Multidimensional refers to the spectral analysis of scalar data (e.g., image data) that is a function of a vector (e.g., two spatial coordinates).

REFERENCES

Alter, D., A Group or Correlation Periodogram, with Application to the Rainfall of the British Isles, *Mon. Weather Rev.*, vol. 56, pp. 263–266, 1927.

Bartlett, M. S., On the Theoretical Specification of Sampling Properties of Autocorrelated Time-Series, *J. R. Stat. Soc.*, Ser. B, vol. 8, pp. 27–41, 1946.

Bartlett, M. S., Smoothing Periodograms from Time Series with Continuous Spectra, *Nature*, London, vol. 161, pp. 686–687, May 1948.

Bartlett, M. S., Periodogram Analysis and Continuous Spectra, *Biometrika*, vol. 37, pp. 1–16, June 1950.

Bernoulli, Daniel, *Hydrodynamica*, Basel, Switzerland, 1738.

Blackman, R. B., and J. W. Tukey, The Measurements of Power Spectra from the Point of View of Communications Engineering, *Bell Syst. Tech. J.*, vol. 33, pp. 185–282, 485–569, 1958; also republished by Dover Publications, New York, 1959.

Burg, John P., Maximum Entropy Spectral Analysis, in *Proceedings 37th Meeting of Society of Exploration Geophysicists*, Oklahoma City, Okla., October 1967. (Also in *Modern Spectrum Analysis*, D. G. Childers, ed., IEEE Press Selected Reprint Series, New York, 1978.)

Cooley, J. W., and J. W. Tukey, An Algorithm for the Machine Calculation of Complex Fourier Series, *Math. Comput.*, vol. 19, pp. 297–301, April 1965.

Daniell, P. J., Discussion of "On the Theoretical Specification and Sampling Properties of Autocorrelated Time-Series," *J. R. Stat. Soc.*, ser. B, vol. 8, pp. 88-90, 1946.

Euler, L., *Institutiones Calculi Differentialis*, St. Petersburg, Russia, 1755.

Fourier, Jean Baptiste Joseph, *Théorie analytique de la chaleur* (Analytical Theory of Heat), Paris, France, 1822.

Heideman, M. T., D. H. Johnson, and C. S. Burrus, Gauss and the History of the Fast Fourier Transform, *IEEE Acoust. Speech, and Signal Process. Magazine*, vol. 1, pp. 14–21, October 1984.

Henrici, O., On a New Harmonic Analyser, *Philos. Mag.*, vol. 38, pp. 110–121, 1894.

Jenkins, G. M., and D. G. Watts, *Spectral Analysis and Its Applications*, Holden-Day, Inc., San Francisco, 1968.

Kay, S. M., and Cedric Demeure, The High-Resolution Spectrum Estimator—A Subjective Entity, *Proc. IEEE*, vol. 72, pp. 1815–1816, December 1984.

Kendall, M. G., On the Analysis of Oscillatory Time Series, *J. R. Stat. Soc.*, vol. 108, p. 93, 1945.

Khintchine, Aleksandr Jakovlevich, Korrelationstheorie der Stationären Stochastischen Prozesse, *Math. Ann.*, vol. 109, pp. 604–615, 1934.

Kolmogoroff, Andrei N., Sur l'interpolation et l'extrapolation des suites stationnaires, *C. R. Acad. Sci.*, vol. 208, p. 2043, 1939.

Levinson, Norman, The Wiener (Root Mean Square) Error Criterion in Filter Design and Prediction, *J. Math. Phys.*, vol. 25, pp. 261–278, 1947.

Michelson, Albert Abraham, and S. W. Stratton, A New Harmonic Analyser, *Philos. Mag.*, vol. 45, pp. 85–91, 1898.

Newton, Isaac, *Phil. Trans.*, vol. VI, 1671. On page 3076: "Comparing the length of this coloured spectrum with its breadth...".

Newton, Isaac, *Principia*, London, England, 1687; *Optics*, London, England, 1704.

Parzen, Emanuel, On Consistent Estimates of the Spectrum of a Stationary Time Series, *Ann. Math. Stat.*, vol. 28, pp. 329–348, 1957.

de Prony, Baron (Gaspard Riche), Essai expérimental et analytique: sur les lois des la dilatabilité de fluides élastiques et sur celles de la force expansive de la vapeur de l'eau et de la vapeur de l'alkool, à différentes températures, *J. Ec. Polytech.*, vol. 1, cahier 2, pp. 24–76, 1795.

Rayleigh, Lord, Investigations in Optics, with Special References to the Spectroscope, *Philos. Mag. J. Sci.*, ser. 5, vol. 8, no. 49, pp. 261–274, October 1879.

Robinson, Enders A., Predictive Decomposition of Time Series with Applications to Seismic Exploration, MIT Geophysical Analysis Group (GAG), Cambridge, Mass., 1954; reprinted in *Geophysics*, vol. 32, pp. 418–484, 1967.

Robinson, Enders A., A Historical Perspective of Spectrum Estimation, *Proc. IEEE*, vol. 70, pp. 885–907, September 1982.

Schove, D. Justin, ed., *Sunspot Cycles*, Hutchinson & Ross Publishing Co., Stroudsburg, Pa., 1983.

Schuster, Sir Arthur, On Interference Phenomenon, *Philos. Mag.*, vol. 37, pp. 509–545, June 1894.

Schuster, Sir Arthur, On Lunar and Solar Periodicities of Earthquakes, *Proc. R. Soc. London*, vol. 61, pp. 455–465, 1897.

Schuster, Sir Arthur, On the Investigation of Hidden Periodicities with Application to a Supposed Twenty-Six-Day Period of Meteorological Phenomena, *Terr. Mag.*, vol. 3, no. 1, pp. 13–41, March 1898.

Schuster, Sir Arthur, The Periodogram of Magnetic Declination as Obtained from the Records of the Greenwich Observatory during the Years 1871–1895, *Trans. Cambridge Philos. Soc.*, vol. 18, pp. 107–135, April 1900.

Schuster, Sir Arthur, *The Theory of Optics*, Cambridge University Press, London, 1904.

Schuster, Sir Arthur, The Periodogram and Its Optical Analogy, *Proc. R. Soc. London*, ser. A, vol. 77, pp. 136–140, 1905. Also, On Sun Spot Periodicities—Preliminary Notice, pp. 141–145, 1905.

Schuster, Sir Arthur, On the Periodicities of Sunspots, *Philos. Trans. R. Soc. London*, ser. A, vol. 206, pp. 69–100, 1906.

Sharp, Archibald, Harmonic Analyser, Giving Direct Readings of the Amplitude and Epoch of the Various Constituent Simple Harmonic Terms, *Philos. Mag.*, vol. 38, pp. 121–125, 1894.

Slutsky, Evgenievich, The Summation of Random Causes as the Source of Cyclic Processes (in Russian), *Probl. Econ. Conditions* (Moscow), vol. 3, no. 1, 1927; English translation in *Econometrica*, vol. 5, pp. 105, 1937.

Stokes, George Gabriel, Comments on the "Preliminary Report to the Committee on Solar Physics on a Method of Detecting the Unknown Inequalities of a Series of Observations," *Proc. R. Soc. London*, vol. 29, pp. 122–123, 29 May 1879.

Thomson, Sir William (Lord Kelvin), On an Instrument for Calculating the Integral of the Product of Two Given Functions, *Proc. R. Soc. London*, vol. 24, pp. 266–268, 1876.

Thomson, Sir William, Harmonic Analyzer, *Proc. R. Soc. London*, vol. 27, pp. 371–373, 1878.

Toeplitz, Otto, Zur Theorie der Quadratischen und Bilinearen Formen von Unendlichvielen Veränderlichen, *Math. Ann.*, vol. 70, pp. 351–376, 1911.

Tukey, John W., The Sampling Theory of Power Spectrum Estimates, *Proceedings Symposium on Applied Autocorrelation Analysis of Physical Problems*, U.S. Office of Naval Research (NAVEXOS-P-725), pp. 47-67, 1949. Reprinted in *J. Cycle Res.*, vol. 6, pp. 31–52, 1957.

Walker, Sir Gilbert, On Periodicity in Series of Related Terms, *Proc. R. Soc. London*, ser. A, vol. 131, pp. 518–532, 1931.

Wiener, Norbert, Generalized Harmonic Analysis, *Acta Math.*, vol. 55, pp. 117–258, 1930.

Wold, Herman O. A., A Study in the Analysis of Stationary Time Series, dissertation, Uppsala University, 1938; reprinted by Almqvist & Wiksell Forlag, Stockholm, 1954.

Wolf, R., Tafel der Relativzahlen, *Astron. Mitteil. Eidgen. Sternwarte, Zurich*, no. 24, vol. 111, 1868.

Yule, George Udny, On a Simple Form of Harmonic Analyses, *Philos. Mag.*, vol. 39, pp. 367–374, 1895.

Yule, George Udny, On a Method of Investigating Periodicities in Disturbed Series, with Special Reference to Wolfer's Sunspot Numbers, *Philos. Trans. R. Soc. London*, ser. A, vol. 226, pp. 267–298, July 1927.

2

REVIEW OF LINEAR SYSTEMS AND TRANSFORM THEORY

2.1 INTRODUCTION

As this is a review chapter, it is assumed that the reader has had some exposure to linear systems theory and Fourier transform theory from an introductory course in both continuous-time and discrete-time systems. Details of properties presented in this chapter may be found in the reference list at the end of the chapter. Another function of this chapter is to introduce many of the notational conventions used throughout the text.

Key concepts in linear systems theory are presented separately for continuous-time and discrete-time signals in Secs. 2.3 and 2.4, respectively. Section 2.5 is devoted to Fourier transform theory for continuous-time signals. Although Fourier transform theory for discrete-time signals is often presented in the literature independently of the continuous-time transform, Secs. 2.6 and 2.7 illustrate that the discrete-time transform may be viewed as a special case of the continuous-time transform. This development provides the link between the continuous-time Fourier transform (CTFT) and the discrete-time Fourier series (DTFS) of a finite sequence of samples of the continuous-time signal. This is in recognition that most realistic scenarios involve processing of sequences from uniformly sampled continuous temporal or spatial waveforms. The DTFS used in this book differs slightly from the traditional discrete Fourier transform (DFT) definition found in the literature. The difference is due to the inclusion of the sampling interval as a scaling factor in the

DTFS. This factor will be important for yielding spectral estimators with proper power units. Section 2.10 summarizes the fast Fourier transfrom (FFT), a very efficient computational algorithm to compute the DTFS. Finally, the important concept of time-bandwidth product (TBP) is discussed at length in Sec. 2.11. The TBP forms the basis of a measure for resolution.

The material in this chapter is based on the assumption that the signal is deterministic. The additional mathematical theory required to treat random signals is covered in Chap. 4.

2.2 SIGNAL NOTATION

A *continuous* signal is any real or complex time waveform $f(t)$, defined as a function of the continuous real temporal variable t, or any real or complex space waveform $g(s)$, defined as a function of the continuous real spatial variable s. Continuous signals are often termed *analog* if they can take on a continuum of values at any point t or s. Unless stated otherwise, all signals considered in this text will be assumed complex valued. The use of complex data has become prevalent with the increase in digital signal processing. Complex data is the natural output, for example, of a complex demodulation process (see Appendix 2.A). Some signals, such as found in radar and communication, have in-phase and quadrature components that lend themselves naturally to a complex representation.

A *discrete* signal is any function $f[n]$ that is a sequence of real or complex numbers defined for every integer n. A continuous temporal function $f(t)$ that is sampled at uniform intervals of T seconds, or a continuous spatial function $g(s)$ that is sampled at uniform intervals of S meters (or other appropriate spatial units), will generate the discrete sequences $f[n] = f(nT)$ or $g[n] = g(nS)$, respectively. Note that the distinguishing feature between continuous and discrete function notation is, respectively, the use of parentheses ( ) versus brackets [ ]. Parentheses are smooth, *continuous* line segments, whereas a bracket is formed by three *discrete* line segments. These symbols should avoid ambiguity between the continuous and discrete functions that use similar letter symbols.

A continuous or discrete signal whose amplitudes can take on a finite number of values, rather than a continuum, at any time t or at any index n is said to be *digital*. Discrete signals are, in practice, most commonly digital. Analog-to-digital converters in hardware naturally quantize the digital samples. Digital computers use finite-word-length registers to represent data values.

2.3 CONTINUOUS LINEAR SYSTEMS

A *linear system*, be it continuous or discrete, is simply a system in which superposition of responses may be applied. Thus, the response of a linear system to the sum of two input signals is simply the sum of the separate system responses to each individual input signal. A linear system will be *time-invariant* if an input $x(t)$ produces an output response $y(t)$ and $x(t - t_0)$ produces an output response $y(t - t_0)$ for any time (or space) shift t_0.

A special input signal is the *unit impulse function* $\delta(t)$, also called the *continuous delta function*. The unit impulse function may be conceptualized as a continuous signal of zero width and infinite height

$$\delta(t) = \begin{cases} \infty & \text{if } t = 0 \\ 0 & \text{if } t \neq 0 \end{cases} \tag{2.1}$$

but with unit area

$$\int_{-\infty}^{\infty} \delta(t)\, dt = 1 \quad . \tag{2.2}$$

The impulse function has the *sifting* property

$$\int_{-\infty}^{\infty} f(\tau)\delta(t - \tau)\, d\tau = \int_{-\infty}^{\infty} f(t - \tau)\delta(\tau)\, d\tau = f(t) \tag{2.3}$$

in that it can isolate, or reproduce, a particular value of a function $f(t)$, provided that the function is continuous at t. *Note that $\delta(t)$ has mathematical meaning only when used within the context of an integral.* For example, the product of a continuous function and an impulse function, $f(t)\delta(t)$, may be interpreted to mean $f(0)\delta(t)$, because

$$\int_{-\infty}^{\infty} g(t - \tau)[f(\tau)\delta(\tau)]\, d\tau = \int_{-\infty}^{\infty} [g(t - \tau)f(\tau)]\delta(\tau)\, d\tau = g(t)f(0) \quad . \tag{2.4}$$

Thus, the product of the function $f(t)$ with the impulse function has "sampled" the function at $t = 0$.

The output response $g(t)$ of a linear time-invariant (LTI) system to an arbitrary input signal $f(t)$ is provided by the *continuous convolution integral*

$$g(t) = \int_{-\infty}^{\infty} h(\tau)f(t - \tau)\, d\tau = \int_{-\infty}^{\infty} h(t - \tau)f(\tau)\, d\tau \quad , \tag{2.5}$$

where $h(t)$ is the *continuous impulse response* of the system, that is, the output response of the system to an impulse function as input

$$h(t) = \int_{-\infty}^{\infty} h(\tau)\delta(t - \tau)\, d\tau \quad . \tag{2.6}$$

A concise notation to represent the convolution operation is the $\star$ symbol. Thus, Eq. (2.5) could be expressed as

$$g(t) = h(t) \star f(t) \quad . \tag{2.7}$$

If the input to a continuous linear time-invariant system with impulse response $h(t)$ is a complex exponential of the form $f(t) = \exp(st)$, where s is an arbitrary complex value, then the output $g(t)$ has the form

$$g(t) = \int_{-\infty}^{\infty} h(\tau) \exp(s[t - \tau]) \, d\tau = H(s) \exp(st) \quad , \tag{2.8}$$

where

$$H(s) = \int_{-\infty}^{\infty} h(\tau) \exp(-s\tau) \, d\tau \quad . \tag{2.9}$$

The function $H(s)$ is the *continuous system function*; it is also recognizable as the *Laplace transform* of the impulse response. The term $\exp(st)$ is said to be an *eigenfunction* of the linear system because both input and output are proportional to it. $H(s)$ is then an *eigenvalue* of the system, because it represents the complex scaling of the eigenfunction.

2.4 DISCRETE LINEAR SYSTEMS

To develop a framework for discrete linear systems, one may proceed in a manner analogous to that for continuous linear systems. A special input signal for discrete systems is the *unit impulse function* $\delta[n]$, also called the *discrete delta sequence*. It is simply defined as

$$\delta[n] = \begin{cases} 1 & \text{if } n = 0 \\ 0 & \text{if } n \neq 0 \end{cases} . \tag{2.10}$$

Unlike its continuous-time counterpart, there are no analytical difficulties in defining $\delta[n]$. Any arbitrary sequence $f[n]$ may be written as a weighted sum of discrete-time impulse functions

$$f[n] = \sum_{k=-\infty}^{\infty} f[k]\delta[n - k] = \sum_{k=-\infty}^{\infty} f[n - k]\delta[k] \quad . \tag{2.11}$$

Let $h[n]$ denote the *discrete impulse response* of a discrete linear system excited by a unit impulse function. The output response $g[n]$ to an arbitrary input sequence $f[n]$ is then provided by the *discrete convolution summation*

$$g[n] = \sum_{k=-\infty}^{\infty} h[n - k]f[k] = h[n] \star f[n] \quad . \tag{2.12}$$

Note that brackets or parentheses on the functions surrounding the operator $\star$ will determine whether a discrete convolution or a continuous convolution operation is intended. A *causal discrete system* is one in which the output at time n depends only on the input $f[k]$ for $k \leq n$, which implies $h[k] = 0$ for $k < 0$.

If the input to a discrete linear system with impulse response $h[n]$ is an exponential sequence $f[n] = z^n$, where z is an arbitrary complex value, then the output response is

$$g[n] = H(z)z^n \quad , \tag{2.13}$$

where

$$H(z) = \sum_{n=-\infty}^{\infty} h[n]z^{-n} = Z\{h[n]\} \quad . \tag{2.14}$$

Thus, z^n is an eigenfunction of a discrete linear system. $H(z)$ is the *discrete system function*; it is defined for those values of z such that the summation in Eq. (2.14) converges. $H(z)$ may be recognized as the two-sided *z-transform* of the sequence $h[n]$. The symbol Z will be used to designate the z-transform operation. Note that $H(z)$ is a continuous function of z, even though it is defined from a discrete sequence. The function $H(z)$ forms a polynomial in which the powers of z^{-1} correspond to the sequence time index (e.g., $h[n]$ is associated with the term z^{-n}). In this sense, z^{-1} may be considered a single sample delay operator. Some important properties of z-transforms used in this text are summarized in Table 2.1. Note that these properties are valid only for the common region of convergence for $F(z)$ and $G(z)$. For proof of these properties, consult Oppenheim and Schafer [1975] or Oppenheim and Willsky [1983].

PROPERTY	DISCRETE TIME FUNCTION	Z-TRANSFORM
Definitions	$f[n] \quad , \quad g[n]$	$F(z) \quad , \quad G(z)$
Linearity	$af[n] + bg[n]$	$aF(z) + bG(z)$
Shift	$f[n-m]$	$z^{-m}F(z)$
Scaling	$a^{-n}f[n]$	$F(az), \quad a > 0$
Conjugation	$f^*[n]$	$F^*(z^*)$
Time Reversal	$f[-n]$	$F(1/z)$
	$f^*[-n]$	$F^*(1/z^*)$
Convolution	$f[n] \star g[n]$	$F(z) \cdot G(z)$

Table 2.1   z-Transform Properties

An important class of discrete system functions are those with rational function z-transforms, that is, a ratio of polynomials in z. Let a causal discrete linear system be described by a constant coefficient linear difference equation, in which the input sequence $x[n]$ and output sequence $y[n]$ are related by

$$\sum_{k=0}^{P} a[k]y[n-k] = \sum_{k=0}^{Q} b[k]x[n-k] \tag{2.15}$$

for $n \geq 0$. The sequences $a[0], \ldots, a[P]$ and $b[0], \ldots, b[Q]$ characterize the linear system. Without loss of generality, one may assume $a[0] = 1$. Given a set of initial conditions of the x and y sequences for indices $n < 0$ and the input sequence $x[n]$ for indices $n \geq 0$, then the output sequence $y[n]$ for indices $n \geq 0$ may be directly computed. For zero initial conditions, the z-transform of Eq. (2.15) yields

$$Y(z) \sum_{k=0}^{P} a[k] z^{-k} = X(z) \sum_{k=0}^{Q} b[k] z^{-k} \quad , \tag{2.16}$$

where the convolution property from Table 2.1 has been used. The system function $H(z)$ relating input and output is therefore

$$H(z) = \frac{Y(z)}{X(z)} = \frac{\displaystyle\sum_{k=0}^{Q} b[k] z^{-k}}{1 + \displaystyle\sum_{k=1}^{P} a[k] z^{-k}} \quad , \tag{2.17}$$

which is a rational polynomial in z^{-1}. An equivalent factored form of $H(z)$ is

$$H(z) = \frac{b[0] \displaystyle\prod_{k=1}^{Q} (1 - z_k z^{-1})}{\displaystyle\prod_{k=1}^{P} (1 - p_k z^{-1})} \quad , \tag{2.18}$$

so that $b[0]$ may be regarded as a gain scaling factor. The roots $z_1, \ldots, z_Q$ of the numerator polynomial are called the *zeros* of $H(z)$; the roots $p_1, \ldots, p_P$ of the denominator polynomial are called the *poles* of $H(z)$. To have a stable system, it can be shown [Oppenheim and Willsky, 1983] that all poles must have the property $|p_k| < 1$. A *minimum-phase* linear system is a causal system in which all the poles and zeros of the system function $H(z)$ lie inside the unit z-plane circle, that is, $|z_k| < 1$ and $|p_k| < 1$.

The system function (2.17) may also be expressed as a partial fraction expansion. Assuming $Q \leq P$ and no repeated poles exist, then

$$H(z) = \sum_{k=1}^{P} \frac{r[k]}{1 - p_k z^{-1}} = \sum_{k=1}^{P} \frac{r[k] z}{z - p_k} \quad . \tag{2.19}$$

The residues $r[k]$ for $k = 1$ to $k = P$ may be found by using the residue theorem

$$r[k] = \left[\frac{H(z)(z - p_k)}{z} \right]_{z = p_k} \quad . \tag{2.20}$$

Repeated poles require a slightly more complicated treatment. The inverse z-transform of Eq. (2.19) will show [Oppenheim and Schafer, 1975] that the discrete system impulse response for zero initial conditions is a sum of discrete exponentials

$$h(n) = \begin{cases} \sum_{k=1}^{P} r[k]p_k^n & \text{for } n \geq 0 \\ 0 & \text{for } n < 0 \end{cases} \tag{2.21}$$

2.5   CONTINUOUS-TIME FOURIER TRANSFORM

Although the Laplace transform $H(s)$ permits general analysis of continuous linear systems for arbitrary exponential inputs, the analysis often of most interest is the evaluation along the imaginary axis, $s = j2\pi f$. The Laplace transform thus reduces to a function of f,

$$H(f) = \int_{-\infty}^{\infty} h(t) \exp(-j2\pi ft)\, dt = \mathcal{F}\{h(t)\} \quad . \tag{2.22}$$

In this form, $H(f)$ is called the *continuous-time Fourier transform* (CTFT). The symbol $\mathcal{F}$ will be used to designate the CTFT operation. The variable f in the complex sinusoid $\exp(-j2\pi ft)$ corresponds to frequency with units in hertz (cycles per second), assuming t has units of time (seconds). For spatial signal processing, the spatial variable x replaces the time variable t, and wavenumber k (in cycles per spatial unit) replaces temporal frequency f. The CTFT, in effect, identifies the frequencies and amplitudes of those complex sinusoids that combine to form an arbitrary waveform. The *inverse Fourier transform* is given by

$$h(t) = \int_{-\infty}^{\infty} H(f) \exp(j2\pi ft)\, df = \mathcal{F}^{-1}\{H(f)\} \quad . \tag{2.23}$$

The symbol $\mathcal{F}^{-1}$ will be used to designate the inverse CTFT operation. Expressions (2.22) and (2.23) form the continuous-time Fourier transform pair.

The existence of a CTFT and its inverse for a given function has been determined under a variety of conditions. One sufficient condition is that a signal $h(t)$ be absolute integrable in the sense

$$\int_{-\infty}^{\infty} |h(t)|\, dt < \infty \quad . \tag{2.24}$$

A less restrictive sufficient condition for the existence of the CTFT is that the signal have finite energy,

$$\int_{-\infty}^{\infty} |h(t)|^2\, dt < \infty \quad .$$

Another sufficient condition for the existence of a CTFT applies to signals that can be represented in the form $h(t) = a(t)\sin(2\pi ft + \theta)$. The function $a(t)$ must be damped, i.e., $a(t + k) < a(t)$ for $k > 0$, and $h(t)$ must also satisfy

$$\int_{-\infty}^{\infty} \left| \frac{h(t)}{t} \right| dt < \infty \quad . \tag{2.25}$$

If the theory of distributions is allowed (a topic which is beyond the mathematical scope intended here), even the CTFT of undamped periodic signals and impulse functions may be defined.

PROPERTY or FUNCTION	FUNCTION	TRANSFORM
Linearity	$ag(t) + bh(t)$	$aG(f) + bH(f)$
Time Shift	$h(t - t_0)$	$H(f)\exp(-j2\pi ft_0)$
Frequency Shift (Modulation)	$h(t)\exp(j2\pi f_0 t)$	$H(f - f_0)$
Scaling	$(1/|\alpha|)\, h(t/\alpha)$	$H(\alpha f)$
Temporal Convolution Theorem	$g(t) \star h(t)$	$G(f) \cdot H(f)$
Frequency Convolution Theorem	$g(t) \cdot h(t)$	$G(f) \star H(f)$
Window Function	$A\,\text{wind}(t/T_0)$	$2AT_0 \,\text{sinc}(2T_0 f)$
Sinc Function	$2AF_0 \,\text{sinc}(2F_0 t)$	$A\,\text{wind}(f/F_0)$
Impulse Function	$A\delta(t)$	A
Sampling (Replicating) Function	$\uparrow\uparrow\uparrow_T(t)$	$F\uparrow\uparrow\uparrow_F(f)\,,\ F = 1/T$

Table 2.2   Important CTFT Properties and Functions

Some key properties and functions of the continuous Fourier transform used frequently in the text are tabulated in Table 2.2. Derivations of these relationships, particularly those involving impulse functions, may be found in many standard texts [Brigham, 1974; Rabiner and Gold, 1975; Oppenheim and Schafer, 1975; Bracewell, 1978]. Note that the rectangular *window* function is defined as

$$\text{wind}(x) = \begin{cases} 1 & |x| < 1 \\ 1/2 & |x| = 1 \\ 0 & |x| > 1 \end{cases} \tag{2.26}$$

and the *sinc* function is defined as

$$\text{sinc}(x) = \frac{\sin(\pi x)}{\pi x} \quad . \tag{2.27}$$

Of special interest in Sec. 2.6 is the *sampling function*, defined as

$$⊔⊔⊔_W(x) = \sum_{n=-\infty}^{\infty} \delta(x - nW) \quad , \tag{2.28}$$

which has a transform that is also a sampling function. It has also been called a *replicating function* for reasons to be explained in the next section.

Another significant property is *Parseval's theorem* for two functions $g(t)$ and $h(t)$,

$$\int_{-\infty}^{\infty} g(t)h^*(t)\,dt = \int_{-\infty}^{\infty} G(f)H^*(f)\,df \quad . \tag{2.29}$$

By setting $g(t) = h(t)$, Parseval's theorem becomes the *energy theorem*

$$E = \int_{-\infty}^{\infty} |h(t)|^2\,dt = \int_{-\infty}^{\infty} |H(f)|^2\,df \tag{2.30}$$

because the left-hand side of Eq. (2.30) is the total energy E in the signal $h(t)$. Expression (2.30) is simply a statement of conservation of energy in the two domains. Thus, the function

$$S(f) = |H(f)|^2 \tag{2.31}$$

represents the distribution of energy as a function of frequency, and is therefore called the *energy spectral density* (ESD) of the deterministic signal $h(t)$.

In addition to the ESD, two other spectral definitions relevant to deterministic signals have been described in the linear system literature. If $h(t)$ represents the impulse response of a filter, then its CTFT

$$H(f) = \int_{-\infty}^{\infty} h(t)\exp(-j2\pi ft)\,dt \tag{2.32}$$

is called the *frequency response function*. $H(f)$ is, in general, a complex quantity and is therefore expressible in polar format as

$$H(f) = |H(f)|\exp(j\theta(f)) \quad , \tag{2.33}$$

where the real functions $|H(f)|$ and $\theta(f)$ are defined as

$$|H(f)| = [\text{Re}\{H(f)\}^2 + \text{Im}\{H(f)\}^2]^{1/2}$$
$$\theta(f) = \tan^{-1}[\text{Im}\{H(f)\}/\text{Re}\{H(f)\}] \quad .$$

The function $|H(f)|$ is termed the *amplitude spectrum* of $h(t)$ and the function $\theta(f)$ is termed the *phase spectrum*.

2.6 SAMPLING AND WINDOWING OPERATIONS

In Sec. 2.7, the discrete-time Fourier series (DTFS) is developed as a special case of the CTFT. The development makes use of two basic signal processing operations: *sampling* and *windowing*. The effect of each operation on a signal and its transform is examined in this section. This will simplify the presentation in Sec. 2.7. A key result of this section is the sampling theorem, which indicates the conditions for which a sampled continuous-time signal or continuous-space signal may be recovered from its samples with no loss of information. The following discussions assume signals that are functions of time, although the presentation could analogously be developed for signals that are functions of space (see Appendix 2.B).

OPERATION	TIME FUNCTION	TRANSFORM FUNCTION
Time Windowing (NT-sec timewidth)	$\mathrm{TW} = \mathrm{wind}(2t/NT - 1)$	$\mathcal{F}\{\mathrm{TW}\} = NT\mathrm{sinc}(NTf)$ $\cdot \exp(-j\pi NTf)$
Frequency Windowing ($1/T$-Hz bandwidth)	$\mathcal{F}^{-1}\{\mathrm{FW}\} = \frac{1}{T}\mathrm{sinc}(t/T)$	$\mathrm{FW} = \mathrm{wind}(2Tf)$
Time Sampling (T-sec intervals)	$\mathrm{TS} = T{\uparrow\uparrow\uparrow}_T(t)$	$\mathcal{F}\{\mathrm{TS}\} = {\uparrow\uparrow\uparrow}_{1/T}(f)$
Frequency Sampling ($1/NT$-Hz intervals)	$\mathcal{F}^{-1}\{\mathrm{FS}\} = {\uparrow\uparrow\uparrow}_{NT}(t)$	$\mathrm{FS} = \frac{1}{NT}{\uparrow\uparrow\uparrow}_{1/NT}(f)$

Table 2.3   Windowing and Sampling Functions

Table 2.3 lists the windowing and sampling functions to be used in this discussion. The uniform *sampling interval* is T seconds. The *sampling frequency*, or *sampling rate*, is $F = 1/T$ Hz. Note that the windowing and sampling functions in the time domain are designated as TW and TS, respectively, whereas the windowing and sampling functions in the frequency domain are designated as FW and FS, respectively.

Assume that a continuous real-valued signal $x(t)$ to be sampled is *bandlimited* (BL) with maximum frequency F_0 Hz, that is, the CTFT of $x(t)$ is zero for $|f| > F_0$. The CTFT of a real signal $x(t)$ is always a symmetrical function with a total

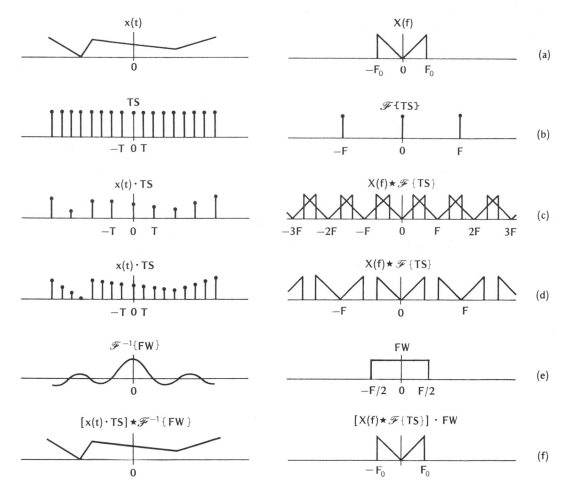

Figure 2.1   Illustration of the temporal sampling theorem for a real band-limited signal. (a) Original bandlimited time function and its transform. (b) Temporal sampling function and its transform. (c) Sampled time function and replicated transform when $F_0 > 1/2T$. (d) Sampled time function and replicated transform when $F_0 < 1/2T$. (e) Frequency window (ideal low-pass filter) and its transform (a sinc function). (f) Original time function recovered by convolution with sinc function.

frequency bandwidth of $2F_0$ Hz, as depicted in Fig. 2.1(a). A sampled function of $x(t)$ may be constructed by multiplication with the sampling function

$$x_S(t) = x(t) \cdot \text{TS} = T \sum_{n=-\infty}^{\infty} x(nT)\delta(t - nT) \quad . \tag{2.34}$$

The reader is cautioned that the above product of $x(t)$ with a train of impulse functions must be interpreted in the manner of Eq. (2.4). By the frequency convolution theorem, the CTFT of $x_S(t)$ is simply the convolution of the transforms of $x(t)$ and TS,

$$X_S(f) = X(f) \star \mathcal{F}\{\text{TS}\} = \sum_{k=-\infty}^{\infty} X(f - kF) \quad . \tag{2.35}$$

Convolving $X(f)$ with the sampling function $\mathcal{F}\{\text{TS}\} = \text{⫿}_{1/T}(f)$ simply *replicates* $X(f)$ at frequency separations of $1/T$ Hz, corresponding to the location of each impulse function. Thus, $X_S(f)$ is a periodic replication of $X(f)$. For this reason, $\text{⫿}(f)$ is often called a *replicating function*. In general, sampling in one domain forces a periodic extension in the transformed domain. If the sampling rate is selected too low such that $F < 2F_0$, then the replicated transforms will overlap with adjacent transforms, as illustrated in Fig. 2.1(c). This overlap is a distorting form of *frequency aliasing*. If the sampling rate is increased such that $F \geq 2F_0$, then there will be no overlap, as indicated in Fig. 2.1(d). The sampling frequency $F_N = 2F_0$ is known as the *Nyquist sampling rate* or *foldover frequency*.

In order to recover the original time signal from its samples, that is, to *interpolate* a continuum of values between the samples, one can filter the sampled data with an ideal rectangular low-pass filter FW, as illustrated in Fig. 2.1(e). The result, illustrated in Fig. 2.1(f),

$$X(f) = X_s(f) \cdot \text{FW} = [X(f) \star \mathcal{F}\{TS\}] \cdot \text{FW} \tag{2.36}$$

recovers the original CTFT. Using both the temporal and frequency convolution theorems, then

$$\begin{aligned} x(t) &= x_s(t) \star \mathcal{F}^{-1}\{\text{FW}\} = [x(t) \cdot \text{TS}] \star \mathcal{F}^{-1}\{\text{FW}\} \\ &= \sum_{n=-\infty}^{\infty} x(nT)\text{sinc}([t - nT]/T) \quad . \end{aligned} \tag{2.37}$$

Expressions (2.36) and (2.37) constitute a concise mathematical statement of the *temporal sampling theorem*. This theorem proves that a bandlimited real signal can be reconstructed exactly, using the bandlimited interpolation formula (2.37), from knowledge of an *infinite* number of samples taken at a sample rate $F \geq 2F_0$. The same arguments can also be used with complex-valued signals with a bandwidth of $2F_0$ Hz.

A dual theorem to expression (2.37) is the *frequency sampling theorem*. Rather than a bandlimited signal, consider a real function that is *time-limited* (TL), that is, a signal $x(t)$ which is zero for $|t| > T_0$. If one now samples in the frequency domain, rather than the time domain, at frequency intervals of $F \leq 1/2T_0$ (otherwise, there will be *time aliasing*), then a nonoverlapping, periodic extension of the TL signal is created. Placement of an ideal rectangular time window will recover the original TL signal; in the frequency domain, this corresponds to a filtering operation for reconstruction of the original transform. The time-domain operations that characterize the frequency sampling theorem are

$$x(t) = [x(t) \star \mathcal{F}^{-1}\{\text{FS}\}] \cdot \text{TW} \quad , \tag{2.38}$$

while the corresponding transform operations

$$\begin{aligned}
X(f) &= [X(f) \cdot \text{FS}] \star \mathcal{F}\{\text{TW}\} \\
&= \sum_{n=-\infty}^{\infty} X(n/2T_0) \operatorname{sinc}(2T_0[f - n/2T_0]) \\
&= \sum_{n=-\infty}^{\infty} X(nF) \operatorname{sinc}([f - nF]/F) \quad ,
\end{aligned} \tag{2.39}$$

in which $F = 1/2T_0$, will represent a time-limited interpolation procedure. Thus, the CTFT $X(f)$ of a time-limited signal may be uniquely recovered from the uniformly sampled transform values if a frequency sampling interval $F \le 1/2T_0$ Hz is selected.

2.7   RELATING THE CONTINUOUS AND DISCRETE TRANSFORMS

In order to generate spectral estimates from data samples that are scaled properly for energy and power units, it is necessary to use a slightly different definition and terminology for the usual definition of the discrete Fourier transform (DFT) found in most digital signal processing textbooks. The transform pair for the usual DFT definition of an N-point time sequence $x[n]$ and its N-point transform sequence $X[k]$ are

$$X[k] = \sum_{n=0}^{N-1} x[n] \exp(-j2\pi kn/N) \tag{2.40}$$

$$x[n] = \frac{1}{N} \sum_{k=0}^{N-1} X[k] \exp(j2\pi kn/N) \quad . \tag{2.41}$$

In this text, the *discrete-time Fourier series* (DTFS) pair

$$X[k] = T \sum_{n=0}^{N-1} x[n] \exp(-j2\pi kn/N)$$

$$x[n] = \frac{1}{NT} \sum_{k=0}^{N-1} X[k] \exp(j2\pi kn/N) \quad ,$$

defined for $0 \leq k \leq N - 1$ and $0 \leq n \leq N - 1$, will instead be used because the dependence on the sampling interval T is incorporated explicitly into the transform definitions. The justification for the DTFS name and definition, as well as the justification for other forms of the Fourier transform, is the subject of this section. The sampling and windowing operations introduced in Sec. 2.6 will be used to directly relate the CTFT to the DTFS and other Fourier transforms. Although the presentation approach here is rather unique, more detailed explanations of some of the developments within this section may be found in books by Brigham [1974], Bloomfield [1976], Papoulis [1977], Geçkinli and Yavuz [1983], and Oppenheim and Willsky [1983].

FW: Frequency-domain window
TW: Time-domain window
FS: Frequency-domain sampling
TS: Time-domain sampling

Figure 2.2   Two possible sequences of two windowing and two sampling operations to relate the CTFT to the DTFS.

The DTFS may be viewed as an approximation of the CTFT based on a finite number of data samples. To develop the exact nature of the relationship, a four-step sequence of linear operations is required. These operations are *windowing* in both the time and frequency domains, and *sampling* in both the time and frequency domains. As was demonstrated in Sec. 2.6, if windowing is performed in one domain, filtering (convolution) with the sinc function is performed in the other domain as a result of the convolution theorem. Similarly, if sampling is performed in one domain, periodic replication is performed in the other domain. Because windowing and sampling are linear and commutative operations, there are many possible ways in which to order the four operations, all of which will yield the identical end result, although the intermediate results will be different. Figure 2.2 suggests two possible sequences for the four operations. Consider first the sequence designated by node numbers 1, 2, 4, 6, and 8. The original continuous-time function $x(t)$ and its transform $X(f)$ are not restricted and may be, in general, nonperiodic, non-bandlimited, and non-time-limited. Assuming that N time samples of $x(t)$ are to be taken at uniform intervals of T seconds, the first operation, FW, bandlimits (windows in frequency) the signal to $\pm 1/2T$ Hz. The second operation, TS, samples the bandlimited signal in time at T-second intervals. The third operation, TW, time-limits the sampled signal to N samples. The fourth operation, FS, samples in frequency at intervals of $1/NT$ Hz, which periodically replicates the original N time samples. Using the function definitions in Table 2.3 that represent these four operations, the sequence of time-domain and frequency-domain operations that lead to the DTFS pair are given by

$$x_{\mathrm{DTFS}} = \Big(\big((x(t) \star \mathcal{F}^{-1}\{\mathrm{FW}\}) \cdot \mathrm{TS}\big) \cdot \mathrm{TW}\Big) \star \mathcal{F}^{-1}\{\mathrm{FS}\} \qquad (2.42)$$

$$X_{\mathrm{DTFS}} = \Big(\big((X(f) \cdot \mathrm{FW}) \star \mathcal{F}\{\mathrm{TS}\}\big) \star \mathcal{F}\{\mathrm{TW}\}\Big) \cdot \mathrm{FS} \quad . \qquad (2.43)$$

The sampling operations between nodes 2–4 and 6–8 are reversible by application of the temporal sampling theorem or the frequency sampling theorem, respectively. The appropriate operations are designated as FW and TW on reverse arrows between nodes 4–2 and 8–6, respectively. The other suggested path illustrated in Fig. 2.2 uses the node sequence 1, 3, 5, 7, and 8. This switches the ordering of the time-window/frequency-sample pair of operations with the frequency-window/time-sample pair of operations.

As a result of the windowing and sampling operations, four different types of Fourier relationships will be encountered at nodes 1, 4, 5, and 8, as indicated on Fig. 2.2: continuous-time Fourier transform, discrete-time Fourier transform, continuous-time Fourier series, and discrete-time Fourier series. A distinction has been made between Fourier *transform* and Fourier *series*. Those nodes at which the frequency-domain function is continuous are termed Fourier transforms; those nodes at which the frequency-domain function is discrete are termed Fourier series. Note that the historical terminology discrete Fourier transform (DFT), in reference to Eqs. (2.40) and (2.41), does *not* follow this convention.

The bandlimiting and time-limiting operations required to relate the DTFS and the CTFT show that the DTFS is a distorted variant of the original continuous-time signal $x(t)$ and transform $X(f)$. The effect of the bandlimiting creates a filtered time function at node 2 of

$$x_{BL}(t) = x(t) \star \mathcal{F}^{-1}\{\mathrm{FW}\} \quad , \qquad (2.44)$$

while the effect of time limiting creates a filtered transform function at node 3 of

$$X_{TL}(f) = X(f) \star \mathcal{F}\{\mathrm{TW}\} \quad . \qquad (2.45)$$

Samples of these functions are designated as $x_{BL}[n] = x_{BL}(nT)$ and $X_{TL}[k] = X_{TL}(k/NT)$.

Two other interesting observations can be made concerning the sequences of windowing and sampling operations depicted on Fig. 2.2. At node 5, the time windowing and frequency sampling operations create the *continuous-time Fourier series* (CTFS). The Fourier relationship at this node relates a continuous-time periodic function of period NT seconds to a discrete line spectrum. The following Fourier transform pairs may easily be established for this case, using the properties in Table 2.2 and the function definitions in Table 2.3, as

$$X_{TL}[k] = \int_0^{NT} x(t)\exp(-j2\pi kt/NT)\,dt \qquad k = 0, \pm 1, \pm 2, \ldots, \pm\infty \quad (2.46)$$

$$x(t) = \frac{1}{NT}\sum_{k=-\infty}^{\infty} X_{TL}[k]\exp(j2\pi kt/NT) \qquad 0 \le t \le NT \quad . \quad (2.47)$$

Note that Eq. (2.47) is a periodic function that matches the original time function at node 1 only over the 0-to-NT time interval. Expression (2.47) represents the traditional Fourier series representation of a periodic signal. Early literature referred to expression (2.46) as *harmonic analysis*. The energy theorem for the CTFS is simply

$$\int_0^{NT} |x(t)|^2\,dt = \frac{1}{NT}\sum_{k=-\infty}^{\infty} |X_{TL}[k]|^2 \quad . \quad (2.48)$$

This represents the energy over a period of NT seconds.

At node 4, the frequency windowing and time sampling operations have created the *discrete-time Fourier transform* (DTFT). It is characterized by a periodic *transform* function of period $1/T$ Hz. The following Fourier transform pairs may be established for this case, between the discrete-time sequence $x[n]$ to the continuous periodic transform $X(f)$

$$X(f) = T\sum_{n=-\infty}^{\infty} x_{BL}[n]\exp(-j2\pi fnT) \qquad -1/2T \le f \le 1/2T \quad (2.49)$$

$$x_{BL}[n] = \int_{-1/2T}^{1/2T} X(f)\exp(j2\pi fnT)\,df \qquad n = 0, \pm 1, \pm 2, \ldots, \pm\infty \quad . \quad (2.50)$$

Note that Eq. (2.49) is a periodic function that matches the original transform function at node 1 only over the $-1/2T$-to-$1/2T$ hertz frequency interval. The energy theorem for the DTFT is

$$T\sum_{n=-\infty}^{\infty} |x_{BL}[n]|^2 = \int_{-1/2T}^{1/2T} |X(f)|^2\,df \quad . \quad (2.51)$$

This represents the energy over a frequency period of $1/T$ Hz. Expression (2.49) is related to the z-transform of a discrete sequence as follows

$$X(f) = T\mathsf{X}(z)\Big|_{z=\exp(j2\pi fT)} \quad , \tag{2.52}$$

where $\mathsf{X}(z)$ is the z-transform of the sequence $x_{BL}[n]$. It is assumed that the region of convergence of the z-transform includes the unit circle. Thus, the discrete-time Fourier transform is simply the z-transform which has been evaluated along the unit circle of the z-plane and scaled by T. The discrete-time Fourier transform will be used frequently throughout this text.

Regardless of which of the two sequences of four operations is selected, the final result at node 8 is the same. At this node, the *discrete-time Fourier series* (DTFS) has been created, with the following transform relationships

$$X_{TL}[k] = T\sum_{n=0}^{N-1} x_{BL}[n]\exp(-j2\pi kn/N) \qquad k = -\frac{N}{2}, \ldots, \frac{N}{2}-1 \tag{2.53}$$

$$x_{BL}[n] = \frac{1}{NT}\sum_{k=-N/2}^{N/2-1} X_{TL}[k]\exp(j2\pi kn/N) \qquad n = 0, \ldots, N-1 \quad , \tag{2.54}$$

which follow from use of the properties in Table 2.3. The energy theorem for the DTFS is simply

$$T\sum_{n=0}^{N-1} |x_{BL}[n]|^2 = \frac{1}{NT}\sum_{k=-N/2}^{N/2-1} |X_{TL}[k]|^2 \quad , \tag{2.55}$$

representing the energy over N data samples.

Both sequences $x_{BL}[n]$ and $X_{TL}[k]$ are periodic modulo N, so the property $X_{TL}[-k] = X_{TL}[N-k]$ for $-N/2 \le k \le 1$ holds. Expression (2.54) may thus be equivalently written as

$$x_{BL}[n] = \frac{1}{NT}\sum_{n=0}^{N-1} X_{TL}[k]\exp(j2\pi kn/N) \tag{2.56}$$

for $0 \le n \le N-1$. Equations (2.53) and (2.54) constitute the discrete-time Fourier series pair related to the original continuous-time and continuous-frequency pair $x(t)$ and $X(f)$. The distinguishing differences between the DTFS equations and the usual discrete Fourier transform equations (2.40) and (2.41) is the factor T. The factor T, which represents the time sample interval in seconds, and the factor $1/NT$, which represents the frequency sample interval in Hz, are required in order that

Eqs. (2.53) and (2.54) represent, in effect, a rectangular integration approximation of the transform integral

$$\sum_{n=0}^{N-1} x[n] \exp(-j2\pi n fT)\, T \approx \int_0^{NT} x(t) \exp(-j\pi ft))\, dt \quad . \tag{2.57}$$

The T and $1/NT$ factors scale the DTFS by the sample rate, so that the correctly scaled energy and power values will be computed.

An examination of Fig. 2.2 will indicate the exact relationship required of the DTFS time sequence or the DTFS transform sequence in order for each to be the original continuous-time function or the original continuous-transform function, respectively. If $x(t)$ is inherently bandlimited to $1/T$ Hz total bandwidth, then the DTFS time sequence preserves the original $x(t)$ values at the sample points, but the DTFS transform sequence is composed of samples of a smeared version of the original transform $X(f)$ [see Eq. (2.44)]. Conversely, if $x(t)$ is inherently time-limited to NT seconds in extent, then the DTFS transform sequence preserves the original $X(f)$ values at the sample points, but the DTFS time sequence is composed of samples of a smeared version of the original signal $x(t)$ [see Eq. (2.43)]. The smeared effects may be mitigated by decreasing T (so that $1/T$ is a broader bandwidth) or by increasing N (so that NT is a broader time duration), thereby making the DTFS a better approximation of the CTFT. Note that the DTFS will be identical to the CTFT only for periodic signals that can be represented as a sum of the N complex sinusoids of frequencies k/NT Hz, for $k = 0$ to $k = N - 1$.

2.8 THE ISSUE OF SCALING FOR POWER DETERMINATION

In a manner analogous to definition (2.31) for the energy spectral density of the continuous-time Fourier transform, the energy spectral density of the discrete-time Fourier transform is

$$S_{\text{DTFT}}(f) = \left| X(f) \right|^2 = \left| T \sum_{n=-\infty}^{\infty} x_{BL}[n] \exp(-j2\pi fnT) \right|^2 , \tag{2.58}$$

based on energy theorem (2.51) and defined for $-1/2T \le f \le 1/2T$. The energy spectral density of the continuous-time Fourier series is

$$S_{\text{CTFS}}[k] = \left| X_{TL}[k] \right|^2 = \left| \int_0^{NT} x(t) \exp(-j2\pi kt/NT)\, dt \right|^2 , \tag{2.59}$$

based on energy theorem (2.48) and defined for $-\infty < k < \infty$. The energy spectral density of the discrete-time Fourier series is

$$S_{\text{DTFS}}[k] = |X_{TL}[k]|^2 = \left| T \sum_{n=0}^{N-1} x_{BL}[n] \exp(-j2\pi kn/N) \right|^2 \quad , \qquad (2.60)$$

based on energy theorem (2.55) and defined for $0 \le k \le N - 1$.

Both the CTFS and DTFS have periodic time functions with period NT seconds. Power is energy per unit time. Therefore, dividing the ESDs represented by Eqs. (2.59) and (2.60) by NT will yield the deterministic *power spectral densities* (PSD)

$$P_{\text{CTFS}}[k] = \frac{1}{NT} S_{\text{CTFS}}[k] \quad , \qquad (2.61)$$

defined for $-\infty < k < \infty$, and

$$P_{\text{DTFS}}[k] = \frac{1}{NT} S_{\text{DTFS}}[k] = \frac{T}{N} \left| \sum_{n=0}^{N-1} x_{BL}[n] \exp(-j2\pi kn/N) \right|^2 \quad , \qquad (2.62)$$

defined for $0 \le k \le N - 1$. Both are in units of power per Hz. The total power P in one period is then obtained by rectangular integration of the *area* under the PSD values,

$$P_{\text{CTFS}} = F \sum_{k=-\infty}^{\infty} P_{\text{CTFS}}[k]$$

$$P_{\text{DTFS}} = F \sum_{k=0}^{N-1} P_{\text{DTFS}}[k],$$

where $F = 1/NT$ is the discrete frequency sample interval in Hz. Some texts define a DTFS "spectrum" as

$$F \cdot P_{\text{DTFS}}[k] = \left| \frac{1}{N} \sum_{n=0}^{N-1} x_{BL}[n] \exp(-j2\pi kn/N) \right|^2 \qquad (2.63)$$

because it does not depend on the sample interval T. The value of Eq. (2.63) at each index k will yield exactly the power of a sinusoid of frequency k/NT Hz (see the Problems). However, Eq. (2.63) does not represent the correctly scaled PSD function; Eq. (2.62) does.

2.9   THE ISSUE OF ZERO PADDING

The discrete-time Fourier series may be modified to interpolate transform values between the N original transform values by a process called *zero padding*.

Consider adding N zero values $x[N], \ldots, x[2N-1]$ to the available data samples $x[0], \ldots, x[N-1]$. The DTFS of the zero-augmented $2N$-point data sequence is

$$X[k] = T \sum_{n=0}^{2N-1} x[n] \exp(-j2\pi nk/2N) = T \sum_{n=0}^{N-1} x[n] \exp(-j2\pi nk/2N) \quad , \quad (2.64)$$

where the range on the right-hand summation has been adjusted to reflect the zero samples. Let $k = 2l$, so that

$$X[l] = T \sum_{n=0}^{N-1} x[n] \exp(-j2\pi nl/N) \tag{2.65}$$

for $l = 0, 1, \ldots, N-1$ represents the even values of $X[k]$. The $2N$-point discrete-time Fourier series, therefore, reduces to that of the N-point discrete-time Fourier series at the even index values. The odd values of k represent the interpolated DTFS values between the original N-point DTFS values.

As more zeros are padded to the original N-point sequence, even more interpolation is obtained. Figure 2.3 illustrates the interpolative impact of zero padding. In the limit of infinite zero padding, the discrete-time Fourier series may be viewed as taking the discrete-time Fourier transform of an N-point windowed data sequence

$$X(f) = T \sum_{n=0}^{N-1} x[n] \exp(-j2\pi fnT) \quad . \tag{2.66}$$

The transform represented by Eq. (2.66) corresponds to node 6 in Fig. 2.2. There is a common misconception that zero padding improves the inherent resolution because it increases the data interval. As may be observed from Fig. 2.3, zero padding does *not* enhance the underlying resolution of the transform made from a given finite sample sequence. The zero padding simply provides an interpolated transform with a smoother appearance. It also removes ambiguities sometimes encountered in practice with the discrete-time Fourier series, due to narrowband signal components with center frequencies that lie between the N frequency evaluation points of a non-zero-padded discrete-time Fourier series, as illustrated in Fig. 2.3. The accuracy of estimating the frequency of spectral peaks is also enhanced with zero padding.

2.10 THE FAST FOURIER TRANSFORM

The fast Fourier transform (FFT) is not another Fourier transform. The name is descriptive of a number of computationally efficient *algorithms* for rapidly evaluating the discrete-time Fourier series. The concepts behind these algorithms have been discussed at length in numerous references [Otnes and Enochson, 1972; Brigham,

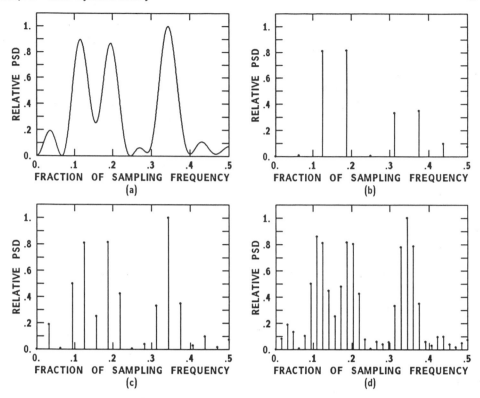

Figure 2.3 Transform interpolation by zero padding. (a) Magnitude of DTFT for a 16-point data record containing three sinusoids. (b) Magnitude of DTFS with no zero padding. Ambiguities are unresolved. (c) Magnitude of DTFS with double padding. Ambiguities are resolved because the three sinusoids can be distinguished. (d) Magnitude of DTFS with eight times zero padding.

1974; Rabiner and Gold, 1975; McClellan and Rader, 1979; Elliott and Rao, 1983; Bergland, 1969; Cochran et al., 1967]. It is not the purpose of this section to present yet another tutorial on this topic, but rather to provide a brief overview of the basis for the computational savings afforded by the FFT algorithm. The FFT is the first of several fast computational algorithms to be presented in this text for use in spectral estimation methods.

The central concept of the FFT is to divide an N-point DTFS into two or more smaller DTFSs, each of which can be individually computed and linearly combined to yield the DTFS of the original N-point sequence. These smaller DTFSs can, in turn, be divided into even smaller DTFSs of correspondingly smaller subsequences. In general, an N-point DTFS requires $\log_2 N$ stages with N adds and $N/2$ multiplies at each stage. Thus, an N-point FFT requires roughly $N \log_2 N$ adds and $N \log_2 N/2$ complex multiplies. This is a significant savings relative to the N^2 operations that would be required to individually evaluate N transform values from the N data points. If using zero padding, then even further reductions in computations may be achieved by eliminating, or *pruning*, computational paths involving only zero values. Details on pruning may be found in papers by Markel [1971] and Sreenivas and Rao [1979].

Appendix 2.C contains a FORTRAN program for a decimation-in-frequency FFT algorithm. More sophisticated FFT program codes may be found in Chap. 1 of the IEEE Press text *Programs for Digital Signal Processing* [1979], or in the text by McClellan and Rader [1979].

2.11 RESOLUTION AND THE TIME-BANDWIDTH PRODUCT

A common rule-of-thumb often used for spectral analysis suggests that the spectral resolution in hertz will be approximately the reciprocal of the signal observation time in seconds. Because the frequency spacing of the DTFS is $1/NT$ Hz, where NT is the total observed time interval, each DTFS frequency "bin" will, according to this rule, represent roughly the spectral resolution limit. This section examines the basis for this rule-of-thumb and places it in proper perspective as a measure of resolution. The results in this section apply to deterministic, finite-energy signals. The time-bandwidth product (TBP) will be revisited in Chap. 5, where it will be shown that a modification into a three-term statistical stability-time-bandwidth product is required to handle random signals of finite power.

A signal $x[n]$ cannot simultaneously be both time-limited and bandlimited. Although a function may not be strictly time-limited or bandlimited, it can still be characterized by an interval of T_e seconds in which most of its temporal energy is concentrated and by an interval B_e Hz in which most of its spectral energy is concentrated. In order to quantify the *temporal concentration* of a discrete-time signal sequence and the associated *frequency concentration* of its transform, several measures have been proposed. Two of these measures are presented here.

The *equivalent time width* T_e of discrete-time signal $x[n]$ is defined as

$$T_e = \frac{T \sum_{n=-\infty}^{\infty} x[n]}{x[0]} \quad , \tag{2.67}$$

that is, the "area" of the discrete signal divided by its central value. The equivalent time width of a signal is the time width of a rectangular signal with height equal to the value of $x[n]$ at the origin and area equal to that of the original signal. This is illustrated in Fig. 2.4(a) and (b). Note that T_e will not, in general, be an integral multiple of the sample interval T. The *equivalent bandwidth* B_e of the discrete-time Fourier transform $X(f)$ of $x[n]$ is defined analogously as

$$B_e = \frac{\int_{-1/2T}^{1/2T} X(f)\,df}{X(0)} \quad . \tag{2.68}$$

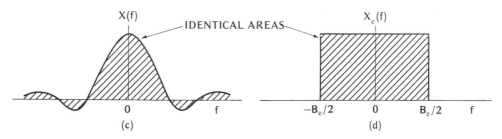

Figure 2.4   (a) Original signal sequence. (b) Equivalent time-width of rectangular signal of equal area and equal height as original signal. (c) Transform of original signal. (d) Equivalent bandwidth of rectangular transform of equal area and equal height as original transform.

This is illustrated in Fig. 2.4(c) and (d). These two measures of the temporal concentration and the frequency concentration apply only to signals that are real-valued and symmetric, that have the maximum value at the origin, and that integrate to a finite nonzero area. These conditions will hold exactly for the window functions to be considered in Chap. 5 in conjunction with the classical spectral estimators.

It is obvious from the transform relationships (2.49) and (2.50) that

$$X(0) = T \sum_{n=-\infty}^{\infty} x[n]$$

$$x[0] = \int_{-1/2T}^{1/2T} X(f)\, df \quad ,$$

$$(2.69)$$

from which it follows that the time-bandwidth product

$$T_e B_e = \frac{T \sum_{n=-\infty}^{\infty} x[n]}{x[0]} \cdot \frac{\int_{-1/2T}^{1/2T} X(f)\, df}{X(0)} = 1 \quad , \qquad (2.70)$$

that is, the equivalent widths of a signal and its transform are reciprocals. It is this unity TBP relationship that is responsible for the rule-of-thumb cited at the beginning of this section, for which T_e is considered to be the observation interval.

An alternative TBP may be defined, based upon mean-square width. The mean-square width is a measure of the variance (mean-square deviation) of a function about its mean value. In order to handle a broader class of functions than possible with equivalent width definitions (2.67) and (2.8), the mean-square width definitions are based on the squared-magnitude functions $|x[n]|^2$ and $|X(f)|^2$. This will permit complex-valued functions, oscillatory functions, and functions that have zero integrated area to have meaningful mean-square widths. The *mean-square time width* $\tilde{T}_e$ of discrete-time signal $x[n]$ is defined as

$$(\tilde{T}_e)^2 = \frac{T \sum_{n=-\infty}^{\infty} (nT)^2 |x[n]|^2}{T \sum_{n=-\infty}^{\infty} |x[n]|^2} \quad , \tag{2.71}$$

and the *mean-square bandwidth* $\tilde{B}_e$ of the DTFT $X(f)$ of $x[n]$ is defined analogously as

$$(\tilde{B}_e)^2 = \frac{\int_{-1/2T}^{1/2T} f^2 |X(f)|^2 \, df}{\int_{-1/2T}^{1/2T} |X(f)|^2 \, df} \quad . \tag{2.72}$$

These definitions assume that the mean values of $x[n]$ and $X(f)$ are located at the origins $x[0]$ and $X(0)$, although the definitions can be modified to handle the case for mean values not at the origin.

Noting that the energy E of $x[n]$ and $X(f)$ is given by Eq. (2.51) as

$$\mathsf{E} = T \sum_{n=-\infty}^{\infty} |x[n]|^2 = \int_{-1/2T}^{1/2T} |X(f)|^2 \, df \quad ,$$

then the mean-square width product $(\tilde{T}_e)^2 (\tilde{B}_e)^2$ is

$$(\tilde{T}_e)^2 (\tilde{B}_e)^2 = \frac{T \sum_{n=-\infty}^{\infty} (nT)^2 |x[n]|^2 \int_{-1/2T}^{1/2T} f^2 |X(f)|^2 \, df}{\mathsf{E}^2} \quad . \tag{2.73}$$

It can be shown [Bracewell, 1978; Papoulis, 1977] using a variation of the Schwartz inequality and assuming that the signal has finite energy E and satisfies

$$\lim_{n \to \infty} (nT) |x[n]|^2 = 0 \quad ,$$

then $(\tilde{T}_e)^2(\tilde{B}_e)^2 \geq 1/16\pi^2$. Therefore, the classical *root-mean-square* (rms) *time-bandwidth product* inequality satisfies

$$\tilde{T}_e \tilde{B}_e \geq \frac{1}{4\pi} \quad . \tag{2.74}$$

If $\tilde{T}_e$ and T_e are approximately the same time width, then the TBP of (2.74) establishes a smaller concentration bandwidth than given by the TBP of (2.70).

The *half-power* (3-dB) *bandwidth* B_h is often used in practice as an approximation for $\tilde{B}_e$ because it is easy to measure. This is the bandwidth about the origin of the transform at which the squared magnitude of the transform is half its squared magnitude at the origin, i.e., $|X(\pm B_h/2)|^2 = |X(0)|^2/2$.

The two TBP expressions (2.70) and (2.74) establish a relationship between the time concentration of a *single* signal and the spectral concentration of its transform. The TBP does *not* explicitly quantify the capability to *resolve* the spectral responses due to *two* or more signals. As a result, many proposed definitions of *resolution* have appeared in the literature. Most concern the capability to resolve the responses of *two* sinusoids that are close in frequency and equal in amplitude. These definitions rely on some measure of how close two sinusoids may be before their spectral responses are indistinguishable. The general concept behind these definitions assumes that the frequency separation of the sinusoids may be no closer than the equivalent bandwidth of the window through which a segment of the two sinusoids is observed. Because most resolution measures deal with signals as seen through windows, the time-bandwidth product $T_e B_e$ is most often used to establish the equivalent bandwidth, and therefore, the resolution. Thus, resolution in hertz is said to be approximately equal to the reciprocal of the observation time. Some spectral estimation methods in this text can achieve resolutions better than this. This suggests that the TBP must be interpreted carefully if used to infer resolution. The high-resolution methods effectively extrapolate the measured signal beyond its observed interval. The effective time interval has a larger time concentration than the original observation interval. This means T_e is effectively larger, so that B_e will be smaller and the resolution correspondingly better.

REFERENCES

Bergland, G. D., A Guided Tour of the Fast Fourier Transform, *IEEE Spectrum*, vol. 6, pp. 41–52, July 1969.

Bloomfield, Peter, *Fourier Analysis of Time Series: An Introduction*, John Wiley & Sons, Inc., New York, 1976.

Bracewell, R., *The Fourier Transform and Its Applications*, McGraw-Hill Book Company, New York, 1978.

Brigham, E. Oran, *The Fast Fourier Transform*, Prentice-Hall, Inc., Englewood Cliffs, N. J., 1974.

Cochran, W. T., et al., What Is the Fast Fourier Transform?, *IEEE Trans. Audio Elec-troacoust.*, vol. AU-15, pp. 45–55, June 1967.

Digital Signal Processing Committee, ed., Fast Fourier Transform Subroutines, Chapter 1 in *Programs for Digital Signal Processing*, IEEE Press, New York, 1979.

Elliott, D. F., and K. R. Rao, *Fast Algorithms–Applications, Analysis, and Application*, Academic Press, Inc., New York, 1983.

Geckinli, N. C., and Davras Yavuz, *Discrete Fourier Transformation and Its Applications to Power Spectra Estimation*, Elsevier Scientific Publishing Company, Amsterdam, 1983.

Markel, J. D., FFT Pruning, *IEEE Trans. Audio Electroacoust.*, vol. AU-19, pp. 305–311, December 1971.

McClellan, J. H., and C. M. Rader, eds., *Number Theory in Digital Signal Processing*, Prentice-Hall, Inc., Englewood Cliffs, N. J., 1979.

Oppenheim, A. V., and R. W. Schafer, *Digital Signal Processing*, Prentice-Hall, Inc., Englewood Cliffs, N. J., 1975.

Oppenheim, A. V., and A. S. Willsky, *Signals and Systems*, Prentice-Hall, Inc., Englewood Cliffs, N. J., 1983.

Otnes, R. K., and L. Enochson, *Digital Time Series Analysis*, John Wiley & Sons, Inc., New York, 1972.

Papoulis, Athanasios, *The Fourier Integral and Its Application*, McGraw-Hall Book Company, New York, 1962.

Papoulis, Athanasios, *Signal Analysis*, McGraw-Hill Book Company, New York, 1977.

Rabiner, L. R., and Ben Gold, *Theory and Application of Digital Signal Processing*, Prentice-Hall, Inc., Englewood Cliffs, N. J., 1975.

Sreenivas, T. V., and P. V. S. Rao, FFT Algorithm for Both Input and Output Pruning, *IEEE Trans. Acoust. Speech Signal Process.*, vol. ASSP-27, pp. 291–292, June 1979.

PROBLEMS

1. Prove that $\delta(at) = \delta(t)/|a|$, that is,

$$\int_{-\infty}^{\infty} \delta(at)\phi(t)\, dt = \frac{1}{|a|} \int_{-\infty}^{\infty} \delta(t)\phi(t/a)\, dt \quad .$$

2. Prove that the complex output of the complex demodulation of a real signal need only be sampled at half the rate of the original real signal.

3. Suppose that only the first $N/2$ of the N transform output values are needed from subroutine FFT. Show how pruning may be incorporated to reduce the computational complexity of the program. What is the amount of computational reduction?

4. Show that

$$\mathrm{III}(ax) = \frac{1}{|a|} \sum_{n=-\infty}^{\infty} \delta\left(x - \frac{n}{a}\right)$$

and

$$\frac{1}{\tau} f(x) \amalg (x/\tau) = \sum_{n=-\infty}^{\infty} f(n\tau) \delta(x - n\tau) \quad .$$

5. A factorization problem: given the function $g(t)$ with a transform $G(f)$ which is non-negative, find a causal function $f(t)$ such that $g(t) = f(t) \star f^*(t)$, which implies that $G(f) = |f(f)|^2$.

6. A TBP problem: define the one-sided exponential

$$x[n] = \begin{cases} A \exp(-\alpha nT) & \text{for } n \geq 0 \\ 0 & \text{for } n < 0 \end{cases} \quad ,$$

where T is the sample interval and α is a positive constant. Find T_e, B_e, $\tilde{T}_e$, and $\tilde{B}_e$ and the respective TBPs for this function. Which TBP is smaller? Why?

7. Find the equivalent time width and equivalent bandwidth of the windows defined in Table 5.1.

8. Define the function

$$x(t) = \begin{cases} \exp(-.1t) + \exp(-.5t) & 0 \leq t \leq 10 \text{ sec} \\ 0 & \text{otherwise} \end{cases} \quad .$$

Compute the CTFT energy E of this function using Eq. (2.30). If $x(t)$ is sampled at intervals of T seconds starting at $t = 0$, what value of T is required so that the DTFT energy equation (2.51) approximates the CTFT energy within 1%? What value of T is required if the match is to be within .01%?

9. Let $x[n] = A \exp(-j2\pi nk/N)$. Show that Eq. (2.63) will yield the power of the complex sinusoid $x[n]$.

10. Prove the energy theorem (2.54) for the discrete-time Fourier series.

APPENDIX 2.A
SOURCE OF COMPLEX-VALUED SIGNALS

Although most discrete-time signals originate as real-valued samples of a continuous-time signal, modern signal processing systems very often convert the real-valued samples into complex-valued samples at some point in the processsing chain because real samples are multiplied with a complex sinusoid $\exp(j\omega t)$. For example, processing in the frequency domain is often a system requirement. This means that the complex-valued DTFS $X[k]$

$$X[k] = T \sum_{n=0}^{N-1} x[n] \exp(-j2\pi kn/N)$$

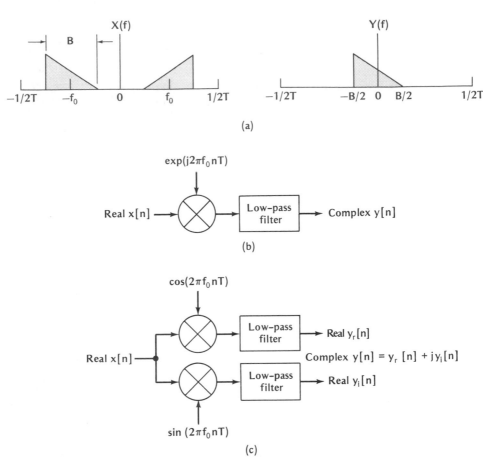

Figure 2.5   Complex demodulation process. (a) Spectra of original real signal (left) and demodulated complex signal (right). (b) Complex demodulator. (c) Scheme to implement complex demodulation.

will be used in the processing, which involves complex sinusoid products.

Complex demodulation of real-valued bandpass signals to complex-valued baseband signals is another common source of complex data. Consider in Fig. 2.5(a) the symmetric spectrum of the real-valued baseband signal and the desired complex-valued baseband signal centered at 0 Hz. This baseband signal of bandwidth B Hz is created by forming the product $x[n] \exp(j2\pi f_0 nT)$, in which f_0 is the center frequency of the bandpass signal, and then filtering the resulting complex signal by a low-pass filter with real-valued coefficients and band edges at $\pm B/2$ Hz, as shown in Fig. 2.5(b). Noting that

$$\exp(j2\pi f_0 nT) = \cos(2\pi f_0 nT) + j\,\sin(2\pi f_0 nT) \quad ,$$

then a practical implementation of complex demodulation is depicted in Fig. 2.5(c).

APPENDIX 2.B
WAVENUMBER PROCESSING WITH LINEAR SPATIAL ARRAYS

A temporal complex sinusoid has the exponential form $\exp(j2\pi fnT)$ for $1 \leq n \leq N$ when sampled at uniform increments of T seconds across a time aperture of NT seconds. Spectral analysis is used to determine the sinusoidal frequency f from the N data samples. The analogous spatial problem is encountered when processing signals from an array of uniformly spaced sensors, as illustrated in Fig. 2.6. A monochromatic plane wave of frequency f impinging on the array at an angle θ will have the exponential form $\exp(j2\pi knD)$ for $1 \leq n \leq N$ when sampled at uniform intersensor spacing increments of D across a spatial aperture of length ND. Spectral analysis is used to determine the wavenumber k from the N sensor samples. The wavenumber is related to the angle-of-incidence θ as follows

$$k = \frac{f}{c} \sin \theta = \frac{1}{\lambda} \sin \theta$$

in which c is the plane wave velocity of propagation and λ is the plane wave wavelength. Thus, spatial spectral analysis may be use for direction finding by relating the angle θ to the estimated wavenumber k.

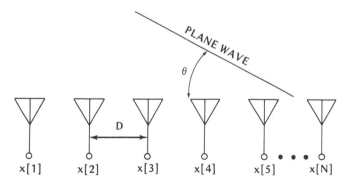

Figure 2.6   Linear array of N sensors with spacing D.

APPENDIX 2.C
FAST FOURIER TRANSFORM PROGRAM

There are a variety of FFT computer programs available, both in commercial sub-routine packages and in the literature (e.g., Chapter 1 in *Programs for Digital Signal Processing* [1979] or the edited text by McClellan and Rader [1979]). For completeness, however, a simple radix–2 decimation-in-frequency FFT program is included. It is used by several programs within this text. Once these programs have been verified with the FFT subroutine here, users may then substitute their own FFT algorithm choice.

Two FORTRAN subroutines are used to compute the FFT. The subroutine PREFFT is called once in order to set up the complex exponential table. Parameter MODE is set to either 0 or 1, depending on whether a forward or inverse DTFS is desired. PREFFT will also verify that the number of samples entered is a power of 2. An error code is returned if N is not a power of 2. Once PREFFT has been called, subroutine FFT may then be called repetitively to process as many N-point data sets as desired. Subroutine FFT is a decimation-in-frequency, radix-2, in-place (original input data array is replaced with output transform values) algorithm. Selecting MODE as 0 will compute the DTFS

$$X[k] = T \sum_{n=0}^{N-1} x[n] \exp(-j2\pi kn/N) \qquad (2.\text{C}.1)$$

and setting MODE to 1 will compute the inverse DTFS

$$x[n] = \frac{1}{NT} \sum_{k=0}^{N-1} X[k] \exp(j2\pi kn/N) \qquad (2.\text{C}.2)$$

for $0 \leq k, n \leq N - 1$. The data and transform are indexed from 1 to N in the subroutine, rather than 0 to $N - 1$ as defined above. To use the program with real data, simply set the imaginary component to zero before calling the subroutine.

If the 64-point test data sequence of Appendix II is used with the parameter selection N=64, MODE=0, and T=1., then the following partial listing of output values should be computed:

```
X( 1) = ( -1.62146,  1.55632)
X( 2) = ( -1.82918,  1.65053)
X( 3) = ( -2.06704,  1.76419)
    :           :         :
    :           :         :
X(62) = ( -1.21244,  1.34462)
X(63) = ( -1.31569,  1.40536)
X(64) = ( -1.45793,  1.48031)   .
```

```
C     These two programs set up the complex exponential table (PREFFT) and
C     compute the discrete-time Fourier series of an array of complex data
C     samples using a decimation-in-frequency fast Fourier transform (FFT)
C     algorithm.
C
      SUBROUTINE PREFFT (N,MODE,NEXP,W)
C
C     Input Parameters:
C
C     N      - Number of data samples to be processed (integer-must be a
C              power of two)
C     MODE   - Set to 0 for discrete-time Fourier series (Eq. 2.C.1) or
C              1 for inverse (Eq. 2.C.2)
C
C     Output Parameters:
C
C     NEXP   - Indicates power-of-2 exponent such that N=2**NEXP .
C              Will be set to -1 to indicate error condition if N
C              is not a power of 2 (this integer used by sub. FFT)
C     W      - Complex exponential array
C
C     Notes:
C
C     External array W must be dimensioned .GE. N by calling program.
C
      COMPLEX W(1),C1,C2
      NEXP=1
5     NT=2**NEXP
      IF (NT .GE. N)  GO TO 10
      NEXP=NEXP+1
      GO TO 5
10    IF (NT .EQ. N)  GO TO 15
      NEXP=-1                    ! Error:  N is not a power of 2
      RETURN
15    S=8.*ATAN(1.)/FLOAT(NT)
      C1=CMPLX(COS(S),-SIN(S))
      IF (MODE .NE. 0)  C1=CONJG(C1)
      C2=(1.,0.)
      DO 20 K=1,NT
        W(K)=C2
20      C2=C2*C1
      RETURN
      END


      SUBROUTINE FFT (N,MODE,T,NEXP,W,X)
C
C     Input Parameters:
C
C     N,MODE,NEXP,W - See parameter list for subroutine PREFFT
C     T             - Sample interval in seconds
C     X             - Array of N complex data samples, X(1) to X(N)
C
C     Output Parameters:
C
C     X - N complex transform values replace original data samples
C         indexed from k=1 to k=N, representing the frequencies
C         (k-1)/NT hertz
```

```
C
C   Notes:
C
C      External array X must be dimensioned .GE. N by calling program.
C
        COMPLEX X(1),W(1),C1,C2
        MM=1
        LL=N
        DO 70 K=1,NEXP
          NN=LL/2
          JJ=MM+1
          DO 40 I=1,N,LL
            KK=I+NN
            C1=X(I)+X(KK)
            X(KK)=X(I)-X(KK)
40          X(I)=C1
          IF (NN .EQ. 1) GO TO 70
          DO 60 J=2,NN
            C2=W(JJ)
            DO 50 I=J,N,LL
              KK=I+NN
              C1=X(I)+X(KK)
              X(KK)=(X(I)-X(KK))*C2
50            X(I)=C1
60        JJ=JJ+MM
          LL=NN
          MM=MM*2
70        CONTINUE
        NV2=N/2
        NM1=N-1
        J=1
        DO 90 I=1,NM1
          IF (I .GE. J)  GO TO 80
          C1=X(J)
          X(J)=X(I)
          X(I)=C1
80        K=NV2
85        IF (K .GE. J)  GO TO 90
          J=J-K
          K=K/2
          GO TO 85
90        J=J+K
        IF (MODE .EQ. 0)  S=T
        IF (MODE .NE. 0)  S=1./(T*FLOAT(N))
        DO 100 I=1,N
100       X(I)=X(I)*S
        RETURN
        END
```

3

REVIEW OF
MATRIX ALGEBRA

3.1 INTRODUCTION

An indispensible tool for describing the mathematical relationships of many digital spectral estimation techniques is linear algebra, with a particular emphasis on matrix operations. Matrices provide a convenient, concise method for systematizing detailed algebraic and numerical relationships that occur frequently in spectral analysis. The section on the Toeplitz matrix is particularly relevant for many spectral estimation methods to be discussed. The goal of this chapter is to introduce basic matrix notation and matrix algebra operations that will be used extensively throughout this book. Some familiarity on the part of the reader with the subject of linear algebra is assumed and, therefore, most results provided in this chapter are provided without proofs. Proofs and other details may be found by consulting the reference list at the end of this chapter, particularly that of Noble and Daniel [1977].

3.2 MATRIX ALGEBRA BASICS

A *matrix* is defined as a set of real or complex numbers arranged in a rectangular array

$$\mathbf{A} = \{a[i,j]\} = \begin{pmatrix} a[1,1] & a[1,2] & \cdots & a[1,n] \\ a[2,1] & a[2,2] & \cdots & a[2,n] \\ \vdots & \vdots & \ddots & \vdots \\ a[m,1] & a[m,2] & \cdots & a[m,n] \end{pmatrix} \tag{3.1}$$

of m rows and n columns. The individual entries in the matrix, such as $a[i,j]$, are the *elements* of the matrix. The mn elements compose a matrix said to be of *dimension*, or size, $m \times n$. Here $a[i,j]$ designates the element in the ith row and jth column of the matrix, where $1 \le i \le m$ and $1 \le j \le n$. Matrices throughout this text will be denoted by boldface capital letters.

A *block matrix* is a matrix composed of elements that are themselves matrices

$$\underline{\mathbf{A}} = \{\mathbf{A}[i,j]\} = \begin{pmatrix} \mathbf{A}[1,1] & \cdots & \mathbf{A}[1,q] \\ \vdots & \ddots & \vdots \\ \mathbf{A}[p,1] & \cdots & \mathbf{A}[p,q] \end{pmatrix}. \tag{3.2}$$

Each matrix element $\mathbf{A}[i,j]$ has the same $m \times n$ dimension. The *block dimension* of $\underline{\mathbf{A}}$ is said to be $p \times q$. The *scalar dimension* of the matrix $\underline{\mathbf{A}}$ is then $pm \times qn$. A block matrix will be denoted by an underlined boldface capital letter. The block definition will be useful later for the presentations on multichannel and two-dimensional spectral estimation.

A *row vector* is a $1 \times n$ matrix

$$\mathbf{b} = \begin{pmatrix} b[1] & b[2] & \cdots & b[n] \end{pmatrix}$$

and is denoted simply with a bold lowercase letter. A *column vector* is a $m \times 1$ matrix

$$\mathbf{c} = \begin{pmatrix} c[1] \\ \vdots \\ c[m] \end{pmatrix}$$

and is also denoted by a bold lowercase letter. A *block column vector* is simply a block matrix of block dimension $p \times 1$ (scalar dimension $pm \times n$)

$$\underline{\mathbf{c}} = \begin{pmatrix} \mathbf{C}[1] \\ \vdots \\ \mathbf{C}[p] \end{pmatrix} \tag{3.3}$$

and is denoted by an underlined bold lowercase letter.

Matrices $\mathbf{A}$ and $\mathbf{B}$ are said to be equal if and only if $\mathbf{A}$ and $\mathbf{B}$ have the same row dimension and the same column dimension and $a[i,j] = b[i,j]$ for all i and j. The sum or difference of two $m \times n$ matrices $\mathbf{A}$ and $\mathbf{B}$ to form a new matrix $\mathbf{C}$

$$\mathbf{C} = \mathbf{A} \pm \mathbf{B} \tag{3.4}$$

is obtained simply by summing or differencing the corresponding elements

$$c[i,j] = a[i,j] \pm b[i,j]$$

for $1 \le i \le m$ and $1 \le j \le n$. Note that matrix addition is both associative and commutative. Multiplication of a matrix $\mathbf{A}$ by a scalar α is defined by

$$\alpha\mathbf{A} = \{\alpha a[i,j]\} \quad . \tag{3.5}$$

Two matrices $\mathbf{A}$ and $\mathbf{B}$ can be multiplied together in the order $\mathbf{AB}$ to yield the resultant matrix $\mathbf{C}$ if and only if the number of columns in $\mathbf{A}$ equals the number of rows in $\mathbf{B}$. The (i,k) element of the product $\mathbf{AB}$ is obtained by multiplication of the elements of the ith row of $\mathbf{A}$ with the elements of the kth column of $\mathbf{B}$. That is, if $\mathbf{A} = \{a[i,j]\}$ is $m \times n$ and $\mathbf{B} = \{b[j,k]\}$ is $n \times p$, then the matrix $\mathbf{C} = \mathbf{AB}$ is an $m \times p$ matrix with elements

$$c[i,k] = \sum_{j=1}^{n} a[i,j]b[j,k] \quad . \tag{3.6}$$

Note that matrix multiplication is associative, but is not, in general, commutative ($\mathbf{AB} \ne \mathbf{BA}$). Note also that $\mathbf{AB} = \mathbf{0}$, where $\mathbf{0}$ is the all-zeros matrix, does not necessarily imply that either $\mathbf{A} = \mathbf{0}$ or $\mathbf{B} = \mathbf{0}$. The relationship $\mathbf{AB} = \mathbf{AC}$ also does not necessarily imply that $\mathbf{B} = \mathbf{C}$.

The *transpose* of an $m \times n$ matrix $\mathbf{A}$ is the $n \times m$ matrix $\mathbf{A}^T$ obtained by interchanging the rows and columns of $\mathbf{A}$

$$\mathbf{A}^T = \begin{pmatrix} a[1,1] & a[2,1] & \cdots & a[m,1] \\ a[1,2] & a[2,2] & \cdots & a[m,2] \\ \vdots & \vdots & \ddots & \vdots \\ a[1,n] & a[2,n] & \cdots & a[m,n] \end{pmatrix} \quad , \tag{3.7}$$

so that the element of $\mathbf{A}^T$ indexed by (i,j) is simply the element of $\mathbf{A}$ indexed by (j,i). The superscript ^{T} will be used to denote the transpose operation. It can be shown that the transpose of the sum of two matrices is the sum of their transposes

$$(\mathbf{A} + \mathbf{B})^T = \mathbf{A}^T + \mathbf{B}^T \quad , \tag{3.8}$$

while the transpose of the product of two matrices is the product of their transposes in reverse order

$$(\mathbf{AB})^T = \mathbf{B}^T\mathbf{A}^T. \tag{3.9}$$

Using the symbol * to denote complex conjugation, the matrix $\mathbf{A}^*$ will designate a matrix whose (i,j) element is the complex conjugate of the (i,j) element of $\mathbf{A}$. The *Hermitian transpose* of an $m \times n$ complex element matrix $\mathbf{A}$ is then the

$n \times m$ matrix $\mathbf{A}^H$ obtained by first complex conjugating all the elements of $\mathbf{A}$ and then transposing the elements in the usual fashion $[\mathbf{A}^H = (\mathbf{A}^T)^* = (\mathbf{A}^*)^T]$,

$$\mathbf{A}^H = \begin{pmatrix} a^*[1,1] & a^*[2,1] & \cdots & a^*[m,1] \\ a^*[1,2] & a^*[2,2] & \cdots & a^*[m,2] \\ \vdots & \vdots & & \vdots \\ a^*[1,n] & a^*[2,n] & \cdots & a^*[m,n] \end{pmatrix} . \tag{3.10}$$

The superscript ^{H} will be used throughout the text to denote the Hermitian transpose operation. Analogous to the transpose, it may be shown that

$$(\mathbf{A} + \mathbf{B})^H = \mathbf{A}^H + \mathbf{B}^H \tag{3.11}$$

$$(\mathbf{AB})^H = \mathbf{B}^H \mathbf{A}^H. \tag{3.12}$$

The *block Hermitian transpose* of a $p \times q$ complex block-element matrix $\underline{\mathbf{A}}$ is the $q \times p$ block matrix $\underline{\mathbf{A}}^H$ obtained by Hermitian transposing all the elements of $\underline{\mathbf{A}}$

$$\underline{\mathbf{A}}^H = \begin{pmatrix} \mathbf{A}^H[1,1] & \cdots & \mathbf{A}^H[p,1] \\ \vdots & \ddots & \vdots \\ \mathbf{A}^H[1,q] & \cdots & \mathbf{A}^H[p,q] \end{pmatrix} . \tag{3.13}$$

The use of bold lower-case letters to designate both column and row vectors is ambiguous. To prevent confusion in the text, bold lower-case letters will be reserved only for column vectors. References to "vector" in this book will mean column vector, unless explicitly indicated to be a row vector. A row vector can always be devised by simply transposing a column vector

$$\mathbf{c}^T = \begin{pmatrix} c[1] & \cdots & c[m] \end{pmatrix} . \tag{3.14}$$

A useful quantity encountered frequently is the vector *inner product* between two $n \times 1$ vectors

$$\mathbf{w} = \begin{pmatrix} w[1] \\ \vdots \\ w[n] \end{pmatrix} \qquad \mathbf{v} = \begin{pmatrix} v[1] \\ \vdots \\ v[n] \end{pmatrix}$$

defined as the scalar

$$\langle \mathbf{w}, \mathbf{v} \rangle = \sum_{j=1}^{n} w^*[j]v[j] . \tag{3.15}$$

Note that this can be expressed with normal matrix multiplication rules as

$$\langle \mathbf{w}, \mathbf{v} \rangle = \mathbf{w}^H \mathbf{v} . \tag{3.16}$$

In an analogous manner, the vector *outer product*, defined as $\mathbf{wv}^H$, forms an $m \times m$ square matrix from the $m \times 1$ vectors $\mathbf{w}$ and $\mathbf{v}$

$$
\mathbf{wv}^H = \begin{pmatrix} w[1]v^*[1] & w[1]v^*[2] & \cdots & w[1]v^*[m] \\ \vdots & \vdots & & \vdots \\ w[m]v^*[1] & w[m]v^*[2] & \cdots & w[m]v^*[m] \end{pmatrix}. \tag{3.17}
$$

A sense of the "size" of a vector can be expressed by either of the *vector norms*

$$
\|\mathbf{v}\|_1 = \sum_{i=1}^{m} |v[i]| \tag{3.18}
$$

$$
\|\mathbf{v}\|_2 = \left(\sum_{i=1}^{m} |v[i]|^2 \right)^{1/2} = \langle \mathbf{v}, \mathbf{v} \rangle^{1/2} \quad . \tag{3.19}
$$

Each of these norms yields nonnegative scalar values.

3.3 SPECIAL VECTOR AND MATRIX STRUCTURES

This section identifies several special vectors and matrices encountered frequently in the subject of spectral estimation. The reader should become familiar with the notations presented here, due to their frequent use throughout the text.

An $m \times 1$ *zero vector* of m zeros is denoted by

$$
\mathbf{0}_m = \begin{pmatrix} 0 \\ \vdots \\ 0 \end{pmatrix} \quad . \tag{3.20}
$$

The sequence $\exp(j2\pi fmT)$ is a *complex sinusoid* of frequency f, sampled at T second intervals. The *complex sinusoid vector* $\mathbf{e}_m(f)$ of frequency f is defined as the $(m+1) \times 1$ vector

$$
\mathbf{e}_m(f) = \begin{pmatrix} 1 \\ \exp(j2\pi fT) \\ \vdots \\ \exp(j2\pi fmT) \end{pmatrix} \quad , \tag{3.21}
$$

in which m designates the highest time index. The discrete-time Fourier transform (DTFT) for N data samples may then be expressed, for example, as the scaled vector inner product

$$
X(f) = T\,\mathbf{e}_{N-1}^H(f)\mathbf{x} \quad , \tag{3.22}
$$

for which the data vector $\mathbf{x}$ is defined as

$$\mathbf{x} = \begin{pmatrix} x[0] \\ \vdots \\ x[N-1] \end{pmatrix} .$$

A matrix for which the number of rows, n, equals the number of columns is said to be a *square matrix* of size $n \times n$. The elements $a[i,i]$ for $i = 1$ to n are said to lie on the *principal diagonal* (or *main diagonal*) of the square matrix $\mathbf{A}$. The elements $a[i, n+1-i]$ are said to be on the *cross diagonal*.

A *symmetric matrix* $\mathbf{S}$ is a square matrix such that

$$\mathbf{S}^T = \mathbf{S} \quad , \tag{3.23}$$

which means $s[i,j] = s[j,i]$ symmetrically about the principal diagonal. An example of a 4×4 symmetric matrix is

$$\mathbf{S} = \begin{pmatrix} s[1,1] & s[1,2] & s[1,3] & s[1,4] \\ s[1,2] & s[2,2] & s[2,3] & s[2,4] \\ s[1,3] & s[2,3] & s[3,3] & s[3,4] \\ s[1,4] & s[2,4] & s[3,4] & s[4,4] \end{pmatrix} . \tag{3.24}$$

A *Hermitian matrix* is a square $n \times n$ matrix $\mathbf{G}$ of complex elements with complex conjugate symmetry

$$\mathbf{G}^H = \mathbf{G}. \tag{3.25}$$

A *diagonal matrix* $\mathbf{D}$ is a square matrix in which all the elements are zero, except for the elements along the principal diagonal (some of which may be zero),

$$\mathbf{D} = \begin{pmatrix} d[1] & 0 & \cdots & 0 \\ 0 & d[2] & \cdots & 0 \\ \vdots & \vdots & \ddots & \vdots \\ 0 & 0 & \cdots & d[n] \end{pmatrix} . \tag{3.26}$$

The abbreviation $\mathbf{D} = \text{diag}\,(d[1], \ldots, d[n])$ will be used as a more compact description of a diagonal matrix.

The *identity matrix* $\mathbf{I}$ is a special case diagonal matrix in which all the diagonal elements are unity

$$\mathbf{I} = \begin{pmatrix} 1 & 0 & \cdots & 0 \\ 0 & 1 & \cdots & 0 \\ \vdots & \vdots & \ddots & \vdots \\ 0 & 0 & \cdots & 1 \end{pmatrix} . \tag{3.27}$$

If the size of the identity matrix is needed within a matrix equation, the dimension will be explicitly noted as a subscript. Thus, $\mathbf{I}_m$ denotes an $m \times m$ identity matrix. For any $m \times n$ matrix $\mathbf{A}$,

$$\mathbf{I}_m \mathbf{A} = \mathbf{A} \mathbf{I}_n = \mathbf{A}.$$

If the dimension subscript is omitted from $\mathbf{I}$, it will be understood from the context what dimension is required.

A close relative to the identity matrix is the *reflection matrix* $\mathbf{J}$ (sometimes called an *exchange matrix*)

$$\mathbf{J} = \begin{pmatrix} 0 & \cdots & 0 & 1 \\ 0 & \cdots & 1 & 0 \\ \vdots & \ddots & \vdots & \vdots \\ 1 & \cdots & 0 & 0 \end{pmatrix}, \tag{3.28}$$

which has unity elements along the cross diagonal. The $\mathbf{J}$ matrix reverses, or exchanges, the order of the rows or columns of a matrix or vector. Premultiplying an $m \times n$ matrix $\mathbf{A}$ by $\mathbf{J}_m$, where the subscript m denotes the reflection matrix size, yields a reversed ordering of rows (reflection about the central horizontal axis)

$$\mathbf{J}_m \mathbf{A} = \begin{pmatrix} a[m,1] & a[m,2] & \cdots & a[m,n] \\ \vdots & \vdots & & \vdots \\ a[2,1] & a[2,2] & \cdots & a[2,n] \\ a[1,1] & a[1,2] & \cdots & a[1,n] \end{pmatrix}, \tag{3.29}$$

whereas postmultiplying by $\mathbf{J}_n$ yields a matrix with reversed ordering of columns (reflection about the central vertical axis)

$$\mathbf{A} \mathbf{J}_n = \begin{pmatrix} a[1,n] & \cdots & a[1,2] & a[1,1] \\ a[2,n] & \cdots & a[2,2] & a[2,1] \\ \vdots & & \vdots & \vdots \\ a[m,n] & \cdots & a[m,2] & a[m,1] \end{pmatrix}. \tag{3.30}$$

As with the identity matrix, the dimension subscript of the $\mathbf{J}$ matrix will often be omitted when its size can be deduced from the context of a matrix equation. In an analogous manner for matrices, $\mathbf{J}\mathbf{c}$ will reverse the element order of the column vector $\mathbf{c}$, and $\mathbf{c}^T \mathbf{J}$ will reverse the element order of the row vector $\mathbf{c}^T$. It may be easily shown that $\mathbf{J}^T = \mathbf{J}$ and $\mathbf{J}^2 = \mathbf{J}\mathbf{J} = \mathbf{I}$.

A *persymmetric matrix* $\mathbf{P}$ is an $n \times n$ square matrix that is symmetric about its cross diagonal, as illustrated by the 4×4 example

$$\mathbf{P} = \begin{pmatrix} p[1,1] & p[1,2] & p[1,3] & p[1,4] \\ p[2,1] & p[2,2] & p[2,3] & p[1,3] \\ p[3,1] & p[3,2] & p[2,2] & p[1,2] \\ p[4,1] & p[3,1] & p[2,1] & p[1,1] \end{pmatrix}. \tag{3.31}$$

Thus, $p[i,j] = p[n-j+1, n-i+1]$. It may easily be shown that $\mathbf{P}^T = \mathbf{JPJ}$ and $\mathbf{P} = \mathbf{JP}^T\mathbf{J}$.

A *centrosymmetric matrix* $\mathbf{R}$ is an $n \times n$ square matrix with the property $r[i,j] = r^*[n-i+1, n-j+1]$. A special class of centrosymmetric matrices are those that are doubly symmetric, that is, Hermitian about the principal diagonal and persymmetric about the cross diagonal, as illustrated by the 4×4 complex matrix

$$\mathbf{R} = \begin{pmatrix} r[1,1] & r^*[2,1] & r^*[3,1] & r^*[4,1] \\ r[2,1] & r[2,2] & r^*[3,2] & r^*[3,1] \\ r[3,1] & r[3,2] & r[2,2] & r^*[2,1] \\ r[4,1] & r[3,1] & r[2,1] & r[1,1] \end{pmatrix}. \tag{3.32}$$

In this special case, $r[i,j] = r^*[j,i] = r[n-j+1, n-i+1] = r^*[n-i+1, n-j+1]$. It may easily be shown that $\mathbf{R} = \mathbf{JRJ}$ if $\mathbf{R}$ is real, or $\mathbf{R} = \mathbf{JR}^*\mathbf{J}$ if $\mathbf{R}$ has complex elements. When the dimension of a centrosymmetric matrix is even $(n = 2r)$, it may be partitioned into the form

$$\mathbf{R}_{even} = \begin{pmatrix} \mathbf{A} & \mathbf{B} \\ \mathbf{JB}^*\mathbf{J} & \mathbf{JA}^*\mathbf{J} \end{pmatrix}, \tag{3.33}$$

where $\mathbf{A}$ and $\mathbf{B}$ are general $r \times r$ matrices of no special structure. Similarly, when the dimension is of odd order, $n = 2r + 1$, then a centrosymmetric matrix may be partitioned as

$$\mathbf{R}_{odd} = \begin{pmatrix} \mathbf{A} & \mathbf{x} & \mathbf{B} \\ \mathbf{x}^H & \alpha & \mathbf{x}^H\mathbf{J} \\ \mathbf{JB}^*\mathbf{J} & \mathbf{Jx} & \mathbf{JA}^*\mathbf{J} \end{pmatrix}, \tag{3.34}$$

where $\mathbf{A}$ and $\mathbf{B}$ are general $r \times r$ matrices, $\mathbf{J}$ is an $r \times r$ reflection matrix, $\mathbf{x}$ is a column vector of dimension r, and α is a real scalar.

A very important matrix in spectral estimation is the *Toeplitz matrix* $\mathbf{T}$ (named after the German mathematician O. Toeplitz). It has the property that all the elements along any diagonal are identical, that is, $t[i,j] = t[i-j]$. A Toeplitz matrix can be, in general, nonsquare. An example of a 5×4 Toeplitz matrix is

$$\mathbf{T} = \begin{pmatrix} t[0] & t[-1] & t[-2] & t[-3] \\ t[1] & t[0] & t[-1] & t[-2] \\ t[2] & t[1] & t[0] & t[-1] \\ t[3] & t[2] & t[1] & t[0] \\ t[4] & t[3] & t[2] & t[1] \end{pmatrix}. \tag{3.35}$$

Note that a square Toeplitz matrix is a special case of a persymmetric matrix,

$$\mathbf{T} = \mathbf{JT}^T\mathbf{J}. \tag{3.36}$$

If a square Toeplitz matrix has the additional property that it is Hermitian, $t^*[k] = t[-k]$, then $\mathbf{T} = \mathbf{JT}^*\mathbf{J}$. Therefore, a Hermitian Toeplitz matrix is centrosymmetric.

A close relative of the Toeplitz matrix is the *Hankel matrix* **H**, which has the property that all the elements along any cross diagonal are identical, that is, $h[i, j] = h[i + j - n - 1]$. A Hankel matrix can be, in general, nonsquare. An example of a 4×5 Hankel matrix is

$$
\mathbf{H} = \begin{pmatrix}
h[-4] & h[-3] & h[-2] & h[-1] & h[0] \\
h[-3] & h[-2] & h[-1] & h[0] & h[1] \\
h[-2] & h[-1] & h[0] & h[1] & h[2] \\
h[-1] & h[0] & h[1] & h[2] & h[3]
\end{pmatrix} . \tag{3.37}
$$

Note that a square $n \times n$ Hankel matrix is a special case of a Hermitian matrix, that is, $\mathbf{H}^H = \mathbf{H}$. Hankel matrices can be related to Toeplitz matrices (see the Problems).

A *circulant matrix* $\mathbf{C}_R$ is a $n \times n$ square matrix composed from n unique complex elements. If the matrix elements have the relationship

$$
c_R[i, j] = \begin{cases} c_R[j - i] & \text{for } j - i \geq 0 \\ c_R[n - j + 1] & \text{for } j - i < 0 \end{cases} \tag{3.38}
$$

over the range $1 \leq i, j \leq n$, then the matrix $\mathbf{C}_R$ is said to be *right-circulant*. An example of a 4×4 right-circulant matrix is

$$
\mathbf{C}_R = \begin{pmatrix}
c_R[0] & c_R[1] & c_R[2] & c_R[3] \\
c_R[3] & c_R[0] & c_R[1] & c_R[2] \\
c_R[2] & c_R[3] & c_R[0] & c_R[1] \\
c_R[1] & c_R[2] & c_R[3] & c_R[0]
\end{pmatrix} . \tag{3.39}
$$

Observe that each row is formed from the row above it by shifting right one element and bringing the rightmost element to the left-hand side of the row. In a similar manner, one may define a *left-circulant* matrix $\mathbf{C}_L$ satisfying

$$
c_L[i, j] = \begin{cases} c_L[n + 1 - i - j] & \text{for } j + i \leq n + 1 \\ c_L[2n + 1 - i - j] & \text{for } j + i > n + 1 \end{cases} . \tag{3.40}
$$

An example of a 4×4 left-circulant matrix is

$$
\mathbf{C}_L = \begin{pmatrix}
c_L[3] & c_L[2] & c_L[1] & c_L[0] \\
c_L[2] & c_L[1] & c_L[0] & c_L[3] \\
c_L[1] & c_L[0] & c_L[3] & c_L[2] \\
c_L[0] & c_L[3] & c_L[2] & c_L[1]
\end{pmatrix} . \tag{3.41}
$$

Note that each row of a left-circulant matrix can be obtained from the row above it by a left shift, bringing the leftmost element to the right-hand side of the row. The right-circulant and left-circulant matrices are special cases of Toeplitz and Hankel matrices, respectively. An interesting alternative method to represent a circulant matrix makes use of the square $n \times n$ *shift matrix*

$$\mathbf{P} = \begin{pmatrix} 0 & 1 & 0 & \cdots & 0 \\ 0 & 0 & 1 & \cdots & 0 \\ \vdots & \vdots & \vdots & \ddots & \vdots \\ 0 & 0 & 0 & \cdots & 1 \\ 1 & 0 & 0 & \cdots & 0 \end{pmatrix}, \tag{3.42}$$

defined as $p[i, i+1] = 1$ for $1 \leq i \leq n-1$, $p[n, 1] = 1$, and zero otherwise. This is a special permutation matrix. The right-circulant matrix then has the representation

$$\mathbf{C}_R = \sum_{m=0}^{n-1} c_R[m] \mathbf{P}^m \tag{3.43}$$

where $\mathbf{P}^m$ denotes matrix exponentiation, that is, $\mathbf{P}$ multiplied by itself m times. Note that $\mathbf{P}^0 = \mathbf{I}$. Likewise, the left-circulant matrix has the representation

$$\mathbf{C}_L = \left(\sum_{m=0}^{n-1} c_L[m] \mathbf{P}^m \right) \mathbf{J} \; . \tag{3.44}$$

Another matrix form that is found in spectral estimation is the $m \times n$ *Vandermonde matrix* $\mathbf{V}$, whose elements are expressed in terms of powers of the n base parameters $x_1, \ldots, x_n$,

$$v[i, j] = x_j^{i-1} \quad \text{for} \quad 1 \leq i \leq m, 1 \leq j \leq n. \tag{3.45}$$

Therefore, an $m \times n$ Vandermonde matrix would have the structure

$$\mathbf{V} = \begin{pmatrix} 1 & 1 & \cdots & 1 \\ x_1 & x_2 & \cdots & x_n \\ x_1^2 & x_2^2 & \cdots & x_n^2 \\ \vdots & \vdots & & \vdots \\ x_1^{m-1} & x_2^{m-1} & \cdots & x_n^{m-1} \end{pmatrix}. \tag{3.46}$$

An *upper triangular matrix* $\mathbf{U}$ is an $n \times n$ square matrix with zero elements below its principal diagonal, i.e., $u[i, j] = 0$ for $j < i$. A 3×3 example is

$$\mathbf{U} = \begin{pmatrix} u[1,1] & u[1,2] & u[1,3] \\ 0 & u[2,2] & u[2,3] \\ 0 & 0 & u[3,3] \end{pmatrix}. \tag{3.47}$$

A *lower triangular matrix* **L** is an $n \times n$ square matrix with zero elements above its principal diagonal, i.e., $l[i, j] = 0$ for $j > i$. An example is

$$\mathbf{L} = \begin{pmatrix} l[1, 1] & 0 & 0 \\ l[2, 1] & l[2, 2] & 0 \\ l[3, 1] & l[3, 2] & l[3, 3] \end{pmatrix}. \tag{3.48}$$

3.4 MATRIX INVERSES

An $n \times n$ square matrix $\mathbf{A}^{-1}$ such that $\mathbf{A}^{-1}\mathbf{A} = \mathbf{A}\mathbf{A}^{-1} = \mathbf{I}$, if such a matrix $\mathbf{A}^{-1}$ exists, is called the *inverse* of the square matrix **A**. A square matrix that possesses such an inverse is said to be *nonsingular*. If it does not possess an inverse, the matrix is said to be *singular*. If **A**, **B**, and the product **AB** are all nonsingular, an important identity that will be used frequently is

$$(\mathbf{AB})^{-1} = \mathbf{B}^{-1}\mathbf{A}^{-1}. \tag{3.49}$$

A set of $n \times 1$ vectors $\mathbf{v}_1, \ldots, \mathbf{v}_n$ is said to be *linearly dependent* if there exists numbers $\alpha_1, \ldots, \alpha_n$, not all zero, such that

$$\alpha_1\mathbf{v}_1 + \alpha_2\mathbf{v}_2 + \ldots + \alpha_n\mathbf{v}_n = 0; \tag{3.50}$$

otherwise, the vector set is *linearly independent*. If the columns of a rectangular $m \times n$ matrix **A** are considered as individual $m \times 1$ vectors, then the *column rank* of **A** is the number of linearly independent column vectors. Similarly, if the rows of **A** are partitioned as individual $1 \times n$ row vectors, then the *row rank* of **A** is the number of linearly independent row vectors. It can be shown [Noble and Daniel, 1977] for any matrix that the row rank is equal to the column rank, so it is sufficient to indicate a single rank number to be associated with each matrix. A square $m \times m$ matrix **A** is nonsingular if and only if its rank is m (i.e., it is invertible). A *rank one* matrix can be expressed in the form of a vector outer product $\mathbf{v}\mathbf{w}^H$, because every column is a multiple of **v** and every row is a multiple of $\mathbf{w}^H$.

Another indicator of the singularity of a square $n \times n$ matrix **A** is a unique scalar number called the *determinant*, denoted $\det \mathbf{A}$. It is defined by the expression

$$\det \mathbf{A} = \sum_{j=1}^{n}(-1)^{1+j}a[1, j]A_{1j} \tag{3.51}$$

where $a[1, j]$ is an element from the top row of matrix **A** and A_{1j} is the determinant of the $(n-1) \times (n-1)$ matrix formed by omitting the first row, and jth column of the $n \times n$ matrix **A**. This is a recursive definition which starts with the fact that a 1×1 matrix (a single element) has a determinant equal to that element. More details on computing determinants may be found in standard linear algebra texts, such as Sec. 6.5 of Noble and Daniel [1977].

An $n \times n$ matrix $\mathbf{A}$ is singular if and only if $\det \mathbf{A} = 0$. Thus, if $\det \mathbf{A} \neq 0$, then the matrix is invertible. It may also be shown that the product of two $n \times n$ square matrices $\mathbf{A}$ and $\mathbf{B}$ has the determinant

$$\det \mathbf{AB} = \det \mathbf{A} \det \mathbf{B}. \tag{3.52}$$

It is also true that if $\mathbf{A}$ is Hermitian ($\mathbf{A}^H = \mathbf{A}$), then $\det \mathbf{A}$ is real-valued.

Two matrix inversion lemmas are frequently used in spectral analysis studies. If $\mathbf{A}$ is a nonsingular $n \times n$ matrix, $\mathbf{C}$ a nonsingular $m \times m$ matrix, $\mathbf{B}$ an $n \times m$ matrix, and $\mathbf{D}$ an $m \times n$ matrix, then the augmented matrix $\mathbf{A} + \mathbf{BCD}$ has the inverse

$$(\mathbf{A} + \mathbf{BCD})^{-1} = \mathbf{A}^{-1} - \mathbf{A}^{-1}\mathbf{B}\left(\mathbf{DA}^{-1}\mathbf{B} + \mathbf{C}^{-1}\right)^{-1}\mathbf{DA}^{-1} \tag{3.53}$$

assuming the inverse of $\mathbf{DA}^{-1}\mathbf{B} + \mathbf{C}^{-1}$ exists. This relationship is known as the *augmented matrix inversion lemma*. One specialized form of this lemma is of interest. If $\mathbf{C}$ is the unity scalar (a 1×1 matrix), $\mathbf{B}$ is an $n \times 1$ column vector $\mathbf{v}$, and $\mathbf{D}$ is a conjugated $1 \times n$ row vector $\mathbf{w}^H$, then

$$(\mathbf{A} + \mathbf{vw}^H)^{-1} = \mathbf{A}^{-1} - \frac{\left(\mathbf{A}^{-1}\mathbf{v}\right)\left(\mathbf{w}^H\mathbf{A}^{-1}\right)}{1 + \mathbf{w}^H\mathbf{A}^{-1}\mathbf{v}} \tag{3.54}$$

is the inverse of a matrix formed by augmenting $\mathbf{A}$ with a rank one matrix $\mathbf{vw}^H$.

Let the $n \times n$ matrix $\mathbf{Y}$ be partitioned in submatrices $\mathbf{A},\mathbf{B},\mathbf{C},\mathbf{D}$ as follows

$$\mathbf{Y} = \begin{pmatrix} \mathbf{A} & \mathbf{D} \\ \mathbf{C} & \mathbf{B} \end{pmatrix}, \tag{3.55}$$

where $\mathbf{A}$ is an $m \times m$ matrix, $\mathbf{B}$ is an $(n-m) \times (n-m)$ matrix, $\mathbf{C}$ is an $(n-m) \times m$ matrix, and $\mathbf{D}$ is an $m \times (n-m)$ matrix. The inverse of $\mathbf{Y}$ is given by

$$\begin{aligned}
\mathbf{Y}^{-1} &= \begin{pmatrix} \mathbf{A}^{-1} + \mathbf{A}^{-1}\mathbf{D}\boldsymbol{\Delta}^{-1}\mathbf{CA}^{-1} & -\mathbf{A}^{-1}\mathbf{D}\boldsymbol{\Delta}^{-1} \\ -\boldsymbol{\Delta}^{-1}\mathbf{CA}^{-1} & \boldsymbol{\Delta}^{-1} \end{pmatrix} \\
&= \begin{pmatrix} \boldsymbol{\Lambda}^{-1} & -\boldsymbol{\Lambda}^{-1}\mathbf{DB}^{-1} \\ -\mathbf{B}^{-1}\mathbf{C\Lambda}^{-1} & \mathbf{B}^{-1} + \mathbf{B}^{-1}\mathbf{C\Lambda}^{-1}\mathbf{DB}^{-1} \end{pmatrix},
\end{aligned} \tag{3.56}$$

assuming either that the inverses of $\mathbf{A}$ and $\boldsymbol{\Delta} = \mathbf{B} - \mathbf{CA}^{-1}\mathbf{D}$ exist, or that the inverses of $\mathbf{B}$ and $\boldsymbol{\Lambda} = \mathbf{A} - \mathbf{DB}^{-1}\mathbf{C}$ exist, whichever is appropriate. The matrices $\boldsymbol{\Delta}$ and $\boldsymbol{\Lambda}$ have been termed the *Schur complements* of $\mathbf{A}$. Equation (3.56) is known as the *partitioned matrix inversion lemma*. In the special case where $\mathbf{Y}$ is $n \times n$, $\mathbf{A}$ is an $(n-1) \times (n-1)$ matrix, $\mathbf{D} = \mathbf{v}$ is an $(n-1) \times 1$ column matrix, $\mathbf{C} = \mathbf{w}^H$ is an $1 \times (n-1)$ row vector, and $\mathbf{B} = \alpha$ is an 1×1 matrix (i.e., a scalar), then

$$\mathbf{Y}^{-1} = \begin{pmatrix} \mathbf{A}^{-1} + \beta\mathbf{A}^{-1}\mathbf{vw}^H\mathbf{A}^{-1} & -\beta\mathbf{A}^{-1}\mathbf{v} \\ -\beta\mathbf{w}^H\mathbf{A}^{-1} & \beta \end{pmatrix}, \tag{3.57}$$

MATRIX FORM	MATRIX INVERSE FORM
Hermitian (Symmetric)	Hermitian (Symmetric)
Persymmetric	Persymmetric
Centrosymmetric	Centrosymmetric
Toeplitz	Persymmetric
Hankel	Symmetric
Right Circulant	Right Circulant
Left Circulant	Left Circulant
Triangular	Triangular

Table 3.1 Matrix Inverse Structures

where the scalar $\beta = (\alpha - \mathbf{w}^H \mathbf{A}^{-1} \mathbf{v})^{-1}$. Thus, the inverse of a matrix formed by bordering the original matrix with an additional row and column (or by omitting a row and column) may be computed simply. Matrices created in this way are known as *border matrices*.

Table 3.1 lists the form of the inverse of the special matrices introduced in Sec. 3.3. Many of these are simple to prove. For example, to prove that the inverse of a persymmetric matrix $\mathbf{P}$ is also persymmetric, use the fact that $\mathbf{JJ} = \mathbf{I}$ to write

$$\mathbf{PP}^{-1} = \mathbf{PJJP}^{-1} = \mathbf{I}$$

and pre- and postmultiply by $\mathbf{J}$

$$\mathbf{J}(\mathbf{PJJP}^{-1})\mathbf{J} = \mathbf{P}^T(\mathbf{JP}^{-1}\mathbf{J}) = \mathbf{I} \quad .$$

This yields

$$\mathbf{JP}^{-1}\mathbf{J} = (\mathbf{P}^{-1})^T. \tag{3.58}$$

The property $(\mathbf{P}^T)^{-1} = (\mathbf{P}^{-1})^T$ has been used.

3.5 LEAST SQUARES NORMAL EQUATIONS

Matrix algebra provides a concise methodology for expressing the simultaneous linear equations of least squares analysis. Consider the approximation $\hat{y}[n]$ of the complex sequence $y[n]$ by a linear combination of the m complex sequences $x_1[n], x_2[n], \ldots, x_m[n]$

$$\hat{y}[n] = a_1 x_1[n] + a_2 x_2[n] + \cdots + a_m x_m[n] \tag{3.59}$$

for $1 \leq n \leq N$. It is assumed that $N > m$, so that Eq. (3.59) represents an overdetermined set of simultaneous equations. One method for uniquely assigning values to the unknown $a_1, \ldots, a_m$ parameters is to minimize the real sum of squared errors

$$E = \sum_{n=1}^{N} |e[n]|^2 \quad , \tag{3.60}$$

in which $e[n] = y[n] - \hat{y}[n]$ is the complex error between the actual sample value $y[n]$ and its linear approximation $\hat{y}[n]$.

An alternative description of the N error equations is

$$\mathbf{y} - \mathbf{Xa} = \mathbf{e} \quad , \tag{3.61}$$

in which the $N \times m$ data matrix $\mathbf{X}$, the $m \times 1$ column vector $\mathbf{a}$, and the $N \times 1$ column vectors $\mathbf{y}$ and $\mathbf{e}$ are defined as

$$\mathbf{X} = \begin{pmatrix} x_1[1] & \cdots & x_m[1] \\ \vdots & & \vdots \\ x_1[N] & \cdots & x_m[N] \end{pmatrix} \quad , \quad \mathbf{a} = \begin{pmatrix} a_1 \\ \vdots \\ a_m \end{pmatrix}$$

and

$$\mathbf{y} = \begin{pmatrix} y[1] \\ \vdots \\ y[N] \end{pmatrix} \quad , \quad \mathbf{e} = \begin{pmatrix} e[1] \\ \vdots \\ e[N] \end{pmatrix}.$$

By defining an $N \times (m+1)$ matrix $\mathbf{Z} = \begin{pmatrix} \mathbf{y} & \mathbf{X} \end{pmatrix}$, the error vector $\mathbf{e}$ may be expressed as

$$\begin{pmatrix} \mathbf{y} & \mathbf{X} \end{pmatrix} \begin{pmatrix} 1 \\ -\mathbf{a} \end{pmatrix} = \mathbf{Z} \begin{pmatrix} 1 \\ -\mathbf{a} \end{pmatrix} = \mathbf{e} \quad . \tag{3.62}$$

The squared error E may be expressed as

$$E = \mathbf{e}^H \mathbf{e} = \mathbf{y}^H \mathbf{y} - \mathbf{y}^H \mathbf{Xa} - \mathbf{a}^H \mathbf{X}^H \mathbf{y} + \mathbf{a}^H \mathbf{X}^H \mathbf{Xa}, \tag{3.63}$$

in which the vector inner product $\mathbf{y}^H \mathbf{y}$ forms a scalar, the matrix-vector product $\mathbf{X}^H \mathbf{y}$ forms an $m \times 1$ column vector, and the matrix-matrix product $\mathbf{X}^H \mathbf{X}$ forms an $m \times m$ square matrix.

The minimization of E may be obtained by inspection by first noting that Eq. (3.63) may be written as

$$\begin{aligned} E = \mathbf{y}^H \mathbf{y} &- \mathbf{y}^H \mathbf{X} (\mathbf{X}^H \mathbf{X})^{-1} \mathbf{X}^H \mathbf{y} \\ &+ (\mathbf{X}^H \mathbf{y} - \mathbf{X}^H \mathbf{Xa})^H (\mathbf{X}^H \mathbf{X})^{-1} (\mathbf{X}^H \mathbf{y} - \mathbf{X}^H \mathbf{Xa}) \end{aligned} \tag{3.64}$$

by "completing the square." Only the last term on the right-hand side of Eq. (3.64) is a function of the unknown parameter vector $\mathbf{a}$. Due to its Hermitian symmetry, this term will always be real and positive. In order to minimize E, this term must be set to zero. This is accomplished by selecting **a** such that

$$\mathbf{X}^H\mathbf{y} - \mathbf{X}^H\mathbf{X}\mathbf{a} = \mathbf{0}_m \quad ,$$

where $\mathbf{0}_m$ is the all-zeros vector. Thus, the vector **a** that minimizes the squared error is found by solving the set of m simultaneous equations

$$\mathbf{X}^H\mathbf{X}\mathbf{a} = \mathbf{X}^H\mathbf{y} \quad . \tag{3.65}$$

The minimum squared error is obtained by substituting Eq. (3.65) into Eq. (3.63), yielding

$$\mathsf{E}_{\min} = \mathbf{y}^H\mathbf{y} - \mathbf{y}^H\mathbf{X}\mathbf{a} \quad . \tag{3.66}$$

Equations (3.65) and (3.66) may be combined into a single set of $m+1$ simultaneous equations as follows

$$\begin{pmatrix} \mathbf{y}^H\mathbf{y} & \mathbf{y}^H\mathbf{X} \\ \mathbf{X}^H\mathbf{y} & \mathbf{X}^H\mathbf{X} \end{pmatrix} \begin{pmatrix} 1 \\ -\mathbf{a} \end{pmatrix} = \begin{pmatrix} \mathbf{y} & \mathbf{X} \end{pmatrix}^H \begin{pmatrix} \mathbf{y} & \mathbf{X} \end{pmatrix} \begin{pmatrix} 1 \\ -\mathbf{a} \end{pmatrix}$$
$$= \mathbf{Z}^H\mathbf{Z} \begin{pmatrix} 1 \\ -\mathbf{a} \end{pmatrix} = \begin{pmatrix} \mathsf{E}_{\min} \\ \mathbf{0}_m \end{pmatrix} \quad . \tag{3.67}$$

Equation (3.67) forms the *normal equations* of least squares analysis. Note that $\mathbf{Z}^H\mathbf{Z}$ forms a Hermitian matrix.

The squared error expression (3.63) is a special case of a matrix quadratic equation of the general form

$$\mathsf{E} = r - \mathbf{r}^H\mathbf{a} - \mathbf{a}^H\mathbf{r} + \mathbf{a}^H\mathbf{R}\mathbf{a} \quad , \tag{3.68}$$

in which r is a known positive scalar, **r** is a known $m \times 1$ column vector, and **R** is a known $m \times m$ Hermitian matrix. The normal equations that provide the solution for the $m \times 1$ vector **a** that minimizes the positive real-valued scalar E is given by

$$\begin{pmatrix} r & \mathbf{r}^H \\ \mathbf{r} & \mathbf{R} \end{pmatrix} \begin{pmatrix} 1 \\ -\mathbf{a} \end{pmatrix} = \begin{pmatrix} \mathsf{E}_{\min} \\ \mathbf{0}_m \end{pmatrix} \quad . \tag{3.69}$$

This follows directly from Eq. (3.67) by making the substitution of r for $\mathbf{y}^H\mathbf{y}$, **r** for $\mathbf{X}^H\mathbf{y}$, and **R** for $\mathbf{X}^H\mathbf{X}$.

3.6   SOLUTION OF LINEAR EQUATIONS

Many spectral estimation methods require the solution of a set of simultaneous linear equations, which may be generally expressed as a matrix equation

$$\mathbf{A}\mathbf{x} = \mathbf{b} \quad , \tag{3.70}$$

where $\mathbf{A}$ is some arbitrary $n \times n$ square matrix, $\mathbf{b}$ is some arbitrary $n \times 1$ column vector, and $\mathbf{x}$ is an $n \times 1$ vector of unknown values whose solution is to be found. An obvious method for obtaining the solution vector $\mathbf{x}$ is to premultiply both sides by $\mathbf{A}^{-1}$, the inverse (assuming it exists), to yield

$$\mathbf{x} = \mathbf{A}^{-1}\mathbf{b}. \tag{3.71}$$

However, this is often neither the most numerically efficient nor the most numerically stable method for solving linear equations. If the inverse does not exist, then the rank k of the matrix $\mathbf{A}$ is less than n. The *null space* of the matrix $\mathbf{A}$ is the linear subspace of nonzero vectors $\mathbf{x}$ that satisfy $\mathbf{Ax} = \mathbf{0}$. The null space will have dimension $n - k$.

If the $n \times n$ matrix $\mathbf{A}$ is triangular and nonsingular (i.e., the diagonal elements are nonzero), then the system of linear equations involving $\mathbf{A}$ can be solved in a number of computations proportional to n^2 by a method known as *back substitution*. Consider the 3×3 case below for an upper triangular matrix

$$\begin{pmatrix} a[1,1] & a[1,2] & a[1,3] \\ 0 & a[2,2] & a[2,3] \\ 0 & 0 & a[3,3] \end{pmatrix} \begin{pmatrix} x[1] \\ x[2] \\ x[3] \end{pmatrix} = \begin{pmatrix} b[1] \\ b[2] \\ b[3] \end{pmatrix}. \tag{3.72}$$

From the last row, observe that $a[3,3]x[3] = b[3]$, from which the solution $x[3] = b[3]/a[3,3]$ may be calculated. If $x[3]$ is substituted back into the matrix expression, then the second row will have only the one unknown $x[2]$, found by solution of $a[2,2]x[2] + a[2,3]x[3] = b[2]$. Continuing to back substitute will eventually solve for all the unknown x components.

For general $n \times n$ nonsingular matrices $\mathbf{A}$, the *Gaussian elimination procedure* may be used to solve $\mathbf{Ax} = \mathbf{b}$ using a three-step procedure. First, the matrix $\mathbf{A}$ is uniquely factored into a product of an upper triangular matrix $\mathbf{U}$ and a lower triangular matrix $\mathbf{L}$ (with 1's along the diagonal),

$$\mathbf{A} = \mathbf{LU} \quad . \tag{3.73}$$

This factorization is followed by two stages of "back" substitution, including the triangular matrix solution for vector $\mathbf{y}$

$$\mathbf{Ly} = \mathbf{b}, \tag{3.74}$$

followed by the triangular matrix solution for the $\mathbf{x}$ vector

$$\mathbf{Ux} = \mathbf{y}. \tag{3.75}$$

This method requires a number of computations proportional to n^3 and memory storage proportional to n^2.

If the matrix $\mathbf{A}$ is square and Hermitian, then the usual triangular factorization takes on the special form

$$\mathbf{A} = \mathbf{R}\mathbf{R}^H \quad , \tag{3.76}$$

where $\mathbf{R}$ is a lower triangular matrix with nonzero real principal diagonal elements. This decomposition is called the *Cholesky decomposition*. Due to the Hermitian symmetry of $\mathbf{A}$, the number of computations required to solve a set of Hermitian equations by Cholesky factorization is about half that required for Gaussian elimination because only the matrix $\mathbf{R}$, rather than the two matrices $\mathbf{L}$ and $\mathbf{U}$, need be computed. Program CHOLESKY in Appendix 3.A is a FORTRAN program to solve a set of linear equations involving complex elements using Cholesky decomposition. Although this algorithm is typically available in many standard computer math libraries, it is rare to find a version written for complex elements.

The solution of a set of linear equations when the matrix is circulant is presented in the next section. It requires a number of computational operations proportional to $n \log_2 n$. The Toeplitz and Hankel linear equations require a number of operations proportional to n^2. Section 3.8 is devoted to a detailed discussion of the Toeplitz case.

3.7   EIGENANALYSIS AND SINGULAR VALUE DECOMPOSITION

3.7.1   General

It was shown in Sec. 2.3 that the exponential $\exp(j2\pi ft)$ is an eigenfunction of a linear system. A linear system operating with an exponential at the input leaves the exponential form unchanged at the output, except for a complex amplitude scaling. In a similar manner, if $\mathbf{q}$ is a nonzero vector that, when operated on by the linear transformation represented by the $n \times n$ square matrix $\mathbf{A}$, is left unchanged except for scaling by a factor λ

$$\mathbf{A}\mathbf{q} = \lambda\mathbf{q}, \tag{3.77}$$

then $\mathbf{q}$ is said to be an *eigenvector* of the matrix $\mathbf{A}$. The scalar λ associated with the eigenvector is an *eigenvalue*. The order n polynomial $f(\lambda) = \det(\mathbf{A} - \lambda\mathbf{I})$ is called the *characteristic polynomial* of $\mathbf{A}$. The n roots of $f(\lambda) = 0$ yield the n eigenvalues λ_i,

$$f(\lambda) = \prod_{i=1}^{n}(\lambda_i - \lambda) = \sum_{k=0}^{n}\gamma_k\lambda^k = 0 \quad . \tag{3.78}$$

The eigenvalues and associated eigenvectors together form the *eigensystem* of $\mathbf{A}$. The set of eigenvalues has been termed, by mathematicians, the *spectrum* of $\mathbf{A}$; however, this is not to be confused with the definitions of spectrum found in Chaps. 2 and 4 of this book. There is always at least one eigenvector associated with each distinct eigenvalue, and eigenvectors associated with distinct eigenvalues are linearly independent of each other. The highest-order coefficient γ_n in (3.78) is $(-1)^n$ and the lowest-order coefficient γ_0 may be shown to satisfy

$$\gamma_0 = \det \mathbf{A} = \prod_{i=1}^{n} \lambda_i \quad . \tag{3.79}$$

Defining the trace of a matrix as the sum of its principal diagonal elements

$$\operatorname{tr} \mathbf{A} = \sum_{i=1}^{n} a[i,i] \quad , \tag{3.80}$$

then it may also be shown that

$$\sum_{i=1}^{n} \lambda_i = \operatorname{tr} \mathbf{A} \tag{3.81}$$

and

$$\gamma_{n-1} = (-1)^{n-1} \operatorname{tr} \mathbf{A} \quad . \tag{3.82}$$

Principal eigenvectors are those eigenvectors associated with the largest magnitude eigenvalues of $\mathbf{A}$. The matrix $k\mathbf{A}$, where k is a scalar, has eigenvalues $k\lambda_i$. The matrix $\mathbf{A}^p$ for p a positive integer has eigenvalues λ_i^p. If $\mathbf{A}$ is nonsingular, then $\mathbf{A}^{-1}$ has eigenvalues $1/\lambda_i$. The matrix $\mathbf{A} + k\mathbf{I}$ has eigenvalues $\lambda_i + k$. An $n \times n$ matrix $\mathbf{P}$ such that $\mathbf{P}^H\mathbf{P} = \mathbf{P}\mathbf{P}^H$ is called *orthogonal*. Furthermore, if $\mathbf{P}$ has the property $\mathbf{P}^H\mathbf{P} = \mathbf{P}\mathbf{P}^H = \mathbf{I}$, then it is said to be an *orthonormal*, or a *unitary*, matrix. Because $\mathbf{P}^{-1}\mathbf{P} = \mathbf{I}$, then $\mathbf{P}^{-1} = \mathbf{P}^H$. A unitary matrix has the properties that $|\det \mathbf{P}| = 1$ and that all eigenvalues are of unit modulus.

Suppose an $n \times n$ matrix $\mathbf{Q}$ is constructed from the n column eigenvectors $\mathbf{q}_1$ to $\mathbf{q}_n$ of the $n \times n$ square matrix $\mathbf{A}$ and an $n \times n$ diagonal matrix $\mathbf{\Lambda} = \operatorname{diag}(\lambda_1, \ldots, \lambda_n)$ is constructed from the n distinct eigenvalues of $\mathbf{A}$. The matrix $\mathbf{A}$ will then have a linearly independent set of n eigenvectors if and only if $\mathbf{A}$ can be expressed as

$$\mathbf{A} = \mathbf{Q}\mathbf{\Lambda}\mathbf{Q}^{-1} \quad , \quad \mathbf{\Lambda} = \mathbf{Q}^{-1}\mathbf{A}\mathbf{Q} \quad , \tag{3.83}$$

where $\mathbf{Q}$ and $\mathbf{\Lambda}$ are nonsingular.

If the nonsingular matrix $\mathbf{A}$ also has Hermitian symmetry, then $\mathbf{A}$ will have the unique decomposition

$$\mathbf{A} = \mathbf{Q}\mathbf{\Lambda}\mathbf{Q}^{-1} = \mathbf{A}^H = (\mathbf{Q}^{-1})^H\mathbf{\Lambda}^H\mathbf{Q}^H. \tag{3.84}$$

In order to have equality, $\mathbf{Q}^{-1} = \mathbf{Q}^H$ and $\mathbf{\Lambda} = \mathbf{\Lambda}^H$. This means that a Hermitian matrix has real eigenvalues and that, if all the eigenvalues are distinct, the eigenvectors form an orthonormal set, because $\mathbf{Q}\mathbf{Q}^H = \sum \mathbf{q}_i\mathbf{q}_i^H = \mathbf{I}$, that is, $\mathbf{Q}$ is a unitary matrix. Thus Hermitian matrices are diagonalized by a unitary transformation,

$$\mathbf{A} = \mathbf{Q}\mathbf{\Lambda}\mathbf{Q}^H. \tag{3.85}$$

An alternative expression based on Eq. (3.85) for the Hermitian matrix $\mathbf{A}$ is the outer product decomposition in terms of eigenvectors and eigenvalues of $\mathbf{A}$,

$$\mathbf{A} = \sum_{i=0}^{n} \lambda_i \mathbf{q}_i \mathbf{q}_i^H \quad . \tag{3.86}$$

Expression (3.86) has been called the "spectral decomposition" of $\mathbf{A}$ in mathematical journals and should not be confused with spectral estimation. Based on the relationship

$$\mathbf{A}^{-1} = (\mathbf{Q}^H)^{-1} \mathbf{\Lambda}^{-1} \mathbf{Q}^{-1} = \mathbf{Q} \mathbf{\Lambda}^{-1} \mathbf{Q}^H \quad , \tag{3.87}$$

then

$$\mathbf{A}^{-1} = \sum_{i=1}^{n} \frac{1}{\lambda_i} \mathbf{q}_i \mathbf{q}_i^H , \tag{3.88}$$

assuming all eigenvalues are nonzero.

The *quadratic form* associated with Hermitian matrix $\mathbf{A}$ is the real scalar quantity $\langle \mathbf{x}, \mathbf{A}\mathbf{x} \rangle = \mathbf{x}^H \mathbf{A}\mathbf{x} = \sum_i \sum_j a_{ij} x_i^* x_j$. The quadratic form is said to be *positive definite* if $\langle \mathbf{x}, \mathbf{A}\mathbf{x} \rangle > 0$ for all nonnull vectors $\mathbf{x}$, and *positive semidefinite*, if $\langle \mathbf{x}, \mathbf{A}\mathbf{x} \rangle \geq 0$ for all $\mathbf{x}$. The matrix $\mathbf{A}$ is said to be positive definite or semidefinite if its corresponding quadratic form is positive definite or semidefinite. If and only if all of the eigenvalues of a Hermitian matrix are positive, then the matrix is positive definite; if and only if the eigenvalues are all nonnegative, then the matrix is positive semidefinite.

The *Rayleigh quotient $R(\mathbf{x})$* of the Hermitian matrix $\mathbf{A}$ is the scalar

$$R(\mathbf{x}) = \frac{\mathbf{x}^H \mathbf{A}\mathbf{x}}{\mathbf{x}^H \mathbf{x}}. \tag{3.89}$$

Denoting the minimum and maximum eigenvalues of $\mathbf{A}$ by λ_{min} and λ_{max} and the associated orthonormal eigenvectors by $\mathbf{x}_{min}$ and $\mathbf{x}_{max}$, then it may be shown [Noble and Daniel, 1977] that

$$\lambda_{min} \leq R(\mathbf{x}) \leq \lambda_{max} \quad \text{for all} \quad \mathbf{x} \neq \mathbf{0}$$

$$\lambda_{min} = \min_{\mathbf{x} \neq 0} R(\mathbf{x}) = R(\mathbf{x}_{min}) \tag{3.90}$$

$$\lambda_{max} = \max_{\mathbf{x} \neq 0} R(\mathbf{x}) = R(\mathbf{x}_{max}).$$

Some of the methods discussed in this text require the computation of the minimum or maximum eigenvalue of a Hermitian matrix $\mathbf{A}$. The *power method* is one technique for finding these eigenvalues. For example, picking some initial vector $\mathbf{x}_0$, then the linear equation

$$\mathbf{y}_{k+1} = \mathbf{A}\mathbf{x}_k \tag{3.91}$$

is used iteratively, normalizing at each step to yield

$$\mathbf{x}_{k+1} = \frac{\mathbf{y}_{k+1}}{\sigma_{k+1}} \quad , \quad \sigma_{k+1} = \mathbf{y}_{k+1}^H \mathbf{y}_{k+1} \tag{3.92}$$

until $\mathbf{x}_k$ converges. The number σ_k after the last step will be the minimum eigenvalue and $\mathbf{x}_k$ will be the associated eigenvector. Convergence is assured provided $\mathbf{x}_0$ is not orthogonal to the eigenvector associated with the maximum eigenvalue. In order to obtain the minimum eigenvalue and its associated eigenvector, the inverse matrix $\mathbf{A}^{-1}$ is used in the linear equation

$$\mathbf{y}_{k+1} = \mathbf{A}^{-1}\mathbf{x}_k \quad , \tag{3.93}$$

which may more conveniently be solved for $\mathbf{y}_k$ as

$$\mathbf{A}\mathbf{y}_{k+1} = \mathbf{x}_k \quad . \tag{3.94}$$

A process of deflation may be used to remove each eigenvalue as it is found, a consequence of Eq. (3.86),

$$\mathbf{A} - \sigma \mathbf{x}\mathbf{x}^H \tag{3.95}$$

and the process repeated to find the other eigenvalues.

3.7.2 Singular Value Decomposition

It was shown in the previous section that an $n \times n$ Hermitian matrix could be decomposed in terms of a $n \times n$ unitary matrix composed of the eigenvectors and an $n \times n$ diagonal matrix composed of the eigenvalues. This concept can be extended to an arbitrary $m \times n$ complex-valued matrix $\mathbf{A}$ of rank k. The *singular value decomposition* (SVD) *theorem* [Forsythe et al., 1977; Klema and Laub, 1980; Lawson and Hanson, 1974] states that there exist positive real numbers $\sigma_1 \geq \sigma_2 \geq \ldots \geq \sigma_k > 0$ (the so-called *singular values* of $\mathbf{A}$), an $m \times m$ unitary matrix $\mathbf{U} = [\mathbf{u}_1 \ldots \mathbf{u}_m]$, and an $n \times n$ unitary matrix $\mathbf{V} = [\mathbf{v}_1 \ldots \mathbf{v}_n]$ such that matrix $\mathbf{A}$ can be expressed as

$$\mathbf{A} = \mathbf{U}\mathbf{\Sigma}\mathbf{V}^H = \sum_{i=1}^{k} \sigma_i \mathbf{u}_i \mathbf{v}_i^H \quad , \tag{3.96}$$

where the $m \times n$ matrix $\mathbf{\Sigma}$ has the structure

$$\mathbf{\Sigma} = \begin{pmatrix} \mathbf{D} & \mathbf{0} \\ \mathbf{0} & \mathbf{0} \end{pmatrix} \tag{3.97}$$

and $\mathbf{D} = \text{diag}\,(\sigma_1, \ldots, \sigma_k)$ is a $k \times k$ diagonal matrix. Noting that $\mathbf{A}^H = \mathbf{V}\mathbf{\Sigma}^H\mathbf{U}^H$, $\mathbf{U}^H\mathbf{U} = \mathbf{I}$, and $\mathbf{V}^H\mathbf{V} = \mathbf{I}$, then

$$\mathbf{A}^H\mathbf{A} = \mathbf{V}(\mathbf{\Sigma}^H\mathbf{\Sigma})\mathbf{V}^H \quad , \quad \mathbf{A}\mathbf{A}^H = \mathbf{U}(\mathbf{\Sigma}\mathbf{\Sigma}^H)\mathbf{U}^H \tag{3.98}$$

and

$$\mathbf{A}^H \mathbf{A} \mathbf{v}_i = \sigma_i^2 \mathbf{v}_i \quad , \quad \mathbf{A} \mathbf{A}^H \mathbf{u}_i = \sigma_i^2 \mathbf{u}_i \tag{3.99}$$

for $1 \leq i \leq k$. The matrix products $\mathbf{\Sigma}^H \mathbf{\Sigma}$ and $\mathbf{\Sigma} \mathbf{\Sigma}^H$ are diagonal matrices of size $n \times n$ and $m \times m$, respectively, with diagonal elements σ_i^2. The matrix products $\mathbf{A}^H \mathbf{A}$ and $\mathbf{A} \mathbf{A}^H$ are Hermitian matrices of size $n \times n$ and $m \times m$, respectively. The columns of $\mathbf{U}$ are, therefore, the orthonormal eigenvectors of $\mathbf{A} \mathbf{A}^H$ and the columns of $\mathbf{V}$ are, therefore, the orthonormal eigenvectors of $\mathbf{A}^H \mathbf{A}$. Both share the same eigenvalues σ_i^2 for $1 \leq i \leq k$. Thus, the singular values are simply the positive square roots of the nonzero eigenvalues of $\mathbf{A}^H \mathbf{A}$ and $\mathbf{A} \mathbf{A}^H$.

Using the unitary properties of $\mathbf{U}$ and $\mathbf{V}$, one can obtain from (3.96)

$$\mathbf{A} \mathbf{V} = \mathbf{U} \mathbf{\Sigma} \mathbf{V}^H \mathbf{V} = \mathbf{U} \mathbf{\Sigma} \quad , \quad \mathbf{U}^H \mathbf{A} = \mathbf{U}^H \mathbf{U} \mathbf{\Sigma} \mathbf{V}^H = \mathbf{\Sigma} \mathbf{V}^H \tag{3.100}$$

or

$$\mathbf{A} \mathbf{v}_i = \sigma_i \mathbf{u}_i \quad , \quad \mathbf{A}^H \mathbf{u}_i = \sigma_i \mathbf{v}_i \tag{3.101}$$

for $1 \leq i \leq k$. Equation (3.101) provides a pair of relationships between the eigenvectors $\mathbf{u}_i$ and $\mathbf{v}_i$ that share the common singular value σ_i. The eigenvectors that are associated with the zero singular values, $\mathbf{u}_i$ for $k+1 \leq i \leq m$ and $\mathbf{v}_i$ for $k+1 \leq i \leq n$, are not relatable in the manner of Eqs. (3.100) and (3.101).

The Moore-Penrose *pseudoinverse* $\mathbf{A}^\#$ of the $m \times n$ matrix $\mathbf{A}$ of rank k is defined in terms of the SVD matrix components as the unique matrix

$$\mathbf{A}^\# = \mathbf{V} \mathbf{\Sigma}^\# \mathbf{U}^H = \sum_{i=1}^{k} \sigma_i^{-1} \mathbf{v}_i \mathbf{u}_i^H \quad , \tag{3.102}$$

where

$$\mathbf{\Sigma}^\# = \begin{pmatrix} \mathbf{D}^{-1} & \mathbf{0} \\ \mathbf{0} & \mathbf{0} \end{pmatrix} . \tag{3.103}$$

The pseudoinverse $\mathbf{A}^\#$ provides the *minimum-norm least squares solution* $\mathbf{x} = \mathbf{A}^\# \mathbf{b}$ to the problem of finding the $n \times 1$ vector $\mathbf{x}$ that simultaneously minimizes the squared equation error $\|\mathbf{A}\mathbf{x} - \mathbf{b}\|_2$, for some given $m \times 1$ vector, and minimizes the solution vector length $\|\mathbf{x}\|_2$. The minimum length constraint is required in order to ensure a unique solution for those cases in which more than one vector $\mathbf{x}$ will minimize $\|\mathbf{A}\mathbf{x} - \mathbf{b}\|_2$. If $m = n$ and rank $\mathbf{A}$ is n (i.e., it is nonsingular), then the pseudoinverse reduces to the usual square matrix inverse $\mathbf{A}^\# = \mathbf{A}^{-1}$. If $m > n$ and rank $\mathbf{A} = n$, then $\mathbf{A}^\# = (\mathbf{A}^H \mathbf{A})^{-1} \mathbf{A}^H$ and $\mathbf{x} = (\mathbf{A}^H \mathbf{A})^{-1} \mathbf{A}^H \mathbf{b}$. This is the usual least squares solution for a set of overdetermined equations (see Sec. 3.5). If $n > m$ and rank $\mathbf{A} = m$, then $\mathbf{A}^\# = \mathbf{A}^H (\mathbf{A} \mathbf{A}^H)^{-1}$ and $\mathbf{x} = \mathbf{A}^H (\mathbf{A} \mathbf{A}^H)^{-1} \mathbf{b}$. This solution is often called the minimum norm solution for a set of underdetermined equations because the pseudoinverse solution will yield the vector $\mathbf{x}$ of minimum length.

Computing the pseudoinverse $\mathbf{A}^\#$ directly from the SVD [Eq. (3.98)] has two advantages over direct computation of $\mathbf{A}^\#$ in the form of either $(\mathbf{A}^H \mathbf{A})^{-1} \mathbf{A}^H$, in the case $m > n$, or $\mathbf{A}^H(\mathbf{A}\mathbf{A}^H)^{-1}$, in the case $n > m$. First, the SVD assists one to determine the rank of $\mathbf{A}$ by examining the number of non-negligible singular values. Second, the computational precision to calculate $\mathbf{A}^\#$ to a given accuracy with the SVD is approximately half that required to calculate $\mathbf{A}^\#$ using the relations $(\mathbf{A}^H\mathbf{A})^{-1}$ or $(\mathbf{A}\mathbf{A}^H)^{-1}$. Program CSVD is a FORTRAN program provided in Appendix 3.B to calculate the SVD of a complex element rectangular matrix.

3.7.3 Eigenanalysis of Some Special Matrices

It may easily be shown that a triangular matrix $\mathbf{A}$ has the determinant

$$\det \mathbf{A} = \prod_{i=1}^{n} a[i,i] \quad . \tag{3.104}$$

Comparing this with Eq. (3.79), it can be seen that the product of the eigenvalues of a triangular matrix are simply the product of the diagonal elements.

A circulant matrix has eigenvalues and eigenvectors related to the discrete-time Fourier series (DTFS) [Cornyn, 1974; McClellan and Parks, 1972]. Recall from Sec. 2.7 that the n-point DTFS $X[0], \ldots, X[n-1]$ of an n-point sequence $x[0], \ldots, x[n-1]$ for $T = 1$ is

$$X[k] = \sum_{i=0}^{n-1} x[i] \exp(-j2\pi ik/n) \quad \text{for} \quad k = 0, \ldots, n-1, \tag{3.105}$$

which may be expressed in matrix form as

$$\begin{pmatrix} X[0] \\ \vdots \\ X[n-1] \end{pmatrix} = \mathbf{Q}_{\text{DTFS}} \begin{pmatrix} x[0] \\ \vdots \\ x[n-1] \end{pmatrix}, \tag{3.106}$$

where the elements of $\mathbf{Q}_{\text{DTFS}}$ are the exponential coefficients

$$q_{\text{DTFS}}[i,k] = \exp\left(-j2\pi ik/n\right) \quad \text{for} \quad 0 \le i, k \le n-1. \tag{3.107}$$

The right-circulant matrix $\mathbf{C}_R$ may be expressed as the eigen-factorization

$$\mathbf{C}_R = \left(\frac{1}{\sqrt{n}}\mathbf{Q}_{\text{DTFS}}\right) \mathbf{\Lambda}_{\text{DTFS}} \left(\frac{1}{\sqrt{n}}\mathbf{Q}_{\text{DTFS}}^H\right), \tag{3.108}$$

where the diagonal matrix $\mathbf{\Lambda}_{\text{DTFS}}$ of eigenvalues is given by

$$\begin{pmatrix} \lambda_0 \\ \lambda_1 \\ \vdots \\ \lambda_{n-1} \end{pmatrix} = \mathbf{Q}_{\text{DTFS}} \begin{pmatrix} c_0 \\ c_1 \\ \vdots \\ c_{n-1} \end{pmatrix}. \tag{3.109}$$

Thus, the eigenvalues of an arbitrary circulant matrix are the DTFS of the circulant elements $c_o, \ldots, c_{n-1}$. The columns of the DTFS matrix $\mathbf{Q}_{\mathrm{DTFS}}$ form the eigenvectors. The normalized eigenvectors $\mathbf{q}_k$ are composed of powers of the n roots of unity,

$$\mathbf{q}_k = \frac{1}{\sqrt{n}} \begin{pmatrix} 1 \\ w_n^k \\ \vdots \\ w_n^{(n-1)k} \end{pmatrix}, \quad w_n = \exp(j2\pi/n). \tag{3.110}$$

A similar development for the left-circulant matrix $\mathbf{C}_L$ can be performed using the *inverse* DTFS, rather than the *forward* DTFS. Linear equations such as $\mathbf{C}_R\mathbf{x} = \mathbf{y}$ may be solved efficiently with FFT algorithms if expression (3.108) is used for $\mathbf{C}_R$.

The eigenvectors of a centrosymmetric matrix $\mathbf{C}$ have either conjugate symmetry or anticonjugate symmetry [Cantoni and Butler, 1976]. A vector $\mathbf{v}$ is conjugate symmetric if $\mathbf{Jv} = \mathbf{v}^*$, where $\mathbf{J}$ is the reflection matrix. A vector $\mathbf{v}$ is anticonjugate symmetric if $\mathbf{Jv} = -\mathbf{v}^*$. It may be inferred from this definition that the center element for a vector of odd dimension must be real if the vector is conjugate symmetric or zero if the vector is anticonjugate symmetric. Assuming unique eigenvalues, a square centrosymmetric matrix of *even* dimension n will have $n/2$ conjugate symmetric orthonormal eigenvectors $\mathbf{v}_i$ for $i = 1, \ldots, n/2$, with corresponding eigenvalues σ_i of the form

$$\mathbf{v}_i = \frac{1}{\sqrt{2}} \begin{pmatrix} \mathbf{y}_i \\ \mathbf{Jy}_i^* \end{pmatrix}, \tag{3.111}$$

where $\mathbf{y}_i$ are the orthonormal eigenvectors of the matrix $\mathbf{A} + \mathbf{JB}$, that is,

$$(\mathbf{A} + \mathbf{JB})\mathbf{y}_i = \sigma_i \mathbf{y}_i, \tag{3.112}$$

and where $\mathbf{A}$ and $\mathbf{B}$ are as given in Eq. (3.33). It will also have $n/2$ anticonjugate symmetric orthonormal eigenvectors $\mathbf{w}_i$ for $i = 1, \ldots, n/2$, with corresponding eigenvalues λ_i of the form

$$\mathbf{w}_i = \frac{1}{\sqrt{2}} \begin{pmatrix} \mathbf{z}_i \\ -\mathbf{Jz}_i^* \end{pmatrix}, \tag{3.113}$$

where $\mathbf{z}_i$ are the orthonormal eigenvectors of the matrix $\mathbf{A} - \mathbf{JB}$, that is,

$$(\mathbf{A} - \mathbf{JB})\mathbf{z}_i = \lambda_i \mathbf{z}_i. \tag{3.114}$$

If a square centrosymmetric matrix has *odd* dimension n and structure as given by Eq. (3.34), then it will have $(n+1)/2$ conjugate symmetric orthonormal eigenvectors $\mathbf{v}_i$ for $i = 1, \ldots, (n+1)/2$, with corresponding eigenvalues σ_i of the form

$$\mathbf{v}_i = \frac{1}{\sqrt{2}} \begin{pmatrix} \mathbf{y}_i \\ 2\beta_i \\ \mathbf{Jy}_i^* \end{pmatrix}, \tag{3.115}$$

where vector $\mathbf{y}_i$ and real scalar β_i are the orthonormal eigenvectors of the augmented matrix

$$\begin{pmatrix} \mathbf{A}+\mathbf{JB} & \sqrt{2}\mathbf{x} \\ \sqrt{2}\mathbf{x}^H & \alpha \end{pmatrix} \begin{pmatrix} \mathbf{y}_i \\ \beta_i \end{pmatrix} = \sigma_i \begin{pmatrix} \mathbf{y}_i \\ \beta_i \end{pmatrix}, \tag{3.116}$$

and $(n-1)/2$ anticonjugate symmetric orthonormal eigenvectors $\mathbf{w}_i$ for $i = 1, 2, 3, 4, \ldots, (n-1)/2$ with corresponding eigenvalues λ_i of the form

$$\mathbf{w}_i = \frac{1}{\sqrt{2}} \begin{pmatrix} \mathbf{z}_i \\ 0 \\ -\mathbf{Jz}_i^* \end{pmatrix}, \tag{3.117}$$

where $\mathbf{z}_i$ are the orthonormal eigenvectors of the matrix $\mathbf{A}-\mathbf{JB}$, that is,

$$(\mathbf{A}-\mathbf{JB})\mathbf{z}_i = \lambda_i \mathbf{z}_i \quad . \tag{3.118}$$

The proof of the above relationships is based on the fact that the centrosymmetric matrix $\mathbf{R}$ is orthogonally similar to the matrices $\mathbf{A}-\mathbf{JB}$ and $\mathbf{A}+\mathbf{JB}$, that is, if $\mathbf{R}_n$ is even, then the orthogonal similarity matrix

$$\mathbf{Q} = \frac{1}{\sqrt{2}} \begin{pmatrix} \mathbf{I} & -\mathbf{J} \\ \mathbf{I} & \mathbf{J} \end{pmatrix} \quad , \quad \mathbf{QQ}^T = \mathbf{I} \tag{3.119}$$

transforms the centrosymmetric matrix to

$$\mathbf{QRQ}^H = \begin{pmatrix} \mathbf{A}-\mathbf{JB} & 0 \\ 0 & \mathbf{A}+\mathbf{JB} \end{pmatrix}, \tag{3.120}$$

and if $\mathbf{R}_n$ is odd, then

$$\mathbf{Q} = \frac{1}{\sqrt{2}} \begin{pmatrix} \mathbf{I} & 0 & -\mathbf{J} \\ 0 & \sqrt{2} & 0 \\ \mathbf{I} & 0 & \mathbf{J} \end{pmatrix} \tag{3.121}$$

transforms it to

$$\mathbf{QRQ}^H = \begin{pmatrix} \mathbf{A}-\mathbf{JB} & 0 & 0 \\ 0 & \alpha & \sqrt{2}\mathbf{x}^H \\ 0 & \sqrt{2}\mathbf{x} & \mathbf{A}+\mathbf{JB} \end{pmatrix}. \tag{3.122}$$

3.8 THE TOEPLITZ MATRIX

The Toeplitz matrix structure comes up frequently in the development of various spectral estimation methods. Because of its importance, this entire section devotes an extended emphasis on the Toeplitz inverse, Toeplitz linear equation solution, and Toeplitz eigenanalysis. The special structure of the Toeplitz matrix will lead to very computationally efficient ("fast") algorithms for these three situations.

3.8.1 Toeplitz Inverse

The inverse of a square non-Hermitian Toeplitz matrix is considered first [Trench, 1964; Zohar, 1969]. Throughout this text, $\mathbf{T}_M$ shall denote the square $(M + 1) \times (M + 1)$ Toeplitz matrix which has $t[M]$ as its highest coefficient:

$$\mathbf{T}_M = \begin{pmatrix} t[0] & t[-1] & \cdots & t[-M] \\ t[1] & \ddots & \ddots & \vdots \\ \vdots & \ddots & \ddots & t[-1] \\ t[M] & \cdots & t[1] & t[0] \end{pmatrix}. \tag{3.123}$$

Note, in general, that $t[k] \neq t[-k]$ for $k = 1, \ldots, M$. Denote the inverse of $\mathbf{T}_M$ by

$$\mathbf{U}_M = \mathbf{T}_M^{-1} = \begin{pmatrix} u[0,0] & \cdots & u[0,M] \\ \vdots & \ddots & \vdots \\ u[M,0] & \cdots & u[M,M] \end{pmatrix}. \tag{3.124}$$

Because a Toeplitz matrix is persymmetric, its inverse $\mathbf{U}_M$ must also be persymmetric. However, the inverse is not Toeplitz, although it will be shown to be composed of sums of products of triangular Toeplitz matrices.

To obtain the complete inverse $\mathbf{U}_M$, it will be necessary only to solve for the first column of the inverse

$$\begin{pmatrix} t[0] & t[-1] & \cdots & t[-M] \\ t[1] & \ddots & \ddots & \vdots \\ \vdots & \ddots & \ddots & t[-1] \\ t[M] & \cdots & t[1] & t[0] \end{pmatrix} \begin{pmatrix} u[0,0] \\ u[1,0] \\ \vdots \\ u[M,0] \end{pmatrix} = \begin{pmatrix} 1 \\ 0 \\ \vdots \\ 0 \end{pmatrix} \tag{3.125}$$

and the last column of the inverse

$$\begin{pmatrix} t[0] & t[-1] & \cdots & t[-M] \\ t[1] & \ddots & \ddots & \vdots \\ \vdots & \ddots & \ddots & t[-1] \\ t[M] & \cdots & t[1] & t[0] \end{pmatrix} \begin{pmatrix} u[0,M] \\ \vdots \\ u[M-1,M] \\ u[M,M] \end{pmatrix} = \begin{pmatrix} 0 \\ \vdots \\ 0 \\ 1 \end{pmatrix}. \tag{3.126}$$

It will be shown that the remaining elements of $\mathbf{U}_M$ may be obtained by using the persymmetry property.

Alternative representations to those of Eqs. (3.125) and (3.126) are obtained by dividing the vectors on both sides of the equal sign in (3.125) by $u[0,0]$ (assuming it is nonzero), substituting $a_M[k] = u[k,0]/u[0,0]$ for $k = 1, \ldots, M$, and setting $\rho_M^a = 1/u[0,0]$ to yield

$$
\begin{pmatrix}
t[0] & t[-1] & \cdots & t[-M] \\
t[1] & \ddots & \ddots & \vdots \\
\vdots & \ddots & \ddots & t[-1] \\
t[M] & \cdots & t[1] & t[0]
\end{pmatrix}
\begin{pmatrix}
1 \\
a_M[1] \\
\vdots \\
a_M[M]
\end{pmatrix}
=
\begin{pmatrix}
\rho_M^a \\
0 \\
\vdots \\
0
\end{pmatrix},
\tag{3.127}
$$

and by dividing the vectors on both sides of the equal sign in (3.126) by $u[M,M]$ (assuming it is nonzero), substituting $b_M[k] = u[M-k,M]/u[M,M]$ for $k = 1, \ldots, M$, and setting $\rho_M^b = 1/u[M,M]$ to yield

$$
\begin{pmatrix}
t[0] & t[-1] & \cdots & t[-M] \\
t[1] & \ddots & \ddots & \vdots \\
\vdots & \ddots & \ddots & t[-1] \\
t[M] & \cdots & t[1] & t[0]
\end{pmatrix}
\begin{pmatrix}
b_M[M] \\
\vdots \\
b_M[1] \\
1
\end{pmatrix}
=
\begin{pmatrix}
0 \\
\vdots \\
0 \\
\rho_M^b
\end{pmatrix}.
\tag{3.128}
$$

Due to the persymmetry of $\mathbf{U}_M$, $u[0,0] = u[M,M]$ so that the complex-valued scalars $\rho_M^a = \rho_M^b = \rho_M$. Equations (3.127) and (3.128) will prove useful in connection with the normal equations of an autoregressive process (see Chaps. 6 and 7).

The solution for the $a_M[k]$ and $b_M[k]$ coefficients may be obtained with a recursive algorithmic procedure that successively yields the coefficients at each order m, starting at $m = 1$ and working recursively to $m = M$. The original recursive algorithm was developed by Levinson [1947] in connection with the solution of the normal equations for linear prediction of a stationary discrete-time process. It was rediscovered by Durbin [1960] for the problem of fitting an autoregressive model to a given correlation sequence. The key components to this recursion are the following partitions of $\mathbf{T}_m$ that depend on the very special structure of a Toeplitz matrix

$$
\mathbf{T}_m = \begin{pmatrix} \mathbf{T}_{m-1} & \mathbf{J}\mathbf{s}_m \\ \mathbf{r}_m^T \mathbf{J} & t[0] \end{pmatrix} = \begin{pmatrix} t[0] & \mathbf{s}_m^T \\ \mathbf{r}_m & \mathbf{T}_{m-1} \end{pmatrix},
\tag{3.129}
$$

where the $(m-1) \times 1$-dimensional column vectors $\mathbf{r}_m$ and $\mathbf{s}_m$ are given by

$$
\mathbf{r}_m = \begin{pmatrix} t[1] \\ \vdots \\ t[m] \end{pmatrix} \qquad \mathbf{s}_m = \begin{pmatrix} t[-1] \\ \vdots \\ t[-m] \end{pmatrix}
\tag{3.130}
$$

and $\mathbf{J}$ is a $(m-1) \times (m-1)$ reflection matrix. Using a process of induction, assume that the vector formed from the $a_m[k]$ coefficients may be obtained as a linear combination of the vectors formed from the $a_{m-1}[k]$ coefficients and from the $b_{m-1}[k]$ coefficients

$$
\begin{pmatrix} 1 \\ a_m[1] \\ \vdots \\ a_m[m-1] \\ a_m[m] \end{pmatrix} = \begin{pmatrix} 1 \\ a_{m-1}[1] \\ \vdots \\ a_{m-1}[m-1] \\ 0 \end{pmatrix} + \alpha \begin{pmatrix} 0 \\ b_{m-1}[m-1] \\ \vdots \\ b_{m-1}[1] \\ 1 \end{pmatrix} , \tag{3.131}
$$

where the right-hand-side vectors have been augmented with zeros and α is a scalar to be determined. Note that $a_m[m] = \alpha$. Equation (3.131) asserts that the first column of the inverse matrix for order m is a linear combination of the first and last columns of the inverse matrix for order $m-1$. By defining the column vectors

$$
\mathbf{a}_m = \begin{pmatrix} a_m[1] \\ \vdots \\ a_m[m] \end{pmatrix} \qquad \mathbf{b}_m = \begin{pmatrix} b_m[1] \\ \vdots \\ b_m[m] \end{pmatrix} \tag{3.132}
$$

then (3.131) may be more concisely expressed as

$$
\begin{pmatrix} 1 \\ \mathbf{a}_m \end{pmatrix} = \begin{pmatrix} 1 \\ \mathbf{a}_{m-1} \\ 0 \end{pmatrix} + a_m[m] \begin{pmatrix} 0 \\ \mathbf{J}\mathbf{b}_{m-1} \\ 1 \end{pmatrix} . \tag{3.133}
$$

In order to determine the scalar $a_m[m]$, it is necessary to premultiply both sides of (3.133) by $\mathbf{T}_m$ and substitute the appropriate partition from Eq. (3.129), yielding

$$
\begin{aligned}
\mathbf{T}_m \begin{pmatrix} 1 \\ \mathbf{a}_m \end{pmatrix} &= \begin{pmatrix} \mathbf{T}_{m-1} & \mathbf{J}\mathbf{s}_m \\ \mathbf{r}_m^T \mathbf{J} & t[0] \end{pmatrix} \begin{pmatrix} 1 \\ \mathbf{a}_{m-1} \\ 0 \end{pmatrix} \\
&\quad + a_m[m] \begin{pmatrix} t[0] & \mathbf{s}_m^T \\ \mathbf{r}_m & \mathbf{T}_{m-1} \end{pmatrix} \begin{pmatrix} 0 \\ \mathbf{J}\mathbf{b}_{m-1} \\ 1 \end{pmatrix} .
\end{aligned} \tag{3.134}
$$

This will yield, based on (3.127) and (3.128), the result

$$
\begin{pmatrix} \rho_m \\ 0 \\ \vdots \\ 0 \\ 0 \end{pmatrix} = \begin{pmatrix} \rho_{m-1} \\ 0 \\ \vdots \\ 0 \\ \Delta_m \end{pmatrix} + a_m[m] \begin{pmatrix} \nabla_m \\ 0 \\ \vdots \\ 0 \\ \rho_{m-1} \end{pmatrix} , \tag{3.135}
$$

where

$$
\Delta_m = \mathbf{r}_m^T \mathbf{J} \begin{pmatrix} 1 \\ \mathbf{a}_{m-1} \end{pmatrix} = \sum_{k=1}^{m} t[k] a_{m-1}[m-k], \quad a_{m-1}[0] = 1 \tag{3.136}
$$

$$\nabla_m = \mathbf{s}_m^T \begin{pmatrix} \mathbf{Jb}_{m-1} \\ 1 \end{pmatrix} = \sum_{k=1}^{m} t[-k]b_{m-1}[m-k], \quad b_{m-1}[0] = 1. \tag{3.137}$$

Note that Δ_m and ∇_m require knowledge of the order $m-1$ coefficients only. In order to have equality in Eq. (3.135), the bottom element on the right-hand side should be zero

$$\Delta_m + a_m[m]\rho_{m-1} = 0 \quad , \tag{3.138}$$

which implies

$$a_m[m] = -\Delta_m/\rho_{m-1} \quad . \tag{3.139}$$

The top element on both sides of Eq. (3.135) then becomes

$$\rho_m = \rho_{m-1} + a_m[m]\nabla_m = \rho_{m-1} - \Delta_m\nabla_m/\rho_{m-1} \quad . \tag{3.140}$$

The analogous order update to Eq. (3.133) for the vector $\mathbf{b}_m$ can also be proved by induction to be

$$\begin{pmatrix} 1 \\ \mathbf{b}_m \end{pmatrix} = \begin{pmatrix} 1 \\ \mathbf{b}_{m-1} \\ 0 \end{pmatrix} + b_m[m] \begin{pmatrix} 0 \\ \mathbf{Ja}_m \\ 1 \end{pmatrix}. \tag{3.141}$$

When premultiplied on both sides by $\mathbf{T}_m$, the result is

$$\begin{pmatrix} \rho_m \\ 0 \\ \vdots \\ 0 \\ 0 \end{pmatrix} = \begin{pmatrix} \rho_{m-1} \\ 0 \\ \vdots \\ 0 \\ \nabla_m \end{pmatrix} + b_m[m] \begin{pmatrix} \Delta_m \\ 0 \\ \vdots \\ 0 \\ \rho_{m-1} \end{pmatrix}, \tag{3.142}$$

where Δ_m and ∇_m were defined previously by Eqs. (3.136) and (3.137). Again, for equality to hold in Eq. (3.142), the selection

$$b_m[m] = -\nabla_m/\rho_{m-1} \tag{3.143}$$

must be made. Substituting for ∇_m in Eq. (3.140),

$$\rho_m = \rho_{m-1} + a_m[m]\left(-\rho_{m-1}b_m[m]\right) = \rho_{m-1}\left(1 - a_m[m]b_m[m]\right) \quad . \tag{3.144}$$

Note from (3.127) that $t[0] = \rho_0$ at order $m = 0$. This initializes the recursion. The complex scalar ρ_m is related to the determinant of the Toeplitz matrix by the expression

$$\det \mathbf{T}_m = \prod_{k=0}^{m} \rho_k = \rho_0^{m+1} \prod_{k=1}^{m} (1 - a_k[k]b_k[k])^{m+1-k} \quad . \tag{3.145}$$

To prove this result, use Eqs. (3.52) and (3.144) and note that the following arbitrary matrix product

$$
\mathbf{T}_m \begin{pmatrix} \mathbf{I}_m & \mathbf{b}_m \\ \mathbf{0_m}^T & 1 \end{pmatrix} = \begin{pmatrix} \mathbf{T}_{m-1} & \mathbf{Js}_m \\ \mathbf{r}_m^T \mathbf{J} & t[0] \end{pmatrix} \begin{pmatrix} \mathbf{I}_m & \mathbf{b}_m \\ \mathbf{0_m}^T & 1 \end{pmatrix} = \begin{pmatrix} \mathbf{T}_{m-1} & \mathbf{0}_m \\ \mathbf{r}_m^T \mathbf{J} & \rho_m \end{pmatrix}
$$
(3.146)

has the determinant $\det \mathbf{T}_m = \rho_m \det \mathbf{T}_{m-1}$, based on the property $\det \mathbf{AB} = \det \mathbf{A} \det \mathbf{B}$. On an element-by-element basis, the recursions indicated by (3.133) and (3.141) are

$$
a_m[k] = a_{m-1}[k] + a_m[m] b_{m-1}[m-k]
$$
(3.147)

$$
b_m[k] = b_{m-1}[k] + b_m[m] a_{m-1}[m-k]
$$
(3.148)

for $k = 1, \ldots, m-1$. Thus, the six equations (3.136), (3.137), (3.139), (3.140), (3.143), (3.147), and (3.148) constitute a closed-form recursion ($m = 0, \ldots, M$) to obtain the vectors $\mathbf{a}_m$ and $\mathbf{b}_m$. This, in effect, provides the first and last columns of the Toeplitz inverse. Note that the submatrices $\mathbf{T}_0, \mathbf{T}_1, \ldots, \mathbf{T}_M$ must all be invertible ($\det \mathbf{T}_n = \rho_n \neq 0$) for this recursion to work. The vector updates given by (3.133) and (3.141), as well as the vector inner products (3.136) and (3.137), require a number of computations proportional to M at each step in the recursion. Because there are M steps, the total computational requirements of this algorithm are proportional to M^2.

In order to compute the remaining elements of the inverse, first note that the inverse Toeplitz matrix may be expressed in the partitioned form

$$
\mathbf{U}_M = \frac{1}{\rho_M} \begin{pmatrix} 1 & \mathbf{b}_M^T \\ \mathbf{a}_M & \rho_M \mathbf{U}_{M-1} + \mathbf{a}_M \mathbf{b}_M^T \end{pmatrix}.
$$
(3.149)

See the Problems for a proof. Because the inverse is persymmetric,

$$
\mathbf{J} \mathbf{U}_M^T \mathbf{J} = \mathbf{U}_M,
$$
(3.150)

then Eq. (3.149) may also be expressed as

$$
\mathbf{U}_M = \frac{1}{\rho_M} \begin{pmatrix} \rho_M \mathbf{U}_{M-1} + \mathbf{Jb}_M \mathbf{a}_M^T \mathbf{J} & \mathbf{Jb}_M \\ \mathbf{a}_M^T \mathbf{J} & 1 \end{pmatrix}.
$$
(3.151)

From (3.149) and (3.151), the following relations for the elements $u_M[j, k]$ of the order M Toeplitz inverse may be found

$$
u_M[0,0] = u_M[M,M] = 1/\rho_m
$$

$$
u_M[0,k] = u_M[M-k,M] = b_M[k]/\rho_M \quad \text{for} \quad 1 \le k \le M
$$

$$
u_M[j,0] = u_M[M,M-j] = a_M[j]/\rho_M \quad \text{for} \quad 1 \le j \le M
$$

$$
u_M[j+1,k+1] = u_{M-1}[j,k] + a_M[j+1] b_M[k+1]/\rho_M \quad \text{for} \quad 0 \le j, k \le M-1
$$

$$u_M[j,k] = u_{M-1}[j,k] + b_M[M-j]a_M[M-k]/\rho_M \quad \text{for} \quad 0 \le j,k \le M-1.$$

By combining the last two of the above expressions, the element $u_{M-1}[j,k]$ can be eliminated:

$$u_M[j+1,k+1] = u_M[j,k] + \frac{1}{\rho_M}\left(a_M[j+1]b_M[k+1] - b_M[M-j]a_M[M-k]\right) ,$$

$$(3.152)$$

which holds for $0 \le j,k \le M-1$. Equation (3.152) is a recursive relationship that permits all inverse elements to be computed from knowledge of only the $\mathbf{a}_M$ and $\mathbf{b}_M$ vectors. The following may also be developed from Eq. (3.152),

$$\mathbf{T}_M^{-1} = \frac{1}{\rho_M}\begin{pmatrix} 1 & 0 & \cdots & 0 \\ a_M[1] & \ddots & \ddots & \vdots \\ \vdots & \ddots & \ddots & 0 \\ a_M[M] & \cdots & a_M[1] & 1 \end{pmatrix}\begin{pmatrix} 1 & b_M[1] & \cdots & b_M[M] \\ 0 & \ddots & \ddots & \vdots \\ \vdots & \ddots & \ddots & b_M[1] \\ 0 & \cdots & 0 & 1 \end{pmatrix} \qquad (3.153)$$

$$-\frac{1}{\rho_M}\begin{pmatrix} 0 & 0 & \cdots & 0 \\ b_M[M] & \ddots & \ddots & \vdots \\ \vdots & \ddots & \ddots & 0 \\ b_M[1] & \cdots & b_M[M] & 0 \end{pmatrix}\begin{pmatrix} 0 & a_M[M] & \cdots & a_M[1] \\ 0 & \ddots & \ddots & \vdots \\ \vdots & \ddots & \ddots & a_M[M] \\ 0 & \cdots & 0 & 0 \end{pmatrix}.$$

Thus, the inverse of a general Toeplitz matrix is not Toeplitz, yet it can be factored into the sum of products of upper and lower triangular Toeplitz matrices.

A case of special interest is that of the inverse of a Hermitian Toeplitz matrix $\mathbf{H}_M$, which has the form

$$\mathbf{H}_M = \begin{pmatrix} t[0] & t^*[1] & \cdots & t^*[M] \\ t[1] & t[0] & \cdots & t^*[M-1] \\ \vdots & \vdots & \ddots & \vdots \\ t[M] & t[M-1] & \cdots & t[0] \end{pmatrix} \qquad (3.154)$$

for complex data. Note that $\mathbf{H}^H = \mathbf{H}$. In this situation, the vectors

$$\mathbf{s}_M = \mathbf{r}_M^* \qquad (3.155)$$

of Eq. (3.129) are related by complex symmetry, so that the recursions simplify to reduce the number of computations for finding the inverse. In particular, it easily follows that the vectors

$$\mathbf{b}_M^* = \mathbf{a}_M \qquad (3.156)$$

and the scalars

$$\nabla_M^* = \Delta_M \qquad (3.157)$$

have complex conjugate relationships. The scalar term ρ_M, which now satisfies

$$\rho_M = \rho_{M-1}\left(1 - \left|a_M[M]\right|^2\right), \tag{3.158}$$

is real and positive. This implies the following

$$\det \mathbf{H}_M = \rho_0 \prod_{k=1}^{M}\left(1 - \left|a_k[k]\right|^2\right) > 0 \quad . \tag{3.159}$$

The number of computations to obtain the $\mathbf{a}_M$ vector is reduced approximately by a factor of 2 in the Hermitian case over the non-Hermitian case due to relationships (3.156), (3.157), and (3.158). Program LEVINSON in Appendix 3.C is a FORTRAN program to solve for the $\mathbf{a}_M$ coefficients and ρ_M in the Hermitian Toeplitz matrix case.

Analogous to the matrix inverse (3.153) for a general Toeplitz matrix is the following inverse for a Hermitian Toeplitz matrix

$$\mathbf{H}_M^{-1} = \frac{1}{\rho_M}\begin{pmatrix} 1 & 0 & \cdots & 0 \\ a_M[1] & \ddots & \ddots & \vdots \\ \vdots & \ddots & \ddots & 0 \\ a_M[M] & \cdots & a_M[1] & 1 \end{pmatrix}\begin{pmatrix} 1 & a_M^*[1] & \cdots & a_M^*[M] \\ 0 & \ddots & \ddots & \vdots \\ \vdots & \ddots & \ddots & a_M^*[1] \\ 0 & \cdots & 0 & 1 \end{pmatrix} \tag{3.160}$$

$$- \frac{1}{\rho_M}\begin{pmatrix} 0 & 0 & \cdots & 0 \\ a_M^*[M] & \ddots & \ddots & \vdots \\ \vdots & \ddots & \ddots & 0 \\ a_M^*[1] & \cdots & a_M^*[M] & 0 \end{pmatrix}\begin{pmatrix} 0 & a_M[M] & \cdots & a_M[1] \\ 0 & \ddots & \ddots & \vdots \\ \vdots & \ddots & \ddots & a_M[M] \\ 0 & \cdots & 0 & 0 \end{pmatrix} .$$

3.8.2   Toeplitz Triangular Decomposition

The Levinson algorithm also provides the elements needed for an efficient Cholesky (triangular) decomposition of the inverse of a Hermitian Toeplitz matrix [Burg, 1968; Therrien, 1983]. Because all lower-order solution vectors from $\mathbf{a}_1$ up to $\mathbf{a}_M$ are computed as part of the algorithm, it is then possible to define the matrix product

$$\mathbf{T}_M \mathbf{A}_M = \mathbf{Q}_M \quad , \tag{3.161}$$

where $\mathbf{T}_M$ is the Hermitian Toeplitz matrix and $\mathbf{A}_M$ is a lower-triangular matrix constructed from the coefficient vectors $\mathbf{a}_m$ from $m = 0$ to $m = M$,

$$\mathbf{A}_M = \begin{pmatrix} 1 & 0 & \cdots & 0 & 0 \\ a_M[1] & 1 & \cdots & 0 & 0 \\ a_M[2] & a_{M-1}[1] & \cdots & 0 & 0 \\ \vdots & \vdots & \ddots & \vdots & \vdots \\ a_M[M-1] & a_{M-1}[M-2] & \cdots & 1 & 0 \\ a_M[M] & a_{M-1}[M-1] & \cdots & a_1[1] & 1 \end{pmatrix} . \tag{3.162}$$

Using Eq. (3.127), it may easily be shown that the right-hand matrix is itself a triangular matrix with the form

$$
\mathbf{Q}_M = \begin{pmatrix}
\rho_M & x & \cdots & x & x \\
0 & \rho_{M-1} & \cdots & x & x \\
\vdots & \vdots & \ddots & \vdots & \vdots \\
0 & 0 & \cdots & \rho_1 & x \\
0 & 0 & \cdots & 0 & \rho_0
\end{pmatrix} , \tag{3.163}
$$

where the x denote nonzero off-diagonal quantities whose specific values are not of interest. If both sides of (3.161) are premultiplied by the conjugate transpose of $\mathbf{A}_M$, then

$$
\mathbf{A}_M^H \mathbf{T}_M \mathbf{A}_M = \mathbf{A}_M^H \mathbf{Q}_M = \mathbf{P}_M , \tag{3.164}
$$

where matrix $\mathbf{P}_M$ is the diagonal matrix

$$
\mathbf{P}_M = \begin{pmatrix}
\rho_M & 0 & \cdots & 0 & 0 \\
0 & \rho_{M-1} & \cdots & 0 & 0 \\
\vdots & \vdots & \ddots & \vdots & \vdots \\
0 & 0 & \cdots & \rho_1 & 0 \\
0 & 0 & \cdots & 0 & \rho_0
\end{pmatrix} \tag{3.165}
$$

formed as the result of the product of two upper triangular matrices. Thus, an alternative decomposition to Eq. (3.161) for the inverse of a Hermitian Toeplitz matrix is the triangular factorization

$$
\mathbf{T}_M^{-1} = \mathbf{A}_M \mathbf{P}_M^{-1} \mathbf{A}_M^H . \tag{3.166}
$$

3.8.3 Solution of Toeplitz Linear Equations

The Levinson algorithm also forms the nucleus for algorithms that solve linear equations involving Toeplitz and Hermitian Toeplitz matrices. Consider the general Toeplitz linear equations of the form

$$
\mathbf{T}_M \mathbf{x}_M = \mathbf{z}_M , \tag{3.167}
$$

where $\mathbf{z}_M$ is a known right-hand-side $(M+1)$-dimensional column vector

$$
\mathbf{z}_M = \begin{pmatrix}
z[0] \\
\vdots \\
z[M]
\end{pmatrix} \tag{3.168}
$$

and $\mathbf{x}_M$ is the unknown $(M + 1)$-dimensional column vector

$$\mathbf{x}_M = \begin{pmatrix} x_M[0] \\ \vdots \\ x_M[M] \end{pmatrix} \qquad (3.169)$$

whose solution is desired. The solution for $\mathbf{x}_M$ may be embedded within the recursions of the Levinson algorithm by noting that the order m solution vector $\mathbf{x}_m$ for the linear equations

$$\mathbf{T}_m \mathbf{x}_m = \mathbf{z}_m, \qquad (3.170)$$

where $m \leq M$ and $\mathbf{z}_m$ is $(m + 1)$-dimensional vector formed from the first $m + 1$ elements of $\mathbf{z}_M$, may be computed recursively from the order $m - 1$ solution vector $\mathbf{x}_{m-1}$ as follows

$$\mathbf{x}_m = \begin{pmatrix} \mathbf{x}_{m-1} \\ 0 \end{pmatrix} + \alpha_m \begin{pmatrix} \mathbf{Jb}_m \\ 1 \end{pmatrix} \qquad (3.171)$$

for some scalar α, to be determined, and $\mathbf{b}_m$ is the vector of Eq. (3.132). To prove Eq. (3.171), simply premultiply both sides of the equality by $\mathbf{T}_m$ and make use of the partition (3.129) to yield

$$\mathbf{z}_m = \begin{pmatrix} \mathbf{z}_{m-1} \\ \beta_m \end{pmatrix} + \alpha_m \begin{pmatrix} 0 \\ \vdots \\ 0 \\ \rho_m \end{pmatrix} \quad , \qquad (3.172)$$

where

$$\beta_m = \mathbf{r}_m^T \mathbf{J} \mathbf{x}_{m-1} = \sum_{k=0}^{m-1} x[k]t[m-k] \quad . \qquad (3.173)$$

Equality will result by selecting

$$\alpha_m = (z[m] - \beta_m)/\rho_m \quad . \qquad (3.174)$$

Thus, starting at order zero with

$$t[0]x[0] = z[0] \quad , \qquad (3.175)$$

the solution vector is updated by Eq. (3.171) at each stage of the Levinson algorithm for $1 \leq m \leq M$. For the case of a Hermitian matrix, the substitution $\mathbf{a}_m^* = \mathbf{b}_m$ is made. Program TOEPLITZ in Appendix 3.D is a FORTRAN program that solves the general case of complex Toeplitz linear simultaneous equations. The algorithm for the general Toeplitz case requires $3M^2$ multiplication/addition operations and memory storage of $6M$, or $5M$ if the solution vector is obtained in place of the original right-hand-side vector. Program HERMTOEP in Appendix

3.E is a FORTRAN program that solves the Hermitian Toeplitz linear equation case. For the Hermitian case, the computational operations reduce to $2M^2$ and memory storage reduces to $4M$ (or $3M$ if in-place operations are used). Cybenko [1980] has found that the Levinson-based algorithms have comparable numerical stability to the more computationally inefficient Cholesky factorization method of linear equation solution. Other implementation aspects are discussed by Carayannis et al. [1982], Farden [1976], Roebuck [1978], Yarlagadda [1980], and Zohar [1974, 1979, 1981].

Although the Levinson recursion is certainly the most well-known algorithm for fast computational solution of Toeplitz linear equations on computers or single microprocessor implementations, it is by no means the only fast solution. For very large scale integrated (VLSI) circuit implementations, an alternative algorithm based on the Schur algorithm has been promoted by Kung and Hu [1983] to take advantage of parallel processor implementations. The inner product operations in the Levinson algorithm [Eqs. (3.136), (3.137), and (3.171)] will require $\log_2 M$ sequential applications of M parallel processors, because only half of the adds can be performed at each time step, for a total processing throughput rate of $M \log_2 M$ operational steps. The Schur algorithm requires a total number of computations proportional to M^2, similar to the Levinson algorithm, but it is structured to avoid inner products operations in order to achieve a processing throughput rate of M operational steps using M parallel processors.

3.8.4 Toeplitz Eigenanalysis

Despite its special structure, there are not many known special properties of the eigenvalues and eigenvectors of finite-dimensional Toeplitz matrices [Datta, 1984; Makhoul, 1981]. Let

$$A(z) = \sum_{k=0}^{M} v[k] z^{-k} \tag{3.176}$$

be the eigenpolynomial formed from the elements $v[k]$ of an eigenvector of the $(M+1) \times (M+1)$ Toeplitz matrix $\mathbf{T}_M$. If $\mathbf{T}_M$ is Hermitian, then $\mathbf{T}_M$ is a special case of a centrosymmetric matrix. The eigenvectors will be either conjugate symmetric or anticonjugate symmetric (see Sec. 3.7.3), which means the polynomial $A(z)$ will similarly be conjugate symmetric or anticonjugate symmetric. Such symmetry in a polynomial can be shown to possess roots that occur in inverse pairs [Makhoul, 1981]. Thus, if z_i is a root, then so is $1/z_i$. If z_i is inside the unit circle, then $1/z_i$ will be outside the unit circle. If z_i is on the unit circle, $1/z_i = z_i^*$ will be its complex conjugate (and on the unit circle as well). If the coefficients of $A(z)$ are real, then the complex zeros will also come in complex conjugate pairs.

If the *maximum* eigenvalue of $\mathbf{T}_M$ is distinct, then it can be shown (see the Problems) that the polynomial formed from the eigenvector of the maximum eigenvalue has its roots *on* the unit circle. The same is true for the eigenvector corresponding to the *minimum* eigenvalue, if it also is distinct. The roots of the polynomials formed from the remaining eigenvectors may or may not have their roots on the unit circle; the same will be true if the maximum or minimum eigenvalues are not unique.

From Eqs. (3.79) and (3.145), the eigenvalues λ_k of a Toeplitz matrix and the ρ_k elements are related by

$$\det \mathbf{T}_M = \prod_{k=0}^{M} \rho_k = \prod_{k=0}^{M} \lambda_k. \tag{3.177}$$

The trace of an $(M+1) \times (M+1)$ Toeplitz matrix $\mathbf{T}_M$ is simply $(M+1)t[0]$. Using (3.81), then

$$t[0] = \frac{1}{M+1} \sum_{k=0}^{M} \lambda_k \quad . \tag{3.178}$$

As will be shown in Chap. 6, the element $t[0]$ will correspond to the zero-lag autocorrelation term for a random process, which is the total power in the process. Thus, the average of the eigenvalues represents the total power in the process.

It is possible to make asymptotic statements concerning the behavior of eigenvalues of Toeplitz matrices by relating them to the eigenvalues of a circulant matrix, for which an analytical structure of the eigenvalues is known. For example, the 4×4 tridiagonal Toeplitz matrix

$$\begin{pmatrix} t[0] & t[-1] & 0 & 0 \\ t[1] & t[0] & t[-1] & 0 \\ 0 & t[1] & t[0] & t[-1] \\ 0 & 0 & t[1] & t[0] \end{pmatrix} \tag{3.179}$$

may be approximated as a circulant matrix

$$\begin{pmatrix} t[0] & t[-1] & 0 & t[1] \\ t[1] & t[0] & t[-1] & 0 \\ 0 & t[1] & t[0] & t[-1] \\ t[-1] & 0 & t[1] & t[0] \end{pmatrix} \tag{3.180}$$

by simply adding the appropriate elements in the opposite corners. As the 4×4 dimension is permitted to grow to dimension $n \times n$, the two matrices become closer in the sense that the n^2 elements agree in all positions, except at the two corners. As $n \to \infty$, the matrices become asymptotically equivalent. Details of the asymptotic behavior of the eigenvalues of Toeplitz matrices of this sort of structure may be found in Grenander and Szegö [1958] and Gray [1972].

There are spectral estimation techniques in this text that require the minimum or maximum eigenvalues of a Toeplitz matrix and the associated eigenvectors. The classical power method may be used to find these eigenvalues, with some computational reduction possible by exploiting the Toeplitz structure. The eigenvector associated with the minimum eigenvalue is the asymptotic solution to a sequence of vectors $\mathbf{v}(k)$ found as the solution to

$$\mathbf{v}(k+1) = \mathbf{T}^{-1}\mathbf{v}(k) \quad \text{for} \quad k = 0, 1, \ldots \tag{3.181}$$

starting with some initial guess for vector $\mathbf{v}(0)$. Equation (3.181) may be rewritten as

$$\mathbf{T}\mathbf{v}(k+1) = \mathbf{v}(k), \tag{3.182}$$

forming a set of linear equations for the unknown vector $\mathbf{v}(k+1)$. Use of the FORTRAN programs of Appendixes 3.D and 3.E, depending on whether the Toeplitz matrix is non-Hermitian or Hermitian, can solve (3.182) in a number of computations per iteration proportional to M^2. After each computation of (3.182), the solution vector $\mathbf{v}(k)$ is scaled by the square root of its magnitude $\mathbf{v}^H(k)\mathbf{v}(k)$ to produce a unit length vector. Usually a few iterations are all that is needed for the vector to converge to the eigenvector of the minimum eigenvalue, with the minimum eigenvalue given by the Rayleigh quotient

$$\lambda_{min} = \frac{\mathbf{v}^H(k)\mathbf{T}\mathbf{v}(k)}{\mathbf{v}^H(k)\mathbf{v}(k)} \quad . \tag{3.183}$$

Convergence may be slow if $\lambda_{max}/\lambda_{min} \gg 1$. Program MINEIGVAL is a FORTRAN program in Appendix 3.F that solves for the minimum eigenvalue of a Hermitian Toeplitz matrix using this approach.

The maximum eigenvector may similarly be found by iterating the matrix equation

$$\mathbf{T}\mathbf{v}(k) = \mathbf{v}(k+1) \tag{3.184}$$

until convergence is achieved. Simple matrix-vector multiplication is all that is required here, so that computations will be proportional to M^2.

REFERENCES

Burg, John P., A New Analysis Technique for Time Series Analysis, NATO Advanced Study Institute on Signal Processing with Emphasis on Underwater Acoustics, Enschede, The Netherlands, August 1968. Paper reprinted in *Modern Spectrum Analysis*, Don Childers, ed., IEEE Press, New York, 1978 (see p. 48).

Businger, P. A., and G. H. Golub, Singular Value Decomposition of a Complex Matrix, *Commun. ACM*, vol. 12, pp. 564–565, 1969.

Cantoni, Antonio, and Paul Butler, Eigenvalues and Eigenvectors of Symmetric Centrosymmetric Matrices, *Linear Algebra and Its Applications*, vol. 13, pp. 275–288, March 1976.

Carayannis, George, Nicholas Kalouptsidis, and Dimitris G. Manolakis, Fast Recursive Algorithms for a Class of Linear Equations, *IEEE Trans. Acoust. Speech Signal Process.*, vol. ASSP-30, pp. 227–239, April 1982.

Cornyn, John J. Jr., Direct Methods for Solving Systems of Linear Equations Involving Toeplitz or Hankel Matrices, *Naval Research Laboratory (NRL) Memorandum Report 2920*, October 1974 (available from NTIS, AD/A-002 931).

Cybenko, George G., The Numerical Stability of the Levinson-Durbin Algorithm for Toeplitz Systems of Equations, *SIAM J. Sci. Stat. Comput.*, vol. 1,pp. 303–319, September 1980.

Datta, Lokesh, and Salvatore D. Morgera, Comments and Corrections "On the Eigenvectors of Symmetric Toeplitz Matrices," *IEEE Trans. Acoust. Speech Signal Process.*, vol. ASSP-32, pp. 440–441, April 1984; reply by Makhoul, vol. ASSP-33, pp. 737–738, June 1985.

Durbin, J., The Fitting of Time Series Models, *Rev. Inst. Int. Stat.*, vol. 28, pp. 233–244, 1960.

Farden, David C., Solution of a Toeplitz Set of Linear Equations, *IEEE Trans. Antennas Propag.*, vol. AP-24, pp. 906–907, November 1976.

Forsythe, G. E., M. A. Malcolm, and C. B. Moler, *Computer Methods for Mathematical Computations*, Prentice-Hall, Inc., Englewood Cliffs, N. J., 1977.

Gray, R. M., On the Asymptotic Eigenvalue Distribution of Toeplitz Matrices, *IEEE Trans. Inf. Theory*, vol. IT-18, pp. 725–730, November 1972.

Grenander, O., and G. Szegö, *Toeplitz Forms and Their Applications*, University of California Press, Berkeley, Calif., 1958.

Klema, Virginia C., and Alan J. Laub, The Singular Value Decomposition: Its Computation and Some Applications, *IEEE Trans. Autom. Control*, vol. AC-25, pp. 164–176, April 1980.

Kung, Sun-Yuan, and Yu Hen Hu, A Highly Concurrent Algorithm and Pipelined Architecture for Solving Toeplitz Systems, *IEEE Trans. Acoust. Speech Signal Process.*, vol. ASSP-31, pp. 66–75, February 1983.

Lawson, C. L., and R. J. Hanson, *Solving Least Squares Problems*, Prentice-Hall, Inc., Englewood Cliffs, N. J., 1974.

Levinson, Norman, The Wiener RMS (Root Mean Square) Error Criterion in Filter Design and Prediction, *J. Math. Phys.*, vol. 25, pp. 261–278, January 1947.

Makhoul, John, On the Eigenvectors of Symmetric Toeplitz Matrices, *IEEE Trans. Acoust. Speech Signal Process.*, vol. ASSP-29, pp. 868–872, August 1981.

McClellan, J. H., and T. W. Parks, Eigenvalue and Eigenvector Decomposition of the Discrete Fourier Transform, *IEEE Trans. Audio Electroacoust.*, vol. AU-20, pp. 66–74, March 1972. See also comments in vol. AU-21, p. 65, February 1973.

Noble, Ben, and James W. Daniel, *Applied Linear Algebra*, 2nd ed., Prentice-Hall, Inc., Englewood Cliffs, N. J., 1977.

Roebuck, Pamela A., and Stephen Barnett, A Survey of Toeplitz and Related Matrices, *Int. J. Syst. Scie.*, vol. 9, pp. 921–934, 1978.

Therrien, C. W., On the Relation between Triangular Matrix Decomposition and Linear Prediction, *Proc. IEEE*, vol. 71, pp. 1459–1460, December 1983.

Trench, William F., An Algorithm for the Inversion of Finite Toeplitz Matrices, *J. Soc. Ind. Appl. Math.*, vol. 12, pp. 515–522, September 1964.

Yarlagadda, R., and B. N. Suresh Babu, A Note on the Application of FFT to the Solution of a System of Toeplitz Normal Equations, *IEEE Trans. Circuits Syst.*, vol. CAS-27, pp. 151–154, February 1980.

Zohar, Shalhav, Toeplitz Matrix Inversion: The Algorithm of W. F. Trench, *J. Assoc. Comput. Mach.*, vol. 16, pp. 592–601, October 1969.

Zohar, Shalhav, The Solution of a Toeplitz Set of Linear Equations, *J. Assoc. Comput. Mach.*, vol. 21, pp. 272–276, April 1974.

Zohar, Shalhav, FORTRAN Subroutines for the Solution of Toeplitz Sets of Linear Equations, *IEEE Trans. Acoust. Speech Signal Process.*, vol. ASSP-27, pp. 656–658, December 1979. See also corrections in: vol. ASSP-28, p. 601, October 1980; vol. ASSP-29, p. 1212, December 1981.

PROBLEMS

1. Prove that a matrix that is both symmetric and persymmetric is also centrosymmetric, but the converse is not true. Construct such a matrix. Also prove that a matrix that possesses any two of the symmetric, persymmetric, centrosymmetric properties will also have the remaining property.

2. Prove that $(\mathbf{AB})^H = \mathbf{B}^H \mathbf{A}^H$.

3. Define the inner product relationship for block vectors.

4. If $\mathbf{H}$ is a Hankel matrix, show that $\mathbf{JH}$ or $\mathbf{HJ}$ are Toeplitz matrices.

5. Prove that $(\mathbf{AB})^{-1} = \mathbf{B}^{-1}\mathbf{A}^{-1}$ if $\mathbf{A}$, $\mathbf{B}$, and $\mathbf{AB}$ are nonsingular.

6. Prove that the inverse of a diagonal matrix is a diagonal matrix with main diagonal elements $1/d[i]$.

7. If $\mathbf{A}$ is a square matrix of size $n \times n$ and $\mathbf{x}$ is a column vector of size $n \times 1$, then show that $\mathbf{x}^H \mathbf{A} \mathbf{x}$ is a non-negative scalar.

8. Prove that $(\mathbf{A}^H)^{-1} = (\mathbf{A}^{-1})^H$.

9. Prove that if $\mathbf{A}$ is symmetric, then $\mathbf{A}^{-1}$ is symmetric (if inverse exists). Prove that if $\mathbf{A}$ is persymmetric, then $\mathbf{A}^{-1}$ is persymmetric. Prove that if $\mathbf{A}$ is Toeplitz, then $\mathbf{A}^{-1}$ is persymmetric. Prove that if $\mathbf{A}$ is Hankel, then $\mathbf{A}^{-1}$ is symmetric. Prove that if $\mathbf{A}$ is centrosymmetric, then $\mathbf{A}^{-1}$ is centrosymmetric.

10. Show that an upper triangular matrix $\mathbf{A}$ with nonzero diagonal elements has linearly independent column vectors, and is, therefore, nonsingular.

11. Show that if $\mathbf{A}$ has rank n, then the rank of $\mathbf{A}^H$ is also n.

12. Show that the determinant of the square Vandermonde matrix

$$\mathbf{V} = \begin{Bmatrix} 1 & \cdots & 1 \\ x_1 & \cdots & x_n \\ \vdots & & \vdots \\ x_1^{n-1} & \cdots & x_n^{n-1} \end{Bmatrix}$$

is given by

$$\det \mathbf{V} = \prod_{i \neq j}(x_j - x_i) \quad .$$

13. An $n \times n$ symmetric tridiagonal Toeplitz matrix has the form

$$\begin{pmatrix} b & a & 0 & \cdots & 0 \\ a & b & a & \ddots & \vdots \\ 0 & a & \ddots & \ddots & 0 \\ \vdots & \ddots & \ddots & \ddots & a \\ 0 & \cdots & 0 & a & b \end{pmatrix} \quad .$$

Show that it has eigenvalues $\lambda_k = a + 2b\cos(k\pi/n + 1)$ for $k = 1$ to n and corresponding eigenvectors

$$\mathbf{v}_k = \sqrt{\frac{2}{n+1}} \begin{pmatrix} \sin(k\pi/n + 1) \\ \vdots \\ \sin(kn\pi/n + 1) \end{pmatrix} \quad .$$

14. Show how the solution $\mathbf{x}$ to the linear equation $\mathbf{Cx} = \mathbf{b}$, in which $\mathbf{C}$ is circulant, can be obtained with three FFT operations. How does the use of left- or right-circulant matrices change whether forward or inverse FFTs are used?

15. Show that if $\mathbf{C}$ is centrosymmetric, then $\mathbf{JC} = \mathbf{CJ}$.

16. Prove Eq. (3.149). Hint: Use the partitions

$$\mathbf{T}_M = \begin{pmatrix} t[0] & \mathbf{s}_M^T \\ \mathbf{r}_M & \mathbf{T}_{M-1} \end{pmatrix}$$

$$\mathbf{T}_M^{-1} = \mathbf{U}_M = \begin{pmatrix} h & \mathbf{g}^T \\ \mathbf{F} & \mathbf{E} \end{pmatrix}$$

and then make use of the matrix inversion lemma, Eq. (3.50). Note that $h = u[0,0] = 1/\rho_M$.

17. Investigate the properties of polynomial roots when a matrix is Hermitian Toeplitz. Show, for example, that the eigenpolynomial has complex conjugate symmetry and that the roots are of unit modulus.

18. Modify subroutines TOEPLITZ and HERMTOEP so that an in-place solution is performed in array Z, that is, the solution comes back in array Z, eliminating the need for array X.

19. The Levinson algorithm was shown to solve the equations

$$\mathbf{T}_M \begin{pmatrix} \mathbf{Jb}_M \\ 1 \end{pmatrix} = \begin{pmatrix} \mathbf{0}_M \\ \rho_M \end{pmatrix}$$

$$\mathbf{T}_M \begin{pmatrix} 1 \\ \mathbf{a}_M \end{pmatrix} = \begin{pmatrix} \rho_M \\ \mathbf{0}_M \end{pmatrix} \quad .$$

Using Eq. (3.129), show that the following relations hold

$$t[0] + \mathbf{s}_M^T \mathbf{a}_M = t[0] + \mathbf{r}_M^T \mathbf{b}_M = \rho_M$$

$$\mathbf{r}_M + \mathbf{T}_{M-1} \mathbf{a}_M = \mathbf{J}\mathbf{s}_M + \mathbf{T}_{M-1}\mathbf{J}\mathbf{b}_M = \mathbf{0}_M.$$

20. SPECIAL CREDIT: Show how to develop an $O(n \log n)$ inversion algorithm for triangular Toeplitz matrices. First show that multiplication of a lower (or upper) triangular Toeplitz matrix by a vector is equivalent to the convolution (or correlation) of the sequences formed by the first column (or row) of the matrix and the vector, and it can be done by the FFT.

APPENDIX 3.A
PROGRAM TO SOLVE HERMITIAN LINEAR EQUATIONS
BY CHOLESKY METHOD

The Cholesky method for solving Hermitian linear simultaneous equations is outlined in Sec. 3.6. The number of computations is proportional to M^3, where M is the dimension of the matrix. The program may be converted to process real-valued data by using the procedure described in Appendix IV at the back of the book. The subroutine uses an in-place procedure to deposit the solution in array B, destroying the original input entries in this array. Only half of matrix A needs to be stored for this subroutine to work. The remaining half is determined by the Hermitian symmetry.

Using the notation (x, y) to represent a complex value $x + jy$, the following test case

$$\begin{pmatrix} (2.,0.) & (.5,-.5) & (-.2,.1) \\ (.5,.5) & (1.,0.) & (.3,-.2) \\ (-.2,-.1) & (.3,.2) & (.5,0.) \end{pmatrix} \begin{pmatrix} x[1] \\ x[2] \\ x[3] \end{pmatrix} = \begin{pmatrix} (1.,3.) \\ (2.,-1.) \\ (.5,.8) \end{pmatrix}$$

will yield the solution

$$\begin{pmatrix} (0.9595, 5.2566) \\ (4.4189, -7.0405) \\ (-5.1351, 6.3514) \end{pmatrix}$$

in complex array B. EPS was set to 10^{-15}.

```
      SUBROUTINE CHOLESKY (M,EPS,A,B,ISTAT)
C
C This program solves a Hermitian symmetric set of complex linear
C simultaneous equations using the Cholesky decomposition method.
C The solution replaces the original contents of array B. Contents
C of array A are destroyed after this routine is called.
C
C                    AX = B
C
C   Input Parameters:
C
```

```
C      M   - Order of the matrix (number of linear equations)
C      EPS - Epsilon (quantity for testing loss of significance;
C            depends on machine precision; suggest 1.E-15)
C      A   - Array of complex matrix elements stored columnwise
C            (i.e., A(1,1) is stored as A(1), A(1,2) as A(2),
C            A(2,2) as A(3), etc. Only the top triangular part
C            of the A matrix is stored since the other half is
C            obtained by Hermitian symmetry)
C      B   - Array of complex elements of right-hand-side vector
C
C
C   Output Parameters:
C
C      B   - Complex solution X vector stored in place of B vector
C      ISTAT - Integer status indicator at time of exit
C               0 for normal exit
C               -1 if matrix is singular
C               +K if there is loss of numerical significance or if
C                   a nonpositive-definite matrix detected at pivot K
C
C   Notes:
C
C      External array A must be dimensioned .GE. M(M+1)/2 and array B
C      must be dimensioned .GE. M in the calling program.
C
C      COMPLEX A(1),B(1),SUM
C
C   Factor into triangular and diagonal form   ! Eq. (3.76)
C
       ISTAT=0
       KPIV=0
       DO 100 K=1,M
         KPIV=KPIV+K
         IND=KPIV
         LEND=K-1
         TINY=ABS(EPS*REAL(A(KPIV)))
         DO 100 I=K,M
           SUM=(0.,0.)
           IF (LEND .EQ. 0)  GO TO 40
           LPIV=KPIV
           DO 30 L=1,LEND
             LPIV=LPIV+L-K-1
30           SUM=SUM+REAL(A(LPIV))*A(IND-L)*CONJG(A(KPIV-L))
40         SUM=A(IND)-SUM
           IF (I .NE. K)  GO TO 80
C
C   Test for negative pivot element and loss of significance
C
           IF (REAL(SUM) .GT. TINY)  GO TO 90
           IF (REAL(SUM) .GT. 0.)  GO TO 70
           ISTAT=-1
           RETURN
70         IF (ISTAT .GT. 0)  GO TO 90
           ISTAT=K
90         A(KPIV)=CMPLX(REAL(SUM),0.)
           DPIV=1./REAL(SUM)
           GO TO 100
80         A(IND)=SUM*DPIV
```

```
100       IND=IND+I
C
C   Back solution for intermediate column vector solution   ! Eq. (3.74)
C
      KPIV=1
      DO 200 K=2,M
        KPIV=KPIV+K
        SUM=B(K)
        DO 210 J=1,K-1
210       SUM=SUM-B(K-J)*CONJG(A(KPIV-J))
200     B(K)=SUM
C
C   Back solution for final column vector solution      ! Eq. (3.75)
C
      KPIV=(M*(M+1))/2
      B(M)=B(M)/REAL(A(KPIV))
      DO 300 K=M,2,-1
        KPIV=KPIV-K
        IND=KPIV
        SUM=B(K-1)/REAL(A(KPIV))
        DO 310 J=K,M
          IND=IND+(J-1)
310       SUM=SUM-B(J)*A(IND)
300     B(K-1)=SUM
      RETURN
      END
```

APPENDIX 3.B
PROGRAM TO FIND COMPLEX SINGULAR VALUE DECOMPOSITION

The subroutine CSVD finds the singular value decomposition of the M row by N column complex matrix A, where $M \geq N$. The maximum possible dimensions of A are $MMAX$ by $NMAX$. The N real singular values $(\sigma_1 \geq \sigma_2 \geq \ldots \geq \sigma_N)$ are stored by decreasing magnitude in vector S. The subroutine also finds the first NV columns of the N by N complex unitary matrix V and the first NU columns of the M by M complex unitary matrix U such that $\|A - U\Sigma V^H\|_2$ is negligible relative to $\|A\|_2$, where $\Sigma = \text{diag}(\sigma_1, \ldots, \sigma_N)$ is a diagonal matrix of the singular values. The only permitted values for NU are 0, N, and M. The only permitted values for NV are 0 and N. The transformation U^H may optionally be applied to the IP vectors in the $N + 1$ through $N + IP$ columns of array A (assuming IP is nonzero). This feature may be used to find the least squares solution of minimal Euclidian length (the pseudoinverse solution) of an overdetermined system $AX \approx B$. The pseudoinverse solution is derived by calling CSVD with $NV = N$ and the IP-column right-hand-side B in the $N + 1$ through $N + IP$ columns of A. The effective rank r of A can be estimated from the singular values in vector S. The negligible singular values from $r + 1$ to N are then zeroed, and the solution is given by $X = V\Sigma^{\#}U^H B$, where $\Sigma^{\#} = \text{diag}(\sigma_1^{-1}, \sigma_2^{-1}, \ldots, \sigma_r^{-1}, 0, \ldots, 0)$ and $U^H B$

is furnished by CSVD in place of each right-hand-side B in the $N + 1$ to $N + IP$ positions of A.

The constants ETA and TOL used by the program are machine-dependent. ETA is the relative machine precision and TOL is the smallest normalized positive number divided by ETA. The values in the program are appropriate for a VAX computer. The internal arrays B, C, and T are dimensioned under the assumption that $N \leq 100$.

Using the notation (x, y) to represent a complex value $x + jy$, the following test matrix

$$\mathbf{A} = \begin{pmatrix} (2.8, -.4) & (1.6, 0.) \\ (3.6, -1.2) & (2.4, -1.8) \\ (2., .4) & (2.8, -4.4) \end{pmatrix}$$

will yield, for $NU = 3$, $NV = 2$, and $IP = 0$, the following values in arrays S, U, and V

$$\mathbf{S} = \begin{pmatrix} 7.5171 \\ 2.9687 \end{pmatrix} \quad , \quad \mathbf{V} = \begin{pmatrix} (.61000, 0.) & (.79240, 0.) \\ (.65719, .44271) & (-.50592, -.34081) \end{pmatrix}$$

$$\mathbf{U} = \begin{pmatrix} (.36710, .06177) & (.47471, -.29045) & (.02914, .74220) \\ (.60797, -.11340) & (.34527, -.28907) & (-.18073, -.61813) \\ (.66622, -.18731) & (-.44845, .53517) & (.02582, .18132) \end{pmatrix} \quad .$$

```
      SUBROUTINE CSVD (A,MMAX,NMAX,M,N,IP,NU,NV,S,U,V)
C
C     Singular value decomposition of an  M by N  complex matrix  A,
C     where M .GT. N .   The singular values are stored in the vector
C     S. The first NU columns of the M by M unitary matrix U and the
C     first NV columns of the N by N unitary matrix V  that minimize
C     Det(A-USV*) are also computed.
C
C
C
C           P.A. Businger and G.H. Golub, "Singular Value Decomposition
C           of a Complex Matrix," Communications of the ACM, vol. 12,
C           pp. 564-565, October 1969.
C
C     This algorithm is reprinted by permission, Association for
C     Computing Machinery; copyright 1969.
C
      COMPLEX A(MMAX,NMAX),U(MMAX,MMAX),V(NMAX,NMAX),Q,R
      REAL S(NMAX),B(100),C(100),T(100)
      DATA ETA,TOL/1.2E-7,2.4E-32/
      NP=N+IP
      N1=N+1
C     Householder reduction
      C(1)=0.
      K=1
   10 K1=K+1
```

```
C    Elimination of A(I,K) , I=K+1,...,M
     Z=0.
     DO 20 I=K,M
20      Z=Z+REAL(A(I,K))**2+AIMAG(A(I,K))**2
     B(K)=0.
     IF (Z .LE. TOL)  GO TO 70
     Z=SQRT(Z)
     B(K)=Z
     W=CABS(A(K,K))
     Q=(1.,0.)
     IF (W .NE. 0.)  Q=A(K,K)/W
     A(K,K)=Q*(Z+W)
     IF (K .EQ. NP)  GO TO 70
     DO 50 J=K1,NP
       Q=(0.,0.)
       DO 30 I=K,M
30        Q=Q+CONJG(A(I,K))*A(I,J)
       Q=Q/(Z*(Z+W))
       DO 40 I=K,M
40        A(I,J)=A(I,J)-Q*A(I,K)
50      CONTINUE
C    Phase transformation
     Q=-CONJG(A(K,K))/CABS(A(K,K))
     DO 60 J=K1,NP
60      A(K,J)=Q*A(K,J)
C    Elimination of A(K,J) , J=K+2,...,N
70   IF (K .EQ. N)  GO TO 140
     Z=0.
     DO 80 J=K1,N
80      Z=Z+REAL(A(K,J))**2+AIMAG(A(K,J))**2
     C(K1)=0.
     IF (Z .LE. TOL)  GO TO 130
     Z=SQRT(Z)
     C(K1)=Z
     W=CABS(A(K,K1))
     Q=(1.,0.)
     IF (W .NE. 0.)  Q=A(K,K1)/W
     A(K,K1)=Q*(Z+W)
     DO 110 I=K1,M
       Q=(0.,0.)
       DO 90 J=K1,N
90        Q=Q+CONJG(A(K,J))*A(I,J)
       Q=Q/(Z*(Z+W))
       DO 100 J=K1,N
100       A(I,J)=A(I,J)-Q*A(K,J)
110     CONTINUE
C    Phase transformation
     Q=-CONJG(A(K,K1))/CABS(A(K,K1))
     DO 120 I=K1,M
120     A(I,K1)=A(I,K1)*Q
130  K=K1
     GO TO 10
C    Tolerance for negligible elements
140  EPS=0.
     DO 150 K=1,N
       S(K)=B(K)
       T(K)=C(K)
150  EPS=AMAX1(EPS,S(K)+T(K))
```

```
            EPS=EPS*ETA
C    Initialization of U and V
            IF (NU .EQ. 0)  GO TO 180
            DO 170 J=1,NU
               DO 160 I=1,M
160              U(I,J)=(0.,0.)
170            U(J,J)=(1.,0.)
180         IF (NV .EQ. 0)  GO TO 210
            DO 200 J=1,NV
               DO 190 I=1,N
190              V(I,J)=(0.,0.)
200            V(J,J)=(1.,0.)
C    QR diagonalization
210         DO 380 KK=1,N
               K=N1-KK
C    Test for split
220            DO 230 LL=1,K
                  L=K+1-LL
                  IF (ABS(T(L)) .LE. EPS)  GO TO 290
                  IF (ABS(S(L-1)) .LE. EPS)  GO TO 240
230            CONTINUE
C    Cancellation of B(L)
240            CS=0.
               SN=1.
               L1=L-1
               DO 280 I=L,K
                  F=SN*T(I)
                  T(I)=CS*T(I)
                  IF (ABS(F) .LE. EPS)  GO TO 290
                  H=S(I)
                  W=SQRT(F*F+H*H)
                  S(I)=W
                  CS=H/W
                  SN=-F/W
                  IF (NU .EQ. 0)  GO TO 260
                  DO 250 J=1,N
                     X=REAL(U(J,L1))
                     Y=REAL(U(J,I))
                     U(J,L1)=CMPLX(X*CS+Y*SN,0.)
250                  U(J,I)=CMPLX(Y*CS-X*SN,0.)
260               IF (NP .EQ. N)  GO TO 280
                  DO 270 J=N1,NP
                     Q=A(L1,J)
                     R=A(I,J)
                     A(L1,J)=Q*CS+R*SN
270                  A(I,J)=R*CS-Q*SN
280            CONTINUE
C    Test for convergence
290            W=S(K)
               IF (L .EQ. K)  GO TO 360
C    Origin shift
               X=S(L)
               Y=S(K-1)
               G=T(K-1)
               H=T(K)
               F=((Y-W)*(Y+W)+(G-H)*(G+H))/(2.*H*Y)
               G=SQRT(F*F+1.)
               IF (F .LT. 0.)  G=-G
```

```
          F=((X-W)*(X+W)+(Y/(F+G)-H)*H)/X
C    QR step
          CS=1.
          SN=1.
          L1=L+1
          DO 350 I=L1,K
            G=T(I)
            Y=S(I)
            H=SN*G
            G=CS*G
            W=SQRT(H*H+F*F)
            T(I-1)=W
            CS=F/W
            SN=H/W
            F=X*CS+G*SN
            G=G*CS-X*SN
            H=Y*SN
            Y=Y*CS
            IF (NV .EQ. 0)  GO TO 310
            DO 300 J=1,N
              X=REAL(V(J,I-1))
              W=REAL(V(J,I))
              V(J,I-1)=CMPLX(X*CS+W*SN,0.)
300           V(J,I)=CMPLX(W*CS-X*SN,0.)
310         W=SQRT(H*H+F*F)
            S(I-1)=W
            CS=F/W
            SN=H/W
            F=CS*G+SN*Y
            X=CS*Y-SN*G
            IF (NU .EQ. 0)   GO TO 330
            DO 320 J=1,N
              Y=REAL(U(J,I-1))
              W=REAL(U(J,I))
              U(J,I-1)=CMPLX(Y*CS+W*SN,0.)
320           U(J,I)=CMPLX(W*CS-Y*SN,0.)
330         IF (N .EQ. NP)   GO TO 350
            DO 340 J=N1,NP
              Q=A(I-1,J)
              R=A(I,J)
              A(I-1,J)=Q*CS+R*SN
340           A(I,J)=R*CS-Q*SN
350         CONTINUE
          T(L)=0.
          T(K)=F
          S(K)=X
          GO TO 220
C    Convergence
360       IF (W .GE. 0.)   GO TO 380
          S(K)=-W
          IF (NV .EQ. 0)   GO TO 380
          DO 370 J=1,N
370         V(J,K)=-V(J,K)
380       CONTINUE
C    Sort singular values
          DO 450 K=1,N
            G=-1.
            J=K
```

```
            DO 390 I=K,N
              IF (S(I) .LE. G)  GO TO 390
              G=S(I)
              J=I
390           CONTINUE
            IF (J .EQ. K)  GO TO 450
            S(J)=S(K)
            S(K)=G
            IF (NV .EQ. 0)  GO TO 410
            DO 400 I=1,N
              Q=V(I,J)
              V(I,J)=V(I,K)
400           V(I,K)=Q
410         IF (NU .EQ. 0)  GO TO 430
            DO 420 I=1,N
              Q=U(I,J)
              U(I,J)=U(I,K)
420           U(I,K)=Q
430         IF (N .EQ. NP)  GO TO 450
            DO 440 I=N1,NP
              Q=A(J,I)
              A(J,I)=A(K,I)
440           A(K,I)=Q
450         CONTINUE
C    Back transformation
            IF (NU .EQ. 0)  GO TO 510
            DO 500 KK=1,N
              K=N1-KK
              IF (B(K) .EQ. 0.)  GO TO 500
              Q=-A(K,K)/CABS(A(K,K))
              DO 460 J=1,NU
460             U(K,J)=Q*U(K,J)
              DO 490 J=1,NU
                Q=(0.,0.)
                DO 470 I=K,M
470               Q=Q+CONJG(A(I,K))*U(I,J)
                Q=Q/(CABS(A(K,K))*B(K))
                DO 480 I=K,M
480               U(I,J)=U(I,J)-Q*A(I,K)
490             CONTINUE
500           CONTINUE
510         IF (NV .EQ. 0)  GO TO 570
            IF (N .LT. 2)  GO TO 570
            DO 560 KK=2,N
              K=N1-KK
              K1=K+1
              IF (C(K1) .EQ. 0.)  GO TO 560
              Q=-CONJG(A(K,K1))/CABS(A(K,K1))
              DO 520 J=1,NV
520             V(K1,J)=Q*V(K1,J)
              DO 550 J=1,NV
                Q=(0.,0.)
                DO 530 I=K1,N
530               Q=Q+A(K,I)*V(I,J)
                Q=Q/(CABS(A(K,K1))*C(K1))
                DO 540 I=K1,N
540               V(I,J)=V(I,J)-Q*CONJG(A(K,I))
550             CONTINUE
```

```
560     CONTINUE
570     RETURN
        END
```

APPENDIX 3.C
PROGRAM OF THE LEVINSON ALGORITHM

The Levinson algorithm will solve

$$\mathbf{T}_M \begin{pmatrix} 1 \\ \mathbf{a}_M \end{pmatrix} = \begin{pmatrix} \rho_M \\ \mathbf{0}_M \end{pmatrix}$$

in the case that $\mathbf{T}_M$ is a Hermitian Toeplitz matrix, as described in Sec. 3.8.1. Solving this equation by Gaussian elimination would require a number of operations proportional to M^3 and storage proportional to M^2. Using this Levinson algorithm, only $M^2 + M$ additions, $M^2 + 2M$ multiplications, M divisions, and storage of $2M$ array elements are required. The program may be converted to process real-valued data by using the procedure described in Appendix IV at the back of this book. Using the notation (x, y) to designate the complex value $x + jy$, the test input parameters $M = 2$, $T0 = 3.$, $T(1) = (-2., .5)$, and $T(2) = (.7, -1.)$ to LEVINSON will return the output values $P = 1.3221$, $A(1) = (.86316, .03158)$, and $A(2) = (.34737, .21053)$.

```
        SUBROUTINE LEVINSON (M,TO,T,P,A,ISTAT)
C
C    Solves the set of complex linear simultaneous equations
C                         TA = P
C    by the Levinson algorithm.  T is M+1 by M+1 Hermitian Toeplitz
C    matrix,  A is column vector with elements 1,a(1),...,a(M), and
C    P  is a column vector with  p as the top element and zeros for
C    the remaining elements.
C
C    Input Parameters:
C
C        M   - Number of unknown A vector components;  dimension of A
C              is M. (This is the autoregressive model order; see
C              Chap. 7.) (integer)
C        TO  - Real scalar corresponding to matrix element t(0)
C              (Hermitian symmetry forces this element to be real.)
C        T   - Array of M complex matrix elements t(1),...,t(M) from
C              the left column of the Toeplitz matrix (These are the
C              autocorrelation lags of the autoregressive model; see
C              Chap. 7.)
C
C    Output Parameters:
C
```

```
C        P  - Real scalar of top element of right-hand-side vector
C             (This is the autoregressive model driving noise
C             variance; see Chap. 7.)
C        A  - Array of M complex elements of solution vector. (These
C             are the autoregressive coefficients; see Chap. 7.)
C        ISTAT - Integer status indicator at time of exit
C                 0 for normal exit
C                 1 if P=0 (singular matrix)
C
C   Notes:
C
C     External arrays A and T must be dimensioned .GE. M by calling
C     program.
C
         COMPLEX T(1),A(1),TEMP,SAVE
         REAL TO,P
         P=TO
         ISTAT=0
C   Handle M=0 as special case
         IF (M .EQ. 0)  RETURN
C
C   Main Levinson recursion
C
         K=0
100      K=K+1
         SAVE=T(K)
         IF (K .EQ. 1)  GO TO 20
         DO 10 J=1,K-1
10         SAVE=SAVE+A(J)*T(K-J)                  ! Eq. (3.136)
20       TEMP=-SAVE/P
         P=P*(1.-REAL(TEMP)**2-AIMAG(TEMP)**2)    ! Eq. (3.158)
         IF (P .GT. 0.)  GO TO 30
         ISTAT=1
         RETURN
30       A(K)=TEMP                                 ! Eq. (3.139)
         IF (K .EQ. 1)  GO TO 50
         KHALF=K/2
         DO 40 J=1,KHALF
           KJ=K-J
           SAVE=A(J)
           A(J)=SAVE+TEMP*CONJG(A(KJ))            ! Eqs. (3.147),(3.156)
           IF (J .EQ. KJ)  GO TO 40
           A(KJ)=A(KJ)+TEMP*CONJG(SAVE)           ! Eqs. (3.147),(3.156)
40         CONTINUE
50       IF (K .LT. M)  GO TO 100
         RETURN
         END
```

APPENDIX 3.D
PROGRAM TO SOLVE GENERAL TOEPLITZ LINEAR EQUATIONS

This subroutine solves the general Toeplitz matrix set of linear simultaneous equations (3.167) described in Sec. 3.8.3. Solving these equations by Gaussian elimination would require a number of computations proportional to M^3 and storage proportional to M^2. This program only requires $3M^2 + M$ additions, $(5/2)M^2 + (5/2)M$ multiplications, $3M$ divisions, and storage of $6M$ array elements. The program may be converted to process real-valued data by using the procedure described in Appendix IV at the back of this book. Following the conventions in the text, the order M given as an input to the program results in a solution vector of dimension $M + 1$. Using the notation (x, y) to designate the complex value $x + jy$, the input parameters $M = 2$, $T0 = (3., 0.)$, $TC(1) = (-2., .5)$, $TC(2) = (.7, -1.)$, $TR(1) = (-.2, -.4)$, $TR(2) = (.3, -.6)$, $Z(1) = (1., 3.)$, $Z(2) = (2., -1.)$, and $Z(3) = (.5, .8)$ to TOEPLITZ will return the output values $X(1) = (.23519, 1.2437)$, $X(2) = (1.0303, .53575)$, and $X(3) = (.47335, .24032)$.

```
      SUBROUTINE TOEPLITZ (M,TO,TC,TR,Z,X,ISTAT)
C
C     Solves the set of complex linear simultaneous equations
C                         TX = Z
C     by a variation of the Levinson algorithm.  T is a complex  M+1
C     by  M+1  nonsymmetric Toeplitz matrix,  Z  is the known right-
C     hand-side complex column vector of M+1 elements, and  X is the
C     solution vector of  M+1  complex elements.
C
C     Input Parameters:
C
C        M  - Order of matrix T (integer)
C        TO - Scalar corresponding to complex matrix element t(0)
C        TC - Array of  M  complex matrix elements  t(1),...,t(M)
C             from the left column of the Toeplitz matrix
C        TR - Array of M complex matrix elements  t(-1),...,t(-M)
C             from the top row of the Toeplitz matrix
C        Z  - Array of M+1 complex elements of the right-hand-side
C             vector.   Program element Z(k+1) corresponds to text
C             element z(k), for k=0 to k=M
C
C     Output Parameters:
C
C        X  - Array of  M+1  complex elements of solution vector.
C             Program element X(k+1) corresponds to text element
C             x(k), for k=0 to k=M
C        ISTAT - Integer status indicator at time of exit
C                0 for normal exit
C                1 if P=0. (singular matrix)
C
C     Notes:
C
C        External arrays TR,TC must be dimensioned .GE. M  and arrays
C        X,Z must be dimensioned .GE. M+1  in the calling program.
C        Internal arrays A and B must be dimensioned .GE. M .
C
      COMPLEX TC(1),TR(1),X(1),Z(1),A(100),B(100)
      COMPLEX TEMP1,TEMP2,SAVE1,SAVE2,ALPHA,BETA
      COMPLEX P,TO
      P=TO
```

```
      ISTAT=1
      IF (P .EQ. (0.,0.))  RETURN
C   Handle  M=0  as special case
      X(1)=Z(1)/T0                    ! Eq. (3.175)
      IF (M .LE. 0)  RETURN
C
C   Main recursion
C
      K=0
100   K=K+1
      SAVE1=TC(K)
      SAVE2=TR(K)
      BETA=X(1)*TC(K)
      IF (K .EQ. 1)  GO TO 20
      DO 10 J=1,K-1
        KJ=K-J
        SAVE1=SAVE1+A(J)*TC(KJ)       ! Eq. (3.136)
        SAVE2=SAVE2+B(J)*TR(KJ)       ! Eq. (3.137)
10      BETA=BETA+X(J+1)*TC(KJ)       ! Eq. (3.173)
20    TEMP1=-SAVE1/P
      TEMP2=-SAVE2/P
      P=P*((1.,0.)-TEMP1*TEMP2)       ! Eq. (3.140)
      IF (P .EQ. (0.,0.))  RETURN
30    A(K)=TEMP1                      ! Eq. (3.139)
      B(K)=TEMP2                      ! Eq. (3.143)
      ALPHA=(Z(K+1)-BETA)/P           ! Eq. (3.174)
      IF (K .EQ. 1)  GO TO 50
      DO 40 J=1,K-1
        KJ=K-J
        SAVE1=A(J)
        A(J)=SAVE1+TEMP1*B(KJ)        ! Eq. (3.147)
        B(KJ)=B(KJ)+TEMP2*SAVE1       ! Eq. (3.148)
40      CONTINUE
50    X(K+1)=ALPHA
      DO 60 J=1,K
60      X(J)=X(J)+ALPHA*B(K-J+1)      ! Eq. (3.171)
      IF (K .LT. M)  GO TO 100
      ISTAT=0
      RETURN
      END
```

APPENDIX 3.E
PROGRAM TO SOLVE HERMITIAN TOEPLITZ LINEAR EQUATIONS

This subroutine solves the Hermitian Toeplitz matrix set of linear simultaneous equation (3.167) described in Sec. 3.8.3. This algorithm requires $2M^2 + 2M$ additions, $2M^2 + 3M$ multiplications, $2M$ divisions, and storage of $4M$ array elements. These numbers are less than those of subroutine TOEPLITZ because of the reduction in computations due to the Hermitian symmetry. The program may be converted to process real-valued data by using the procedure described in Appendix IV at the back of this book. Following the conventions of the text, the order M input to the program will result in a solution vector of dimension $M + 1$. Using the notation (x, y) to designate the complex value $x + jy$, the input parameters $M = 2$, $T0 = 3.$, $T(1) = (-2., .5)$, $T(2) = (.7, -1.)$, $Z(1) = (1., 3.)$, $Z(2) = (2., -1.)$, and $Z(3) = (.5, .8)$ to HERMTOEP will return the output values $X(1) = (2.2970, 1.6990)$, $X(2) = (3.3185, 1.2970)$, and $X(3) = (1.4928, 0.94745)$.

```
      SUBROUTINE HERMTOEP (M,TO,T,Z,X,ISTAT)
C
C     Solves the set of complex linear simultaneous equations
C                         TX = Z
C     by a variation of the Levinson algorithm.  T is a complex  M+1
C     by  M+1  Hermitian Toeplitz matrix, Z is the known right-hand-
C     side complex column vector of  M+1  elements,  and  X  is the
C     solution vector of  M+1  complex elements.
C
C     Input Parameters:
C
C        M   - Order of matrix T (integer)
C        TO  - Scalar corresponding to real matrix element t(0)
C              (This element must be real due to Hermitian symmetry.)
C        T   - Array of  M  complex matrix elements t(1),...,t(M)
C              from the left column of the Toeplitz matrix
C        Z   - Array of M+1 complex elements of the right-hand-side
C              vector.   Program element Z(k+1) corresponds to text
C              element z(k), for k=0 to k=M
C
C     Output Parameters:
C
C        X   - Array of  M+1  complex elements of solution vector.
C              Program element X(k+1) corresponds to text element
C              x(k), for k=0 to k=M
C        ISTAT - Integer status indicator at time of exit
C                   0 for normal exit
C                   1 if P=0. (singular matrix)
C
C     Notes:
C
C     External array T must be dimensioned .GE. M and arrays X,Z must
C     be dimensioned .GE. M+1 in the calling program.   Internal array
C     A must be dimensioned .GE. M .
C
         COMPLEX T(1),X(1),Z(1),A(100)
         COMPLEX TEMP,SAVE,ALPHA,BETA
         REAL P,TO
         P=TO
         ISTAT=1
         IF (P .EQ. 0.)  RETURN
C     Handle  M=0  as a special case
         X(1)=Z(1)/TO                              ! Eq. (3.175)
         IF (M .LE. 0)  RETURN
C
C     Main recursion
C
         K=0
```

```
100   K=K+1
      SAVE=T(K)
      BETA=X(1)*T(K)
      IF (K .EQ. 1)  GO TO 20
      DO 10 J=1,K-1
        SAVE=SAVE+A(J)*T(K-J)                    ! Eq. (3.136)
10      BETA=BETA+X(J+1)*T(K-J)                  ! Eq. (3.173)
20    TEMP=-SAVE/P
      P=P*(1.-REAL(TEMP)**2-AIMAG(TEMP)**2)      ! Eq. (3.158)
      IF (P .LE. 0.)  RETURN
30    A(K)=TEMP                                  ! Eq. (3.139)
      ALPHA=(Z(K+1)-BETA)/P                      ! Eq. (3.174)
      IF (K .EQ. 1)  GO TO 50
      KHALF=K/2
      DO 40 J=1,KHALF
        KJ=K-J
        SAVE=A(J)
        A(J)=SAVE+TEMP*CONJG(A(KJ))              ! Eqs. (3.147),(3.157)
        IF (J .EQ. KJ)  GO TO 40
        A(KJ)=A(KJ)+TEMP*CONJG(SAVE)             ! Eqs. (3.147),(3.157)
40    CONTINUE
50    X(K+1)=ALPHA
      DO 60 J=1,K
60      X(J)=X(J)+ALPHA*CONJG(A(K-J+1))          ! Eq. (3.171)
      IF (K .LT. M)  GO TO 100
      ISTAT=0
      RETURN
      END
```

APPENDIX 3.F
PROGRAM TO SOLVE FOR MINIMUM EIGENVALUE
AND EIGENVECTOR OF A HERMITIAN TOEPLITZ MATRIX

This subroutine solves for the minimum eigenvalue and its associated eigenvector of a matrix with Hermitian Toeplitz structure. The power method described in Sec. 3.8.4 is used. The program may be converted to process real-valued data by using the procedure described in Appendix IV at the back of this book. Following conventions used in the text, selection of input order M means that the actual dimension of the matrix is $(M+1) \times (M+1)$. Using the notation (x, y) to designate the complex value $x + jy$, the input parameters $M = 2$, $TOL = 1 \times 10^{-10}$, $T0 = 3.$, $T(1) = (-2., .5)$, and $T(2) = (.7, -1.)$ to MINEIGVAL will return the output values $EVAL = .48869$, $EVEC(1) = (.13791, -.01741)$, $EVEC(2) = (.21272, 0.)$, and $EVEC(3) = (.13791, .01741)$.

```
      SUBROUTINE MINEIGVAL (M,T0,T,TOL,EVAL,EVEC,ISTAT)
C
C     This program finds the  minimum  eigenvalue and its associated
C     eigenvector of a Hermitian Toeplitz matrix.      The classical
```

```
C    power method is used together with a  fast  Toeplitz  equation
C    solution routine.  The eigenvector is normalized to unit length.
C
C    Input parameters:
C
C      M    - Order of matrix T (integer)
C      T0   - Scalar corresponding to real matrix element t(0)
C      T    - Array of  M  complex matrix elements t(1),...,t(M)
C             from the left column of the Toeplitz matrix
C      TOL  - Real scalar tolerance; routine exits when
C                   [ EVAL(k) - EVAL(k-1) ]/EVAL(k-1) < TOL ,
C             where the index k denotes the iteration number.
C
C    Output Parameters:
C
C      EVAL - Real scalar denoting the minimum eigenvalue of matrix
C      EVEC - Array of  M  complex eigenvector elements associated
C             with minimum eigenvalue. Note EVEC(1) normalized to 1.
C      ISTAT - Integer status indicator at time of exit
C              0 for normal exit
C              1 if a singular matrix is detected
C
C    Notes:
C
C      External array T must be dimensioned .GE. M and array EVEC must
C      be dimensioned .GE. M+1 in the calling program.  Internal array
C      E must be dimensioned .GE. M+1 .  Subroutine HERMTOEP (Appendix
C      3.D) is required.
C
       COMPLEX T(1),EVEC(1),E(100),SAVE
       M1=M+1
       EVAL=10.                             ! Initialize the eigenvalue
       DO 10 K=1,M1
10       EVEC(K)=(1.,0.)                    ! Initialize the eigenvector
20     EVALOLD=EVAL
       CALL HERMTOEP (M,T0,T,EVEC,E,ISTAT)       ! Eq. (3.182)
       SUM=0.
       SAVE=(0.,0.)
       DO 30 K=1,M1
         SUM=SUM+REAL(E(K))**2+AIMAG(E(K))**2    !
30       SAVE=SAVE+E(K)*CONJG(EVEC(K))           ! Eq. (3.183)
       SUM=1./SUM
       EVAL=REAL(SAVE)*SUM                       !
       DO 40 K=1,M1
40       EVEC(K)=SUM*E(K)
       IF (ABS(EVAL-EVALOLD) .GE. TOL*EVALOLD)  GO TO 20
       RETURN
       END
```

4

REVIEW OF RANDOM
PROCESS THEORY

4.1 INTRODUCTION

An assumption is made that the reader already has some familiarity with probability, random variable, and random process theory. This chapter serves simply as
a review. A primary topic of this chapter is the formal introduction of the *power
spectral density* (PSD) concept. It will be seen that the PSD is a statistical extension of the energy spectral density of Chap. 2. Another important topic is the
property of *ergodicity*, which permits the substitution of time averages for statistical averages. This will establish the foundation for the classical methods of power
spectral density estimation that are covered in Chap. 5. For those readers needing a
more extensive review than covered in this chapter, the excellent texts by Papoulis
[1977,1984], Brillinger [1974], and Gardner [1985] are highly recommended.

4.2 PROBABILITY AND RANDOM VARIABLES

Consider a discrete event E, which is one of a finite number of possible discrete
outcomes of a random experiment. The *probability* of this event, denoted as Pr(E),
may be intuitively considered to be the limit of the ratio of the number of times E
occurred to the number of times the experiment was attempted. The probability is
bounded, therefore, between 0 and 1. A *random variable* x is, in simplest terms, a

variable which takes on values at random from a continuum of possible values. The manner of specifying the probability with which different values are taken by the random variable is quantified by the *probability distribution function* $F(x)$, defined by $F(x) = \text{Pr}(x \le x)$, that is, the probability that random variable x has a value less than or equal to x is given by $F(x)$. The *probability density function* (PDF) $p(x)$ is the derivative given by $p(x) = \partial F(x)/\partial x$.

The *expectation* of a random variable x, denoted as $\mathcal{E}\{x\}$, is given by

$$\mathcal{E}\{x\} = \int_{-\infty}^{\infty} x\, p(x)\, dx = \bar{x} \quad . \tag{4.1}$$

This is also called the *mean value* of x, or the *first moment* of x. It represents the value toward which the average of a number of observations of x tends, in the probabilistic sense, as the number of observations increases. The expectation of a function of random variable x, say $g(x)$, can be directly calculated from the PDF of x by

$$\mathcal{E}\{g(x)\} = \int_{-\infty}^{\infty} g(x)p(x)\, dx \quad . \tag{4.2}$$

The expectation of the squared magnitude of x

$$\mathcal{E}\{|x|^2\} = \int_{-\infty}^{\infty} |x|^2 p(x)\, dx \tag{4.3}$$

is called the *mean squared value*, or the *second moment* of x. The *variance* ρ of a random variable is the mean squared deviation of the random variable from its mean,

$$\text{var}\{x\} = \int_{-\infty}^{\infty} |x - \mathcal{E}\{x\}|^2 p(x)\, dx = \mathcal{E}\{|x|^2\} - |\mathcal{E}\{x\}|^2 = \rho \quad . \tag{4.4}$$

Note that the mean squared value and the variance are equal only for a zero-mean random variable. An indication of the statistical correlation to which one random variable is related to another random variable is given by the *covariance*,

$$\begin{aligned}
\text{cov}\{xy\} &= \mathcal{E}\{(x - \mathcal{E}\{x\})(y^* - \mathcal{E}\{y\}^*)\} \\
&= \int_{-\infty}^{\infty}\int_{-\infty}^{\infty} (x - \mathcal{E}\{x\})(y^* - \mathcal{E}\{y\}^*)p(x,y)\, dx\, dy \\
&= \mathcal{E}\{xy^*\} - \mathcal{E}\{x\}\mathcal{E}\{y\}^*
\end{aligned} \tag{4.5}$$

in which $p(x, y)$ represents the *joint* probability density function of random variables x and y. In this expression, $\mathcal{E}\{xy\}$ represents the joint second moment of x and y. For convenience, the contrasting notation between a random variable x and its value x will not be used past this point in order to simplify this review.

In the presentation of various parameter estimators in later chapters, several terms are used to describe the behavior of the estimators. These terms are defined here. The *bias* $B(\hat{\alpha})$ of an estimator $\hat{\alpha}$ of the parameter α is the difference between the true value of the parameter and the expected value of the estimate,

$$B(\hat{\alpha}) = \alpha - \mathcal{E}\{\hat{\alpha}\} \quad . \tag{4.6}$$

An *unbiased* estimator is one in which $B(\hat{\alpha}) = 0$. The *mean square error* of the estimator $\hat{\alpha}$ is

$$\text{mse}\{\hat{\alpha}\} = \mathcal{E}\left\{|\alpha - \hat{\alpha}|^2\right\} = \text{var}\{\hat{\alpha}\} + |B(\hat{\alpha})|^2 \quad . \tag{4.7}$$

An estimator is said to be *consistent* if, as the number of observations increases, the bias and variance both tend to zero. A *maximum likelihood estimator* is one in which the value of the parameter for which the probability of having obtained the observed value is a maximum. The Cramer-Rao (CR) inequality is frequently used to lower bound the variance performance of an unbiased estimator of a scalar parameter. Assuming that the random vector $\mathbf{x}$ is used to estimate parameter α, then the CR inequality takes the form

$$\text{var}\{\hat{\alpha}\} \geq \mathcal{E}\left\{ \left(\frac{\partial \ln p(\mathbf{x}|\alpha)}{\partial \alpha} \right)^2 \right\}^{-1} \tag{4.8}$$

evaluated at the true value of the parameter α, in which $p(\mathbf{x}|\alpha)$ is the PDF of random variable $\mathbf{x}$ with dependence on α shown explicitly. An estimator that attains the CR bound is said to be *efficient*.

Two important probability density functions are used in this book. The *uniform distribution* of a real variable x is characterized by a uniform (constant) PDF

$$p(x) = \frac{1}{b - a} \tag{4.9}$$

over the finite real interval $a \leq x \leq b$. The *Gaussian distribution* of a real random variable x with mean x and variance ρ is characterized by a PDF given by

$$p(x) = [2\pi\rho]^{-1/2} \exp\left[-\frac{1}{2\rho}(x - \bar{x})^2 \right] \tag{4.10}$$

for $-\infty < x < \infty$. A *multivariate* Gaussian PDF for a vector of K real random variables $\mathbf{x} = [x_1 \, x_2 \ldots x_K]^T$ has the structure

$$p(\mathbf{x}) = [(2\pi)^K \det \mathbf{C}_K]^{-1/2} \exp\left[-\frac{1}{2}(\mathbf{x} - \bar{\mathbf{x}})^T \mathbf{C}_K^{-1}(\mathbf{x} - \bar{\mathbf{x}}) \right] \quad , \tag{4.11}$$

in which the K-element mean vector $\bar{\mathbf{x}}$ is defined as

$$\bar{\mathbf{x}} = \mathcal{E}\{\mathbf{x}\} \tag{4.12}$$

and the $K \times K$ covariance matrix $\mathbf{C}_K$ is defined as

$$\begin{aligned}
\mathbf{C}_K &= \mathcal{E}\{(\mathbf{x} - \bar{\mathbf{x}})(\mathbf{x} - \bar{\mathbf{x}})^T\} \\
&= \begin{pmatrix}
\text{var}\{x_1\} & \text{cov}\{x_1 x_2\} & \cdots & \text{cov}\{x_1 x_K\} \\
\text{cov}\{x_2 x_1\} & \text{var}\{x_2\} & \cdots & \text{cov}\{x_2 x_K\} \\
\vdots & \vdots & \ddots & \vdots \\
\text{cov}\{x_K x_1\} & \text{cov}\{x_K x_2\} & \cdots & \text{var}\{x_K\}
\end{pmatrix}.
\end{aligned} \tag{4.13}$$

A Gaussian PDF for complex random variables can also be defined (see Appendix E of Monzingo and Miller [1980]). Let $z = x_r + jx_i$ be the complex random variable, where x_r, the real part of z, is a real random variable with mean $\bar{x}_r$ and variance $\rho_z/2$ and x_i, the imaginary part of z, is a real random variable with mean $\bar{x}_i$ and identical variance $\rho_z/2$. The random variables x_r and x_i are assumed to be independent, i.e., $\text{cov}\{x_r x_i\} = 0$. A Gaussian PDF for the complex random variable z may then be embedded in a special case *bivariate* Gaussian PDF for two real random variables, in which

$$\mathbf{x} = \begin{pmatrix} x_r \\ x_i \end{pmatrix} \quad , \quad \bar{\mathbf{x}} = \begin{pmatrix} \bar{x}_r \\ \bar{x}_i \end{pmatrix} \quad , \quad \mathbf{C}_2 = \begin{pmatrix} \rho_z/2 & 0 \\ 0 & \rho_z/2 \end{pmatrix}. \tag{4.14}$$

Substituting these into Eq. (4.11) for $K = 2$ will yield, after some argument simplification,

$$p(z) = p(\mathbf{x}) = [\pi \rho_z]^{-1} \exp\left[-\frac{1}{\rho_z}|z - \bar{z}|^2\right] \quad , \tag{4.15}$$

in which $\bar{z} = \mathcal{E}\{z\} = \bar{x}_r + j\bar{x}_i$ and $\text{var}\{z\} = \text{var}\{x_r\} + \text{var}\{x_i\} = \rho_z$. A multivariate Gaussian PDF for a vector $\mathbf{z}$ of K complex random variables can be embedded into a Gaussian PDF for $2K$ real random variables with the form

$$p(\mathbf{z}) = [\pi^K \det \mathbf{C}_K]^{-1} \exp[-(\mathbf{z} - \bar{\mathbf{z}})^H \mathbf{C}_K^{-1}(\mathbf{z} - \bar{\mathbf{z}})] \quad , \tag{4.16}$$

in which complex mean $\bar{\mathbf{z}}$ and Hermitian covariance matrix $\mathbf{C}_K$ are given by

$$\bar{\mathbf{z}} = \mathcal{E}\{\mathbf{z}\} \tag{4.17}$$
$$\mathbf{C}_K = \mathcal{E}\{(\mathbf{z} - \bar{\mathbf{z}})(\mathbf{z} - \bar{\mathbf{z}})^H\} \quad . \tag{4.18}$$

The assumption has been made that the real and imaginary components of each complex random variable z_k in complex random vector $\mathbf{z}$ are independent and have identical variance, i.e., $\text{cov}\{\text{Re}[z_k]\text{Im}[z_l]\}$ is zero for $k = l$ and nonzero for $k \neq l$, and $\text{var}\{\text{Re}[z_k]\} = \text{var}\{\text{Im}[z_k]\}$.

4.3 RANDOM PROCESSES

A discrete *random process* may be thought of as a collection, or *ensemble*, of real or complex discrete sequences of time (or space), any one of which might be observed on any trial of an experiment. The ensemble of sequences will be denoted as $x[n; i]$, in which i is the ith sequence out of the ensemble and n is the time index. For a given i representing the ensemble member under observation, the abbreviated notation $x[n]$ will be used. For a fixed time index n, the value of the observed element over all ensembles sequences will be a random variable. The range of values will, in general, be a continuum, even though $x[n; i]$ is discrete in both n and i. The probability that $x[n]$ takes values in a certain range α is given by the probability distribution function $F(\alpha; n) = \Pr(x[n] \le \alpha)$, in which the dependence on the time of observation is shown explicitly in the notation. The corresponding PDF is $p(\alpha; n) = \partial F(\alpha; n)/\partial \alpha$.

The *mean* or *expected value* of a random process $x[n]$ at time index n is defined as

$$\bar{x}[n] = \mathcal{E}\left\{x[n]\right\} \quad . \tag{4.19}$$

The *autocorrelation* of a random process at two different time indices n_1 and n_2 is defined as

$$r_{xx}[n_1, n_2] = \mathcal{E}\left\{x[n_1]x^*[n_2]\right\} \quad . \tag{4.20}$$

Equation (4.20) is the engineering definition for autocorrelation, as first suggested by Wiener. Statisticians reserve the term autocorrelation for a related quantity that is normalized to have magnitude lying between zero and unity. The autocorrelation of the process $x[n]$ with the mean removed is the *autocovariance*, defined as

$$c_{xx}[n_1, n_2] = \mathcal{E}\left\{(x[n_1] - \bar{x}[n_1])(x^*[n_2] - \bar{x}^*[n_2])\right\} \quad , \tag{4.21}$$

which can be shown to satisfy

$$c_{xx}[n_1, n_2] = r_{xx}[n_1, n_2] - \bar{x}[n_1]\bar{x}^*[n_2] \quad . \tag{4.22}$$

If the random process has zero mean for all n, then the autocorrelation and the autocovariance are identical

$$c_{xx}[n_1, n_2] = r_{xx}[n_1, n_2] \quad .$$

The terms "correlation" and "covariance" are often used synonymously in the literature, but are formally identical only for zero-mean processes.

When two different random processes $x[n]$ and $y[n]$ are involved, then one may define the *cross correlation* as

$$r_{xy}[n_1, n_2] = \mathcal{E}\left\{x[n_1]y^*[n_2]\right\} \tag{4.23}$$

and the *cross covariance* as

$$
\begin{aligned}
c_{xy}[n_1, n_2] &= \mathcal{E}\left\{(x[n_1] - \bar{x}[n_1])(y^*[n_2] - \bar{y}^*[n_2])\right\} \\
&= r_{xy}[n_1, n_2] - \bar{x}[n_1]\bar{y}^*[n_2] \quad .
\end{aligned}
\tag{4.24}
$$

Two random processes are said to be *uncorrelated* if $c_{xy}[n_1, n_2] = 0$ for all n_1 and n_2.

The definitions to this point have shown an explicit dependence on the time indices. A random process is *wide-sense stationary* (WSS) if its mean is constant for all time indices (i.e., independent of time) and its autocorrelation depends only on the time index difference $m = n_2 - n_1$. A pair of random processes are jointly wide-sense stationary if the cross correlation depends only on the time index difference. Processes that are jointly stationary must also be individually stationary. Note that WSS applies *only* to the first- and second-moment statistics of random processes. Higher-order moments are not constrained. In summary, WSS discrete random process $x[n]$ is statistically characterized by a constant mean

$$
\bar{x}[n] = \bar{x} \quad ,
\tag{4.25}
$$

an *autocorrelation sequence* (ACS)

$$
r_{xx}[m] = \mathcal{E}\left\{x[n+m]x^*[n]\right\} \quad ,
\tag{4.26}
$$

that is a function of the time-difference index m, and an *autocovariance sequence*

$$
c_{xx}[m] = \mathcal{E}\left\{(x[n+m] - \bar{x})(x^*[n] - \bar{x}^*)\right\} = r_{xx}[m] - |\bar{x}|^2 \quad .
\tag{4.27}
$$

The jointly WSS discrete random processes $x[n]$ and $y[n]$ are statistically characterized by a *cross correlation sequence* (CCS)

$$
r_{xy}[m] = \mathcal{E}\left\{x[n+m]y^*[n]\right\}
\tag{4.28}
$$

that is a function of the time-difference index m, and a *cross covariance sequence*

$$
c_{xy}[m] = \mathcal{E}\left\{(x[n+m] - \bar{x})(y^*[n] - \bar{y}^*)\right\} = r_{xy}[m] - \bar{x}\bar{y}^* \quad .
\tag{4.29}
$$

Useful properties are

$$
\begin{aligned}
r_{xx}[0] &\geq |r_{xx}[m]| \\
r_{xx}[-m] &= r_{xx}^*[m] \\
r_{xx}[0]r_{yy}[0] &\geq |r_{xy}[m]|^2 \\
r_{xy}[-m] &= r_{yx}^*[m] \quad ,
\end{aligned}
\tag{4.30}
$$

which apply for all integers m. It is easy to see from these properties that the ACS of a WSS random process must be a maximum at the origin ($m = 0$). If the Hermitian Toeplitz autocorrelation matrix

$$\mathbf{R}_M = \begin{pmatrix} r_{xx}[0] & r_{xx}[-1] & \cdots & r_{xx}[-M] \\ r_{xx}[1] & r_{xx}[0] & \cdots & r_{xx}[-M+1] \\ \vdots & \vdots & \ddots & \vdots \\ r_{xx}[M] & r_{xx}[M-1] & \cdots & r_{xx}[0] \end{pmatrix} \qquad (4.31)$$

is formed from $(M + 1)$ ACS components, then the quadratic form

$$\mathbf{a}^H \mathbf{R}_M \mathbf{a} = \sum_{m=0}^{M} \sum_{n=0}^{M} a[m] a^*[n] \, r_{xx}[m-n] \geq 0 \qquad (4.32)$$

must be positive semidefinite for any arbitrary $M \times 1$ vector $\mathbf{a}$ if $r_{xx}[m]$ is a valid autocorrelation sequence. The ACS is said to have a positive-semidefinite property.

The *power spectral density* (PSD) is defined as the discrete-time Fourier transform (DTFT) of the autocorrelation sequence

$$P_{xx}(f) = T \sum_{m-\infty}^{\infty} r_{xx}[m] \exp(-j2\pi f m T) \quad . \qquad (4.33)$$

The PSD, which is assumed to be bandlimited to $\pm 1/2T$ Hz, is periodic in frequency with period $1/T$ Hz. The power spectral density function describes how the variance of a random process is distributed with frequency. To justify the name, consider the inverse DTFT

$$r_{xx}[m] = \int_{-1/2T}^{1/2T} P_{xx}(f) \exp(j2\pi f m T) \, df \qquad (4.34)$$

evaluated for $m = 0$,

$$r_{xx}[0] = \int_{-1/2T}^{1/2T} P_{xx}(f) \, df \quad . \qquad (4.35)$$

It will be shown in Sec. 4.4 that the autocorrelation at zero lag ($m = 0$) represents the *average power* in the random process. The area under $P_{xx}(f)$ must also represent the average power, as indicated by Eq. (4.35). Therefore, $P_{xx}(f)$ is a density function (power per unit of frequency) that represents the distribution of power with frequency. The Fourier transform pairs (4.33) and (4.34) are often termed the discrete-time *Wiener-Khintchine theorem*. Due to the property $r_{xx}[-m] = r_{xx}^*[m]$, the PSD must be strictly a real, positive function. If the ACS is strictly real-valued, then $r_{xx}[-m] = r_{xx}[m]$ and the PSD can be expressed as the cosine transform

$$P_{xx}(f) = 2T \sum_{m=0}^{\infty} r_{xx}[m] \cos(2\pi f m T) \quad , \qquad (4.36)$$

which also makes $P_{xx}(f) = P_{xx}(-f)$, a symmetric function.

The *cross power spectral density* (CPSD) of two jointly stationary processes $x[n]$ and $y[n]$ is defined as the DTFT of the cross correlation sequence

$$P_{xy}(f) = T \sum_{m=-\infty}^{\infty} r_{xy}[m] \exp(-j2\pi fmT) \quad . \tag{4.37}$$

Because $r_{xy}[-m] \neq r_{xy}^*[m]$, the CPSD is, in general, a complex-valued function. However, the property $P_{xy}(f) = P_{yx}^*(f)$ does hold.

A zero-mean random process $w[n]$ of special interest is that of a discrete-time white noise. A white noise process is uncorrelated with itself for all lags, except at $m = 0$, for which its variance is ρ_w. The ACS has the form

$$r_{ww}[m] = \rho_w \delta[m] \quad , \tag{4.38}$$

where $\delta[m]$ is the discrete delta sequence. The PSD of the white noise autocorrelation sequence is, therefore,

$$P_{ww}(f) = T\rho_w \quad , \tag{4.39}$$

which is a constant for all frequencies, justifying the name *white* noise.

Let $y[n]$ denote the output of a discrete linear time-invariant system

$$y[n] = x[n] \star h[n] \quad , \tag{4.40}$$

in which $h[n]$ is a fixed impulse response sequence and input $x[n]$ is a zero-mean wide-sense stationary discrete random process. The output process $y[n]$ will also be WSS and can be shown (see the Problems) to have the following relationships among the autocorrelations of the input and output process and the cross correlation between the input and output

$$r_{yx}[m] = r_{xx}[m] \star h[m] = \sum_{k=-\infty}^{\infty} r_{xx}[k-m]h[k]$$

$$r_{xy}[m] = r_{xx}[m] \star h^*[-m]$$

$$r_{yy}[m] = r_{xy}[m] \star h[m] = r_{xx}[m] \star (h^*[-m] \star h[m]) \tag{4.41}$$

$$= r_{xx}[m] \star \left(\sum_{k=-\infty}^{\infty} h[k+m]h^*[k] \right) \quad .$$

Denoting the z-transforms of the various correlations as $P_{xx}(z) = Z\{r_{xx}[m]\}$, $P_{xy}(z) = Z\{r_{xy}[m]\}$, and $P_{yy}(z) = Z\{r_{yy}[m]\}$ and the system function as $H(z) = Z\{h[m]\}$, then the convolution theorem applied to relationships (4.41) will yield

$$P_{xy}(z) = P_{xx}(z)H^*(1/z^*)$$

$$P_{yx}(z) = P_{xy}(z)H(z) \tag{4.42}$$

$$P_{yy}(z) = P_{xx}(z)H(z)H^*(1/z^*) \quad ,$$

where the property $Z\{h^*[-m]\} = H^*(1/z^*)$ has been used. If $h[m]$ is real, then $H^*(1/z^*) = H(1/z)$. Based on relationship (2.52), definition (4.33), and Eq. (4.42), the power spectral density $P_{yy}(f)$ of the output process is related to the power spectral density $P_{xx}(f)$ of the input process as follows

$$P_{yy}(f) = TP_{yy}(z)|_{z=\exp(j2\pi fT)} = P_{xx}(\overset{\curvearrowleft}{f}) |H(\exp[j2\pi fT])|^2 \quad , \tag{4.43}$$

where the time domain is discrete and the frequency domain is continuous.

One special case will serve as the basis for the spectral estimation techniques of Chaps. 6–10. If the input process is white noise, so that $P_{xx}(z) = Z\{\rho_w\delta[m]\} = \rho_w$, and the rational system function (2.17) is selected, such that the gain is unity ($b[0] = 1$), then the transform relationship between input and output has the form

$$P_{yy}(z) = \rho_w H(z)H^*(1/z^*) \quad , \tag{4.44}$$

where

$$H(z) = \frac{1 + \sum\limits_{k=1}^{q} b[k]z^{-k}}{1 + \sum\limits_{k=1}^{p} a[k]z^{-k}} \quad . \tag{4.45}$$

Two important random processes used in this text are the Gaussian random process and the sinusoidal random process. If a random process is stationary and Gaussian, then the PDF of $x[n]$ for any time index n is the Gaussian PDF of either Eq. (4.10) or Eq. (4.15), depending on whether $x[n]$ is real or complex, respectively. The sequence samples $x[n], x[n+1], \ldots, x[n+M]$ will have a joint PDF given by either Eq. (4.11) or Eq. (4.16), depending on whether $x[n]$ is real or complex. If complex, for example, assuming a zero-mean process, accounting for the successive times that the samples are taken, and defining $\mathbf{x} = [x[n]\, x[n+1]\ldots x[n+M]]^T$, then the joint Gaussian PDF is

$$p(\mathbf{x}) = [\pi^{M+1} \det \mathbf{R}_M]^{-1} \exp[-\mathbf{x}^H \mathbf{R}_M^{-1}\mathbf{x}] \quad , \tag{4.46}$$

in which the covariance matrix

$$\mathbf{R}_M = \mathbf{C}_M = \begin{pmatrix} r_{xx}[0] & r_{xx}^*[1] & \cdots & r_{xx}^*[M] \\ r_{xx}[1] & r_{xx}[0] & \cdots & r_{xx}^*[M-1] \\ \vdots & \vdots & \ddots & \vdots \\ r_{xx}[M] & r_{xx}[M-1] & \cdots & r_{xx}[0] \end{pmatrix} \tag{4.47}$$

is a Hermitian Toeplitz autocorrelation matrix of order M and, therefore, has dimension $(M+1) \times (M+1)$. This matrix will be encountered frequently in the chapters ahead.

Consider a deterministic real sinusoid process

$$x[n] = A \sin(2\pi f nT + \theta) \quad ,$$

in which T is the sample interval and the amplitude A, frequency f, and phase θ are all fixed values. The mean and autocorrelation sequence for this case are

$$
\begin{aligned}
\bar{x}[n] &= A \sin(2\pi f nT + \theta) \\
r_{xx}[n+m, n] &= A \sin(2\pi[n+m]T + \theta) A \sin(2\pi f nT + \theta) \\
&= \frac{A^2}{2}\left[\cos(2\pi f mT) - \cos(2\pi f[2n+m]T + 2\theta)\right] \quad .
\end{aligned}
\tag{4.48}
$$

The mean is not constant and the ACS is not a function only of the time difference m. A completely deterministic sinusoid cannot be modeled, therefore, as a wide-sense stationary random process. If the phase is now assumed to be a random variable that is uniformly distributed on the interval 0 to 2π, then the sinusoidal process will be stationary because the mean

$$\bar{x} = \int_0^{2\pi} A \sin(2\pi f nT + \theta)\frac{1}{2\pi}\, d\theta = 0$$

and ACS

$$
\begin{aligned}
r_{xx}[m] &= \int_0^{2\pi} A \sin(2\pi f[n+m]T + \theta) A \sin(2\pi f mT + \theta)\frac{1}{2\pi}\, d\theta \\
&= \frac{A^2}{2}\cos(2\pi f mT)
\end{aligned}
\tag{4.49}
$$

are both independent of time index n. If there are L real sinusoids

$$x[n] = \sum_{l=1}^{L} A_l \sin(2\pi f_l nT + \theta_l) \quad ,$$

each of which has a phase that is uniformly distributed on the interval 0 to 2π, independent of the other phases, then the mean of the L sinusoids is zero and the ACS is

$$r_{xx}[m] = \sum_{l=1}^{L} \frac{A_l^2}{2}\cos(2\pi f_l mT) \quad .
\tag{4.50}$$

If the process consists of L complex sinusoids

$$x[n] = \sum_{l=1}^{L} A_l \exp[j(2\pi f_l nT + \theta_l)] \quad ,$$

then the ACS will have the form

$$r_{xx}[m] = \sum_{l=1}^{L} A_l^2 \exp(j2\pi f_l mT) \quad . \tag{4.51}$$

If an independent white noise process $w[n]$, with variance ρ_w, is added to complex sinusoids with random phases, then the combined process $y[n] = x[n] + w[n]$ will have an ACS

$$\begin{aligned} r_{yy}[m] &= r_{xx}[m] + r_{ww}[m] \\ &= \sum_{l=1}^{L} A_l^2 \exp(j2\pi f_l mT) + \rho_w \delta[m] \quad . \end{aligned} \tag{4.52}$$

The autocorrelation matrix (4.47) for the random process of complex sinusoids with additive white noise can be succintly expressed, based on Eq. (4.52), as

$$\mathbf{R}_{yy} = \sum_{l=1}^{L} A_l^2 \mathbf{e}_M(f_l) \mathbf{e}_M^H(f_l) + \rho_w \mathbf{I} \quad , \tag{4.53}$$

where $\mathbf{I}$ is an $(M+1) \times (M+1)$ identity matrix and

$$\mathbf{e}_M(f_l) = \begin{pmatrix} 1 \\ \exp(j2\pi f_l T) \\ \vdots \\ \exp(j2\pi f_l MT) \end{pmatrix}$$

is a complex sinusoid vector at frequency f_l.

4.4 ERGODICITY: FROM ENSEMBLE AVERAGES TO TIME AVERAGES

Up to this point in this chapter, only statistical ensemble averaging has been used to define the mean, correlation, covariance, and power spectral density descriptors of random processes. However, in practice one does not typically have an ensemble of waveforms from which to evaluate these statistical descriptors. It is desirable to *estimate* all these statistical properties from a *single* sample waveform $x(t)$ by substituting *time* averages for *ensemble* averages. The property required to accomplish this is *ergodicity*. A random process is said to be ergodic if, with probability 1, all its statistics can be predicted from a single waveform of the process ensemble via time averaging; that is, the time averages of almost all possible single waveforms are equal to the same constant (the ensemble average). The mathematical analysis of random processes is greatly simplified with the property of ergodicity.

   The concept of ergodicity requires the assumption that the data be stationary up to fourth moments. For a process to be stationary, the statistics must be

independent of the time origin selected. This seems intuitively appropriate since a
time-averaged quantity is independent of time and therefore cannot approximate a
statistically nonstationary parameter that depends on time. Thus, if one were to
look at a single waveform $x[n]$ at time points n_1, n_2, and so forth, then, on average,
the value seen should be $\bar{x}$. In the limit as one looks at all time points, one would
expect the average to be

$$\lim_{M \to \infty} \frac{1}{2M+1} \sum_{n=-M}^{M} x[n] = \mathcal{E}\left\{x[n]\right\} = \bar{x}. \qquad (4.54)$$

This limit, if it exists, can be shown to be true if and only if the variance of the
time average (4.54)

$$\lim_{M \to \infty} \frac{1}{2M+1} \sum_{m=-2M}^{2M} \left(1 - \frac{|m|}{2M+1}\right) c_{xx}[m] = 0 \qquad (4.55)$$

approaches zero, where $c_{xx}[m]$ is the true ensemble covariance of the random process
$x[n]$. In this case, $x[n]$ is said to be *ergodic in the mean*. In a similar manner, if one
were to look in several places at the product of the sample values at two instants
of time that are separated by lag m, say $x[n_1 + m]x[n_1]$, $x[n_2 + m]x[n_2]$, and so
forth, then, on average for a stationary process, the product should yield the value
of $r_{xx}[m]$. In the limit as one looks at all product values, one would expect the
average to be

$$\lim_{M \to \infty} \frac{1}{2M+1} \sum_{n=-M}^{M} x[n + m]x^*[n] = \mathcal{E}\left\{x[n + m]x^*[n]\right\} = r_{xx}[m] \quad . \qquad (4.56)$$

This can be shown to be true if and only if the variance of the above time average
approaches zero in the limit, that is,

$$\lim_{M \to \infty} \frac{1}{2M+1} \sum_{m=-2M}^{2M} \left(1 - \frac{|m|}{2M+1}\right) c_{zz}[m] = 0 \quad , \qquad (4.57)$$

where $c_{zz}[m]$ is the true ensemble covariance of the autocorrelation random process
$z_m[n] = x[n + m]x^*[n]$ (the lagged product of the process $x[n]$). Note that $c_{zz}[m]$
involves a fourth-order statistical moment of the process $x[n]$. If the above is true,
then $x[n]$ is said to be *autocorrelation ergodic*. If the stationary process $x[n]$ is zero-
mean Gaussian, then it is straightforward to show that $x[n]$ is both mean ergodic
and autocorrelation ergodic [Papoulis, 1977]. Although it is more difficult to prove
ergodicity for non-Gaussian processes, suffice it to say that almost all practical data
processes that are stationary are also ergodic. *Hereafter, it shall be assumed that a*

measured process is stationary so that time averages of the mean and autocorrelation can replace their ensemble averages.

The assumption of ergodicity not only permits time average definitions for the mean and autocorrelation, but also permits the equivalent time average definition for the power spectral density

$$P_{xx}(f) = \lim_{M \to \infty} \mathcal{E} \left\{ \frac{1}{(2M+1)T} \left| T \sum_{n=-M}^{M} x[n] \exp(-j2\pi f nT) \right|^2 \right\} \tag{4.58}$$

to be used. This equivalent PSD is obtained by a statistical average of the squared magnitude of the DTFT of a windowed data set divided by its data record length, in which the number of data points grows to infinity. The statistical average is required because the DTFT is a random variable itself, varying for each realization of $x[n]$ used. In order to prove that Eq. (4.58) is equivalent to the Wiener-Khintchine theorem, expand the squared magnitude DTFT and exchange the order of the summation and the expectation operations,

$$P_{xx}(f) = \lim_{M \to \infty} \mathcal{E} \left\{ \frac{T}{2M+1} \sum_{m=-M}^{M} \sum_{n=-M}^{M} x[m]x^*[n] \exp(-j2\pi f[m-n]T) \right\}$$

$$= \lim_{M \to \infty} \frac{T}{2M+1} \sum_{m=-M}^{M} \sum_{n=-M}^{M} r_{xx}[m-n] \exp(-j2\pi f[m-n]T) \quad .$$

$$\tag{4.59}$$

Using the simply proven fact

$$\sum_{m=-M}^{M} \sum_{n=-M}^{M} r_{xx}[m-n] = \sum_{m=-2M}^{2M} (2M+1-|m|) r_{xx}[m] \quad , \tag{4.60}$$

Eq. (4.59) will reduce to

$$P_{xx}(f) = \lim_{M \to \infty} \frac{T}{2M+1} \sum_{m=-2M}^{2M} (2M+1-|m|) r_{xx}[m] \exp(-j2\pi f mT)$$

$$= \lim_{M \to \infty} T \sum_{m=-2M}^{2M} \left(1 - \frac{|m|}{2M+1} \right) r_{xx}[m] \exp(-j2\pi f mT) \tag{4.61}$$

$$= T \sum_{m=-\infty}^{\infty} r_{xx}[m] \exp(-j2\pi f mT) \quad .$$

An assumption has been made in the last step of Eq. (4.61) that the ACS decays such that

$$\sum_{m=-\infty}^{\infty} |m| \, r_{xx}[m] < \infty \quad , \tag{4.62}$$

otherwise, it would not be true that the discrete-time Fourier transform of the temporal ACS will tend to the true ensemble PSD as the data record length increases, even if the ACS is itself ergodic. For example, the condition is violated for random processes with non-zero means or processes with sinusoidal components, although the use of impulse functions can correct this. Thus, the two expressions for the PSD, Eqs. (4.33) and (4.58), are equivalent under the assumption (4.62).

The two equivalent definitions of the PSD are highlighted by the triangle diagram shown in Fig. 4.1 . The PSD definition that uses the autocorrelation approach is termed an *indirect* method because the random process $x[n]$ is not used directly to estimate the PSD. The PSD definition (4.58) is termed the *direct* method because it uses $x[n]$ directly to compute the PSD.

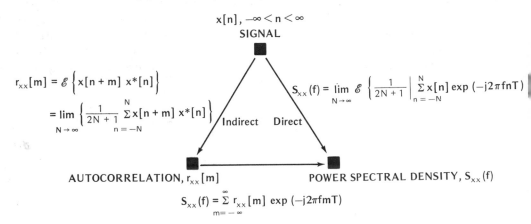

Figure 4.1   Equivalent definitions of the power spectral density under the assumption of ergodicity.

Disregarding the expectation operation of Eq. (4.58) yields the PSD estimator

$$\tilde{P}_{xx}(f) = \lim_{M \to \infty} \frac{1}{(2M+1)T} \left| T \sum_{n=-M}^{M} x[n] \exp(-j2\pi f nT) \right|^2 , \qquad (4.63)$$

termed the *sample spectrum*. This is also the original Schuster *periodogram*, as described in Chap. 1. The sample spectrum is shown in Appendix 4.A to be an inconsistent estimator of the true PSD. Although the mean of the sample spectrum will tend to the true PSD value in the limit, the variance will not tend to zero in the limit of infinite data, but it will, in fact, be comparable in magnitude to the mean value of the sample spectrum. Early users of the periodogram failed to regard the expectation operation and obtained, as a result, unreliable spectral estimates, even though Schuster himself (see Chap. 1) had warned of the need to perform some sort of averaging or smoothing operation when using the periodogram. As a result, the periodogram method fell into disregard by the applications community until its revival in the early 1950s, when smoothing techniques were introduced in the context of a well-understood statistical framework.

4.5 ENTROPY CONCEPTS

Claude Shannon introduced the concept of information measure in statistics. For example, an event that has M possibilities x_i, with $p[x_i]$ representing the probability of occurrence of the ith possibility, has a *self-information* of

$$I[x_i] = \ln(1/p[x_i]) = -\ln p[x_i]. \qquad (4.64)$$

The expected value, or mean, of the information is the *entropy*

$$H[x] = \sum_{i=1}^{M} p[x_i] I[x_i] = -\sum_{i=1}^{M} p[x_i] \log p[x_i]. \qquad (4.65)$$

Entropy is a measure of "uncertainty" associated with the outcome of an event. The higher the entropy, the higher the uncertainty as to which possibility will occur. The discrete event entropy will be maximized when the distribution is uniform, that is, all outcomes are equally likely.

In an analogous way, a continuous multivariate random variable with a continuous probability density function $p(x)$ has an entropy

$$H(x) = -\int_{-\infty}^{\infty} p(x) \ln p(x)\, dx. \qquad (4.66)$$

In the discrete case, $H[x]$ was strictly nonnegative. In the continuous case, however, entropy may be negative. Substituting the zero-mean multivariate Gaussian PDF [Eq. (4.46)] into Eq. (4.66) yields the entropy for a Gaussian process [Smylie et al., 1973]

$$H = \frac{1}{2} \ln\left[\det \mathbf{R}_{xx}\right] \quad . \qquad (4.67)$$

As the dimension M of $\mathbf{R}_{xx}$ grows, the Gaussian entropy may diverge. In such a case, the entropy rate

$$h = \lim_{M \to \infty} \frac{H}{M+1} \qquad (4.68)$$

may be used. It can be shown [Smylie et al., 1973] that the entropy rate for a zero-mean Gaussian process of bandwidth $B = 1/2T$ is alternatively expressed

$$h = \frac{1}{2} \ln(2B) + \frac{1}{4B} \int_{-B}^{B} \ln[P_{xx}(f)]\, df \quad . \qquad (4.69)$$

This will be used in Chap. 7 in the discussion on the maximum entropy method.

REFERENCES

Brillinger, D. R., Fourier Analysis of Stationary Processes, *Proc. IEEE*, vol. 62, pp. 1628–1643, December 1974.

Gardner, W. A., *Introduction to Random Processes*, Macmillan Publishing Company, 1985.

Jenkins, G. M., and D. G. Watts, *Spectral Analysis and Its Applications*, Holden-Day, Inc., San Francisco, 1968.

Kay, S. M., *Modern Spectral Estimation*, Prentice-Hall, Inc., Englewood Cliffs, N. J., 1987.

Monzingo, R. A., and T. W. Miller, *Introduction to Adaptive Arrays*, John Wiley and Sons, Inc., New York, 1980.

Papoulis, Athanasios, *Signal Analysis*, McGraw-Hill Book Company, New York, 1977.

Papoulis, Athanasios, *Probability, Random Variables, and Stochastic Processes*, 2nd ed., McGraw-Hill Book Company, New York, 1984.

Smylie, D. E., G. K. C. Clarke, and T. J. Ulrych, Analysis of Irregularities in the Earth's Rotation, in *Methods in Computational Physics*, R. Alder et al., eds., vol. 13, pp. 391–430, Academic Press,Inc., New York, 1973.

PROBLEMS

1. Let $x[n] = A\sin(2\pi f nT + \theta)$ be a sinusoid process. Using Eq. (4.56), determine the temporal autocorrelation in the limit as $M \to \infty$. Is the sinusoid an ergodic process, i.e., does the temporal autocorrelation yield the same result given by Eq. (4.49)?

2. Show that a wide-sense stationary process has a complex conjugate even autocorrelation, $r_{xx}(\tau) = r_{xx}^*(-\tau)$.

3. For $x(t)$ and $y(t)$ real-valued processes, prove that $\mathsf{P}_{xx}(z) = \mathsf{P}_{xx}(1/z), \mathsf{P}_{xy}(z) = \mathsf{P}_{yx}^*(1/z^*)$.

4. For a deterministic signal as described in Chap. 2, show that the energy spectral densities (ESDs) of the input and output $y(t)$ of a linear filter are related by

$$|Y(f)|^2 = |X(f)|^2|H(f)|^2 \quad .$$

   Use this result and the direct defintion (4.58) of the power spectral density to show that the input and output power spectral densities have the relationship

$$P_{yy}(f) = P_{xx}(f)|H(f)|^2.$$

   This is an alternative proof of relationship (4.43).

5. Prove that power spectral density $P_{xx}(f)$ is a real, even, positive function if $r[m]$ is real-valued.

6. Prove the relationships given by Eq. (4.41).

7. Let the real L sinusoid-plus-noise process be

$$x[n] = \sum_{l=1}^{L} A_l \sin(2\pi f_l nT + \theta_l) + w[n] \quad ,$$

where the initial phases are all uniformly-distributed independent random variables on the interval 0 to 2π and $w[n]$ is a white noise process of variance ρ_w. Compute the statistical autocorrelation sequence. Is this random process ergodic?

8. Show that the autocorrelation matrix for the signal described in the problem above can be expressed as

$$\mathbf{R}_{xx} = \sum_{l=1}^{L} \frac{A_l^2}{4} \left[\mathbf{e}_M(f_l)\mathbf{e}_M^H(f_l) + \mathbf{e}_M^*(f_l)\mathbf{e}_M^T(f_l) \right] + \rho_w \mathbf{I}.$$

APPENDIX 4.A
BIAS AND VARIANCE OF THE SAMPLE SPECTRUM

Statistical analysis of the periodogram for the general case is mathematically complicated. The analysis that follows is for the special case of a zero-mean white Gaussian process; the results may then be used as guidelines to the behavior of the periodogram spectral estimate in more general situations [Jenkins and Watts, 1968].

The sample spectrum of the finite-length sequence $x[n]$ for $n = 0$ to $n = N-1$ is

$$\tilde{P}_{xx}(f) = \frac{1}{NT}|X(f)|^2 \quad ,$$

where $X(f)$ is the discrete-time Fourier transform

$$X(f) = T \sum_{n=0}^{N-1} x[n] \exp(-j2\pi fnT).$$

This is identical (see Problem 1 in Chap. 5) to the discrete-time Fourier transform of the estimated autocorrelation sequence

$$\tilde{P}_{xx}(f) = T \sum_{m=-(N-1)}^{N-1} \hat{r}_{xx}[m] \exp(-j2\pi fmT) \quad ,$$

where the biased autocorrelation estimate

$$\hat{r}_{xx}[m] = \frac{1}{N} \sum_{n=0}^{N-m-1} x[n+m]x^*[n]$$

has been used for the maximum number of lag estimates $[m = 0, \ldots, N - 1]$.

The mean of the sample spectrum is simply

$$\mathcal{E}\left\{\tilde{P}_{xx}(f)\right\} = T \sum_{m=-(N-1)}^{N-1} \mathcal{E}\left\{\hat{r}_{xx}[m]\right\} \exp(-j2\pi f mT)$$

$$= T \sum_{m=-(N-1)}^{N-1} \left[\frac{N - |m|}{N}\right] r_{xx}[m] \exp(-j2\pi f mT)$$

$$= W(f) \star S_{xx}(f) \quad,$$

where $W(f)$ is the DTFT of the Bartlett window,

$$w[m] = \begin{cases} 1 - |m|/N & \text{for } |m| \leq N - 1 \\ 0 & \text{for } |m| > N - 1 \end{cases} .$$

Thus, the mean of the sample spectrum is the convolution of the true PSD with the Fourier transform of the Bartlett window. The sample spectrum is, therefore, *biased* for finite N, but *unbiased* as $N \to \infty$ because

$$\lim_{N \to \infty} \mathcal{E}\left\{\tilde{P}_{xx}(f)\right\} = P_{xx}(f),$$

thus yielding the true spectrum.

The autocorrelation of the periodogram is given by

$$\mathcal{E}\left\{\tilde{P}_{xx}(f_1)\tilde{P}_{xx}(f_2)\right\} =$$

$$\left(\frac{T}{N}\right)^2 \sum_{k=0}^{N-1}\sum_{l=0}^{N-1}\sum_{m=0}^{N-1}\sum_{n=0}^{N-1} \mathcal{E}\left\{x[k]x[l]x[m]x[n]\right\} \exp\{j2\pi T[f_1(k - l) + f_2(m - n)]\}.$$

The variance of the sample spectrum involves *fourth-order* moments, which are difficult to evaluate in the general case. However, because $x[k]$ is white and Gaussian, the fourth-order statistical moment reduces to a sum of second-order moments:

$$\mathcal{E}\left\{x[k]x[l]x[m]x[n]\right\} = \begin{cases} \rho_w^2 & \text{if } k = l \text{ and } m = n, \text{ or } k = m \text{ and } l = n, \\ & \text{or } k = n \text{ and } l = m \\ 0 & \text{otherwise} \end{cases},$$

where ρ is the variance of the Gaussian process. This means that

$$\mathcal{E}\left\{\tilde{P}_{xx}(f_1)\tilde{P}_{xx}(f_2)\right\}$$

$$= (T\rho_w)^2 \left[1 + \left(\frac{\sin \pi NT(f_1 + f_2)}{N \sin \pi T(f_1 + f_2)}\right)^2 + \left(\frac{\sin \pi NT(f_1 - f_2)}{N \sin \pi T(f_1 - f_2)}\right)^2\right].$$

The covariance is then

$$\text{cov}\{\tilde{P}_{xx}(f_1)\tilde{P}_{xx}(f_2)\} = \mathcal{E}\left\{\tilde{P}_{xx}(f_1)\tilde{P}_{xx}(f_2)\right\} - \mathcal{E}\left\{\tilde{P}_{xx}(f_1)\right\}\mathcal{E}\left\{\tilde{P}_{xx}(f_2)\right\}.$$

Noting that $\mathcal{E}\left\{\tilde{P}_{xx}(f)\right\} = T\rho_w$ for a white Gaussian process,

$$\text{cov}\{\tilde{P}_{xx}(f_1)\tilde{P}_{xx}(f_2)\}$$
$$= (T\rho_w)^2\left[\left(\frac{\sin \pi T(f_1 + f_2)N}{N\sin \pi T(f_1 + f_2)}\right)^2 + \left(\frac{\sin \pi T(f_1 - f_2)N}{N\sin \pi T(f_1 - f_2)}\right)^2\right].$$

Looking at the variance at a particular frequency

$$\text{var}\left\{\tilde{P}_{xx}(f)\right\} = \text{cov}\{\tilde{P}_{xx}(f)\tilde{P}_{xx}(f)\} = (T\rho_w)^2\left[1 + \left(\frac{\sin 2\pi fTN}{N\sin 2\pi fT}\right)^2\right]$$
$$= P_{xx}^2(f)\left[1 + \left(\frac{\sin 2\pi fTN}{N\sin 2\pi fT}\right)^2\right].$$

Note that $\text{var}\{\tilde{P}_{xx}(f)\}$ does not tend to zero no matter how large N may get. Thus, the sample spectrum is *not* a *consistent* estimator of the PSD. The variance is of the order of $P_{xx}^2(f)$ for any N, i.e., the standard deviation is as large as the mean to be estimated.

The selection of harmonic frequencies (frequencies which are integer multiples of $1/NT$) $f_1 = m/NT$ and $f_2 = n/NT$, such that $m \neq n$, results in a zero covariance

$$\text{cov}\{\tilde{P}_{xx}(f_1)\tilde{P}_{xx}(f_2)\} = 0 \quad,$$

that is, the values of the periodogram separated in frequency by integer multiples of $1/(NT)$ Hz are uncorrelated. As the number of data samples N increases, these uncorrelated periodogram samples come closer together in frequency. This feature, coupled with the nondecreasing variance for increasing N, leads to a rapidly fluctuating periodogram as the record length increases (see Fig. 1.3 for an example).

In general, any nonwhite process $x[n]$ can be generated by passing white noise of variance ρ_w through a linear filter of magnitude-squared response $|H(f)|^2$. Because the true PSD $P_{xx}(f)$ is related by

$$P_{xx}(f) = T\rho_w|H(f)|^2 \quad,$$

then it could be argued that the following is approximately true

$$\text{var}\left\{\tilde{P}_{xx}(f)\right\} \approx |H(f)|^4\rho_w^2\left[1 + \left(\frac{\sin 2\pi fTN}{N\sin 2\pi fT}\right)^2\right] \geq \mathcal{E}\left\{\tilde{P}_{xx}(f)\right\}^2.$$

Thus, as N increases, the sample spectrum variance does not approach zero, but becomes proportional to the square of the expected value of the PSD (i.e., the square of the true PSD), making an unmodified periodogram a *nonconsistent* estimator of the PSD. That is, $\tilde{P}_{xx}(f)$ does not converge in the mean to $P_{xx}(f)$ at any value f where $P_{xx}(f) > 0$.

5

CLASSICAL SPECTRAL ESTIMATION

5.1 INTRODUCTION

Two formal, but equivalent, definitions of power spectral density (PSD) were introduced in Chap. 4. The indirect approach used an infinite sequence of data values to compute the autocorrelation sequence, which in turn was Fourier transformed to yield the PSD. The direct approach obtained the PSD by taking the squared magnitude of the Fourier transform of the infinite data sequence with appropriate statistical averaging. If this averaging was disregarded, then the resultant function, termed a *sample spectrum*, was shown to be unsatisfactory due to the statistically erratic spectral estimates that it produces, that is, the standard deviation was as large as the estimate mean. In this chapter, averaging approaches that provide smooth and statistically stable spectral estimates from a finite number of data samples are summarized. PSD estimates based on direct transformation of the data followed by averaging are collectively termed *periodograms*. PSD estimates based on forming correlation estimates first from the data are collectively termed *correlogram* methods of spectral estimation. Both names are based on historic roots cited in Chap. 1.

Unlike the continuous-time presentations of spectral estimation often found in other texts, all classical methods covered in this chapter are presented for discrete-time sample sequences. For each PSD estimation method, the user is faced with many trade-offs in an effort to produce statistically reliable spectral estimates of highest possible resolution with a finite amount of data samples. Trade-offs among data windowing, lag windowing, time-domain averaging, and frequency-domain averaging are required to balance the need to reduce sidelobes, to perform effective ensemble averaging, and to ensure adequate spectral resolution. Stable results (small spectral fluctuations) with good fidelity (small bias from the true spectral value at all frequencies) are achievable only if the product $T_e B_e$, where T_e is the total data record interval and B_e is the effective frequency resolution, is much larger than unity. These trade-offs can be quantified analytically for Gaussian processes. Despite detailed analytical studies of the statistical behavior of classical spectral estimators for Gaussian processes, the selection of a particular method for use with non-Gaussian processes is often motivated only by experimental evidence. The selection of a window is also very frequently based more on experimental findings and less on analytical studies.

To adequately describe the statistical *performance* of each method presented would require several chapters. However, only highlights are given here. References that provide greater detail of the classical spectral estimation techniques include Jenkins and Watts [1968], Blackman and Tukey [1958], Koopmans [1974], Yuen and Fraser [1979], and Gardner [1987]. Following the summary, Secs. 5.3–5.6 introduce some basic topics needed for a proper discussion of the classical spectral estimators. Windowing, an important component common to all of the classical spectral estimators, is presented in Sec. 5.3. The time-bandwidth product of Chap. 2 must be augmented with a third term in order to quantify the statistical stability of these estimators. Section 5.4 discusses this stability-time-bandwidth product. Estimation of the correlation function, required for the correlogram method of spectral estimation, is presented in Sec. 5.5. Following these preliminary sections, Secs. 5.6–5.8 present the correlogram method, the periodogram method, and the combined correlogram-periodogram method of PSD estimation. The chapter ends in Sec. 5.9 with an application of the classical methods to sunspot data.

All of the methods presented here have similar statistical behavior and similar gross appearance, although some visual differences in the fine detail of the spectral shape will be apparent. Because all yield similar statistical behavior, often the method selected is the one that may be computed most efficiently. Before the extensive availability of computers, the correlogram method as outlined by Blackman and Tukey [1958] was predominant. The advent of the FFT algorithm and the introduction of signal processing integrated circuits have promoted a shift of interest to methods based on periodogram methods [Jones, 1965].

5.2 SUMMARY

Corresponding to the two equivalent definitions for the PSD presented in Chap. 4, there are two basic classical PSD estimation approaches. The direct method, or *periodogram*, operates directly on the data set to yield a PSD estimate. On the other

```
• ACQUIRE DATA
    N samples
    T seconds/sample

• TREND REMOVAL (optional)
    See Chapter 14

• SELECT SEGMENT PARAMETERS
    NSAMP samples/segment
    NSHIFT sample shift between segments

• COMPUTE PERIODOGRAM
    Subroutine PERIODOGRAM, Appendix 5.C

• WINDOW CLOSING
    Adjust segment parameters for
    variance/resolution trade-off
```

Figure 5.1 Flowchart of periodogram PSD based on Welch estimation procedure.

hand, the indirect method must first make an estimate of the correlation sequence, or correlogram, and then Fourier transform it to obtain the PSD estimate.

Figure 5.1 is a summary of the steps of the periodogram method, described in detail in Sec. 5.8.3. This flowchart is intended to guide those wishing to implement the technique without an in-depth reading of this chapter. The computer program that implements the periodogram method is found in Appendix 5.C. Acquisition of N data samples at a sample rate of T samples per second is followed by optional trend removal. Failure to remove large sample means or other trends in the data may result in distorted or biased spectral estimates. Chapter 14 discusses methods of trend removal. In order to produce a statistically stable spectral estimate, the data must be segmented into possibly overlapping intervals and the sample spectrum of each segment averaged. This averaging is controlled by the selection of the parameters that set the number of samples per segment (NSAMP) and the number of samples to shift to the beginning of the next segment (NSHIFT). The amount of segmentation involves a trade-off between the degree of smoothness required in the spectral estimate versus the desired frequency resolution. Making NSAMP small will provide more segments for averaging and, therefore, a spectral estimate with less variance, but it will also decrease the spectral resolution. Increasing NSAMP will increase the spectral resolution, but at the price of increased variance due to fewer segments being averaged. The periodogram of Appendix 5.C uses a Hamming window to reduce the sidelobes in the spectral estimate. Sidelobes need to be suppressed in order to reveal the presence of weak signal components that may be in the spectrum. Other possible window functions that could have been used are discussed in Sec. 5.3.

A return arrow is illustrated on Fig. 5.1, indicating several passes should be made through the data, varying the length and number of segments. This serves to investigate the data for different frequency resolution/stability settings to learn more about the measured unknown process. If there is much detail in the spectrum, it may be necessary to give up stability (fewer segments averaged) for improved resolution (longer segments). Trial settings of the options may help determine the best trade-off among the options. A procedure that starts with low resolution and high stability and works progressively to periodogram estimates of higher resolution and lower stability is termed *window closing*. This name refers to the window width that is set by the selection of parameter NSAMP. Window closing is achieved by decreasing the number of segments while increasing at the same time the segment length.

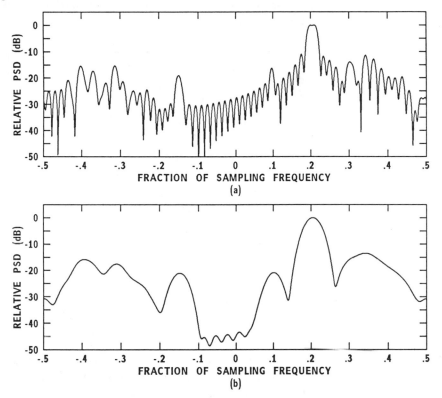

Figure 5.2   Periodogram estimates of the 64-point test sequence. (a) One segment and no window. (b) Three segments and Hamming window.

To illustrate the short data record behavior of the periodogram, consider the analysis of the 64-point complex test sequence, discussed in Chap. 1 and listed in Appendix II at the end of the book. The periodogram of this sample sequence with maximum resolution and minimum stability is illustrated in Fig. 5.2(a). It was produced by selecting only one segment (the entire data record), and no windowing (effectively a rectangular data window). Note that the close sinusoidal components are unresolved. This is not surprising. The time-bandwidth product of Chap. 2 indicates that a resolution of $1/64T$ Hz is the maximum possible, where T is the sample interval. Expressed as a fractional frequency, this becomes $1/64T \div 1/T = .0156$. The two closest sinusoids are spaced .01 apart. Also, the weak sinusoid at .1 is almost lost in the sidelobes from the strong sinusoids. Figure 5.2(b) illustrates the smooth, low-resolution averaged periodogram that results by dividing the data into three segments of 32 samples each, with 16 samples of overlap between segments. The weaker sinusoidal responses are clearly visible.

Figure 5.3 Flowchart of correlogram method of PSD based on Bartlett estimation.

Figure 5.3 is a summary of the steps of the correlogram method of PSD estimation; a program is included in Appendix 5.B. It is based on a method popularized by Blackman and Tukey [1958] that is presented in Sec. 5.6. Like Fig. 5.1, this chart is intended to guide those wishing to implement the correlogram method without detailed examination of this chapter. The trend removal option is similar to that for the periodogram. The only parameter available for selection is the length of the autocorrelation sequence to be estimated, given by the value of LAG, which corresponds to the highest lag index. This parameter serves the same purpose as parameter NSAMP in the periodogram method; its adjustment determines the amount of smoothness and the degree of resolution in the spectral estimate. A stability versus resolution trade-off using a window-closing approach similar to that of the periodogram can be made for the correlogram method; the window in this case is applied to the autocorrelation sequence rather than to a data segment sequence. As the number of estimated lags increases, the resolution increases and the stability decreases.

Figure 5.4   Correlogram method PSD estimate of 64-point test sequence. The absolute value of the PSD has been plotted. The shaded areas designate negative PSD values. (a) 16 lags and Hamming window. (b) 32 lags and Hamming window

Examples of PSD estimates made from the correlogram are shown in Fig. 5.4. The 64-point complex data sequence again was used. Sixteen and 32 unbiased autocorrelation values from lag 0 seconds to lag $15T$ seconds and lag $31T$ seconds, respectively, were estimated. A Hamming window was applied to the autocorrelation estimates. Negative sidelobes have been shaded on the logarithmic plots of Fig. 5.4. This figure is similar, but not identical, to the periodogram estimate of Fig. 5.2(b). The resolution/smoothness trade-off is apparent in the two plots of Fig. 5.4.

Again, if one does not know how to make the stability/resolution trade-off, a suggested procedure is to start with maximum stability (smoothest PSD estimate), and therefore the least resolution, and progressively increase the segment lengths (periodogram) or increase the number of correlation terms (correlogram). This will increase the estimate variance and narrow the spectral bandwidth (increase the resolution). Although there are no rigid rules for stopping this procedure, generally it should be continued until the resolution captures the narrowest *important* detail in the spectrum. Some prior knowledge of anticipated signals that may be in the spectrum might be required in order to determine what is important and what is not of importance. Lacking that, then one should stop when there are no major changes to the spectral estimate as either the data segment length or the lag interval increases.

5.3   WINDOWS

An important topic that is an integral part of all classical spectral estimation methods is that of windowing. Windowing is used to control the effect of sidelobes in these spectral estimators. These effects are discussed in this section. The term *weighting* may also be used synonymously for windowing in this text. This is in contrast to those who would reserve the term window only for the transform of a time-domain weighting function. The function $W(f)$ designates a *frequency window* if it is the discrete-time Fourier transform of a discrete-time *data window* $w[n]$. Data windows have also been called *tapering functions*. The function $\Omega(f)$ designates a *spectral window* if it is the discrete-time Fourier transform of a *lag window* $\omega[m]$ applied to a discrete-time autocorrelation sequence. The primary effect of a data window is to reduce the bias in periodogram spectral estimates. The primary effect of a lag window is to reduce the PSD estimator variance of the correlogram method.

It is convenient to consider a known finite data record or known finite correlation sequence as a portion of an infinite-duration sequence as seen through a window. For example, the observed data sequence $x_0[n]$ of N points may be mathematically expressed as the product of a unit amplitude rectangle function

$$\text{rect}[n] = \begin{cases} 1 & 0 \leq n \leq N - 1 \\ 0 & \text{otherwise} \end{cases} \tag{5.1}$$

and the infinite sequence x[n],

$$x_0[n] = x[n] \cdot \text{rect}[n] \quad . \tag{5.2}$$

An implicit assumption has been made that all unobserved samples are effectively zero, whether or not this is true. The discrete-time Fourier transform of the windowed sequence, expressed in terms of the transforms of $x[n]$ and rect$[n]$, is the convolution of transforms

$$X_0(f) = X(f) \star D_N(f) \quad , \tag{5.3}$$

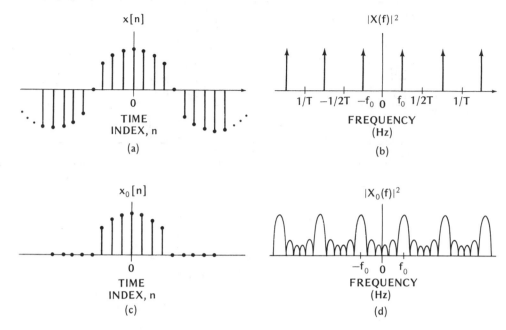

Figure 5.5   Illustration of discrete-time Fourier transform (DTFT) bias due to leakage of windowed data. (a) Original discrete-time sinusoidal sequence. (b) Magnitude of periodic DTFT of sinusoidal sequence. (c) Windowed sinusoidal sequence. (d) Magnitude of DTFT of windowed sequence.

where

$$D_N(f) = T \exp(-j2\pi ft[N-1]) \frac{\sin(\pi fTN)}{\sin(\pi fT)} \quad . \tag{5.4}$$

The function $D_N(f)$, known as the *digital sinc* or the *Dirichlet kernel*, is the discrete-time Fourier transform of the rectangle function. The transform of the observed finite sequence is a distorted version of the infinite sequence transform. Figure 5.5 illustrates the effect of rectangular windowing on a discrete-time sinusoid of frequency f_0. The sharp impulsive discrete-time Fourier transform of the infinite sinusoidal sequence has been broadened by the replication of the shape of the window transform. Thus, the narrowest spectral response of a windowed sequence is limited to that set by the mainlobe of the window transform, independent of the data. Sidelobes of the window transform, sometimes called *leakage*, will bias the amplitudes of adjacent frequency responses. Because the discrete-time Fourier transform is periodic, sidelobe aliasing from adjacent spectral periods can

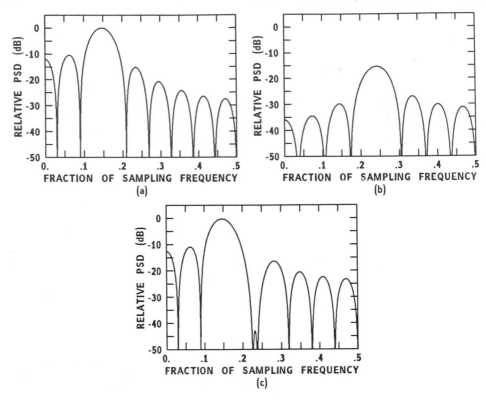

Figure 5.6 Illustration of windowing effect of weak signal masking by an adjacent strong signal. (a) Log of DTFT magnitude of strong sinusoid (16 samples, amplitude 1., fractional sample frequency .15, initial phase 45°). (b) Log of DTFT magnitude of weak sinusoid (16 samples, amplitude .19, fractional sample frequency .24, initial phase 162°). (c) Log of DTFT magnitude of combined signals. Weak signal response is nearly obliterated.

contribute additional bias. Increasing the sample rate can mitigate the effect of aliased sidelobes. Similar distortion will also occur for nonsinusoidal signals.

Leakage not only produces an amplitude bias in a discrete signal spectral response, but it may also mask the presence of weak signals and prevent their detection. Consider the discrete-time Fourier transform of 16 samples of the two-sinusoid signal shown in Fig. 5.6. The weaker sinusoid has approximately 17 dB less power than the stronger sinusoid. In this extreme case, the sidelobes of the stronger sinusoid have almost canceled the mainlobe response of the weaker sinusoid.

Other window functions have been devised to achieve better sidelobe levels than those of the rectangular window. Decreasing the sidelobe levels will reduce the bias. However, this can be achieved only by broadening the window's mainlobe frequency response, resulting in a reduction of spectral resolution. A trade-off must, therefore, be made between mainlobe width and level of sidelobe suppression. Several figures of merit have been devised to categorize window functions.

The mainlobe frequency bandwidth is indicative of the frequency resolution. Two measures are used to quantify the mainlobe bandwidth. The traditional measure is the *half-power bandwidth*, which is 3 dB down from the peak response. An alternative measure is the *equivalent bandwidth*, defined in Chap. 2. Two measures are used to quantify the sidelobe behavior. The *peak sidelobe level* is one indicator of how well a window suppresses leakage. The *sidelobe decay rate* indicates the rate at which the sidelobes closest to the mainlobe fall off. The sidelobe decay rate is actually a function of the number of sample points N, but it tends to approach an asymptotic value as N is increased. The asymptotic value is normally expressed in dB per octave of bandwidth.

Table 5.1 defines some common discrete-time windows among many that have been proposed for use in spectral estimation (e.g., Harris [1978], Nuttall [1981a], Geçkinli and Yavuz [1983]). Figure 5.7 illustrates typical 51-point windows and their frequency responses obtained by taking the magnitude of the discrete-time Fourier transform of each window. Table 5.1 defines N-point symmetric windows with two different origin points. For data windows, the origin point is $n = 0$. For lag windows, the origin point is $-(N-1)/2$. Only odd-length windows are used for lag windows. For an odd-length window, the point of symmetry falls on the middle element of the window. This middle element will always have a value of one if it is a lag window. For an even-length window, the point of symmetry falls between the two window elements at the window center. Other subtle variations on window definitions are often found in the literature. For example, some authors prefer to omit the zero-value endpoints on windows. For operations with the DTFS involving no zero padding, the highest time index point is usually dropped so that a periodic replication of the window is correctly generated [Harris, 1978]. Table 5.2 lists the characteristics of the windows described in Table 5.1. The bandwidth entries are normalized with respect to a discrete-time Fourier series frequency bin of $1/NT$ Hz.

The frequency response of the rectangular window has the narrowest mainlobe among the windows illustrated, but it has the highest sidelobe level of any window. The triangular window was first described by Bartlett in connection with his analysis of the periodogram spectral estimate and, therefore, often carries his name. The autocorrelation of a rectangular window is a triangular window of twice the width of the rectangular window. The squared cosine window is named after the Austrian meteorologist Julius Van Hann. It is often mistakenly termed a *hanning* window. The historic appeal of the Hann window is that it may be easily implemented in the frequency domain with only three adds and two shift operations that effectively multiply by factors of 1/2 and 1/4 at each frequency point. The raised cosine window was introduced by R.W. Hamming, so it often bears his name. The factors .54 and .46 were selected to roughly eliminate the highest sidelobe of the $D_N(f)$ function. This approach can be generalized to a whole family of weighted cosine windows [Nuttall, 1981a; Harris, 1978; Blackman and Tukey, 1958]. The weights of the cosines may be selected to be optimal with respect to a number of conditions, including minimum sidelobes, maximum sideloble decay

Table 5.1 Definitions of Typical N–Point Discrete-Time Windows

WINDOW NAME	DISCRETE-TIME FUNCTION $w[n]$ or $\omega[m]$	FREQUENCY RESPONSE $W(f)$ or $\Omega(f)$
Rectangle (Uniform)	1	$D_N(f)$
Triangle (Bartlett)	$1 - 2|t[n]|$	$\frac{2}{N} D_N^2(f/2)$
Squared Cosine (Hann)	$\cos^2(\pi t[n]) =$ $.50 + .50\cos(2\pi t[n])$	$.50D_N(f) + .25\left[D_N(f - \frac{1}{NT}) + D_N(f + \frac{1}{NT})\right]$
Raised Cosine (Hamming)	$.54 + .46\cos(2\pi t[n])$	$.54D_N(f) + .23\left[D_N(f - \frac{1}{NT}) + D_N(f + \frac{1}{NT})\right]$
Weighted Cosines (Nuttall,R=3)	$\sum_{r=0}^{R} a_r \cos(2\pi r t[n])$	$\sum_{r=0}^{R} .5a_r\left[D_N(f - \frac{r}{NT}) + D_N(f + \frac{r}{NT})\right]$
Truncated Gaussian ($\alpha = 2.5$)	$\exp\left[-\frac{1}{2}(2\alpha t[n])^2\right]$	$(\sqrt{2\pi}/2\alpha)\exp\left[-\frac{1}{2}(2\pi fT/\alpha)^2\right] * D_N(f)$
Equiripple (Chebyshev) ($\beta = 50$ dB)	Inverse DTFT of frequency response	$\cos[(N-1)\cos^{-1}\{\alpha\cos(\pi fT)\}]/\cosh[(N-1)\cosh^{-1}(\alpha)]$ $\alpha = \cosh[\cosh^{-1}(10^{\beta/20})/(N-1)]$ β =ratio of mainlobe to sidelobe level (dB)

T is the sample interval.
Data window $w[n]$ is defined over the index range $0 \leq n \leq N - 1$ and N may be even or odd.
Lag window $\omega[m]$ is defined over the index range $-(N-1)/2 \leq m \leq (N-1)/2$ and N is always odd.
Function $t[n] = (n - [N-1]/2)/[N-1]$ for $w[n]$ and $t[m] = m/N$ for $\omega[m]$.
Function $D_N(f) = T\,\text{sinc}(fNT)$ for $w[n]$ and $D_N(f) = T\exp(j2\pi fT)\text{sinc}(fNT)$ for $\omega[m]$.

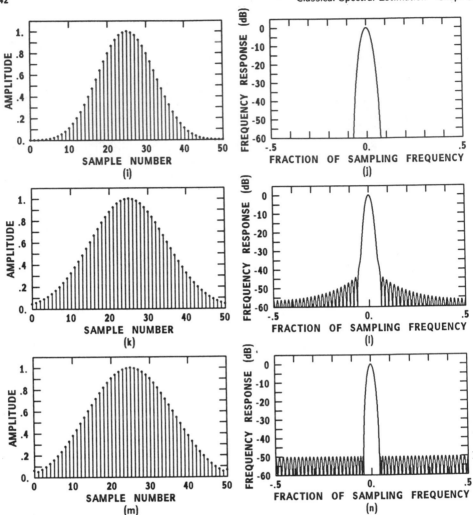

Figure 5.7   Typical discrete-time windows (left side) and the log of their DTFT magnitude (right side). (a-b) Rectangular. (c-d) Triangular. (e-f) Hann. (g-h) Hamming. (i-j) Nuttall. (k-l) Gaussian. (m-n) Chebyshev.

rate, or maximum smoothness (highest number of derivatives without a discontinuity). For example, the window of Fig. 5.7(i) is a four-term cosine window with minimum relative sidelobe levels of -98 dB, obtained by selecting $a_0 = .3635819$, $a_1 = .4891775$, $a_2 = .1365995$, and $a_3 = .0106411$ [Nuttall, 1981a]. The Gaussian window was shown in a Chap. 2 problem to have the smallest time-bandwidth product of all functions, although this is not strictly true when truncated to a finite window. The Gaussian window of Fig. 5.7(k) used a parameter setting of $\alpha = 2.5$. The Chebyshev (equiripple) window has all of its sidelobes at a constant level. It was first used in antenna array theory. It has the property of having, among all

WINDOW NAME	HIGHEST SIDELOBE LEVEL	ASYMPTOTIC SIDELOBE DECAY RATE	EQUIV. BW (DTFS bins)	1/2–POWER BW (DTFS bins)
Rectangle	−13.3 dB	−6 dB/octave	1.00	0.89
Triangle	−26.5 dB	−12 dB/octave	1.33	1.28
Hann	−31.5 dB	−18 dB/octave	1.50	1.44
Hamming	−43 dB	−6 dB/octave	1.36	1.30
Nuttall ($r = 3$)	−98 dB	−6 dB/octave	1.80	1.70
Gaussian	−42 dB	−6 dB/octave	1.39	1.33
Equiripple	−50 dB	0 dB/octave	1.39	1.33

Table 5.2   Characteristics of Windows of Table 5.1

N-point discrete windows with sidelobes at or below a given peak sidelobe level, the narrowest mainlobe. A parameter setting of $\beta = 50$ dB was used to define the Chebyshev window of Fig. 5.7(m).

Figure 5.8   Window selection strategy. (a) Equiripple sidelobes for situations with both close and distant interferences of comparable level. (b) Rapidly decaying sidelobes for distant strong interference. (c) Nontraditional special window with low adjacent sidelobes for very close interference and increasing sidelobes.

The strategy for window selection is dictated by a trade-off between bias due to interferers in nearby sidelobes versus bias due to interferers in distant sidelobes. For example, if there are moderate signal components both close and distant in frequency to a weaker signal component, then a window should be selected with equiripple sidelobes around the mainlobe in order to keep the bias small, as illustrated in Fig. 5.8(a). The decay rate is not important in this situation. If there is a distant strong component, as illustrated in Fig. 5.8(b), then a window with rapidly decaying sidelobes should be used. The sidelobe level in the immediate vicinity of the mainlobe is not important in this situation. In situations where high resolution between very close signal components is desired, and there are no distant signal components, then it is even conceivable that a window with *increasing* sidelobes, but with very narrow mainlobe, could be designed, as illustrated by Fig. 5.8(c). If the range of signal levels is limited, then sidelobe characteristics are not a consideration, so that a window may be selected for its ease of computation. If the spectrum is relatively flat, then no windowing at all may be needed. Windows that can adjust, or "adapt," themselves in some sense to the data conditions, such as that of Fig. 5.8(c), may be found in Chap. 13 on minimum variance spectral estimation.

5.4 RESOLUTION AND THE STABILITY-TIME-BANDWIDTH PRODUCT

In Sec. 2.11, the time-bandwidth product relationship for deterministic signals was introduced. It was shown that, for a temporal (spatial) signal of duration (aperture) $T_e = NT$ seconds (feet), the time-bandwidth product satisfies the equality

$$T_e B_e = 1 \quad ,$$

where B_e is the equivalent bandwidth in Hz. The resolution of the *energy* spectral density made from a finite sequence of samples of a *deterministic* signal was therefore said to have a resolution of B_e Hz, equal approximately to the reciprocal of the data record interval. In order to determine the resolution of the *power* spectral density made from a finite sequence of samples of a *random* signal, the time-bandwidth product must first be modified to account for the random nature of the signal that affects the statistical "quality" of the spectral estimate.

An appropriate modification is the *stability-time-bandwidth product* $QT_e B_s$, where Q is the statistical *quality ratio*, defined as the ratio of the variance of the PSD estimate to the squared mean of the PSD estimate

$$Q = \frac{\text{var}\{\hat{P}(f)\}}{\left[\mathcal{E}\{\hat{P}(f)\}\right]^2} \quad . \tag{5.5}$$

The quality ratio Q is effectively an inverted signal-to-noise ratio (SNR) that relates directly to the statistical stability of the spectral estimate. Values of Q much less than unity would indicate smooth spectral estimates with small fluctuations (low variance). Values of Q much greater than unity would indicate very noisy spectral estimates with large fluctuations (large variance). The equivalent bandwidth B_e in the TBP has been replaced with B_s, the *effective statistical bandwidth* [Blackman and Tukey 1958], defined for the spectral window $\Omega(f)$ as

$$B_s = \frac{\left[\displaystyle\int_{-1/2T}^{1/2T} \Omega(f)\,df\right]^2}{\displaystyle\int_{-1/2T}^{1/2T} \Omega^2(f)\,df} \quad . \tag{5.6}$$

B_s represents the bandwidth of an equivalent rectangular window with an identical ratio of output variance to output squared mean as that of window $\Omega(f)$ when a white noise process is the input (see Sec. B.8 of Blackman and Tukey [1958] for a discussion). The effective statistical bandwidth B_s, rather than the equivalent deterministic bandwidth B_e, must be used due to the random nature of the signal. However, the two bandwidths may be related as $B_s = \alpha B_e$, where α is approximately .8 for a rectangular window, 1.3 for a Hann window, and 1.4 for a Hamming window (see the Problems). The bandwidth B_s may be used to roughly indicate the resolution of the spectral estimate, although the bandwidth B_e is closer to the actual resolution in Hz.

It is shown in Sec. 5.8 that, for a Gaussian noise process, the inequality

$$Q T_e B_s \geq 1 \tag{5.7}$$

is applicable to all the classical spectral estimation procedures presented in this chapter. If $T_e B_s \approx 1$, then generally $Q T_e B_s > 1$. On the other hand, if the time-bandwidth product $T_e B_s$ is selected to be much greater than unity, then the approximation

$$Q T_e B_s \approx 1 \tag{5.8}$$

will hold for all classical spectral estimators. Even though all the classical spectral estimation procedures have similar statistical stability (small fluctuations), each estimator will manifest some slight visual differences on an estimate by estimate basis when processing a given data record.

The stability-time-bandwidth product epitomizes the interrelationship of the three fundamental parameters that affect the performance of spectral estimators. For a given available record length T_e, it is not possible simultaneously to have fine resolution (small values of B_s) and highly stable spectral estimates (small Q). For example, if the desired variance of the spectral estimate is selected to be one-tenth of its mean, then $Q = .1$ and the achievable resolution will be $B_s \approx 10/T_e$ Hz. This resolution bandwidth is ten times larger than the rule-of-thumb $1/T_e$ for deterministic signal resolution given in Chap. 2. For this value of Q, only variations in the PSD estimate greater than $\sqrt{Q} \times$ mean PSD may be considered confidently as spectral features rather than noise variations. This example emphasizes the compromise required to strike a balance between statistical stability and resolution necessary for all spectral estimation methods. Note that increasing the number of samples by increasing the sample rate, but holding the interval T_e constant, will have no effect on the ultimate resolution; only the time interval of the data record has an effect, not the number of samples. Much of the literature on classical spectral estimation is concerned with procedures that attain the ultimate stability (smallest Q) for a given record interval and specified resolution (e.g., Jenkins and Watts [1968] and Nuttall [1981b]).

Analytic determination of the stability factor Q for arbitrary PSD estimation methods operating on arbitrary random processes is generally mathemetically intractable. Analytic investigations, such as the one leading to Eq. (5.7), are usually restricted for this reason to stationary Gaussian processes under the assumptions of a large $T_e B_s$ product and a constant PSD level within a resolution bin width. Because fourth-order statistical moments of Gaussian processes can be expressed as sums of products of second-order variances, the study of the variance of PSD estimators is greatly simplified, as Appendix 4.A illustrates. Although the inequality of Eq. (5.7) depends on the Gaussian assumption, it still serves as a reasonable approximation in practice for non-Gaussian processes. Thus, it may be used as a guideline to structure spectral estimation procedures that attain good statistical stability. Some trial variations of a spectral estimation procedure may still be necessary to "tune" it to yield the best spectral estimation performance in any given data situation. As Blackman and Tukey [1958, p. 21] state, "We must rely on observed changes from trial to trial as basically the safest measure of the lack of stability of our spectral density estimates."

5.5 AUTOCORRELATION AND CROSS CORRELATION ESTIMATION

The autocorrelation sequence $r_{xx}[m]$ of an ergodic process was defined by Eq. (4.56) as the limit of a time average. In practice, the autocorrelation sequence is rarely known, so that it must be estimated with the available finite data record. Assuming N data samples $x[n]$ indexed from $n = 0$ to $n = N - 1$, an obvious discrete-time autocorrelation estimate is

$$\hat{r}_{xx}[m] = \frac{1}{(N-m)T} \sum_{n=0}^{N-m-1} x[n+m]x^*[n]\, T = \frac{1}{N-m} \sum_{n=0}^{N-m-1} x[n+m]x^*[n] \quad .$$

$$(5.9)$$

This estimate follows from Eq. (4.56) if $(N - m)$ is substituted for $(2M + 1)$ and the summation index range adjusted for the available data range. Equation (5.9) is applicable only for the positive lag indices $0 \leq m \leq N - 1$ (the lags are mT seconds). Autocorrelation estimates for lags greater than $N - 1$ are not possible due to the finite data available. For negative lag indices $-(N-1) \leq m < 0$, the estimate must be modified to

$$\hat{r}_{xx}[m] = \frac{1}{(N+m)} \sum_{n=-m}^{N-1} x[n+m]x^*[n] = \frac{1}{N-|m|} \sum_{n=0}^{N-|m|-1} x^*[n+|m|]x[n] \quad .$$

(5.10)

It may be readily shown that this autocorrelation estimate is conjugate symmetric because it satisfies $\hat{r}_{xx}[m] = \hat{r}_{xx}^*[-m]$, a property also found for the known autocorrelation sequence. When computing the estimate $\hat{r}_{xx}[m]$, only the positive lag indices need be computed, as the negative lag indices are obtained by simple conjugate symmetry. Thus, $2N-1$ total lags of the autocorrelation may be estimated from N data samples.

The discrete sequence $\hat{r}_{xx}[m]$ forms *unbiased* estimates of the true autocorrelation,

$$\mathcal{E}\{\hat{r}_{xx}[m]\} = \frac{1}{N-m} \sum_{n=0}^{N-m-1} \mathcal{E}\{x[n+m]x^*[n]\} = r_{xx}[m] \quad .$$

(5.11)

The variance of this autocorrelation estimate for Gaussian processes as a function of the number of data samples has been shown by Jenkins and Watts [1968] to be approximately

$$\text{var}\{\hat{r}_{xx}[m]\} \approx \frac{N}{(N-m)^2} \sum_{k=-\infty}^{\infty} \left(r_{xx}^2[k] + r_{xx}[k+m]r_{xx}[k-m]\right)$$

(5.12)

for $N \gg m$, that is, the lag index is much smaller than the number of data samples. Observe that the variance increases as the lag index increases. Because there are fewer data values to average at the larger lags, the statistical uncertainty of the autocorrelation estimate is increased. The variance tends to zero as N increases, so that $\hat{r}_{xx}[m]$ is a statistically consistent estimate of the discrete-time autocorrelation sequence.

An alternative autocorrelation estimate is

$$\check{r}_{xx}[m] = \begin{cases} \dfrac{1}{N} \displaystyle\sum_{n=0}^{N-m-1} x[n+m]x^*[n] & \text{for } 0 \leq m \leq N-1 \\[4mm] \dfrac{1}{N} \displaystyle\sum_{n=0}^{N-|m|-1} x^*[n+|m|]x[n] & \text{for } -(N-1) \leq m < 0 \quad . \end{cases}$$

(5.13)

This estimate differs from $\hat{r}_{xx}[m]$ only in the normalizing factor,

$$\check{r}_{xx}[m] = \frac{N-|m|}{N} \hat{r}_{xx}[m] \quad .$$

(5.14)

This is a *biased* estimate for finite N because

$$\mathcal{E}\{\check{r}_{xx}[m]\} = \left(1 - \frac{|m|}{N}\right) r_{xx}[m] \quad , \tag{5.15}$$

but it is asymptotically unbiased as $N \rightarrow \infty$. The bias forms a triangular window about the zero lag of the true autocorrelation. The variance of this estimate is approximately

$$\text{var}\{\check{r}_{xx}[m]\} = \frac{N - |m|}{N}\text{var}\{\hat{r}_{xx}[m]\} \approx \frac{1}{N} \sum_{k=-\infty}^{\infty} \left(r_{xx}^2[k] + r_{xx}[k + m]r_{xx}[k - m]\right). \tag{5.16}$$

The variance asymptotically approaches zero as the number of samples increases, for fixed lag index m. For typical applications, the mean square error (sum of variance and squared bias) tends to be higher for estimator $\hat{r}_{xx}[m]$ than for estimator $\check{r}_{xx}[m]$, especially as the highest lag index approaches the number of data samples. The unbiased autocorrelation estimate can also yield autocorrelation estimates that are not valid autocorrelation sequences. Consider, for example, the data sequence $x[1] = 1.$, $x[2] = 1.1$, and $x[3] = 1$. The three lags of the autocorrelation estimate yield $\hat{r}_{xx}[0] = 1.07$, $\hat{r}_{xx}[1] = 1.1$, and $\hat{r}_{xx}[2] = 1$. Observe that $\hat{r}_{xx}[0] < \hat{r}_{xx}[1]$, which violates property (4.30). The unbiased autocorrelation estimates can thus lead to autocorrelation matrices (to be studied in Chap. 6) that are not positive semidefinite, which means certain matrix equations have no solution, whereas the autocorrelation matrices formed from the biased autocorrelation estimate will always be positive semidefinite. For these reasons, the biased autocorrelation estimator is often the preferred estimator.

Both autocorrelation estimates yield identical values at zero lag

$$\hat{r}_{xx}[0] = \check{r}_{xx}[0] = \frac{1}{N} \sum_{n=0}^{N-1} |x[n]|^2 \quad . \tag{5.17}$$

This represents the total sample power of the measured signal. Thus, both estimates preserve the power in the measured signal.

The summation in Eqs. (5.9) and (5.13) may be expressed as a linear convolution

$$\sum_{n=0}^{N-m-1} x[n+m]x^*[n] = x[n] \star x^*[-n] \quad . \tag{5.18}$$

Computationally efficient procedures that perform fast convolutions with FFT algorithms may therefore be used to efficiently compute the discrete autocorrelation estimates. Consult references such as Otnes and Enochson [1978], Rader [1970], Chap. 6 in Rabiner and Gold [1975], or Oppenheim and Schafer [1975] for details.

The cross correlation estimate may similarly be defined. For example, assuming the two sequences $x[n]$ and $y[n]$ have been measured for $n = 0$ to $n = N - 1$, then the biased cross correlation estimate is

$$
\check{r}_{xy}[m] = \begin{cases} \dfrac{1}{N} \displaystyle\sum_{n=0}^{N-m-1} x[n+m]y^*[n] & \text{for } 0 \le m \le N - 1 \\[2ex] \dfrac{1}{N} \displaystyle\sum_{n=0}^{N-|m|-1} x[n]y^*[n+|m|] & \text{for } -(N-1) \le m < 0 \end{cases} \quad . \tag{5.19}
$$

The unbiased cross correlation estimate uses $1/(N - |m|)$, rather than $1/N$. Unlike the autocorrelation estimate, the cross correlation estimate for negative lag indices must be computed separately because $\check{r}_{xy}[m] \ne \check{r}_{xy}^*[-m]$. The biased cross correlation estimate may be shown to have essentially identical bias and variance behavior as that of the biased autocorrelation.

The FORTRAN subroutine CORRELATION is provided in Appendix 5.A for computing autocorrelation or cross correlation estimates. Either the unbiased or the biased estimators may be obtained from this computer program.

5.6   CORRELOGRAM METHOD PSD ESTIMATORS

The power spectral density was shown in Chap. 4 to be the discrete-time Fourier transform of the autocorrelation sequence

$$
P_{xx}(f) = T \sum_{m=-\infty}^{\infty} r_{xx}[m] \exp(-j2\pi fmT) \quad . \tag{5.20}
$$

The *correlogram method* of PSD estimation simply substitutes a finite sequence of autocorrelation estimates (the *correlogram*) for the infinite sequence of unknown true autocorrelation values. For example, substitution of the unbiased autocorrelation estimates $\hat{r}_{xx}[m]$ that have been computed to maximum lag indices $\pm L$ yields one possible PSD estimator

$$
\hat{P}_{xx}(f) = T \sum_{m=-L}^{L} \hat{r}_{xx}[m] \exp(-j2\pi fmT) \quad , \tag{5.21}
$$

defined for $-1/2T \le f \le 1/2T$. The maximum lag index L is typically much less than the number of data samples N. A maximum of $L \approx N/10$ was suggested by Blackman and Tukey [1958], who were the first to extensively study and popularize the discrete-time correlogram method of PSD estimation. The basis for this maximum is to avoid the greater statistical variance associated with the higher lags of the autocorrelation estimate. This increased variance would yield a more unstable PSD estimate.

The expected (mean) value of the estimate $\hat{P}_{xx}(f)$ is

$$
\begin{aligned}
\mathcal{E}\{\hat{P}_{xx}(f)\} &= T \sum_{m=-L}^{L} \mathcal{E}\{\hat{r}_{xx}[m]\} \exp(-j2\pi fmT) \\
&= T \sum_{m=-L}^{L} r_{xx}[m] \exp(-j2\pi fmT) \\
&= P_{xx}(f) \star D_L(f) \quad ,
\end{aligned}
\tag{5.22}
$$

where $D_L(f)$ is the Dirichlet kernel. Even though the PSD is computed with unbiased autocorrelation estimates, it will be a biased, or smeared, estimate of the true PSD. The windowing effect of a finite autocorrelation sequence has produced an estimate that is effectively the convolution of the true PSD with the transform of the discrete-time rectangular window.

Another PSD estimator may also be formed by using the biased autocorrelation estimate $\check{r}_{xx}[m]$, yielding

$$
\check{P}_{xx}(f) = T \sum_{m=-L}^{L} \check{r}_{xx}[m] \exp(-j2\pi fmT) \quad ,
\tag{5.23}
$$

defined for $-1/2T \leq f \leq 1/2T$. An alternative matrix formulation of this PSD estimator is

$$
\check{P}_{xx}(f) = T\mathbf{e}_L^H(f)\check{\mathbf{R}}_L\mathbf{e}_L(f) \quad ,
\tag{5.24}
$$

in which $\mathbf{e}_L(f)$ is the complex sinusoid vector

$$
\mathbf{e}_L(f) = \begin{pmatrix} 1 \\ \exp(j2\pi fT) \\ \vdots \\ \exp(j2\pi fLT) \end{pmatrix}
$$

and $\check{\mathbf{R}}_L$ is a Hermitian Toeplitz matrix of autocorrelation estimates

$$
\check{\mathbf{R}}_L = \begin{pmatrix}
\check{r}_{xx}[0] & \check{r}_{xx}^*[1] & \cdots & \check{r}_{xx}^*[L] \\
\check{r}_{xx}[1] & \check{r}_{xx}[0] & \cdots & \check{r}_{xx}^*[L-1] \\
\vdots & \vdots & \ddots & \vdots \\
\check{r}_{xx}[L] & \check{r}_{xx}[L-1] & \cdots & \check{r}_{xx}[0]
\end{pmatrix} .
\tag{5.25}
$$

The expected (mean) value of the estimate $\check{P}_{xx}(f)$ is

$$\mathcal{E}\left\{\check{P}_{xx}(f)\right\} = T \sum_{m=-L}^{L} \left(1 - \frac{|m|}{N}\right) r_{xx}[m]\exp(-j2\pi fmT)$$

$$= P_{xx}(f) \star \frac{2}{L}D_L^2(f/2) \quad . \tag{5.26}$$

The PSD estimate in this case will have a bias as a result of the convolution of the true PSD with the transform of the discrete-time triangular window. If the special case $L = N - 1$ is selected, i.e., the maximum lag is set equal to the number of available data samples less one, then the estimator $\check{P}_{xx}(f)$ is identical to the sample spectrum computed from the N data samples (see the Problems). Because the sample spectrum is known to be statistically unstable (see Appendix 4.A), this is another indication that one must choose $L << N$ in order to produce a statistically reliable spectral estimator.

To reduce the effect of leakage of the implicit rectangular or triangular window, and therefore to reduce the bias in the estimate, an odd-length $(2L + 1)$-point lag window $\omega[m]$ over the interval $-L \leq m \leq L$ and symmetric about the origin is normally used. The most general form of the correlogram method of PSD estimation then takes the form

$$\hat{P}_{\mathrm{BT}}(f) = T \sum_{m=-L}^{L} \omega[m]\hat{r}_{xx}[m]\exp(-j2\pi fmT) \quad , \tag{5.27}$$

where the unbiased autocorrelation estimate $\hat{r}_{xx}[m]$ is to be used. A subscript BT has been added to designate this PSD estimate as the one promoted by Blackman and Tukey. The window is normalized so that $\omega[0] = 1$. Therefore, $\hat{r}_{xx}[0]$ will be unbiased, the sample power is conserved, and estimator $\hat{P}_{\mathrm{BT}}(f)$ will be scaled correctly as a PSD. If one desires the *peaks* in the BT PSD estimator to be proportional to power for impulses in the spectrum, rather than the *area* under the PSD to be proportional to power, then Eq. (5.27) should be scaled by $F = 1/NT$. The average value of the BT spectral estimate is

$$\mathcal{E}\left\{\hat{P}_{\mathrm{BT}}(f)\right\} = T \sum_{m=-L}^{L} \omega[m] r_{xx}[m]\exp(-j2\pi fmT) = P_{xx}(f) \star \Omega(f) \quad , \tag{5.28}$$

where $\Omega(f)$ is the discrete-time Fourier transform of the lag window. Lag windows with regions where $\Omega(f) < 0$ should be avoided, as this generates negative PSD estimates, contrary to the positive property of a PSD. For instance, a rectangular window should be avoided as it will generate regions of negative PSD values. The correlogram method of PSD estimation is asymptotically unbiased as the number of lags increases. Blackman and Tukey have suggested that the standard deviation of the PSD should be no more than one-third of the PSD mean value, i.e., $Q =$

$(1/3)^2$. Based on the stability-time-bandwidth product, $1/B_s \approx T_e Q = T_e/9$. Assuming that the lag interval $T_L = (2L+1)T$ is approximately the reciprocal of the B_s bandwidth, then $T_L \approx T_e/9$, that is, the number of lags of the discrete-time autocorrelation to be estimated should be about 10% of the available data samples.

The FFT algorithm may be used to evaluate the PSD estimate of Eq. (5.27) on a grid of $K+1$ frequency points $f_i = i/KT$ for $0 \le i \le K$. The value of K is arbitrary, but generally $K \gg L$, so that sharp details in the PSD estimate will not be missed. Zero padding of data samples will be required for time indices $L+1$ to K. Program CORRELOGRAMPSD in Appendix 5.B will compute the PSD estimator of Eq. (5.27). A more sophisticated computer program for computing the correlogram method of PSD estimation is available as program 2.2 in the IEEE Press book *Programs for Digital Signal Processing* [1979]. It uses an FFT to perform a fast correlation estimation by the convolution method.

The correlogram method of PSD estimation for the cross power spectral density has the form

$$\hat{P}_{xy}(f) = T \sum_{m=-L}^{L} \omega[m] \hat{r}_{xy}[m] \exp(-j2\pi fmT) \quad . \tag{5.29}$$

This PSD estimate can have a large bias if the cross correlation sequence is not maximum at or near zero lag, where the lag window will generally be centered. This bias can be minimized by realigning the two discrete-time sequences so that the cross correlation peaks at zero lag. If this is done, then the PSD estimate (5.27) has similar statistical properties as autospectral estimate (5.25). Program CORRELOGRAMPSD in Appendix 5.B will compute the cross power spectral density by the correlogram method.

5.7 PERIODOGRAM PSD ESTIMATORS

The alternative formal definition of the PSD, based on ergodicity, has the discrete-time form

$$P_{xx}(f) = \lim_{N \to \infty} \mathcal{E} \left\{ \frac{1}{(2N+1)T} \left| T \sum_{n=-N}^{N} x[n] \exp(-j2\pi fnT) \right|^2 \right\} \quad . \tag{5.30}$$

Ignoring the expectation operation and assuming a finite data set $x[0], \ldots, x[N-1]$ of N samples, the sample spectrum

$$\tilde{P}_{xx}(f) = \frac{1}{NT} \left| T \sum_{n=0}^{N-1} x[n] \exp(-j2\pi fnT) \right|^2 = \frac{T}{N} \left| \sum_{n=0}^{N-1} x[n] \exp(-j2\pi fnT) \right|^2 \tag{5.31}$$

may be computed from the finite data sequence. This was the original unmodified periodogram PSD estimate. It was shown in Chap. 4 that the sample spectrum will yield statistically inconsistent (unstable) PSD estimates because the expectation operation of Eq. (5.30) has been ignored. One must resort to pseudo ensemble averaging in order to smooth the periodogram PSD estimate. Three types of basic averaging schemes have been considered. The method of Daniell [1946] smooths the periodogram by averaging over adjacent frequency bins. The method of Bartlett [1948] averages multiple periodograms produced from segments of the original data sequence. The method of Welch [1967] extends the Bartlett approach by over-lapping the segments and introducing data windows to improve the bias caused by leakage. Other optimal methods of smoothing the periodogram have appeared in the literature, but the methods are usually optimal only with respect to some restrictive class of signals. The three methods presented in this section may not always be optimum, but they have been proven by usage to be robust for many classes of signals.

5.7.1 Daniell Periodogram

Daniell suggested that a method to smooth the rapid fluctuations of the sample spectrum was to average over adjacent spectral frequencies. If an FFT is used to evaluate the sample spectrum $\tilde{P}_{xx}(f)$ at a set of frequencies $f_k = k/KT$ for $0 \leq k \leq K - 1$, then a modified periodogram estimate at frequency f_i could be obtained by averaging the P points on either side of this frequency

$$\hat{P}_{\mathrm{D}}[f_i] = \frac{1}{2P + 1} \sum_{n=i-P}^{i+P} \tilde{P}_{xx}[f_n] \quad . \tag{5.32}$$

The generalization of this concept is to pass the sample spectrum through a low-pass filter with frequency response $H(f)$. The Daniell periodogram may therefore be expressed as the convolution of the sample spectrum with a low-pass filter

$$\hat{P}_{\mathrm{D}}(f) = \tilde{P}_{xx}(f) \star H(f) \quad , \tag{5.33}$$

where subscript D will distinguish this periodogram estimator from other PSD estimators.

5.7.2 Bartlett Periodogram

Bartlett's scheme to smooth the sample spectrum is to create a pseudo ensemble by dividing the data sequence of N samples into P nonoverlapping segments of D samples each, so that $DP \leq N$. The pth segment will then consist of the samples

$$x^{(p)}[n] = x[pD + n] \tag{5.34}$$

for $0 \leq n \leq D - 1$, where the superscript (p) denotes the segment number. An independent sample spectrum

$$\tilde{P}_{xx}^{(p)}(f) = \frac{1}{DT} \left| T \sum_{m=0}^{D-1} x^{(p)}[m] \exp(-j2\pi f mT) \right|^2 \qquad (5.35)$$

for each segment $0 \leq p \leq P - 1$ is computed over the range $-1/2T \leq f \leq 1/2T$, possibly with an FFT over a grid of frequency points. At each frequency of interest, the P individual unmodified periodograms are averaged to produce the Bartlett averaged periodogram

$$\hat{P}_{\mathrm{B}}(f) = \frac{1}{P} \sum_{p=0}^{P-1} \tilde{P}_{xx}^{(p)}(f) \quad . \qquad (5.36)$$

The bias of the Bartlett average of modified periodograms is

$$\mathcal{E}\left\{\hat{P}_{\mathrm{B}}(f)\right\} = \frac{1}{P} \sum_{p=0}^{P-1} \mathcal{E}\left\{\tilde{P}_{xx}^{(p)}(f)\right\} = \mathcal{E}\left\{\tilde{P}_{xx}(f)\right\} \quad . \qquad (5.37)$$

Thus, $\hat{P}_{\mathrm{B}}(f)$ suffers from the same window bias as that of the sample spectrum of a single segment periodogram. If the P segment periodograms are statistically independent, which will be approximately true if autocorrelation $r_{xx}[m]$ is small for lags $m > D$, then $\hat{P}_{\mathrm{B}}(f)$ may be interpreted as the sample mean of a set of P independent observations of $\tilde{P}_{xx}(f)$. The Bartlett averaged periodogram can be shown, using a generalized variance expression developed in Sec. 5.8, to have a variance inversely proportional to the number of segments

$$\mathrm{var}\left\{\hat{P}_{\mathrm{B}}(f)\right\} \propto \frac{P_{xx}^2(f)}{P} \quad . \qquad (5.38)$$

The spectral estimate stability improves, therefore, roughly as the inverse of the number of segments P. The variance reduction with increasing P will be less if the segment periodograms are not statistically independent. The resolution has been degraded due to the segmentation into data lengths of D samples each, where $D < N$. The effective spectral window will then have a broader mainlobe bandwidth. For fixed $N = PD$, there is the usual trade-off between high spectral resolution (D is as large as possible) and minimizing estimation variance (P is as large as possible).

5.7.3 Welch Periodogram

Welch modified the basic Bartlett segment-and-average scheme by using data windows and by permitting the data segments to overlap. A data window is applied to the data in each segment prior to the computation of the segment periodogram.

The purpose of the window is to reduce the effect of sidelobes and to decrease the estimation bias, at the price of a slight decrease in resolution. The purpose of overlapping segments is to increase the number of segments that are averaged for a given data record length and, therefore, to decrease the PSD estimate variance. Welch also provided a computationally efficient procedure using the FFT for his method of averaging periodograms of weighted and overlapped data segments. It is this latter feature that has made the Welch method the most frequently used periodogram estimation approach in use today.

If the complex data record $x[0], \ldots, x[N-1]$ of N samples is divided into P segments of D samples each, with a shift of S samples between adjacent segments ($S \leq D$), then the maximum number of segments P is given by the integer part of $(N - D)/S + 1$. The weighted pth segment will consist of the samples

$$x^{(p)}[n] = w[n]x[n + pS] \tag{5.39}$$

for $0 \leq n \leq D - 1$. The index range of segments is $0 \leq p \leq P - 1$. The sample spectrum of the weighted pth segment is given by

$$\tilde{P}_{xx}^{(p)}(f) = \frac{1}{UDT}X^{(p)}(f)[X^{(p)}(f)]^* = \frac{1}{UDT}\left|X^{(p)}(f)\right|^2 \tag{5.40}$$

over the frequency range $-1/2T \leq f \leq 1/2T$, where $X^{(p)}(f)$ is the discrete-time Fourier transform of the pth segment

$$X^{(p)}(f) = T\sum_{n=0}^{D-1} x^{(p)}[n]\exp(-j2\pi fnT) \tag{5.41}$$

and U is the discrete-time window energy

$$U = T\sum_{n=0}^{D-1} w^2[n] \quad . \tag{5.42}$$

The average of the windowed segment periodograms yields the Welch periodogram estimate,

$$\hat{P}_{\mathrm{W}}(f) = \frac{1}{P}\sum_{p=0}^{P-1}\tilde{P}_{xx}^{(p)}(f) \quad . \tag{5.43}$$

The factor U removes the effect of the window energy bias in the PSD estimator $\hat{P}_{\mathrm{W}}(f)$. The average value of the Welch periodogram may be shown (see the Problems) to be

$$\mathcal{E}\left\{\hat{P}_{\mathrm{W}}(f)\right\} = \frac{1}{P}\sum_{p=0}^{P-1}\mathcal{E}\left\{\tilde{P}_{xx}^{(p)}(f)\right\} = P_{xx}(f)\star|W(f)|^2/U \quad , \tag{5.44}$$

where

$$W(f) = T \sum_{n=0}^{D-1} w[n] \exp(-j2\pi fnT) \tag{5.45}$$

is the discrete-time Fourier transform of the data window and $P_{xx}(f)$ is the true PSD. The inverse discrete-time Fourier transform of Eq. (5.48) yields the expected value of the effective autocorrelation sequence of the Welch periodogram

$$\mathcal{E}\left\{\hat{r}_{xx}^W[m]\right\} = r_{xx}[m] \cdot \phi[m]/U \quad, \tag{5.46}$$

where

$$\phi[m] = w[m] \star w^*[-m] = T \sum_{n=0}^{D-m-1} w[n+m]w[n] \tag{5.47}$$

is the autocorrelation of the data window. Note that $U = \phi[0]$, so that $\phi[m]/\phi[0]$ is effectively a lag window with a unit value at lag 0. The total power in the original sample data sequence is given by the zero lag autocorrelation term; because

$$\mathcal{E}\left\{\hat{r}_{xx}^W[0]\right\} = r_{xx}[0]\phi[0]/U = r_{xx}[0] \tag{5.48}$$

equals $r_{xx}[0]$, this will imply $\hat{r}_{xx}^W[0]$ is an unbiased estimate of the power.

Welch specifically proposed the use of the Hann window and 50% overlap of the segments. This particular amount of overlap leads to a very efficient implementation with the FFT algorithm, which evaluates Eq. (5.43) on a grid of frequency points. A 50% overlap also uses all data samples twice, except for the $D/2$ samples on each end of the original N-point data sequence. This tends to equalize the treatment of most of the data samples, giving a sample which received a small weight in one segment a larger weight in the next segment. A study of the variance of the Welch periodogram for Gaussian processes indicates, based on expressions given in the next section, that the minimum variance for a Hann window is achieved with an overlap of 65%, with an increase in variance of approximately 8% when using 50% overlap. Like the Bartlett periodogram, the variance of the Welch periodogram is roughly inversely proportional to the number of segments

$$\text{var}\left\{\hat{P}_W(f)\right\} \propto \frac{P_{xx}^2(f)}{P} \quad, \tag{5.49}$$

assuming segment independence (overlapping, though, will tend to introduce some segment dependence). Due to overlapping, more segments are constructed from a fixed data record for use by the Welch method than for the Bartlett method. As a result, the Welch periodogram will tend to have less variance than the Bartlett periodogram.

Unlike the lag window of the correlogram method, the merits of the use of data windows in spectral estimation have occasionally been the subject of debate in the literature. It has been shown that the primary use of data windows is to reduce the bias effects of sidelobes in spectra with large amplitude range among signals. Examples of such spectra that provide compelling motivation for data windowing have been provided by Thompson [1977] and Van Schooneveld and Frijling [1981]. The importance of data windowing for sidelobe control is diminished as the spectrum becomes flatter (has decreased amplitude range). Some published studies claim that data windows give some data samples more importance than others and also serve only to decrease resolution (broadened mainlobe of frequency window) without a compensating decrease in variance. These claims are certainly true for a sample spectrum produced by using all the data samples of a signal with a relatively flat spectral response. However, the claims are not true for the Welch periodogram, because overlapping segments serves to equalize data treatment and increasing the number of segments serves to decrease PSD estimate variance. The claims are also not true for spectra involving large amplitude differences among signals.

The Welch periodogram can be implemented for complex data by using the program PERIODOGRAM in Appendix 5.C . Another computer program for real data only is available in the IEEE Press book *Digital Signal Processing Algorithms* [1979] as program 2.1 .

The Welch procedure for estimation of the cross power spectral density is very similar to the autospectral estimate. The N-sample sequences $x[n]$ and $y[n]$ are segmented and weighted

$$x^{(p)}[n] = w[n]x[n + pS]$$
$$y^{(p)}[n] = w[n]y[n + pS] \tag{5.50}$$

for $0 \leq n \leq D - 1$ and $0 \leq p \leq P - 1$, and the sample cross spectrum computed

$$\tilde{P}_{xy}^{(p)}(f) = \frac{1}{UDT} X^{(p)}(f) \left[Y^{(p)}(f) \right]^* \quad, \tag{5.51}$$

where $X^{(p)}(f)$ and $Y^{(p)}(f)$ are the discrete-time Fourier transforms

$$X^{(p)}(f) = T \sum_{n=0}^{D-1} x^{(p)}[n] \exp(-j2\pi fnT)$$
$$Y^{(p)}(f) = T \sum_{n=0}^{D-1} y^{(p)}[n] \exp(-j2\pi fnT) \tag{5.52}$$

and U is identical to Eq. (5.42). Averaging over the segment periodograms yields the final periodogram estimate

$$\hat{P}_{xy}(f) = \frac{1}{P} \sum_{p=0}^{P-1} \tilde{P}_{xy}^{(p)}(f) \quad. \tag{5.53}$$

The mean and variance of the cross spectral estimate is very similar to that of the autospectral estimate when the two processes are Gaussian. Program PERIODOGRAM in Appendix 5.C will compute the cross spectral density estimate for complex data.

5.8 COMBINED PERIODOGRAM/CORRELOGRAM ESTIMATORS

Schemes that combine aspects of both the periodogram and correlogram methods of PSD estimation have frequently been promoted in the literature in an attempt to unify the classical PSD estimation methods (e.g., see Otnes and Enochson [1978] or Van Schoeneveld and Frijling [1981]). One of the more definitive generalizations has been presented by Nuttall and Carter [1982]. It includes all the methods in Secs. 5.6–5.7 as special cases. Their generalization led to a discovery of an alternative to the popular Welch periodogram method with comparable statistical performance and half the computational burden.

The combined periodogram/correlogram method requires four steps. First, the usual Welch periodogram $\hat{P}_{W}(f)$ is computed according to Eqs. (5.39), (5.40), and (5.43). Arbitrary overlap S and data window $w[n]$ are permitted. Second, an inverse discrete-time Fourier transform of $\hat{P}_{W}(f)$ is computed to produce a symmetric autocorrelation estimate $\hat{r}_{xx}^{W}[m]$ of $2D + 1$ lags. The autocorrelation $\hat{r}_{xx}^{W}[m]$ spans the lags $|m| \leq D$ due to the effect of the window autocorrelation $\phi[m] = w[n] \star w[n]$, as illustrated by Fig. 5.9(a) and (b) for the rectangular data window. Third, an odd-length real symmetric lag window $\omega[m]$ of $2L + 1$ lags is applied to produce the windowed autocorrelation $\hat{r}_{xx}^{C}[m] = \omega[m]\hat{r}_{xx}^{W}[m]$ for the combined method. The lag window will be selected to be smaller than the width of the autocorrelation $\phi[m]$ of the data window ($L < D$). Fourth, a DTFT of $\hat{r}_{xx}^{C}[m]$ will yield the final PSD estimate. The final combined PSD estimate is given by

$$\hat{P}_{C}(f) = \hat{P}_{W}(f) \star \Omega(f) \quad , \tag{5.54}$$

where $\Omega(f)$ is the transform of the lag window $\omega[m]$.

The combined method achieves sidelobe control (leakage suppression) by a mixture of temporal weighting and lag weighting. Stability is achieved by a combination of segment averaging and frequency smoothing (lag weighting). By restricting windows and overlaps appropriately, either the Welch periodogram or the Blackman-Tukey PSD estimates are obtained as special cases.

The mean of the combined method PSD estimate and the mean of the combined method autocorrelation are easily shown to satisfy

$$\mathcal{E}\left\{\hat{P}_{C}(f)\right\} = P_{xx}(f) \star \Omega_{e}(f) \tag{5.55}$$

$$\mathcal{E}\left\{\hat{r}_{xx}^{C}[m]\right\} = r_{xx}[m]\omega_{e}[m] \quad , \tag{5.56}$$

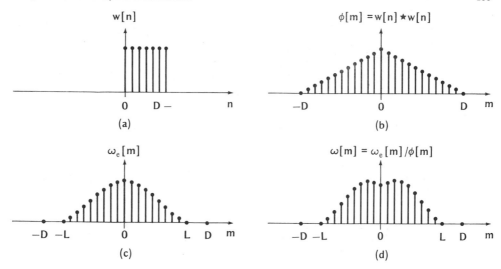

Figure 5.9   Illustration of lag reshaping. (a) Original discrete-time data window of length D. (b) Autocorrelation of discrete-time data window of length $2D + 1$. (c) Desired discrete-time effective lag window of length $2L + 1$, $L < D$. (d) Actual discrete-time lag window applied to compensate for the effect of $\phi[m]$.

where the *effective lag window* $w_e[m]$ and its transform $\Omega_e(f)$ are given by

$$\Omega_e(f) = \Omega(f) \star |W(f)|^2 \tag{5.57}$$

$$w_e[m] = w[m]\phi[m]/U = w[m]\phi[m]/\phi[0] \ . \tag{5.58}$$

The only assumption required to obtain these is that $x[n]$ be stationary. In order that $\hat{r}_{xx}^C[0]$ be an unbiased estimate of the total power, one must select $w_e[0] = 1$. Selecting a lag window $w[m]$ such that $w[0] = 1$ will satisfy the requirement. An interesting observation can be made at this point. Suppose a desired effective lag window is selected in advance, such as the one illustrated in Fig. 5.9(c). If $D > L$, then the data window $w[n]$ may be selected arbitrarily because its effect may be undone by selecting the lag window $w[m]$ as follows,

$$w[m] = \frac{w_e[m]}{\phi[m]/U} \tag{5.59}$$

for $|m| \le L$. The effect of *lag window reshaping* is illustrated in Fig. 5.9(d) for the case of a rectangular data window. Other data windows could also have been used.

The variance of the combined approach has been shown by Nuttall [1971, 1981b] to be approximately

$$\mathrm{var}\left\{\hat{P}_C(f)\right\} \approx P^2(f)\frac{1}{P} \sum_{p=-(P-1)}^{P-1} \left(1 - \frac{|p|}{P}\right) T \sum w^2[m]\psi[m, pS] \ , \tag{5.60}$$

where the third-order correlation sequence $\psi[m,n]$ of the data window is

$$\psi[m,n] \tag{5.61}$$
$$= T\sum_l w\left[l+\frac{n-m}{2}\right] w\left[l+\frac{-n-m}{2}\right] w\left[l+\frac{n+m}{2}\right] w\left[l+\frac{-n+m}{2}\right].$$

Note that this correlation sequence is symmetric, $\psi[m,n] = \psi[-m,-n]$. The only assumptions required to make this approximation are that $x[n]$ be a complex Gaussian process and that the true PSD $P_{xx}(f)$ be relatively constant within the frequency band $f \pm B_s/2$, representing the bandwidth of the effective lag window. This latter assumption also permits the mean to be approximated as

$$\mathcal{E}\left\{\hat{P}_C(f)\right\} \approx P_{xx}(f)\int_{-1/2T}^{1/2T}\Omega_e(f)\,df = P_{xx}(f)w_e[0] = P_{xx}(f) \quad . \tag{5.62}$$

The equivalent statistical bandwidth B_s may be explicitly expressed as a function of the data and lag window functions as

$$B_s = \frac{\left[\int \Omega_e(f)\,df\right]^2}{\int \Omega_e^2(f)\,df} = \frac{\omega_e^2[0]}{T\displaystyle\sum_{m=-L}^{L}\omega_e^2[m]} = \frac{1}{T\displaystyle\sum_{m=-L}^{L}\phi^2[m]\omega^2[m]} \quad . \tag{5.63}$$

The stability-time-bandwidth product for the combined approach is obtained by substituting the variance equation (5.60), squared mean equation (5.62), and equivalent statistical bandwidth equation (5.63) to yield

$$QT_eB_s \approx \frac{\dfrac{1}{P}\displaystyle\sum_{p=-(P-1)}^{P-1}\left(1-\frac{|p|}{P}\right)T\displaystyle\sum_{m=-L}^{L}\omega^2[m]\psi[m,pS]}{\displaystyle\sum_{m=-L}^{L}\omega^2[m]\phi^2[m]} \quad . \tag{5.64}$$

This triple product is a function of the available data record length T_e, the number of segments P, the amount of overlap S, the data window $w[n]$, and the lag window $\omega[m]$.

To obtain the Blackman-Tukey PSD estimate, select one segment ($P = 1$), a lag window much less than the number of data points ($L \ll D = N$), and a rectangular data window ($w[n] = 1$ for $n = 0$ to $n = N - 1$). Nuttall [1981b] has shown that $QT_eB_s \approx 1$ in this case. To obtain the Welch periodogram, select $P = 2N/D-1$ segments, no lag weighting ($\omega[m] = 1$ for $|m| \leq L = D$), 62% overlap ($S = .38D$), and Hann weighting for the data window. It may similarly be shown in this case that $QT_eB_s \approx 1$. If 50% overlap is selected, then $QT_eB_s \approx 1.08$. An interesting combined approach is to select a rectangular data window ($w[n] = 1$), no overlap ($S = D$), half the number of segments as the Welch periodogram, and lag window reshaping to obtain an effective lag window $w_e[m]$ which is a Hann weighting, as illustrated by Fig. 5.9. A flowchart of the four steps of the Nuttall-Carter combined PSD estimator is provided in Fig. 5.10. Nuttall and Carter [1982] have shown, using Eq. (5.64), that these conditions will yield $QT_eB_s \approx 1$. This special case of the combined approach will therefore have the same statistical behavior for a given time-bandwidth product T_eB_s as the popular Welch periodogram. However, it requires about half the computational effort of the Welch method because it uses the FFT for half as many segments as the Welch method and no multiplications for data windowing the segments are required.

```
• COMPUTE BARTLETT PERIODOGRAM (Sec. 5.7.2)
    No segment overlap
    Rectangular data window

• INVERSE FFT OF PERIODOGRAM
    Yields correlation estimate

• WINDOW THE CORRELATION ESTIMATE
    Use lag window reshaping, Eq. (5.63)

• FFT OF WINDOWED CORRELATION
    Final PSD estimate
```

Figure 5.10   Flowchart of the Nuttall-Carter combined method.

5.9   APPLICATION TO SUNSPOT NUMBERS

An interesting application of classical spectral estimation that has a long historical basis has been the search for periodicities in sunspot numbers. Section 1.2 provided background information on this special data sequence. A preliminary periodogram analysis is shown in Fig. 5.11. The 1728 monthly sunspot numbers from Appendix I for the years 1841 to 1984 were processed using 24-year segments (288 samples per segment), 12 year overlap (144 samples), and a Hamming data window for each segment. It is apparent from Fig. 5.11 that there are no significant features at frequencies higher than 1 sunspot cycle per year. Although not shown, this lack of features is also borne out by the Blackman-Tukey spectral estimator and by the autoregressive spectral estimator (this method is presented in Chaps. 7 and 8). A large 0-Hz component, due to the positive numerical property of the sunspot

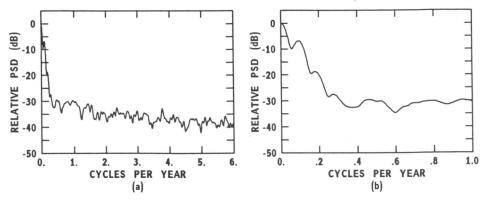

Figure 5.11   (a) Periodogram of monthly sunspot numbers for years 1841–
1984. (b) Expansion of the frequency interval within 0 to 1 cycle/year.

numbers, is apparent in Fig. 5.11. The classical 11-year sunspot period (frequency
of .09 cycle per year) is also clearly apparent in this figure.

In order to study the details in the spectrum between 0 and 1 cycle per
year, the monthly sunspot numbers were filtered by a low-pass filter, decimated
by a factor of 6 to reduce the sample rate to twice yearly, and finally filtered by
a high-pass filter. Linear-phase filter designs using the Parks-McClellan program
5.1 in *Programs for Digital Signal Processing* [1979] were used to create the low-
and high-pass filters. The low-pass filter had 49 coefficients and a transition zone
from .5 to 1.0 cycle per year, as shown in Fig. 5.12(a). This eliminated the high-
frequency noise in the monthly sunspot numbers. The output of the low-pass filter
was decimated by 6 to yield a twice-yearly sample rate. The decimated samples
were high-pass filtered to remove the biasing effect of the large DC component.
The high-pass filter had 51 coefficients and a transition zone from 0. to .0455 cycle
per year, as shown in Fig. 5.12(b). This transition zone was selected to permit the
detection of a possible 22-year harmonic period in the sunspot numbers, due to
the sunspot magnetic polarity, which is known to switch roughly every 22 years.
The resultant bandpass-filtered data record consisted of 230 samples of biyearly
data running from July 1855 to January 1970 (the decimated data samples fell on
January and July of each year).

Spectral estimates made from the filtered sunspot data by the classical methods are shown in Fig. 5.13. The periodogram used four segments of 46-year intervals
(92 samples per segment) and 23-year overlap (46 samples) between segments. A
Hamming window was applied to each segment. The PSD estimate by the correlogram method was based on a sequence of unbiased autocorrelation estimates from
lag 0 to lag 45 that had been weighted with a Hamming window. The periodogram
indicates two strong peaks at .095 cycle per year (10.5 years per cycle) and .194 cycle per year (5.16 years per cycle). The correlogram method positions these peaks
at .095 cycle per year and .188 cycle per year (5.32 years per cycle). Thus, the
second peak is probably a harmonic of the 10.5-year primary period of the sunspot

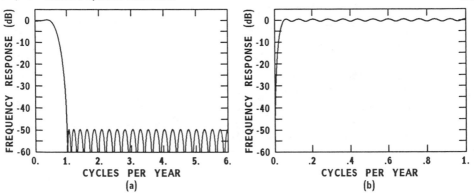

Figure 5.12   Log of frequency response magnitude. (a) 49-term linear-phase low-pass filter. (b) 51-term linear-phase high-pass filter.

activity. Other similar features between the spectra of Fig. 5.13 are also observable around .25 and .45 cycle per year.

Figure 5.13   Spectral estimates of the filtered sunspot numbers. (a) Periodogram. (b) Correlogram method with negative PSD values shown shaded. (c) Stack of single-segment periodograms.

A useful indicator of the nonstationary characteristics of sunspot numbers is shown by Fig. 5.13(c). Single-segment periodograms of 23-year intervals each are stacked one above the other. A 50-dB plotting range is depicted for each periodogram. The starting year for each segment is indicated along the abscissa. Observe that an overlap of 11.5 years between segments has been used. The two strong peaks do not stay at a fixed frequency, but instead tend to wander about the mean peak location indicated by Fig. 5.13(a) and (b). Thus, the use of spectral estimation methods based on the stationary assumption must be used cautiously when applied to the sunspot numbers.

5.10 CONCLUSION

Classical spectral estimation techniques that have been outlined in this chapter are among the most robust of the spectral estimation methods presented in this text. They may be employed for just about any signal and noise classes that have stationary properties, whereas alternative high-resolution methods, such as those to be presented in Chaps. 6–14, are robust for a restricted class of stationary signals. The classical methods typically employ the FFT algorithm and are, therefore, the most computationally efficient spectral estimation methods available. The PSD estimates are linearly proportional to the power of sinusoids present in the data; the methods of Chaps. 6–14 do not often have a linear relationship between spectral peaks and sinusoidal power.

The key disadvantage of the classical spectral estimation techniques is the distorting impact of sidelobe leakage due to the inherent windowing of finite data sets. Window weighting was shown to mitigate the effect of sidelobes at the expense of decreasing the spectral resolution. The resolution of the classical methods can be no better than the reciprocal of the data record duration, independent of the characteristics of the data. In order to improve the statistical stability of the spectral estimate, pseudo ensemble averaging by segmenting the data was introduced at the price of further decreasing the resolution. For a finite data record, trade-offs among resolution, stability (minimizing the estimate variance), and leakage suppression are necessary. Often, very short data records are forced upon us and practical needs for highest resolution may require that the entire data record be used in a single-segment analysis. This is done by sacrificing statistical stability. Alternative methods that may improve or maintain high resolution without sacrificing as much stability are the subject of the next chapter.

REFERENCES

Bartlett, M. S., Smoothing Periodograms from Time Series with Continuous Spectra, *Nature*, London, vol. 161, pp. 686–687, May 1948.

Blackman, R. B., and J. W. Tukey, *The Measurement of Power Spectra from the Point of View of Communication Engineering*, Dover Publications, Inc., New York, 1958; also appeared in the January 1958 and March 1958 *Bell Syst. Tech. J.*

Daniell, P. J.,Discussion of "On the Theoretical Specification and Sampling Properties of Autocorrelated Time-Series," *J. R. Stat. Soc.*, ser. B, vol. 8, pp. 88–90, 1946.

Digital Signal Processing Committee, ed., *Programs for Digital Signal Processing*, IEEE Press, New York, 1979.

Gardner, W. A., *Statistical Spectral Analysis: A Non-Probabilistic Theory*, Prentice-Hall, Inc., Englewood Cliffs, N. J., 1987.

Geçkinli, N. C., and D. Yavuz, *Discrete Fourier Transformation and Its Applications to Power Spectra Estimation*, Elsevier Scientific Publishing Company, Amsterdam, 1983.

Harris, F. J., On the Use of Windows for Harmonic Analysis with the Discrete Fourier Transform, *Proc. IEEE*, vol. 66, pp. 51–83, January 1978.

Jenkins, G. M., and D. G. Watts, *Spectral Analysis and Its Applications*, Holden-Day, Inc., San Francisco, 1968.

Jones, R. H., A Reappraisal of the Periodogram in Spectral Analysis, *Technometrics*, vol. 7, pp. 531–542, November 1965.

Koopmans, L. H., *The Spectral Analysis of Time Series*, Academic Press, Inc., New York, 1974.

Nuttall, Albert H., Spectral Estimation by Means of Overlapped Fast Fourier Transform Processing of Windowed Data, *Naval Underwater Systems Center Technical Report 4169*, New London, Conn., October 1971.

Nuttall, Albert H., Some Windows with Very Good Sidelobe Behavior, *IEEE Trans. Acoust. Speech Signal Process.*, vol. ASSP-29, pp. 84–91, February 1981a.

Nuttall, Albert H., Spectral Analysis via Quadratic Frequency-Smoothing of Fourier-Transformed, Overlapped, Weighted Data Segments, *Naval Underwater Systems Center Technical Report 6459*, New London, Conn., June 1981b.

Nuttall, A. H., and G. C. Carter, Spectral Estimation Using Combined Time and Lag Weighting, *Proc. IEEE*, vol. 70, pp. 1115–1125, September 1982.

Oppenheim, A. V., and R. W. Schafer, *Digital Signal Processing*, Prentice-Hall, Inc., Englewood Cliffs, N. J., 1975.

Otnes, R. K., and L. Enochson, *Applied Time Series Analysis*, John Wiley & Sons, Inc., New York, 1978.

Rabiner, L. R., and Ben Gold, *Theory and Application of Digital Signal Processing*, Prentice-Hall, Inc., Englewood Cliffs, N. J., 1975.

Rader, C. M., An Improved Algorithm for High Speed Autocorrelation with Applications to Spectral Estimation, *IEEE Trans. Audio Electroacoust.*, vol. AU-18, pp. 439–442, December 1970.

Thompson, D. J., Spectrum Estimation Techniques for Characterization and Development of WT4 Waveguide-II, *Bell Syst. Tech. J.*, vol. 56, pp. 1983–2005, December 1977; Part I, vol. 50, pp. 1769–1815, November 1977.

Van Schooneveld, C., and D. J. Frijling, Spectral Analysis: On the Usefulness of Linear Tapering for Leakage Suppression, *IEEE Trans. Acoust. Speech Signal Process.*, vol. ASSP-29, pp. 323-329, April 1981.

Welch, P. D., The Use of Fast Fourier Transform for the Estimation of Power Spectra: A Method Based on Time Averaging over Short Modified Periodograms, *IEEE Trans. Audio Electroacoust.*, vol. AU-15, pp. 70-73, June 1967.

Yuen, C. K., and D. Fraser, *Digital Spectral Analysis*, Pitman Publishing Ltd., London, 1979.

PROBLEMS

1. Show that the Bartlett periodogram estimator [Eq. (5.36)] can be expressed in the matrix form

$$\hat{P}_{\mathrm{B}}f) = \frac{T}{DP} \mathbf{e}_D^H(f) \left(\sum_{p=0}^{P} \mathbf{x}^{(p)} \mathbf{x}^{(p)\,H} \right) \mathbf{e}_D(f) \quad ,$$

   in which $\mathbf{e}_D(f)$ is a complex sinusoid vector [see definition (3.21)] and $\mathbf{x}^{(p)} = \left(x[pD] \quad x[pD+1] \quad \ldots \quad x[pD+D-1] \right)^T$ is the vector of data samples for the pth segment.

2. Prove the bias result shown in the text for Eq. (5.44).

3. Show that the matrix (5.25) of the biased autocorrelation estimate may alternatively be written as

$$\check{\mathbf{R}}_L = \frac{1}{N} \sum_{k=0}^{N-1} \mathbf{x}_L[k] \mathbf{x}_L[k]^H \quad ,$$

   in which $\mathbf{x}_L[k] = \left(x[k] \quad x[k-1] \quad \ldots \quad x[k-L] \right)^T$ is a data vector. Assume $x[n] = 0$ for $n < 0$ or $n > N - 1$.

4. Develop a more computationally efficient subroutine CORRELATION that uses the FFT to compute the correlation estimates.

5. Show that for real $\hat{r}_{xx}[m]$ that

$$\hat{P}_{\mathrm{BT}}(f) = T\,\hat{r}_{xx}[0] + 2T \sum_{m=1}^{M} \hat{r}_{xx}[m] \cos(2\pi f mT) \quad .$$

6. Derive the B_s and B_e bandwidths for the windows of Table 5.1, normalized to an FFT bin of $1/NT$ Hz. What is the ratio $\alpha = B_s/B_e$ for each window?

7. What is the quality ratio Q for the sample spectrum of Appendix 4.A? What is the $QT_e B_s$ product for the sample spectrum?

8. The correlogram method spectral estimate of Fig. 5.4 possessed negative PSD lobes. Choose or design a window that will yield only a positive PSD for all frequencies for the test data case. Substitute this window in program CORRELOGRAMPSD. Plot

the resultant spectral estimate. How does this estimate compare with the estimate of Fig. 5.4?

9. Assuming N data samples $x[0], \ldots, x[N-1]$, show that the correlogram method PSD estimator

$$\check{P}_{xx}(f) = T \sum_{m=-(N-1)}^{N-1} \check{r}_{xx}[m] \exp(-j2\pi fmT) \quad ,$$

that uses the biased autocorrelation estimator for the maximum number of posssible lags, and the sample spectrum

$$\tilde{P}_{xx}(f) = \frac{T}{N} \left| \sum_{n=0}^{N-1} x[n] \exp(-j2\pi fnT) \right|^2$$

are identical.

APPENDIX 5.A
PROGRAM TO COMPUTE CORRELATION ESTIMATES

Subroutine CORRELATION will compute either the unbiased or the biased auto-correlation or cross correlation estimate for complex data (see Sec. 5.5), depending on the value selected for parameter MODE. If array X is passed in parameter position Y, as in CALL CORRELATION (N,LAG,MODE,X,X,R), then the autocorrelation is computed; otherwise, the cross correlation is computed. Only correlation estimates for positive lag indices are calculated. To obtain the negative lag indices of the autocorrelation, simply conjugate the autocorrelations returned by the subroutine. To obtain the negative lag indices of the cross correlation, simply reverse the X and Y vectors, call the subroutine again, and then conjugate the result. This is a consequence of the property $r_{xy}[-m] = r_{yx}^*[m]$. Use Appendix IV in order to convert this program to process real-valued data.

If $N = 64$, $LAG = 15$, and $MODE = 0$, the 16-term autocorrelation sequence estimated from the 64-point test sequence of Appendix II is

```
R[ 0] = (  1.780459,  0.000000)
R[ 1] = (  0.325858,  1.529764)
R[ 2] = ( -1.341396,  0.772292)
R[ 3] = ( -1.012166, -0.989743)
R[ 4] = (  0.534418, -1.295556)
R[ 5] = (  1.444954,  0.189344)
R[ 6] = (  0.226535,  1.458697)
R[ 7] = ( -1.327125,  0.588727)
R[ 8] = ( -0.908952, -1.137790)
R[ 9] = (  0.769808, -1.127676)
R[10] = (  1.298158,  0.388247)
R[11] = ( -0.029651,  1.296811)
```

```
            R[12] = ( -1.235431,  0.412799)
            R[13] = ( -0.629708, -1.094549)
            R[14] = (  0.824489, -0.898308)
            R[15] = (  1.021054,  0.549560)  .
```

```
        SUBROUTINE CORRELATION (N,LAG,MODE,X,Y,RO,R)
C
C   This program computes either the unbiased or biased complex correlation
C   estimates between complex data sample arrays X and Y.  If X=Y, then the
C   autocorrelation is computed.
C
C   Input Parameters:
C
C     N    - Number of data samples in arrays X and Y (integer)
C     LAG  - Number of correlation lags to compute [ lags from  0  to  LAG
C            are computed and stored in RO and R(1) to R(LAG) ] (integer)
C     MODE - Set to 0 for unbiased correlation estimates; otherwise, biased
C            correlation estimates are computed (integer)
C     X    - Array of complex data samples X(1) through X(N)
C     Y    - Array of complex data samples Y(1) through Y(N)
C
C   Output Parameters:
C
C     RO   - Complex correlation estimate for lag 0
C     R    - Array of complex correlation estimates for lags 1 to LAG
C
C   Notes:
C
C     External arrays X,Y must be dimensioned .GE. N and array R must be
C     dimensioned .GE. LAG in the calling program.
C
        COMPLEX X(1),Y(1),R(1),RO,SUM
        DO 30 K=0,LAG
          NK=N-K
          SUM=(0.,0.)
          DO 10 J=1,NK
10          SUM=SUM+X(J+K)*CONJG(Y(J))
          IF (K .NE. 0)  GO TO 20
          RO=SUM/FLOAT(N)
          GO TO 30
20        IF (MODE .EQ. 0)  R(K)=SUM/FLOAT(N-K)     ! Eq.  (5.9)
          IF (MODE .NE. 0)  R(K)=SUM/FLOAT(N)       ! Eqs. (5.13),(5.19)
30      CONTINUE
        RETURN
        END
```

APPENDIX 5.B
PROGRAM TO COMPUTE THE CORRELOGRAM METHOD PSD ESTIMATE

Subroutine CORRELOGRAMPSD computes a set of autospectral or cross-spectral estimates by the Blackman-Tukey correlogram method of PSD estimation, based on Eq. (5.27).   The FFT is used to efficiently evaluate the PSD transform.   If array X is passed in parameter position Y, as in CALL CORRELOGRAMPSD (N,LAG,T,X,X,PSD), then the autospectrum is computed; otherwise, the cross spectrum is computed. Real data sequences are processed by setting the imaginary part of the data to zero.

Using $N = 64$, $LAG = 15$, $T = 1.$, and the 64-point test sequence of Appendix II, the following selected PSD values were generated

```
PSD(   1) =  0.131417E+00
PSD(1000) =  0.795428E+01
PSD(2000) =  0.106389E+00
PSD(3000) =  0.219200E+00
PSD(4000) = -0.344072E-01
PSD(4096) =  0.132312E+00 .
```

```
      SUBROUTINE CORRELOGRAMPSD (N,LAG,T,X,Y,PSD)
C
C   Note that Rxy[-k] is computed as Conjugate(Ryx[k]).
C
C   Input Parameters:
C
C     N   - Number of data samples
C     LAG - Highest lag index to compute
C     T   - Sample interval in seconds
C     X   - Array of complex data samples X(1) to X(N)
C     Y   - Array of complex data samples Y(1) to Y(N)
C
C   Output Parameters:
C
C     PSD - Array of real power spectral density estimate values
C
C   Notes:
C
C     External arrays X and Y must be dimensioned .GE. N and array PSD
C     must be dimensioned .GE. NPSD in the calling program.   Internal
C     array W must be dimensioned .GE. NPSD,  arrays R and WINDOW must
C     be dimensioned .GE. LAG. External subroutines used:  CORRELATION
C     (Appendix 5.A), PREFFT and FFT (Appendix 2.C).
C
      PARAMETER (NPSD=4096, PI=3.141592654)
      COMPLEX X(1),Y(1),PSD(1),W(NPSD),R(64),RO
      REAL WINDOW(64)
C  Can use any window here
      DO 10 K=1,LAG
10       WINDOW(K)=0.538+0.462*COS(PI*FLOAT(K)/FLOAT(LAG))
      CALL CORRELATION (N,LAG,0,X,Y,RO,R)
      PSD(1)=RO
      DO 20 K=1,LAG
20       PSD(K+1)=R(K)*WINDOW(K)
      CALL CORRELATION (N,LAG,0,Y,X,RO,R)
      DO 30 K=1,LAG
30       PSD(NPSD+1-K)=CONJG(R(K))*WINDOW(K)
      DO 40 K=LAG+2,NPSD-LAG
40       PSD(K)=(0.,0.)
```

```
CALL PREFFT (NPSD,0,NEXP,W)
CALL FFT (NPSD,0,T,NEXP,W,PSD)
RETURN
END
```

APPENDIX 5.C
PROGRAM TO COMPUTE THE PERIODOGRAM METHOD PSD ESTIMATE

Subroutine PERIODOGRAM computes a set of autospectral or cross-spectral estimates by the Welch periodogram method, based on Eq. (5.43). The FFT is used to evaluate the periodogram. If array X is passed in parameter position Y, as in CALL PERIODOGRAM (N,NSHIFT,NSAMP,T,X,X,NSEG,PSD), then the autospectrum is computed; otherwise, the cross spectrum is computed. Real data sequences are processed by setting the imaginary part of the input data array to zero.

Using $N = 64$, $NSHIFT = 16$, $NSAMP = 32$, $T = 1.$, and the 64-point test sequence of Appendix II, the following selected PSD values were generated

```
PSD(   1) = 0.341366E-03
PSD(1000) = 0.989954E+00
PSD(2000) = 0.812411E-02
PSD(3000) = 0.505813E-01
PSD(4000) = 0.378735E-03
PSD(4096) = 0.336007E-03   .
```

```
      SUBROUTINE PERIODOGRAM (N,NSHIFT,NSAMP,T,X,Y,NSEG,PSD)
C
C    This subroutine computes the averaged periodogram based on Eq.(5.43).
C    It computes the nearest integer number of segments, NSEG.  A Hamming
C    window is used, although other windows may be substituted from Table
C    5.1 .  NPSD power spectral density estimate values over the frequency
C    range -1/2T to 1/2T, where T is the sample interval in seconds, are
C    returned.  Some additional computational efficiency may be gained in
C    the autospectral estimate by eliminating the lines of code that deal
C    with data vector Y.  The PSD is complex, in general, for cross PSD.
C    The PSD is real for auto PSD.
C
C    Input Parameters:
C
C      N      - Number of data samples
C      NSHIFT - Number of samples shift between segments
C      NSAMP  - Number of samples per segment (must be even)
C      T      - Sample interval in seconds
C      X      - Array of complex samples X(1) to X(N)
C      Y      - Array of complex samples Y(1) to Y(N)
C
C    Output Parameters:
C
C      NSEG   - Number of segments averaged
```

```
C     PSD    - Real array of NPSD power spectral density estimate values
C
C   Notes:
C
C     External arrays X,Y must be dimensioned .GE. N and array PSD must be
C     dimensioned .GE. NPSD in the calling program.    Internal arrays W,
C     XSEG,YSEG must be dimensioned .GE. NPSD and array WINDOW must be
C     dimensioned .GE. NSAMP . External subroutines used: PREFFT and FFT
C     in Appendix 2.C .
C
        PARAMETER NPSD=4096           ! Must be a power of 2
        COMPLEX X(1),Y(1),PSD(1),W(NPSD),XSEG(NPSD),YSEG(NPSD),TEMP
        REAL WINDOW(127)
        PI2=8.*ATAN(1.)
        CALL PREFFT (NPSD,0,NEXP,W)
C   A Hamming window is used.  The next two lines may be replaced by any
C   other desired window function
        DO 10 K=1,NSAMP
10      WINDOW(K)=0.538+0.462*COS(PI2*(-.5+FLOAT(K-1)/FLOAT(NSAMP-1)))
C   Compute the number of whole segments NSEG such that NSEG .LE. N
        NSEG=(N-NSAMP)/NSHIFT + 1
        DO 50 K=1,NSEG
          DO 20 J=1,NSAMP
            INDEX=J+(K-1)*NSHIFT
            XSEG(J)=X(INDEX)*WINDOW(J)
20          YSEG(J)=Y(INDEX)*WINDOW(J)
          DO 30 J=NSAMP+1,NPSD
            XSEG(J)=(0.,0.)
30          YSEG(J)=(0.,0.)
          CALL FFT (NPSD,0,T,NEXP,W,XSEG)
          CALL FFT (NPSD,0,T,NEXP,W,YSEG)
          DO 40 J=1,NPSD
            IF (K .EQ. 1)  PSD(J)=XSEG(J)*CONJG(YSEG(J))
40          IF (K .NE. 1)  PSD(J)=PSD(J)+XSEG(J)*CONJG(YSEG(J))
50      CONTINUE
C   Need to add window energy correction factor
        DO 60 K=1,NPSD
60      PSD(K)=PSD(K)/FLOAT(NSEG*NSAMP)
        RETURN
        END
```

6

PARAMETRIC MODELS OF RANDOM PROCESSES

6.1 INTRODUCTION

The power spectral density (PSD) was defined in Chap. 4 as the discrete-time Fourier transform of an infinite autocorrelation sequence (ACS). This transform relationship between the PSD and ACS may be considered as a *nonparametric* description of the second-order statistics of a random process. Other nonparametric spectral estimators that are strictly functions of the ACS are considered in Chaps. 12 and 13. A *parametric* description of the second-order statistics may also be devised by assuming a time-series model of the random process. The PSD of the time-series model will then be a function of the model parameters rather than the ACS. A special class of models, driven by white noise processes and possessing rational system functions, is described in this chapter. This class includes the autoregressive (AR) process model, the moving average (MA) process model, and the autoregressive–moving average (ARMA) process model. The output processes of this class of models have power spectral densities that are totally described in terms of the model parameters and the variance of the white noise process. The parameters and the white noise variance are obtained from the autocorrelation sequence through relationships described in this chapter. Chapters 8–10 describe methods to estimate the model parameters and the white noise variance from a finite data record.

The motivation for parametric models of random processes is the ability to achieve better PSD estimators based upon the model than produced by classical spectral estimators. Better spectral resolution is one key improvement area. Both the periodogram and correlogram methods of Chap. 5 yield PSD estimates from a windowed set of data or ACS estimates. The unavailable data or unestimated ACS values outside the window are implicitly zero, normally an unrealistic assumption that leads to distortions in the spectral estimate. Some knowledge about the process from which the data samples are taken is often available. This information may be used to construct a model that approximates the process that generated the observed time sequence. Such models will make more realistic assumptions about the data outside the window other than the zero assumption. Thus, the need for window functions can be eliminated, along with their distorting impact. The degree of improvement in resolution and spectral fidelity, if any, is determined by the appropriateness of the selected model and the ability to fit the measured data or the ACS (known or estimated from the data) with a few model parameters.

Given the PSD or the ACS, one must require filter stability and/or causality in order to obtain a unique model. This topic receives special attention in Sec. 6.6.

6.2 SUMMARY

The parametric approach to spectral estimation involves three steps. In step one, an appropriate parametric time-series model is selected to represent the measured data record. This chapter is concerned with three types of parametric time-series models: autoregressive, moving average, and combined autoregressive–moving average. In step two, an estimate of the parameters of the model is made. In step three, the estimated parameters are inserted into the theoretical power spectral density expression appropriate for that model.

KEY RELATIONSHIPS	ARMA	AR	MA
TIME SERIES DEFINITION	6.1	6.13	6.11
AUTOCORRELATION SEQUENCE	6.29	6.31	6.35
PSD (based on parameters)*	6.8	6.14	6.12
PSD (based on ACS)	–	6.33	6.36
AR(∞) EQUIVALENCE	6.17	–	6.17
MA(∞) EQUIVALENCE	6.24	6.24	–

*See also subroutine ARMAPSD in Appendix 6.A

Table 6.1   Summary of Key Relationships for Parametric Models

A summary of the key equation relationships for AR, MA, and ARMA time-series models that are developed in this chapter are provided in Table 6.1. Appendix 6.A contains computer program ARMAPSD that computes the PSD values, given the appropriate model parameters. The selection of one of the three models of Table 6.1 requires some knowledge concerning the likely spectral shape. If spectra with sharp peaks, but no deep nulls, are required, then the AR model is appropriate. If spectra with deep nulls, but no sharp peaks, are required, then the MA model is appropriate. The ARMA model can represent, in general, both kinds of extremes. If the spectral shape is reasonably modeled by any two or more of the three models, then the model that results in the fewest number of parameters should probably be selected. This is the principle of parsimony promoted by Box and Jenkins [1970]. The reasoning for this principle is that better estimation statistics are usually possible if the number of parameters to be estimated is minimized. The computational burden to estimate AR parameters is often significantly less than required to estimate MA or ARMA parameters. Thus, an AR time series may still be the model of choice, even though it may not be the model of least number of parameters. The question of how to select the number of parameters, once a model is selected, is left to Chaps. 8 and 10.

6.3   AR, MA, AND ARMA RANDOM PROCESS MODELS

A time-series model that approximates many discrete-time deterministic and stochastic processes encountered in practice is represented by the filter linear difference equation of complex coefficients

$$x[n] = -\sum_{k=1}^{p} a[k]x[n-k] + \sum_{k=0}^{q} b[k]u[n-k] \tag{6.1}$$

$$= \sum_{k=0}^{\infty} h[k]u[n-k] \quad , \tag{6.2}$$

in which $x[n]$ is the output sequence of a causal filter ($h[k] = 0$ for $k < 0$) that models the observed data and $u[n]$ is an input driving sequence. The assumption $b[0] = 1$ can be made without loss of generality because the input $u[n]$ can always be scaled to account for any filter gain. The system function $\mathsf{H}(z)$ between input and output was shown [see Eq. (2.17)] to have the rational form

$$\mathsf{H}(z) = \frac{\mathsf{B}(z)}{\mathsf{A}(z)} \quad , \tag{6.3}$$

for which the polynomials are

$$A(z) = 1 + \sum_{k=1}^{p} a[k]z^{-k} \tag{6.4}$$

$$B(z) = 1 + \sum_{k=1}^{q} b[k]z^{-k} \tag{6.5}$$

$$H(z) = 1 + \sum_{k=1}^{\infty} h[k]z^{-k}. \tag{6.6}$$

Both polynomials $A(z)$ and $B(z)$ will be assumed to have all of their zeros within the unit circle in the z-plane to guarantee that $H(z)$ is a stable minimum-phase causal filter.

The z-transform of the output sequence $x[n]$ is related to the z-transform of the input random process $u[n]$ by

$$P_{xx}(z) = P_{uu}(z)H(z)H^*(1/z^*) = P_{uu}(z)\frac{B(z)B^*(1/z^*)}{A(z)A^*(1/z^*)} \quad , \tag{6.7}$$

as shown by Eq. (4.42). The input driving process $u[n]$ is not usually available for purposes of spectral analysis. Many things could be assumed for the driving process. It could be a unit impulse, an impulse train, or white noise. If an impulse is assumed, then the methods of Chap. 11 would apply. Here it will be assumed that the driving sequence is a white noise process of zero mean and variance ρ_w, so that $P_{uu}(z) = \rho_w$. An *autoregressive–moving average* (ARMA) model for the time series $x[n]$ is determined by Eq. (6.1), with $u[n]$ a white noise sequence. The ARMA model is illustrated in Fig. 6.1(a). The $a[k]$ parameters form the autoregressive portion of the ARMA model. The $b[k]$ parameters form the moving average portion of the ARMA model. The ARMA power spectral density is obtained by substituting $z = \exp(j2\pi fT)$ into Eq. (6.7) and scaling by the sampling interval T [see Eq. (4.43)], yielding

$$P_{\mathrm{ARMA}}(f) = T\rho_w \left|\frac{B(f)}{A(f)}\right|^2 = T\rho_w \frac{\mathbf{e}_q^H(f)\mathbf{bb}^H\mathbf{e}_q(f)}{\mathbf{e}_p^H(f)\mathbf{aa}^H\mathbf{e}_p(f)} \quad , \tag{6.8}$$

in which the polynomials $A(f)$ and $B(f)$ are defined as

$$A(f) = 1 + \sum_{k=1}^{p} a[k]\exp(-j2\pi fkT)$$

$$B(f) = 1 + \sum_{k=1}^{q} b[k]\exp(-j2\pi fkT) \quad , \tag{6.9}$$

Figure 6.1   Time-series models that have rational system functions.   (a) Autoregressive-moving average filter of order (p, q). (b) ARMA with observation noise. (c) Moving average filter of order q. (d) Autoregressive filter of order p.

and the complex sinusoid vectors $\mathbf{e}_q(f)$ and $\mathbf{e}_p(f)$ and parameter vectors $\mathbf{a}$ and $\mathbf{b}$ are defined as

$$
\mathbf{e}_p(f) = \begin{pmatrix} 1 \\ \exp(j2\pi fT) \\ \vdots \\ \exp(j2\pi fpT) \end{pmatrix} \quad , \quad \mathbf{a} = \begin{pmatrix} 1 \\ a[1] \\ \vdots \\ a[p] \end{pmatrix} \quad ,
$$

$$
\mathbf{e}_q(f) = \begin{pmatrix} 1 \\ \exp(j2\pi fT) \\ \vdots \\ \exp(j2\pi fqT) \end{pmatrix} \quad , \quad \mathbf{b} = \begin{pmatrix} 1 \\ b[1] \\ \vdots \\ b[q] \end{pmatrix} \quad .
$$

(6.10)

The ARMA power spectral density is evaluated over the range $-1/2T \leq f \leq 1/2T$.

The notation ARMA(p,q) is often used for convenience to indicate an ARMA model of *order p* autoregressive parameters and *order q* moving average parameters. Specification of the AR parameters, the MA parameters, and the white noise variance ρ_w entirely characterizes the ARMA PSD of process $x[n]$. Any additive *observation* noise present in the measured sequence must be modeled as a *separate* and *distinguishable* noise source from the *driving* noise source that is an integral part of the ARMA model, as illustrated in Fig. 6.1(b). Effects of observation noise are considered in Chap. 8.

If all the autoregressive parameters are zero, except $a[0] = 1$, then

$$
x[n] = \sum_{k=1}^{q} b[k]u[n-k] + u[n]
$$

(6.11)

is strictly a moving average (MA) process of order q, or simply an MA(q). The MA power spectral density, obtained by setting $p = 0$ in Eq. (6.8), is

$$
P_{\mathrm{MA}}(f) = T\rho_w \, |B(f)|^2 = T\rho_w \mathbf{e}_q^H(f)\mathbf{b}\mathbf{b}^H\mathbf{e}_q(f) \quad .
$$

(6.12)

The MA model is illustrated in Fig. 6.1(c).

If all the moving average parameters are zero, except $b[0] = 1$, then

$$
x[n] = -\sum_{k=1}^{p} a[k]x[n-k] + u[n]
$$

(6.13)

is strictly an autoregressive (AR) process of order p, or simply an AR(p). The AR power spectral density, obtained by setting $q = 0$ in Eq. (6.8), is

$$
P_{\mathrm{AR}}(f) = \frac{T\rho_w}{|A(f)|^2} = \frac{T\rho_w}{\mathbf{e}_p^H(f)\mathbf{a}\mathbf{a}^H\mathbf{e}_p(f)} \quad .
$$

(6.14)

Figure 6.2 Typical parametric model spectra. (a) AR(4) spectrum. (b) MA(4) spectrum. (c) ARMA(4,4) spectrum.

The AR model is illustrated in Fig. 6.1(d). The ARMA, MA, and AR power spectral densities may be evaluated, given the parameters and variance ρ_w, with subroutine ARMAPSD in Appendix 6.A.

Figure 6.2 illustrates typical ARMA, AR, and MA spectra. The sharp peaks that characterize autoregressive spectra and the deep nulls that characterize moving average spectra are apparent in this figure. The ARMA spectrum shown in Fig. 6.2(c) is the result of combining the AR and MA of Fig. 6.2(a) and (b). The ARMA spectrum is able to model both sharp peaks and deep nulls. Other insight into the spectral shape characteristics of these parametric models can be found in Gutowski et al. [1978] and Kay [1987].

6.4 RELATIONSHIPS AMONG AR, MA, AND ARMA MODEL PARAMETERS

Given an AR, MA, or ARMA model of a finite number of parameters, it is possible to express that model in terms of the other two models. An ARMA or MA process can be represented by a unique AR model of generally infinite order. An ARMA or AR process can be represented by a unique MA model of generally infinite order. This concept is important because any of the three models may be selected and still obtain a reasonable approximation if a sufficiently large order is used. There may be certain algorithmic benefits to estimating the parameters of one model from the data and then calculating the parameters of another model from the parameters of the first model. The AR model is a particular case for which many efficient algorithms exist. As will be shown in Chap. 10, a large order AR estimate is often the first step in an MA or an ARMA estimation algorithm.

Let

$$C(z) = 1 + \sum_{k=1}^{\infty} c[k]z^{-k} \tag{6.15}$$

represent the denominator polynomial of an $AR(\infty)$ model. The $c[k]$ parameters of the $AR(\infty)$ model that are equivalent to an $ARMA(p,q)$ model are obtained by equating

$$\frac{B(z)}{A(z)} = \frac{1}{C(z)} \quad , \tag{6.16}$$

or by forming the inverse z-transform of $C(z)B(z) = A(z)$. This will yield

$$c[n] = \begin{cases} 1 & \text{for } n = 0 \\ -\displaystyle\sum_{k=1}^{q} b[k]c[n-k] + a[n] & \text{for } 1 \le n \le p \\ -\displaystyle\sum_{k=1}^{q} b[k]c[n-k] & \text{for } n > p \end{cases} \tag{6.17}$$

with initial conditions $c[-1] = \cdots = c[-q] = 0$. Conversely, if given the parameters of an $AR(\infty)$ model that is known to be equivalent to an $ARMA(p,q)$ model, then the MA parameters may be recovered by solving

$$\begin{pmatrix} c[p] & c[p-1] & \cdots & c[p-q+1] \\ c[p+1] & c[p] & \cdots & c[p-q+2] \\ \vdots & \vdots & \ddots & \vdots \\ c[p+q-1] & c[p+q-2] & \cdots & c[p] \end{pmatrix} \begin{pmatrix} b[1] \\ b[2] \\ \vdots \\ b[q] \end{pmatrix} = - \begin{pmatrix} c[p+1] \\ c[p+2] \\ \vdots \\ c[p+q] \end{pmatrix} . \tag{6.18}$$

for the $b[k]$ terms using relationship (6.17) over the range $p + 1 \le n \le p + q$. The matrix of $c[n]$ parameters in Eq. (6.18) is Toeplitz. Subroutine TOEPLITZ in Appendix 3.D may be used to obtain the solution. Once the MA parameters have been found, then the AR parameters of the ARMA model may be recovered by the convolution

$$a[n] = c[n] + \sum_{k=1}^{q} b[k]c[n-k] \quad , \tag{6.19}$$

for $1 \le n \le p$. Fast convolution algorithms based on the FFT are available. Equation (6.19) is derivable from Eq. (6.17).

Note that only the autoregressive parameters $c[1], \ldots, c[p+q]$ of the $AR(\infty)$ model are used by Eqs. (6.18) and (6.19). If the parameters $c[k]$ for $k > p + q$ are truncated to zero, then the resulting truncated $AR(p+q)$ model can only *approximate* the $ARMA(p,q)$ model from which it came. It approximates the ARMA in the sense that the inverse ARMA polynomial

$$G(z) = \frac{1}{H(z)} = \frac{A(z)}{B(z)} = 1 + \sum_{k=1}^{\infty} g[k]z^{-k} \tag{6.20}$$

Figure 6.3   Finite AR approximation to an ARMA model. (a) ARMA(4,4) spectrum. (b) Spectrum of AR(25) approximation. (c) Spectrum of AR(50) approximation.

and the truncated AR polynomial

$$C(z) = 1 + \sum_{k=1}^{p+q} c[k] z^{-k} \qquad (6.21)$$

match, i.e., $g[k] = c[k]$, only for $1 \leq k \leq p + q$. This approximation of a rational function of finite–order polynomials with a polynomial of higher order is the Padé approximation problem [Padé, 1892; Weiss and McDonough, 1963]. This procedure will be useful in Chap. 10 for deriving approximations of ARMA models from high–order AR models. Figure 6.3 illustrates typical high-order AR approximations to a low-order ARMA model.

Figure 6.4   Finite MA approximation to an ARMA model. (a) ARMA(4,4) spectrum. (b) Spectrum of MA(25) approximation. (c) Spectrum of MA(50) approximation.

In a similar manner, let

$$D(z) = 1 + \sum_{k=1}^{\infty} d[k]z^{-k} \tag{6.22}$$

represent the numerator polynomial of an $MA(\infty)$ model. The $b[k]$ parameters of the $MA(\infty)$ model that are equivalent to an $ARMA(p,q)$ model are obtained by equating

$$\frac{B(z)}{A(z)} = D(z) \quad , \tag{6.23}$$

or by forming the inverse z–transform of $D(z)A(z) = B(z)$. This will yield

$$d[n] = \begin{cases} 1 & \text{for } n = 0 \\ -\sum_{k=1}^{p} a[k]d[n-k] + b[n] & \text{for } 1 \leq n \leq q \\ -\sum_{k=1}^{p} a[k]d[n-k] & \text{for } n > q. \end{cases} \tag{6.24}$$

Expressions similar to Eqs. (6.18) and (6.19) may be formed (see the Problems). Figure 6.4 illustrates typical MA approximations to an ARMA model.

6.5 RELATIONSHIP OF AR, MA, AND ARMA PARAMETERS TO THE AUTOCORRELATION SEQUENCE

This section is concerned with the determination of the model parameters when the autocorrelation sequence is known. If Eq. (6.1) is multiplied by $x^*[n-m]$ and the expectation taken, then the result is

$$\mathcal{E}\{x[n]x^*[n-m]\} = -\sum_{k=1}^{p} a[k]\mathcal{E}\{x[n-k]x^*[n-m]\} + \sum_{k=0}^{q} b[k]\mathcal{E}\{u[n-k]x^*[n-m]\} \tag{6.25}$$

or

$$r_{xx}[m] = -\sum_{k=1}^{p} a[k]r_{xx}[m-k] + \sum_{k=0}^{q} b[k]r_{ux}[m-k] \quad . \tag{6.26}$$

The cross correlation $r_{ux}[i]$ between the input and the output can be expressed in terms of the $h[k]$ parameters of Eq. (6.6) by using Eq. (6.2) to yield

$$r_{ux}[i] = \mathcal{E}\{u[n+i]x^*[n]\} = \mathcal{E}\left\{ u[n+i]\left[u^*[n] + \sum_{k=1}^{\infty} h^*[k]u^*[n-k] \right] \right\}$$

$$= r_{uu}[i] + \sum_{k=1}^{\infty} h^*[k]r_{uu}[i+k] \quad . \tag{6.27}$$

As $u[k]$ was assumed to be a white noise process, then

$$r_{ux}[i] = \begin{cases} 0 & \text{for } i > 0 \\ \rho_w & \text{for } i = 0 \\ \rho_w h^*[-i] & \text{for } i < 0 \end{cases} \qquad (6.28)$$

The final relationship between the ARMA parameters and the autocorrelation of process $x[k]$ is therefore

$$r_{xx}[m] = \begin{cases} r_{xx}^*[-m] & \text{for } m < 0 \\ -\sum_{k=1}^{p} a[k]r_{xx}[m-k] + \rho_w \sum_{k=m}^{q} b[k]h^*[k-m] & \text{for } 0 \le m < q \\ -\sum_{k=1}^{p} a[k]r_{xx}[m-k] & \text{for } m > q \end{cases} \qquad (6.29)$$

where the reader is reminded that $h[0] = 1$ by definition [see Eq. (6.2)].

The autoregressive parameters of an ARMA model are related by a set of linear equations to the autocorrelation sequence. Equation (6.29) may be evaluated for the p lag indices $q + 1 \le m \le q + p$, for example, and grouped into the matrix expression

$$\begin{pmatrix} r_{xx}[q] & r_{xx}[q-1] & \cdots & r_{xx}[q-p+1] \\ r_{xx}[q+1] & r_{xx}[q] & \cdots & r_{xx}[q-p+2] \\ \vdots & \vdots & \ddots & \vdots \\ r_{xx}[q+p-1] & r_{xx}[q+p-2] & \cdots & r_{xx}[q] \end{pmatrix} \begin{pmatrix} a[1] \\ a[2] \\ \vdots \\ a[p] \end{pmatrix} = - \begin{pmatrix} r_{xx}[q+1] \\ r_{xx}[q+2] \\ \vdots \\ r_{xx}[q+p] \end{pmatrix}. \qquad (6.30)$$

If given, therefore, the autocorrelation sequence for lags $q - p + 1$ to $q + p$, then the autoregressive parameters may be found separately from the moving average parameters as the solution to the simultaneous equations (6.30). This relationship is known as the *ARMA Yule-Walker normal equations*, sometimes referenced as the *modified Yule-Walker equations*. The autocorrelation matrix of Eq. (6.30) is Toeplitz, so that subroutine TOEPLITZ in Appendix 3.D may be used to solve this equation. The number of computations required is proportional to p^2. Unfortunately, the moving average parameters of an ARMA model cannot be found simply as the solution to a set of linear equations. The MA parameters are convolved with the impulse response coefficients $h[k]$, as indicated by Eq. (6.29), resulting in a nonlinear relationship with the ACS.

The relationship between the autocorrelation sequence and a pure autoregressive model may be found by setting $q = 0$, yielding

$$r_{xx}[m] = \begin{cases} -\sum_{k=1}^{p} a[k]r_{xx}[m-k] & \text{for } m > 0 \\ -\sum_{k=1}^{p} a[k]r_{xx}[-k] + \rho_w & \text{for } m = 0 \\ r_{xx}^*[-m] & \text{for } m < 0 \end{cases} \qquad (6.31)$$

This relationship may be evaluated for the $p + 1$ lag indices $0 \leq m \leq p$ and formed into the matrix expression

$$
\begin{pmatrix}
r_{xx}[0] & r_{xx}[-1] & \cdots & r_{xx}[-p] \\
r_{xx}[1] & r_{xx}[0] & \cdots & r_{xx}[-p+1] \\
\vdots & \vdots & \ddots & \vdots \\
r_{xx}[p] & r_{xx}[p-1] & \cdots & r_{xx}[0]
\end{pmatrix}
\begin{pmatrix}
1 \\
a[1] \\
\vdots \\
a[p]
\end{pmatrix}
=
\begin{pmatrix}
\rho_w \\
0 \\
\vdots \\
0
\end{pmatrix} .
\tag{6.32}
$$

If given, therefore, the autocorrelation sequence for lags 0 to p, then the AR parameters may be found as the solution to Eq. (6.32). This relationship forms the *AR Yule-Walker normal equations*. The autocorrelation matrix of Eq. (6.32) is both Toeplitz and Hermitian because $r_{xx}[-k] = r_{xx}^*[k]$. Subroutine LEVINSON in Appendix 3.C may be used to obtain the solution for $\rho_w, a[1], \ldots, a[p]$, given the ACS over the 0-to-p lag range. The number of computations is proportional to p^2.

Using the autocorrelation sequence given by Eq. (6.31), an alternative expression for the autoregressive PSD is

$$
P_{\mathrm{AR}}(f) = \frac{T\rho_w}{|A(f)|^2} = T \sum_{k=-\infty}^{\infty} r_{xx}[k] \exp(-j2\pi f k T) .
\tag{6.33}
$$

Note that autocorrelation lags 0 to p uniquely describe the autoregressive process of order p, as the lags for $|k| > p$ are obtained recursively from

$$
r_{xx}[m] = -\sum_{k=1}^{p} a[k] r_{xx}[m-k] ,
\tag{6.34}
$$

as indicated by Eq. (6.29) with $q = 0$.

The relationship between the ACS and a pure moving average model may be found by specializing Eq. (6.29) with the setting of $p = 0$ and noting that $h[k] = b[k]$ for $1 \leq k \leq q$, yielding

$$
r_{xx}[m] = \begin{cases}
0 & \text{for } m > q \\
\rho_w \sum_{k=m}^{q} b[k] b^*[k-m] & \text{for } 0 \leq m \leq q \\
r_{xx}^*[-m] & \text{for } m < 0 .
\end{cases}
\tag{6.35}
$$

This is a nonlinear convolutional relationship between the ACS and the MA parameters. Using the autocorrelation sequence given by Eq. (6.35), an alternative expression for the moving average PSD is

$$
P_{\mathrm{MA}}(f) = T\rho_w |B(f)|^2 = T \sum_{k=-q}^{q} r_{xx}[k] \exp(-j2\pi f k T) .
\tag{6.36}
$$

Note that Eq. (6.36) has a finite summation range. This simply reflects the fact that a moving average process of order q is uncorrelated for lags $|k| > q$. Equation (6.36) is identical in form to the classical correlogram method of PSD estimation

$$\hat{P}_{\text{CORR}}(f) = T \sum_{k=-q}^{q} \hat{r}_{xx}[k] \exp(-j2\pi f kT) \quad , \tag{6.37}$$

if autocorrelation estimates $\hat{r}_{xx}[k]$ up to lag q are used. The distinction between the two spectral methods is the manner in which the data is used. The correlogram method uses the data to estimate the autocorrelation sequence directly. The moving average method uses the data to estimate the MA parameters (see Chap. 10 for MA estimation procedures), then uses Eq. (6.12) to compute the PSD. Both methods will yield spectra with similar features.

6.6 SPECTRAL FACTORIZATION

Consider the z-transform for an AR(p) process, defined by Eq. (6.7) as

$$P_{\text{AR}}(z) = \frac{\rho_w}{A(z)A^*(1/z^*)} \quad , \tag{6.38}$$

in which $A(z)A^*(1/z^*)$ is a polynomial in z of order $2p$. The poles of Eq. (6.38) will occur in conjugate reciprocal pairs. For example, if z_k is a root of $A(z)$, then $(1/z_k)^* = 1/z_k^*$ will be a root of $A^*(1/z^*)$ (see the Problems). If z_k is inside the unit circle, then $1/z_k^*$ will be outside the unit circle. If z_k is on the unit circle, then so will be $1/z_k^*$. Furthermore, the roots of $A(z)$ will also come in complex conjugate pairs if the polynomial coefficients are all real.

Consider the z-transform function $A(z)A^*(1/z^*)$. Figure 6.5(a) illustrates a typical pole plot of the product polynomial $A(z)A^*(1/z^*)$. There are 2^p possible combinations of p poles for $A(z)$ that would yield the identical polynomial $A(z)A^*(1/z^*)$. Figure 6.5(b) and (c) show two possible *spectral factorizations* of the poles indicated in Fig. 6.5(a) for $A(z)A^*(1/z^*)$. A unique factorization is imposed by requiring that the time-series model be both *stable* and *causal*, as was the assumption for Eq. (6.1). Linear systems theory (see Chap. 2) shows that such requirements force $A(z)$ to be minimum phase, that is, to have all of its roots *inside* the unit z-plane circle, as indicated in Fig. 6.5(c). The polynomial $A^*(1/z^*)$ will, therefore, have all of its roots *outside* the unit circle. The polynomial $A^*(1/z^*)$ is associated with the *stable anticausal* autoregressive process

$$x[n] = -\sum_{k=1}^{p} a^*[k]x[n+k] + e[n] \tag{6.39}$$

defined for $n \leq 0$, rather than the causal AR process index range of $n \geq 0$.

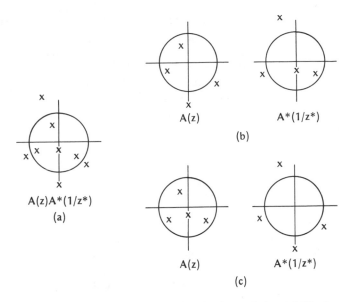

Figure 6.5   Illustration of spectral factorization and the stability issue.

The reader should not confuse the filter stability issue associated with spectral factorization with the statistical stability issue. Filter stability is concerned with the need to choose AR or MA parameters that form valid autocorrelation recursions, such as those of Eq. (6.29) or (6.31). Statistical stability is concerned with methods that reduce the spectral estimator variance for a given finite data record. Chapter 8 will present linear prediction estimation techniques that have good statistical stability, but which do not necessarily guarantee a minimum-phase estimate of $A(z)$. From the standpoint of a PSD estimate, it does not matter whether or not $A(z)$ is minimum phase, as the PSD can be created from any $A(z)$ with arbitrary root locations, as shown in Fig. 6.5. If a filter implementation of the estimated coefficients of $A(z)$ is required, then stability becomes an issue. In this case, a minimum-phase filter can be created by reflecting any poles of $A(z)$ that are outside the unit circle to the inside. That is, one can simply form $A(z)A^*(1/z^*)$ and perform a minimum-phase factorization.

REFERENCES

Box, G. E. P., and G. M. Jenkins, *Time Series Analysis Forecasting and Control*, Holden-Day, Inc., San Francisco, 1970.

Gutowski, P. R., E. A. Robinson, and S. Treitel, Spectral Estimation: Fact or Fiction?, *IEEE Trans. Geosci. Electron.*, vol. GE-16, pp. 80–84, April 1978.

Kay, S. M., *Modern Spectral Estimation*, Prentice-Hall, Inc., Englewood Cliffs, N. J., 1987.

Padé, H. E., Sur la representation approachée d'une function par des fractions rationnelles, *Ann. Sci. Ec. Norm. Sup.* (Paris), no. 3, vol. 9, pp. 1–98 (suppl.), 1892.

Weiss, L., and R. N. McDonough, Prony's Method, z-Transforms, and Padé Approximation, *SIAM Rev.*, vol. 5, pp. 145–149, April 1963.

PROBLEMS

1. Find an explicit relationship for $r_{xx}[m]$ in terms of $a[1]$ and $b[1]$ assuming an ARMA(1,1) model.

2. Take the inverse z-transform of Eq. (6.7) to prove the validity of Eq. (6.29).

3. Using Eq. (6.24), find matrix expressions comparable to Eqs. (6.18) and (6.19) to relate the MA(∞) parameters to the ARMA(p, q) parameters.

4. Let $\mathsf{A}(z) = 1 + .7z^{-1} + .2z^{-2}$ represent the z-transform of an AR(2) process. Approximate this AR(2) by an MA(2), an MA(4), and an MA(10). Plot the results. How good is the MA approximation?

5. Prove that the autocorrelation matrix of the AR Yule-Walker equations (6.32) is positive semidefinite.

6. Suppose a stable ARMA(p, q) filter is approximated by an AR($p+q$) using the Pade approximation. Show that the AR approximation is not guaranteed to be stable.

7. Show that if z_i is a root of $\mathsf{A}(z)$, the polynomial defined by Eq. (6.4), then $(1/z_i)^*$ is a root of $\mathsf{A}^*(1/z^*)$.

APPENDIX 6.A
PROGRAM TO COMPUTE THE ARMA, AR, AND MA
POWER SPECTRAL DENSITY

Subroutine ARMAPSD computes a set of power spectral density values for either an ARMA, an AR, or an MA process, given the arrays of model parameters (A or B or both) and the white noise variance (RHO). An FFT is used to efficiently evaluate the polynomials $A(f)$ and $B(f)$ for a range of frequencies. The program may be used with real data by simply setting the imaginary component of arrays A and B to zero.

Using $A(1) = (.8, .9)$, $B(1) = (.1, -.3)$, $IP = 1$, $IQ = 1$, $RHO = 2.$, and $T = 1.$, then a partial list of output values from the program are as follows

```
PSD(    1) = 0.211765E+01
PSD(1000) = 0.573554E+01
PSD(2000) = 0.687682E+00
PSD(3000) = 0.238198E+00
PSD(4000) = 0.143373E+01
PSD(4096) = 0.210874E+01   .
```

```
      SUBROUTINE ARMAPSD (IP,IQ,RHO,T,A,B,PSD,ISTAT)
C
C  This subroutine computes a set of NPSD power spectral density values
C  across the frequency band from -1/2T to 1/2T Hz, where T is the sam-
C  ple interval in sec. ,  given the complex ARMA parameters of an ARMA
C  model.  The   FFT  is used to efficiently evaluate the numerator and
C  denominator polynomials of the ARMA PSD function.   For the case of
C  real  ARMA  parameters,  the spectral values are symmetric about the
C  element indexed as NPSD/2 + 1 .
C
C  The PSD for just an AR model may be obtained as a special case  of
C  this subroutine by setting IQ to zero. Similarly, the PSD for just
C  a MA model may be obtained as a special case by setting IP to zero.
C
C  Input parameters:
C
C        IP    - AR model order (integer)
C        IQ    - MA model order (integer)
C        RHO   - White noise variance of model input (real)
C        T     - Sample interval in seconds (real)
C        A     - Complex array of autoregressive parameters A(1) to A(IP)
C        B     - Complex array of moving average parameters B(1) to B(IQ)
C
C  Output parameters:
C
C        PSD   - Real array of power spectral density values
C        ISTAT - Integer status indicator at time of exit:
C                    0 for normal exit
C                    1 if IP or IQ < 0
C
C  Notes:
C
C     External array A must be dimensioned .GE. IP, array B must be
C     dimensioned .GE. IQ, and array PSD must be dimensioned .GE.
C     NPSD in the calling program.  Subroutines PREFFT and FFT (in
C     Appendix 2.A) are required.
C
      PARAMETER NPSD=4096           ! Must be a power of 2
      COMPLEX A(1),B(1),W(NPSD),DEN(NPSD),NUM(NPSD)
      REAL PSD(1),RHO,T
      ISTAT=0
C  Determine if error condition exists with order values
      IF (IP .GE. 0 .AND. IQ .GE. 0)  GO TO 5
      ISTAT=1
      RETURN
C  Set up exponential table for the FFT (no zero padding)
5     CALL PREFFT (NPSD,0,NEXP,W)
      IF (IP .EQ. 0)  GO TO 30
      DEN(1)=(1.,0.)
      DO 10 K=1,IP
10      DEN(K+1)=A(K)
      DO 20 K=IP+2,NPSD
20      DEN(K)=(0.,0.)
      CALL FFT (NPSD,0,1.,NEXP,W,DEN)
30    IF (IQ .EQ. 0)  GO TO 60
      NUM(1)=(1.,0.)
      DO 40 K=1,IQ
40      NUM(K+1)=B(K)
```

```
        DO 50 K=IQ+2,NPSD
50         NUM(K)=(0.,0.)
        CALL FFT (NPSD,0,1.,NEXP,W,NUM)
60      IF (IP .EQ. 0)  GO TO 80
        IF (IQ .EQ. 0)  GO TO 100
C  Equation (6.8)
        DO 70 K=1,NPSD
70         PSD(K)=RHO*T*(REAL(NUM(K))**2+AIMAG(NUM(K))**2)/
     *            (REAL(DEN(K))**2+AIMAG(DEN(K))**2)
        RETURN
C  Equation (6.12)
80      DO 90 K=1,NPSD
90         PSD(K)=RHO*T*(REAL(NUM(K))**2+AIMAG(NUM(K))**2)
        RETURN
C  Equation (6.14)
100     DO 110 K=1,NPSD
110        PSD(K)=RHO*T/(REAL(DEN(K))**2+AIMAG(DEN(K))**2)
        RETURN
        END
```

7

AUTOREGRESSIVE PROCESS AND SPECTRUM PROPERTIES

7.1 INTRODUCTION

The autoregressive (AR) spectral estimate has received the most attention in the technical literature of all the time-series models introduced in Chap. 6. The interest stems from two reasons. First, autoregressive spectra tend to have sharp peaks, a feature often associated with high-resolution spectral estimates. Second, estimates of the AR parameters can be obtained as solutions to linear equations. Equation (6.32) illustrated, for example, that the AR parameters and the autocorrelation sequence were related by a set of linear equations. Estimates of MA and ARMA parameters, however, require the solution of nonlinear equations, such as those of Eqs. (6.29) and (6.35).

The large body of material on autoregressive spectral estimation has necessitated a division of the presentation of the AR method into three chapters. Properties and features of the AR process and the AR spectrum are covered in this chapter under the assumption that the ACS is known, which is not generally the case in practice. These properties have led to alternative names for AR spectral analysis, such as the maximum entropy method (MEM) or linear prediction (LP) spectral estimation. Some of these properties have been utilized in the development of algorithms to estimate the autoregressive process parameters from only data samples. These algorithms are described in the two sequel chapters. Chapter

8 describes AR parameter estimation algorithms and programs based on processing the data as a block. Chapter 9 describes AR parameter estimation algorithms based on processing the data sequentially one sample at a time.

7.2 SUMMARY

This chapter has been divided into two main sections: properties of autoregressive processes and properties of autoregressive spectra. These properties are developed under the assumption that the autocorrelation sequence is known. Table 7.1 summarizes the key AR process properties and the section where each property is discussed. A major result of these properties is the ability to represent the AR process as any one of three unique sequences, as summarized in Sec. 7.3.4.

TOPIC	PROPERTY	SECTION
LINEAR PREDICTION FILTER	WHITENS AR PROCESS	3.7.1
LEVINSON ALGORITHM	FAST COMPUTATIONAL ALGORITHM	3.7.2
REFLECTION COEFFICIENTS	AR PROCESS AS A LATTICE FILTER	3.7.3

Table 7.1   Summary of AR Process Properties

Table 7.2 summarizes the key AR spectrum properties and the section where each property is discussed. The maximum entropy interpretation is appropriate when the process is Gaussian. If the process consists of sinusoids in noise, then the content of Sec. 7.4.3 will be of interest to the reader.

PROPERTY	SECTION
MAXIMUM ENTROPY INTERPRETATION	7.4.1
BASIS FOR HIGH RESOLUTION	7.4.2
SINUSOIDAL POWER ESTIMATION	7.4.3

Table 7.2   Summary of AR Power Spectral Density Properties

7.3 AUTOREGRESSIVE PROCESS PROPERTIES

7.3.1 Relationship to Linear Prediction Analysis

The equations of linear prediction analysis will be shown in this section to be structurally identical to the Yule-Walker equations of an autoregressive process. A close relationship, therefore, exists between a linear prediction filter and an AR process. This relationship is exploited by several of the algorithms presented in Chaps. 8 and 9.

Consider the *forward* linear prediction estimate

$$\hat{x}^f[n] = -\sum_{k=1}^{m} a^f[k]x[n-k] \tag{7.1}$$

of the sample $x[n]$, where $a^f[k]$ is the forward linear prediction coefficient at time index k. The hat $\hat{\ }$ is used to denote an estimate and the superscript f is used to denote that this is a forward estimate. The prediction is forward in the sense that the estimate at time index n is based on m samples indexed earlier in time. The complex forward linear prediction error

$$e^f[n] = x[n] - \hat{x}^f[n] \tag{7.2}$$

has a real variance

$$\rho^f = \mathcal{E}\{|e^f[n]|^2\} \quad . \tag{7.3}$$

Substituting Eqs. (7.1) and (7.2) into the above expression will yield

$$\rho^f = r_{xx}[0] + \sum_{k=1}^{m} a^f[k]r_{xx}[-k] + \sum_{j=1}^{m}(a^f[j])^* r_{xx}[j] + \sum_{k=1}^{m}\sum_{j=1}^{m} a^f[k](a^f[j])^* r_{xx}[j-k]$$

$$= r_{xx}[0] + \mathbf{r}_m^H \mathbf{a}^f + (\mathbf{a}^f)^H \mathbf{r}_m + (\mathbf{a}^f)^H \mathbf{R}_{m-1}\mathbf{a}^f \tag{7.4}$$

in which

$$\mathbf{a}^f = \begin{pmatrix} a^f[1] \\ \vdots \\ a^f[m] \end{pmatrix}, \mathbf{r}_m = \begin{pmatrix} r_{xx}[1] \\ \vdots \\ r_{xx}[m] \end{pmatrix}, \mathbf{R}_{m-1} = \begin{pmatrix} r_{xx}[0] & \cdots & r_{xx}^*[m-1] \\ \vdots & & \vdots \\ r_{xx}[m-1] & \cdots & r_{xx}[0] \end{pmatrix}.$$

The assumption that $x[n]$ is a wide-sense stationary process has been made, so that $r_{xx}[-k] = r_{xx}^*[k]$. This expression is identical in form to the quadratic matrix equation (3.70). Therefore, the forward linear prediction coefficient vector $\mathbf{a}^f$ that minimizes the variance ρ^f is found as the solution to the normal equations given by

$$\begin{pmatrix} r_{xx}[0] & \mathbf{r}_m^H \\ \mathbf{r}_m & \mathbf{R}_{m-1} \end{pmatrix} \begin{pmatrix} 1 \\ \mathbf{a}^f \end{pmatrix} = \begin{pmatrix} \rho^f \\ \mathbf{0}_m \end{pmatrix} , \tag{7.5}$$

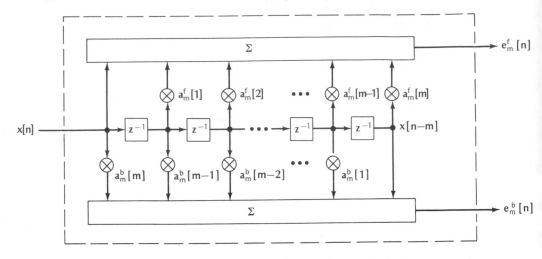

Figure 7.1   Linear prediction error filter implemented using a transversal filter structure. If $x[n]$ is an $AR(m)$ process, then $e^f[n]$ and $e^b[n]$ are white processes. The boxes with z^{-1} denote a delay of one sample.

which follows directly from Eq. (3.71). The structure of normal equations (7.5) become more apparent if rewritten as

$$
\begin{pmatrix}
r_{xx}[0] & r_{xx}^*[1] & \cdots & r_{xx}^*[m] \\
r_{xx}[1] & r_{xx}[0] & \cdots & r_{xx}^*[m-1] \\
\vdots & \vdots & \ddots & \vdots \\
r_{xx}[m] & r_{xx}[m-1] & \cdots & r_{xx}[0]
\end{pmatrix}
\begin{pmatrix}
1 \\
a^f[1] \\
\vdots \\
a^f[m]
\end{pmatrix}
=
\begin{pmatrix}
\rho^f \\
0 \\
\vdots \\
0
\end{pmatrix}. \tag{7.6}
$$

This matrix expression is structurally identical to the Yule-Walker equations (6.32) of an autoregressive process. If one rearranges Eq. (7.3) as

$$
x[n] = -\sum_{k=1}^{m} a^f[k]x[n-k] + e^f[n] \quad , \tag{7.7}
$$

then the similarity with Eq. (6.13), which describes an autoregressive process, may be seen. There are, however, two distinctions between the forward linear prediction process and the AR process. The sequence $u[n]$ of Eq. (6.13) is a *white noise* process used as the *input* to an autoregressive filter. The sequence $x[n]$ is the *output* of the autoregressive filter. The error sequence $e^f[n]$ of Eq. (7.7) is the *output* of a forward linear prediction error filter, as depicted in Fig. 7.1. The sequence $x[n]$ is the *input* to the prediction error filter. The linear prediction error sequence will be uncorrelated with the linear prediction estimate $\hat{x}^f[n]$, but it is not, in general, a white process *unless $x[n]$ was generated as an AR(p) process and $m = p$.* The error sequence in this case will be a white process, the forward linear prediction coefficients will be identical to the AR parameters ($a^f[k] = a[k]$), and the prediction error filter may be regarded as a whitening filter [Papoulis, 1981].

A *backward* linear prediction error estimate

$$\hat{x}^b[n] = -\sum_{k=1}^{m} a^b[k]x[n+k] \tag{7.8}$$

may also be formed, in which $a^b[k]$ is the backward linear prediction coefficient at time index k. A superscript b is used to tag elements associated with the backward linear prediction estimate. The prediction is backward in the sense that the estimate at time index n is based on m samples indexed later in time. The backward linear prediction error is

$$e^b[n] = x[n-m] - \hat{x}^b[n-m] \quad . \tag{7.9}$$

The backward error has been intentionally indexed for notational convenience with respect to n, rather than $n-m$, so that $e^f[n]$ and $e^b[n]$ will be functions of the same set of data samples (namely, $x[n]$, $x[n-1]$, ... ,$x[n-m]$) that are present in the linear prediction filter, as may be seen by examining Fig. 7.1. The complex backward linear prediction error has real variance

$$\rho^b = \mathcal{E}\{|e^b[n]|^2\} \quad . \tag{7.10}$$

Substituting Eqs. (7.8) and (7.9) into the expression above will yield

$$\rho^b = r_{xx}[0] + \sum_{k=1}^{m} a^b[k]r_{xx}[k] + \sum_{j=1}^{m} (a^b[j])^* r_{xx}[-j] + \sum_{k=1}^{m}\sum_{j=1}^{m} a^b[k](a^b[j])^* r_{xx}[k-j]$$

$$= r_{xx}[0] + \mathbf{r}_m^T \mathbf{a}^b + (\mathbf{a}^b)^H \mathbf{r}_m^* + (\mathbf{a}^b)^H \mathbf{R}_{m-1}^* \mathbf{a}^b \tag{7.11}$$

where $\mathbf{r}_m$ and $\mathbf{R}_{m-1}$ have been previously defined, and

$$\mathbf{a}^b = \begin{pmatrix} a^b[1] \\ \vdots \\ a^b[m] \end{pmatrix} \quad .$$

Based on Eq. (3.70), the backward linear prediction coefficient vector $\mathbf{a}^b$ that minimizes the variance ρ^b is found as the solution of the normal equations given by

$$\begin{pmatrix} r_{xx}[0] & \mathbf{r}_m^T \\ \mathbf{r}_m^* & \mathbf{R}_{m-1}^* \end{pmatrix} \begin{pmatrix} 1 \\ \mathbf{a}^b \end{pmatrix} = \begin{pmatrix} \rho^b \\ \mathbf{0}_m \end{pmatrix} \quad . \tag{7.12}$$

Rewriting Eq. (7.11) to explicitly show the structure will produce

$$\begin{pmatrix} r_{xx}[0] & r_{xx}[1] & \cdots & r_{xx}[m] \\ r_{xx}^*[1] & r_{xx}[0] & \cdots & r_{xx}[m-1] \\ \vdots & \vdots & \ddots & \vdots \\ r_{xx}^*[m] & r_{xx}^*[m-1] & \cdots & r_{xx}[0] \end{pmatrix} \begin{pmatrix} 1 \\ a^b[1] \\ \vdots \\ a^b[m] \end{pmatrix} = \begin{pmatrix} \rho^b \\ 0 \\ \vdots \\ 0 \end{pmatrix} \quad ,$$

which can be rearranged as

$$
\begin{pmatrix}
r_{xx}[0] & r_{xx}^{*}[1] & \cdots & r_{xx}^{*}[m] \\
r_{xx}[1] & r_{xx}[0] & \cdots & r_{xx}^{*}[m-1] \\
\vdots & \vdots & \ddots & \vdots \\
r_{xx}[m] & r_{xx}[m-1] & \cdots & r_{xx}[0]
\end{pmatrix}
\begin{pmatrix}
a^{b}[m] \\
\vdots \\
a^{b}[1] \\
1
\end{pmatrix}
=
\begin{pmatrix}
0 \\
\vdots \\
0 \\
\rho^{b}
\end{pmatrix} .
\tag{7.13}
$$

It can now be seen that Eqs. (7.6) and (7.13) both involve the identical Hermitian Toeplitz autocorrelation matrix. It was shown in Sec. 3.8.1, especially Eq. (3.156), that the solutions to Eqs. (7.6) and (7.13) must have the properties

$$
\rho^{b} = \rho^{f}
\tag{7.14}
$$

and

$$
a^{b}[k] = (a^{f}[k])^{*}
\tag{7.15}
$$

for $1 \le k \le m$. Thus, the backward and forward linear prediction error variances are identical. The backward linear prediction coefficients are simply the complex conjugates of the forward linear prediction coefficients when both prediction filters are the same length m. If the forward linear prediction error filter is a whitening filter of an AR process, then the backward linear prediction error filter is a whitening filter for the anticausal realization of the AR process.

7.3.2 Levinson Algorithm

The solution of the Hermitian Toeplitz equations (7.6) and (7.13) can be computed with Levinson's algorithm, as described in Sec. 3.8.1. If the associations $t[k] = r_{xx}[k]$, $a_m[k] = a_m^f[k]$, and $\rho_m = \rho_m^f$ are made with the parameters of Sec. 3.8.1, then the solution for a linear prediction filter of M coefficients is given by the recursion

$$
\Delta_m =
\begin{cases}
r_{xx}[1] & \text{if } m = 1 \\
\displaystyle\sum_{k=1}^{m-1} a_{m-1}^f[k] r_{xx}[m-k] + r_{xx}[m] & \text{if } m > 1
\end{cases}
\tag{7.16}
$$

$$
a_m^f[k] =
\begin{cases}
-\Delta_m/\rho_{m-1}^f & \text{for } k = m \\
a_{m-1}^f[k] + a_m^f[m](a_{m-1}^f[m-k])^{*} & \text{for } 1 \le k \le m-1 \\
& \text{and } m > 1
\end{cases}
\tag{7.17}
$$

$$
\rho_m^f = \rho_{m-1}^f\left(1 - |a_m^f[m]|^2\right)
\tag{7.18}
$$

for $m = 1$ to $m = M$. The single initial condition required is

$$
\rho_0^f = r_{xx}[0] .
\tag{7.19}
$$

The backward linear prediction coefficients are obtained simply by conjugating the forward linear prediction coefficients. A subscript m or $m - 1$ has been added to the elements to distinguish the order of the linear prediction filter. Observe that all minimum variance linear prediction coefficients from order 1 to order M are obtained automatically with the Levinson algorithm. It is possible, then, to produce all lower-order AR models with no additional computational effort.

If the Hermitian Toeplitz matrix of Eq. (7.6) is positive definite, then the polynomial

$$A_m^f(z) = 1 + \sum_{k=1}^{m} a_m^f[k] z^{-k} \tag{7.20}$$

formed from the linear prediction coefficients of the Levinson algorithm solution will have its roots inside the unit circle [Markel and Gray, 1976]. This will yield a *minimum-phase* linear prediction error filter. A variety of proofs have been developed to prove this property [Kay, 1987; Pakula and Kay, 1983; Lang and McClellan, 1979; Burg, 1975]. The typical proof demonstrates that the variance ρ^f may be reduced by reflecting roots outside the unit circle to the inside. The minimum-phase property ensures that the solution of the Yule-Walker equations yields a stable autoregression filter $1/A(z)$. A stable filter means the ACS recursion of Eq. (6.31) will generate autocorrelation values that remain finite and bounded in value by the magnitude of $r_{xx}[0]$, as required for a stationary process.

If the $x[n]$ process is actually an AR(p) process, then the linear prediction solution given by the Levinson algorithm at order $m = p$ yields

$$\begin{aligned} a_p[k] &= a_p^f \qquad \text{for} \quad 1 \le k \le p \\ \rho_p &= \rho_p^f \quad , \end{aligned} \tag{7.21}$$

where $a_p[k]$ are the AR parameters and ρ_p is the driving white noise variance. The variance will be constant for a linear prediction order equal to or greater than the correct order and, therefore, $a_m^f[m] = 0$ for $m > p$. Thus, the Levinson algorithm may be used to generate successively higher-order linear prediction error filters until the variance reaches a point at which it does not change. This can then be used as an indicator of the correct, or most likely, autoregressive model order.

It will be shown in the next section that $|a_m[m]| \le 1$. The prediction error variance ρ_m^f, as given by Eq. (7.18), must therefore be a monotonically decreasing function, reaching a minimum at $m = p$ if the process is an AR(p). This will also be a useful property for model order selection, as discussed in Chap. 8.

7.3.3   Reflection Coefficients

The linear prediction coefficients $a_1^f[1]$, ..., $a_p^f[p]$ are often termed the *reflection coefficients* due to their interpretation as physical parameters of an acoustical tube model of speech [Makhoul, 1975, 1981] or in seismic layered earth models [Robinson and Treitel, 1980]. A special symbol $k_m = a_m^f[m]$ for $1 \le m \le p$ is typically applied to distinguish these particular linear prediction coefficients from the remaining coefficients. The negated reflection coefficient $-k_m$ has been called a *partial correlation*

(PARCOR) in the statistical literature [Box and Jenkins, 1970] because it represents the normalized correlation between $x[n]$ and $x[n-m]$ with the correlation of $x[n-1], \ldots , x[n-m+1]$ removed. The reflection coefficients also have an interpretation as the negative normalized correlation coefficient between the forward and backward linear prediction errors with one unit of delay

$$k_m = \frac{-\mathcal{E}\{e^f_{m-1}[n]e^{b*}_{m-1}[n-1]\}}{\sqrt{\mathcal{E}\{|e^f_{m-1}[n]|^2\}}\sqrt{\mathcal{E}\{|e^b_{m-1}[n-1]|^2\}}} \quad . \tag{7.22}$$

This may be derived by using definition equations (7.2), (7.4), and (7.9) to obtain

$$\mathcal{E}\{e^f_{m-1}[n]e^{b*}_{m-1}[n-1]\}$$

$$= \mathcal{E}\{(x[n] + \sum_{k=1}^{m-1} a^f_{m-1}[k]x[n-k])(x^*[n-m] + \sum_{k=1}^{m-1} a^{b*}_{m-1}[k]x^*[n-m+k])\}$$

$$= r_{xx}[m] + \sum_{k=1}^{m-1} a^f_{m-1}[k]r_{xx}[m-k] = \Delta_m \tag{7.23}$$

and noting that

$$\rho^f_{m-1} = \rho^b_{m-1} = \mathcal{E}\{|e^f_{m-1}[n]|^2\} = \mathcal{E}\{|e^b_{m-1}[n]|^2\} = \mathcal{E}\{|e^b_{m-1}[n-1]|^2\} \quad , \tag{7.24}$$

which is a consequence of the stationary property and the Hermitian Toeplitz property of the autocorrelation matrix. Substituting Eqs. (7.23) and (7.24) into the definition

$$k_m = a_m[m] = -\frac{\Delta_m}{\rho^f_{m-1}} = -\frac{\Delta_m}{\sqrt{\rho^f_{m-1}}\sqrt{\rho^b_{m-1}}} \tag{7.25}$$

will yield Eq. (7.22). It is straightforward to show, using Eq. (7.22), that $|k_m| \leq 1$ for $1 \leq m \leq p$ (see the Problems). Having k_m bounded by unit magnitude is a necessary and sufficient condition for the autocorrelation matrix to be positive semidefinite.

If the recursion (7.17) is substituted for $a^f_m[k]$ or $a^b_m[k] = a^{f*}_m[k]$ in definitions (7.2) and (7.9) for the forward and backward linear prediction errors, then it is simple to show (see the Problems) that

$$e^f_m[n] = e^f_{m-1}[n] + k_m e^b_{m-1}[n-1] \tag{7.26}$$

$$e^b_m[n] = e^b_{m-1}[n-1] + k^*_m e^f_{m-1}[n] \tag{7.27}$$

with initial conditions $x[n] = e^f_0[n] = e^b_0[n]$. Relationships (7.26) and (7.27) yield an alternative interpretation of the prediction error filter as a lattice structure, as depicted in Fig. 7.2. The parameters at each stage of the lattice filter are the reflection coefficients. Note that both the forward and backward linear prediction errors are propagated simultaneously in the lattice filter. The lattice filter has been found to offer implementation advantages over tapped delay line filters such as Fig. 7.1 because they suffer from less round-off noise and less sensitivity to coefficient value perturbations [Friedlander, 1982]. The lattice filter is also an orthogonalizing filter because the backward prediction errors at each stage are mutually orthogonal [Makhoul, 1978] (see the Problems).

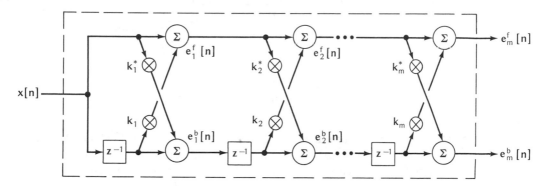

Figure 7.2 Linear prediction error filter implemented using a lattice filter structure. The boxes with z^{-1} denote a delay of one sample.

7.3.4 Summary of Equivalent Representations for Autoregressive Processes

An AR(p) process has three equivalent representations: as an infinite-duration autocorrelation sequence, as a finite sequence of autoregressive parameters, or as a finite sequence of reflection coefficients. These equivalences are depicted by the triangle diagram of Fig. 7.3. Although the ACS for an AR(p) process is infinite, the entire ACS is determined uniquely by the finite autocorrelation sequence $r_{xx}[0]$, ..., $r_{xx}[p]$. The remainder of the ACS can be obtained from the recursion given by Eq. (6.34). The Levinson algorithm of Sec. 7.3.2 provides both AR parameters and reflection coefficients, given the finite ACS from lag 0 to lag p. Using only Eq. (7.17) and the initial condition $a_1[1] = k_1$, a simple recursion can be evolved to yield the AR parameters at all orders from $m = 1$ to $m = p$ based on knowledge of just the reflection coefficient sequence k_1 to k_p, thereby forming a mapping from the reflection coefficients to the autoregressive parameters. The recursions of the Levinson algorithm may also be run in reverse to provide descending-order recursions from order m to order $m - 1$. This enables one to compute the autocorrelation sequence from lag p to lag 0 using either the AR parameter set $\{\rho_p, a_p[1], \ldots, a_p[p]\}$

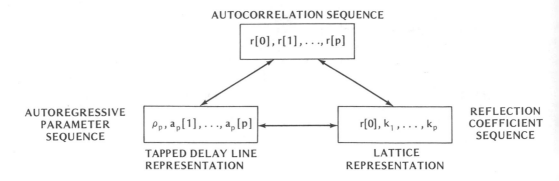

Figure 7.3   The three equivalent representations of an autoregressive process.

or the reflection coefficient set $\{r_{xx}[0], k_1, \ldots, k_p\}$ (see the Problems). A mapping from the AR parameters to the reflection coefficients is also possible.

The following three equivalent statements represent the required conditions for the mappings depicted in Fig. 7.3 to be possible:

- $r_{xx}[0], \ldots, r_{xx}[p]$ is a positive-definite sequence.
- $A(z) = 1 + \sum_{k=1}^{p} a_p[k] z^{-k}$ is minimum phase.
- $\rho_m > 0$ and $|k_m| < 1$ for $1 \le m \le p$.

7.4 AUTOREGRESSIVE POWER SPECTRAL DENSITY PROPERTIES

7.4.1 Maximum Entropy Interpretation

The estimate of the autoregressive power spectral density has frequently been termed the *maximum entropy method* (MEM) of spectral analysis in the literature. This interpretation was introduced by Burg [1975]. If the finite autocorrelation sequence $r_{xx}[0], \ldots, r_{xx}[p]$ is assumed known, then a question may be posed as to how the remaining unknown lags $r_{xx}[p+1], r_{xx}[p+2], \ldots$ should be specified in order to guarantee that the entire autorcorrelation sequence is positive semidefinite. There are an infinite number of possible extrapolations that will yield valid autocorrelation sequences. Burg argued that the extrapolation should be made in such a way as to maximize the entropy of the time series characterized by the extrapolated ACS. This time series would then be the most random, in an entropy sense, of all series that have known ACS for lags 0 to p. A spectral estimate produced from this extrapolated ACS would then be for a process of maximum entropy.

In particular, the entropy rate for a Gaussian random process was shown in Sec. 4.5 to be proportional to

$$\int_{-1/2T}^{1/2T} \ln P_{\mathrm{MEM}}(f)\, df \quad , \tag{7.28}$$

where $P_{\mathrm{MEM}}(f)$ is the PSD of the process. $P_{\mathrm{MEM}}(f)$ is found by maximizing Eq. (7.28), subject to the constraints that it satisfy the Wiener-Khintchine relationship (4.34) for the $p+1$ known autocorrelation values

$$\int_{-1/2T}^{1/2T} P_{\mathrm{MEM}}(f) \exp(j2\pi f n T)\, df = r_{xx}[n] \tag{7.29}$$

over $0 \le n \le p$. The solution, found by the Lagrange multiplier technique (see, for example, Haykin and Kesler [1983]), is

$$P_{\mathrm{MEM}}(f) = \frac{T\rho_w}{\left|1 + \sum_{k=1}^{p} a_p[k] \exp(-j2\pi f k T)\right|^2} \quad , \tag{7.30}$$

for which $\rho_w, a_p[1], \ldots, a_p[p]$ are found via the solution of the Yule-Walker equations. Thus, MEM and AR PSD analysis are identical for *Gaussian random processes* and a *known* autocorrelation sequence of uniform spacing. It is incorrect to say Eq. (7.30) is a maximum entropy spectral analysis if the process is not Gaussian or if the parameters were estimated from data rather than the known ACS. A MEM analysis can also be performed over a nonuniform spacing of the ACS. In this case, the AR and MEM power spectral densities will not be identical. Other maximum entropy interpretations may be found in Jaynes [1982], Van Den Bos [1971], and Nikias and Raghuveer [1985].

7.4.2 Basis for High Resolution

The autoregressive PSD in Chapter 6 [Eqs. (6.14) and (6.33)] was shown to have the equivalent representations [see also DuBroff, 1975]

$$P_{\mathrm{AR}}(f) = \frac{T\rho_w}{\left|1 + \sum_{k=1}^{p} a[p] \exp(-j2\pi f k T)\right|^2} \tag{7.31}$$

$$= T \sum_{k=-\infty}^{\infty} r_{xx}[k] \exp(-j2\pi f k T) \quad . \tag{7.32}$$

Given the autocorrelation sequence for lags 0 to p, one may solve the Yule-Walker equations for the white noise variance ρ_w and the autoregressive parameters $a[1]$, ..., $a[p]$ and then use Eq. (7.31) to evaluate the AR PSD. Alternatively, the extrapolation

$$r_{xx}[n] = -\sum_{k=1}^{p} a[k] r_{xx}[n-k] \qquad (7.33)$$

for $n > p$, which follows from Eq. (6.34), may be used to extend the autocorrelation sequence so that Eq. (7.32) may be used to compute the AR PSD (although this would not be very practical). As a contrast, consider the correlogram method of power spectral density estimation presented in Chap. 5. This method would use the given $p+1$ autocorrelation values to produce the spectral estimator

$$P_{\text{CORR}}(f) = T \sum_{k=-p}^{p} r_{xx}[k] \exp(-j2\pi f k T) \quad . \qquad (7.34)$$

Comparing Eqs. (7.32) and (7.34), it may be seen that the AR PSD estimator matches the autocorrelation sequence over the summation range of the correlogram method of PSD estimation up to lag p, but then uses a nonzero ACS extrapolation given by Eq. (7.33), rather than the zero extension assumed by the correlogram method, to generate the unavailable lags. This is depicted in Fig. 7.4. The implied extrapolation of the autocorrelation sequence when computing the AR PSD using Eq. (7.31) is the basis for the high-resolution property attributed to the AR PSD estimator. There is no windowing of the autocorrelation sequence as there is with the classic spectral estimators. Autoregressive power spectral density estimators, for this reason, do not possess the sidelobe phenomena of the classic spectral estimators.

The degree of improved resolution of the AR PSD estimator for processes consisting of sinusoids in white noise is, however, a function of signal-to-noise ratio (SNR). Consider the AR(8) PSD estimates for three equal power sinusoids in white noise shown in Fig. 7.5. The estimates were produced using lags 0 through 8 of the exact autocorrelation for sinusoids in noise [Eq. (4.52)]. As the SNR decreases from 30 dB to 10 dB, the number of resolved sinusoids decreases from three to two; the frequency estimates given by the peak locations are also biased when the SNR is 10 dB. A measure of the sinusoidal resolution of equal-power sinusoids has been analytically determined in the case of known autocorrelation [Marple, 1982] to be roughly

$$F = \frac{1.03}{Tp[\text{SNR}(p+1)]^{0.31}} \quad , \qquad (7.35)$$

where F is the resolution in Hz, T is the sample interval in sec, p is the highest lag of the autocorrelation sequence, and SNR is the signal-to-noise ratio of a single sinusoid expressed in linear (rather than dB) units.

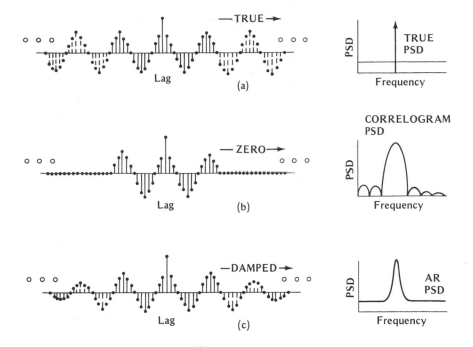

Figure 7.4 Implied extrapolation of the autocorrelation sequence (ACS). (a) Original infinite ACS and true spectrum of a single real sinusoid in white noise. (b) Zero ACS extrapolation implied by the correlogram method PSD estimator and associated spectral estimate. (c) Autoregressive ACS extrapolation and associated spectral estimate.

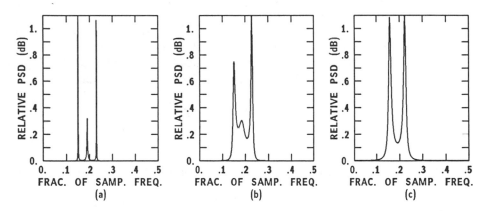

Figure 7.5 Autoregressive PSD estimates based on nine ACS terms for three equal-power sinusoids in white noise. The sinusoids have fractional sampling frequencies of .15, .19, and .23. (a) SNR of 30 dB. (b) SNR of 20 dB. (c) SNR of 10 dB.

7.4.3 Sinusoidal Power Estimation

Autoregressive PSD estimation is often used to indicate the presence of sinusoidal components in the data. The power associated with components in the AR PSD estimate is correctly computed by integrating the area under the power spectral density. This is computationally expensive. As an alternative, it is tempting to use the height of each spectral peak as an indicator of sinusoidal power. The height is a reliable indicator of relative power with the classic spectral estimators because their peaks are linearly proportional to the sinusoidal power when the input consists of sinusoids in white noise. This will *not* work with AR spectral estimators. Consider the autocorrelation sequence for a single complex sinusoid in white noise

$$r_{xx}[k] = P \exp(j2\pi f_0 kT) + \rho_w \delta[k] \quad , \tag{7.36}$$

as given by Eq. (4.52). Lacoss [1971] has used Eq. (7.36) to prove analytically that the mth-order autoregressive PSD function for a single sinusoid in white noise process can be represented as (see the Problems for proof)

$$P_{\mathrm{AR}}(f) = \frac{T\rho_w[1 + p/(mP + \rho_w)]}{\left|1 - \dfrac{P}{mP + \rho_w} \displaystyle\sum_{k=1}^{m} \exp(-j2\pi k[f - f_0]T)\right|^2} \quad . \tag{7.37}$$

The function $P_{\mathrm{AR}}(f)$ reaches its maximum at $f = f_0$,

$$P_{\mathrm{AR}}(f_0) = \rho_w T[1 + m\,\mathrm{SNR}][1 + (m+1)\,\mathrm{SNR}] \approx T(m\,\mathrm{SNR})^2 \quad , \tag{7.38}$$

where $\mathrm{SNR} = P/\rho_w$ and the assumption $m\,\mathrm{SNR} \gg 1$ (high SNR) has been made. Thus, the peak is proportional to the *square* of the power; the area under the peak is, however, linearly proportional to the power.

One method to estimate the power of multiple real sinusoids from the peaks in an AR spectrum was suggested by Johnsen and Andersen [1978]. The method generally works only for well-separated peaks of high-SNR sinusoidal components in the data. If the AR PSD is expressed in z-transform notation

$$\mathsf{P}_{\mathrm{AR}}(z) = \frac{T\rho_w}{\mathsf{A}(z)\mathsf{A}^*(1/z^*)} \quad , \tag{7.39}$$

then a peak observed at f_k in the AR spectrum will have an estimated power of

$$\mathrm{Power}\,(f_k) = 2\,\mathrm{Re}\left\{\mathrm{Residue\ of}\frac{\mathsf{P}_{\mathrm{AR}}(z)}{z}\mathrm{evaluated\ at\ } z_k = \exp(j2\pi f_k T)\right\}. \tag{7.40}$$

The residue is defined by Eq. (2.20). Negative power estimates can occur with this technique if peaks are very close together. The power estimation technique of the Prony method (Chap. 11) is probably a more reliable estimate if the data is known to consist solely of sinusoids in noise.

REFERENCES

Box, G. E.P., and G. M. Jenkins, *Time Series Analysis Forecasting and Control*, Holden-Day, Inc., San Francisco, 1970.

Burg, J. P., Maximum Entropy Spectral Analysis, Ph.D. dissertation, Department of Geophysics, Stanford University, Stanford, Calif., 1975.

DuBroff, R. E., The Effective Autocorrelation Function of Maximum Entropy Spectra, *Proc. IEEE*, vol. 63, pp. 1622–1623, November 1975.

Friedlander, B., Lattice Filters for Adaptive Processing, *Proc. IEEE*, vol. 70, pp. 829–867, August 1982.

Haykin, S. S., and S. Kesler, Prediction-Error Filtering and Maximum-Entropy Spectral Estimation, Chapter 2 in *Nonlinear Methods of Spectral Analysis*, 2nd ed., S. Haykin, ed., Springer-Verlag, New York, 1983.

Jaynes, E. T., On the Rationale of Maximum-Entropy Method, *Proc. IEEE*, vol. 70, pp. 939–952, September 1982.

Johnsen, S. J., and N. Andersen, On Power Estimation in Maximum Entropy Spectral Analysis, *Geophysics*, vol. 43, pp. 681–690, June 1978.

Kay, S. M., *Modern Spectral Estimation*, Prentice-Hall, Inc., Englewood Cliffs, N. J., 1987.

Lacoss, R. T., Data Adaptive Spectral Analysis Methods, *Geophysics*, vol. 36, pp. 661–675, August 1971.

Lang, S. W., and J. H. McClellan, A Simple Proof of Stability for All-Pole Linear Prediction Models, *Proc. IEEE*, vol. 67, pp. 860–861, May 1979.

Makhoul, J., Linear Prediction: A Tutorial Review, *Proc. IEEE*, vol. 63, pp. 561–580, April 1975; corrections in vol. 64, p. 285, February 1976.

Makhoul, J., A Class of All-Zero Lattice Digital Filters: Properties and Applications, *IEEE Trans. Acoust. Speech Signal Process.*, vol. ASSP-26, pp. 304–314, August 1978.

Makhoul, J., Lattice Methods in Spectral Estimation, in *Applied Time Series Analysis II*, D. F. Findley, ed., Academic Press, Inc., New York, pp. 301–324, 1981.

Markel, J. D., and A. H. Gray, *Linear Prediction of Speech*, Springer-Verlag, New York, 1976.

Marple, S. L., Jr., Frequency Resolution of Fourier and Maximum Entropy Spectral Estimates", *Geophysics*, vol. 47, pp. 1303–1307, September 1982.

Nikias, C. L., and M. Raghuveer, Discussion on Higher Order Autospectra by MEM, *Geophysics*, vol. 50, pp. 165–166, January 1985.

Pakula, L., and S. M. Kay, Simple Proofs of the Minimum Phase Property of the Prediction Error Filter, *IEEE Trans. Acoust. Speech Signal Process.*, vol. ASSP-31, p. 501, April 1983.

Papoulis, A., Maximum Entropy and Spectral Estimation: A Review, *IEEE Trans. Acoust. Speech Signal Process.*, vol. ASSP-29, pp. 1176–1186, December 1981.

Robinson, E. A., and S. Treitel, *Geophysical Signal Analysis*, Prentice-Hall, Inc., Englewood Cliffs, N. J., 1980.

Satorius, E. H., and J. Zeidler, Maximum Entropy Spectral Analysis of Multiple Sinusoids in Noise, *Geophysics*, vol. 43, pp. 1111-1118, October 1978.

Van Den Bos, A., Alternative Interpretation of Maximum Entropy Spectral Analysis, *IEEE Trans. Inf. Theory*, vol. IT–17, pp. 493–494, July 1971.

PROBLEMS

1. Show that any set of numbers $\{\rho_p, k_1, \ldots, k_p\}$ such that $\rho_p > 0$ and $|k_i| < 1$ will uniquely determine a valid autocorrelation sequence.

2. Assume that $\{r_{xx}[0], \ldots, r_{xx}[m]\}$ is a valid autocorrelation sequence. Show that the Toeplitz autocorrelation matrices are related by

$$\det \mathbf{R}_{m+1} = -(\det \mathbf{R}_{m-1})r^2[m+1] + \beta r_{xx}[m+1] + \alpha \quad ,$$

where β and α are functions of $\det \mathbf{R}_{m-1}$ and $\sum a_m[i] r_{xx}[m+1-i]$. Show that as a function of $r[m+1]$, for given $\{r_{xx}[0], \ldots, r_{xx}[m]\}$, $\det \mathbf{R}_{m+1}$ has a single maximum and, therefore, that the admissible amplitude range of $r_{xx}[m+1]$ is $2\rho_m^f$, which is a nonincreasing function of m. Show that by choosing $r_{xx}[m+1]$ as the midpoint of the admissible range

$$r_{xx}[m+1] = -\sum_{i=1}^{m} a_m[i] r_{xx}[m+1-i]$$

yields $k_{m+1} = 0$ and $\rho_{m+1}^f = \rho_m^f$. Show that this maximizes $\det \mathbf{R}_{m+1}$.

3. Prove that $|k_m| \leq 1$ using Eq. (7.22).

4. Prove the recursive order relationship between the forward and backward linear prediction errors given by Eqs. (7.26) and (7.27).

5. Use Eq. (7.36) to prove Eq. (7.37).

6. Find the mapping from the autoregressive parameter sequence to the autocorrelation sequence, as shown on Fig. 7.3.

7. The Levinson recursion Eq. (7.17) can be viewed as a mapping of a set of p reflection coefficients k_i into a set of p linear prediction filter coefficients $a[i]$.
   (a) Prove that such a mapping is one-to-one.
   (b) Derive the descending-order Levinson recursion that maps a set of linear prediction filter coefficients into a set of reflection coefficients.
   (c) State a stability test for all-pole filters in terms of the reflection coefficients based on the stability test for the linear prediction coefficients.
   (d) Is the filter

$$H(z) = \frac{1}{1 - 2z^{-1} - 6z^{-2} + z^{-3} - 2z^{-4}}$$

   stable?

8. Show that the lattice filter is an orthogonalizing filter by proving that the backward linear prediction errors are orthogonal to each other in the lattice, i.e.,

$$\mathcal{E}\{e^b[m]e^{b\,*}[n]\} = \rho_w \delta[m-n] \quad .$$

Hint: use Eq. (3.164).

9. The analysis of an $\mathrm{AR}(p)$ spectrum of a process consisting of M complex sinusoids in additive white noise may be simplified whenever $p > M$ by creating a reduced-order equation set [Satorius and Zeidler, 1978; Kay, 1987]. Using the analytic expression,

Eq. (4.52), for the autocorrelation function of M complex sinusoids in additive white noise, show that the autoregresive parameters satisfy the relationship

$$a_p[k] = \sum_{i=1}^{M} \gamma_i \exp(j2\pi f_i[k-1]T)$$

for $1 \le k \le p$ and $p > M$, where

$$\gamma_m + \sum_{\substack{n=1 \\ n \ne m}}^{M} c_{mn}\gamma_n = -\frac{P_m}{pP_m + \rho_w}\exp(j2\pi f_m T)$$

and

$$c_{mn} = \frac{P_m}{pP_m + \rho_w}\left(\frac{1 - \exp(j2\pi[f_n - f_m]pT)}{1 - \exp(j2\pi[f_n - f_m]T)}\right) \quad .$$

Also show that

$$\rho_p = \rho_w\left[1 - \sum_{i=1}^{M}\gamma_i \exp(-j2\pi f_i T)\right] \quad .$$

[Hint: Substitute the vector form of the autocorrelation sequence into the Yule-Walker equations.] This procedure replaces the p Yule-Walker equations with a smaller set of M equations in the γ_i coefficients.

8

AUTOREGRESSIVE SPECTRAL ESTIMATION: BLOCK DATA ALGORITHMS

8.1 INTRODUCTION

Basic properties and relationships of the autoregressive (AR) model and its associated PSD function have been presented in Chaps. 6 and 7. The underlying assumption in these chapters was the availability of the exact autocorrelation function of the random process. In practice, though, the autocorrelation is usually not available, so one must make an AR spectral estimate based on the available data. Both this chapter and the next chapter are concerned with algorithmic techniques for producing AR spectral estimates from data samples. These techniques actually make estimates of the AR model parameters, and from these, the AR PSD function may be evaluated.

The techniques have been divided into two categories: algorithms for *block* data and algorithms for *sequential* data. This chapter presents block data methods, that is, algorithms that process an entire fixed-size block of accumulated data samples. Chapter 9 presents sequential data methods, that is, algorithms that process the data sequentially as each sample becomes available. The block techniques in this chapter may be succinctly described as fixed-time, recursive-in-order algorithms in the sense that they operate on a fixed block of time samples and recursively yield higher-order AR model parameter estimates based on lower-order AR parameter estimates. This is an advantage in situations where the appropriate

AR model order is not known and many different orders must be tried and compared in order to select a suitable order. The sequential techniques of Chap. 9, on the other hand, may be described as fixed-order, recursive-in-time algorithms in the sense that they process the data sequentially to update the estimates of a fixed-order AR model. This is an advantage in situations in which tracking, or adapting to, a slowly time varying spectrum is required.

Conceptually, the simplest procedure to obtain an AR spectral estimate from data samples would be to produce estimates of the autocorrelation sequence from the data using program CORRELATION of Chap. 5. These autocorrelation estimates would then be used, in lieu of the unavailable true autocorrelation sequence, in the Yule-Walker equations of Chap. 6 to yield the AR coefficients, and from these the AR PSD function. However, better results are obtained, particularly for short data segments, by algorithms that yield the AR model parameters directly from the data, without the need for autocorrelation estimates, as examples in this chapter will illustrate.

The block data techniques considered in this chapter fall into three categories, with a section devoted to each. In Chap. 7, it was shown that the AR parameters could be obtained through the equivalent representations of either the autocorrelation sequence or the reflection coefficient sequence. The so-called *Yule-Walker method* of AR parameter estimation from autocorrelation sequence estimates is covered in Sec. 8.3. Two methods of AR parameter estimation from reflection coefficient sequence estimates are provided in Sec. 8.4, including the popular *Burg algorithm*. An important category of AR parameter estimation methods is based on a least squares linear prediction approach. Techniques in this category, which are discussed in Sec. 8.5, are further distinguished by the type of linear prediction estimate used. One class of techniques performs *separate* minimization of the forward and backward linear prediction squared errors. Included in this class are the *autocorrelation* and *covariance* methods. Another class of techniques performs combined minimization of the forward and backward linear prediction squared errors. Included in this class is the *modified covariance* method. Other sections in this chapter present methods for AR model order selection and cover modifications required to handle observation noise in data measurements.

8.2   SUMMARY

In order to produce an autoregressive PSD estimate directly from a block of data samples, computer programs have been included in this chapter to provide the reader with a choice of four possible algorithms. Figure 8.1 is a flowchart of the steps required to estimate the AR power spectral density. One of four subroutines for estimating the AR parameters must be selected. The Yule-Walker method (Sec. 8.3) produces AR spectra for short data records with the least resolution among the four methods. The Burg (Sec. 8.4.2) and covariance (Sec. 8.5.1) methods produce comparable AR spectral estimates. The modified covariance method (Sec. 8.5.2) is

- ACQUIRE DATA
  N samples
  T seconds/sample

- TREND REMOVAL (optional)
  See Chapter 14

- SELECT AR MODEL ORDER
  Parameter IP

- ESTIMATE AR PARAMETERS
  Select one of the following:
  — Yule–Walker method
    (Subroutine YULEWALKER, Appendix 8.A)
  — Burg method
    (Subroutine BURG, Appendix 8.B)
  — Covariance method
    (Subroutine COVAR, Appendix 8.C)
  — Modified covariance method
    (Subroutine MODCOVAR, Appendix 8.D)

- COMPUTE AR PSD ESTIMATE
  Subroutine ARMAPSD, Appendix 6.B

- ORDER CLOSING
  Adjust order for variance/resolution trade–off

Figure 8.1 Flowchart for four AR PSD block estimation algorithms implemented in this chapter.

best for sinusoidal components in the data. The Yule-Walker and Burg methods make direct AR parameter estimates $\hat{a}[n]$. The covariance and modified covariance methods actually make estimates of the linear prediction coefficients, which are then used as the AR parameter estimates by equating the AR parameters to the forward linear prediction coefficients, $\hat{a}[n] = a^f[n]$, or to the complex conjugated backward linear prediction coefficients, $\hat{a}[n] = (a^b[n])^*$. Once the AR parameters have been estimated, then the AR spectral estimate is computed as

$$\hat{P}_{AR}(f) = \frac{T\hat{\rho}_w}{\left|1 + \sum_{n=1}^{p} \hat{a}[n]\exp(-j2\pi fnT)\right|^2} \quad , \tag{8.1}$$

in which $\hat{\rho}_w$ is an estimate of the driving noise variance, which is also provided by all four methods of Fig. 8.1. The subroutine names and the appendix where each program listing may be found are shown on the flowchart. Note that the AR model order must be provided as an input parameter, in addition to the input data. The order determines the trade-off between resolution and estimate variance in AR spectra, analogous to the effect of windows in classical spectral estimates. Many different orders should be tried in a fashion similar to the window-closing approach of classical spectral estimation in order to determine the most suitable order to use. This will be called *order closing*, in analogy with the window closing scheme of classical spectral estimation. Section 8.7 presents methods for automatic order selection that could be incorporated into the program code of any algorithm, thereby relieving the need to enter an order parameter.

Examples of the four AR PSD estimates made from the 64-point test sequence of Appendix II are shown in Fig. 8.2. A 15th-order AR process was selected for all four methods. An inset on the covariance method also shows an 8th-order spectral estimate to illustrate the resolution/smoothing trade-off that order selection permits. These estimates should be compared with the true spectrum depicted in Fig. 1.8. The chapter appendices contain listings of the AR coefficients obtained from each method. These may be used to verify the implementation of the computer program on the reader's computer. The spectra of Fig. 8.2 exhibit very sharp spectral lines. To ensure that the PSD function has been adequately sampled in frequency by subroutine ARMAPSD, so that no sharp peaks are missed, one need only sum the PSD values over all frequencies. This sum should be equal to the total power in the process and, therefore, should agree closely in value with the zero-lag autocorrelation term, which also represents the total power in the process. If the values do not agree, then a denser frequency grid (requires the input parameter N to subroutine ARMAPSD to be increased) is necessary in order to find one or more missed sharp peaks.

8.3 CORRELATION FUNCTION ESTIMATION METHOD

The most obvious approach to AR PSD estimation from data samples is to use autocorrelation function estimates in lieu of the unknown autocorrelation function for the solution of the Yule-Walker equations. This will be termed the *Yule-Walker algorithm*. If the unbiased autocorrelation estimate is selected, it may result in a nonpositive-definite autocorrelation matrix, so that a stable AR filter will not be assured. The biased correlation estimates will always yield positive-semidefinite autocorrelation matrices, so that a stable AR filter will be assured. For long data records, this AR parameter estimator can produce reasonable spectral estimates. For short data records, the use of the Yule-Walker approach produces poor-resolution spectral estimates relative to other AR methods; other techniques can produce better spectral estimates, as illustrated in Fig. 8.2. Program YULE-WALKER in Appendix 8.A implements this technique.

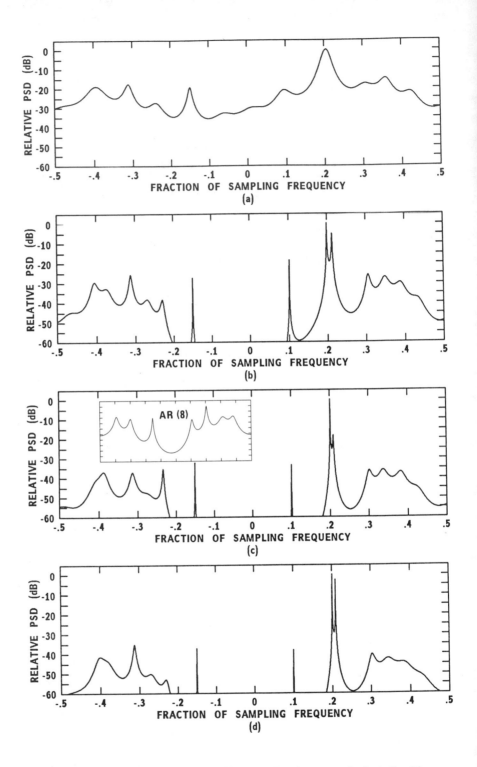

Figure 8.2 Examples of four AR(15) spectral estimates made from the 64-point test data sequence. (a) Yule-Walker method. (b)Burg method. (c) Covariance method. (d) Modified covariance method.

8.4 REFLECTION COEFFICIENT ESTIMATION METHODS

The Levinson recursive solution to the Yule-Walker equations relates the order p AR parameters to the order $p-1$ parameters as

$$a_p[n] = a_{p-1}[n] + k_p a_{p-1}^*[p-n] \qquad (8.2)$$

for $n = 1$ to $n = p - 1$, where the reflection coefficient k_p is found by using the known autocorrelation function for lags 0 to $p - 1$,

$$k_p = a_p[p] = \frac{-\displaystyle\sum_{n=0}^{p-1} a_{p-1}[n] r_{xx}[p-n]}{\rho_{p-1}} . \qquad (8.3)$$

The recursion for the driving white noise variance was given by

$$\rho_p = \rho_{p-1}(1 - |k_p|^2), \qquad (8.4)$$

where $\rho_0 = r_{xx}[0]$. Among the quantities in Eqs. (8.2)–(8.4), only the reflection coefficient depends directly on the autocorrelation function. This suggests that one procedure for yielding an AR PSD estimate, when only a block of data samples is available, is to use the data samples to estimate the reflection coefficient at each stage of the Levinson recursion. Three methods have evolved from this concept, one based on the geometric mean of the forward and backward linear prediction squared errors, one based on the arithmetic mean of these squared errors, and one based on an approximate maximum likelihood approach.

8.4.1 Geometric Algorithm

The forward linear prediction error is given by

$$e_p^f[n] = x[n] + \sum_{m=1}^{p} a_p^f[m] x[n-m] \qquad (8.5)$$

and the backward linear prediction error is given by

$$e_p^b[n] = x[n-p] + \sum_{m=1}^{p} a_p^{f*}[m] x[n+m-p] . \qquad (8.6)$$

Substitution of Eq. (8.2) into these definitions yields the recursive relationships

$$\begin{aligned}
e_p^f[n] &= e_{p-1}^f[n] + k_p e_{p-1}^b[n-1] \\
e_p^b[n] &= e_{p-1}^b[n-1] + k_p^* e_{p-1}^f[n]
\end{aligned} \qquad (8.7)$$

that relate the order $p-1$ prediction errors to the order p prediction errors. In Chap. 7, it was shown that k_p has an interpretation as a partial correlation coefficient between the forward and backward linear prediction errors, with the property

$$k_p = -\frac{\mathcal{E}\{e^f_{p-1}[n]e^{b*}_{p-1}[n-1]\}}{\mathcal{E}\{|e^f_{p-1}[n]|^2\}^{1/2}\,\mathcal{E}\{|e^b_{p-1}[n-1]|^2\}^{1/2}}. \tag{8.8}$$

This represents the "geometric" mean† between the forward prediction partial correlation $\mathcal{E}\{e^f_{p-1}[n]e^{b*}_{p-1}[n-1]\}/\mathcal{E}\{|e^f_{p-1}[n]|^2\}$ and the backward prediction partial correlation $\mathcal{E}\{e^f_{p-1}[n]e^{b*}_{p-1}[n-1]\}/\mathcal{E}\{|e^b_{p-1}[n-1]|^2\}$. By substituting the prediction error autocorrelation and cross correlation estimates

$$\frac{1}{N}\sum_{n=p+1}^{N} e^f_{p-1}[n]e^{b*}_{p-1}[n-1]$$

$$\frac{1}{N}\sum_{n=p+1}^{N} |e^f_{p-1}[n]|^2 \tag{8.9}$$

$$\frac{1}{N}\sum_{n=p+1}^{N} |e^b_{p-1}[n-1]|^2,$$

the reflection coefficient may be approximated as

$$\hat{k}_p = \frac{-\sum_{n=p+1}^{N} e^f_{p-1}[n]e^{b*}_{p-1}[n-1]}{\left(\sum_{n=p+1}^{N}|e^f_{p-1}[n]|^2\right)^{1/2}\left(\sum_{n=p+1}^{N}|e^b_{p-1}[n-1]|^2\right)^{1/2}}. \tag{8.10}$$

Note that it did not matter whether the biased or unbiased correlation estimator was used, as the scale factor divides out. It has been assumed in Eq. (8.10) that there are N samples $x[1],\ldots,x[N]$, and prediction errors $e^f_p[n]$ and $e^b_p[n]$ only in the index range from $n=p+1$ to $n=N$ are formed, because this uses only the available data samples. It is easy to show that $\hat{k}_p$ has magnitude less than unity, so that a stable AR filter (poles within the unit circle) will be ensured.

The geometric algorithm, therefore, will use the Levinson algorithm, substituting estimate $\hat{k}_p$ for the usual reflection coefficient computation based on known

---

† The geometric mean between two numbers a and b is $\sqrt{ab}$, the arithmetic mean is $(a+b)/2$, and the harmonic mean is $2ab/(a+b)$.

correlation values. The basic Levinson algorithm is supplemented with the prediction error recursions given by Eq. (8.7), which are initialized at order zero by

$$e_0^f[n] = e_0^b[n] = x[n] \tag{8.11}$$

for $1 \leq n \leq N$. The linear prediction error variance is initialized by the estimate

$$\rho_0 = \frac{1}{N} \sum_{n=1}^{N} |x[n]|^2, \tag{8.12}$$

which represents the sample power in the N data samples. A multichannel version of the geometric algorithm is developed in Chap. 15 and a computer program is provided in Appendix 15.A. Selecting the case of one channel (NUMCHS=1) for that program will yield solutions identical to the geometric algorithm presented here.

8.4.2 Harmonic (Burg) Algorithm

One of the earliest and best known algorithms for AR spectral estimation was introduced by John Burg [1967], and later was described in detail by Andersen [1974], Datta [1977], Haykin and Kesler [1976], and Ulrych et al. [1973]. This algorithm has been called a maximum entropy algorithm, but it should be considered as a separate and distinct contribution from Burg's maximum entropy concept [1975].

The Burg algorithm is identical to the geometric algorithm, except that an alternative estimate for the reflection coefficient is determined, based on a least squares criteria. At each order p, the arithmetic mean of the forward and backward linear prediction error power (sample prediction error variance)

$$\rho_p^{fb} = \frac{1}{2}\left[\frac{1}{N}\sum_{n=p+1}^{N}|e_p^f[n]|^2 + \frac{1}{N}\sum_{n=p+1}^{N}|e_p^b[n]|^2\right] \tag{8.13}$$

is minimized, subject to the recursion given by Eq. (8.7). Note again that the summation ranges only over the available data. Thus, ρ_p^{fb} is a function of a single parameter, namely the complex-valued reflection coefficient k_p, because the prediction errors from order $p-1$ will be known. Setting the complex derivative of Eq. (8.13) to zero

$$\frac{\partial \rho_p^{fb}}{\partial \operatorname{Re}\{k_p\}} + j\frac{\partial \rho_p^{fb}}{\partial \operatorname{Im}\{k_p\}} = 0$$

and solving for k_p yields the least squares estimate

$$\hat{k}_p = \frac{-2\displaystyle\sum_{n=p+1}^{N} e_{p-1}^f[n]e_{p-1}^{b*}[n-1]}{\displaystyle\sum_{n=p+1}^{N}|e_{p-1}^f[n]|^2 + \sum_{n=p+1}^{N}|e_{p-1}^b[n-1]|^2}. \tag{8.14}$$

This estimate of the reflection coefficient represents the "harmonic" mean between the forward and backward partial correlation coefficients. It is easy to prove that this estimate of the reflection coefficient has magnitude less than or equal to unity, thereby ensuring a stable all-pole filter. A further recursion that simplifies the evaluation of the denominator term in Eq. (8.14) was discovered by Andersen [1978]. Define

$$\text{DEN}_p = \sum_{n=p+1}^{N} \left(|e_{p-1}^f[n]|^2 + |e_{p-1}^b[n-1]|^2 \right); \qquad (8.15)$$

then

$$\text{DEN}_p = \left(1 - |\hat{k}_{p-1}|^2 \right) \text{DEN}_{p-1} - |e_{p-1}^f[p]|^2 - |e_{p-1}^b[N]|^2. \qquad (8.16)$$

The proof of this is left as an exercise for the reader (see the Problems). A FORTRAN program of the Burg algorithm is provided in Appendix 8.B. It is annotated with equation references to the text. A computational complexity analysis (counting only second-order terms) will show that $3Np - p^2$ complex adds and multiplies, as well as p real divisions, are required. Storage of $3N + p$ complex values is also required.

The harmonic method exhibits some bias in the estimation of sinusoidal frequencies, as will be illustrated in Sec. 8.6. This has led some researchers to propose variations of the harmonic method in order to mitigate these biases. The basic variation is a weighting of the squared prediction errors,

$$\rho_p^{fb} = \frac{1}{2} \left[\frac{1}{N} \sum_{n=p+1}^{N} w_p[n] \{ |e_p^f[n]|^2 + |e_p^b[n]|^2 \} \right] \quad ,$$

leading to the reflection coefficient estimate

$$\hat{k}_p = \frac{-2 \sum_{n=p+1}^{N} w_{p-1}[n] e_{p-1}^f[n] e_{p-1}^{b*}[n-1]}{\sum_{n=p+1}^{N} w_{p-1}[n] \left(|e_{p-1}^f[n]|^2 + |e_{p-1}^b[n-1]|^2 \right)} \quad , \qquad (8.17)$$

where $w_{p-1}[n]$ represents the weighting function. As long as $w[n] \geq 0$, then $|\hat{k}_p| \leq 1$. The Burg algorithm selects the uniform weighting $w_{p-1}[n] = 1/N$. Swingler [1979b, 1980] provided simulations that indicated a Hamming taper function reduced the frequency bias. Kaveh and Lippert [1983] found that a special quadratic window could also achieve a reduction in the sinusoidal frequency bias over most of the frequency range. Helme and Nikias [1984] propose the data-adaptive weighting

$$w_{p-1}[n] = \sum_{k=n-p+1}^{n-1} |x[k]|^2 \quad \text{for} \quad p \geq 2,$$

which represents the common data energy in the forward and backward linear prediction errors $e_{p-1}^{f}[n]$ and $e_{p-1}^{b}[n-1]$ at time index n.

8.4.3 Recursive MLE Method

The recursive MLE [Kay, 1983] derives its name based upon the MLE principles that are used to develop an estimate of the reflection coefficients and the order update of the autoregressive coefficients provided by the Levinson recursion. The derivation details are quite extensive; only a summary of the algorithm is given here. The reader may consult Kay [1983] for a derivation assuming real data. The extension to the complex data case is not yet available.

If the probability density function of a zero-mean Gaussian autoregressive process at order p is maximized with respect to the reflection coefficient k_p and the driving noise variance ρ_p, assuming the order $p - 1$ autoregressive coefficients have previously been computed, then the k_p and ρ_p estimates that maximize the PDF for a given data sequence $x[0]$, $x[1]$, ..., $x[N - 1]$ are given as the solution of the cubic equation

$$\hat{k}_p^3 + \left(\frac{N - 2p}{N - p}\right)\left(\frac{\alpha_p}{\beta_p}\right)\hat{k}_p^2 - \left(\frac{p\delta_{p-1} + N\alpha_p}{[N - p]\beta_p}\right)\hat{k}_p - \left(\frac{N}{N - p}\right)\left(\frac{\alpha_p}{\beta_p}\right) = 0 \quad ,$$

for which the real root within the interval $[-1, 1]$ that maximizes the PDF is selected, and the linear equations

$$\delta_p = \delta_{p-1} + 2\alpha_p\hat{k}_p + \beta_p\hat{k}_p^2$$
$$\hat{\rho}_p = \delta_p/N$$

are used. The real coefficients α_p and β_p are determined from the quadratic forms

$$\alpha_p = \begin{pmatrix} \mathbf{a}_{p-1}^T & 0 \end{pmatrix} \mathbf{S}_p \begin{pmatrix} \mathbf{Ja}_{p-1} \\ 0 \end{pmatrix}$$

$$\beta_p = \begin{pmatrix} 0 & \mathbf{a}_{p-1}^T\mathbf{J} \end{pmatrix} \mathbf{S}_p \begin{pmatrix} \mathbf{Ja}_{p-1} \\ 0 \end{pmatrix} \quad ,$$

for which $\mathbf{a} = (1 \quad a_{p-1}[1] \quad \cdots \quad a_{p-1}[p - 1])^T$ is the autoregressive coefficient vector, $\mathbf{J}$ is a $p \times p$ reflection matrix, and $\mathbf{S}_p$ is a $(p + 1) \times (p + 1)$ matrix with elements

$$s_p[i, j] = \sum_{n=p}^{N-1+i+j-p} x[n - i]x[n - j]$$

defined for $0 \leq i, j \leq p$. Once $\hat{k}_p$ has been estimated, then the usual Levinson recursion [Eq. (8.2)] is used to update the order $p - 1$ autoregressive coefficients to the order p coefficients. The initial condition

$$\delta_0 = \sum_{n=0}^{N-1} x^2[n]$$

is required to initialize the recursive MLE algorithm. A computer program that implements this algorithm may be found in Kay [1987].

8.5 LEAST SQUARES LINEAR PREDICTION ESTIMATION METHODS

By constraining the AR coefficients to satisfy the Levinson recursive relationship, Eq. (8.2), Burg was able to perform a least squares optimization with respect to a single parameter, namely, the reflection coefficient. An alternative approach would be to perform a least squares minimization with respect to *all* of the linear prediction coefficients, entirely removing the Levinson recursion constraint. Such an approach will yield some improvement to the spectral estimate, as Sec. 8.6 will demonstrate. Two types of least squares estimates will be considered. The first type utilizes separate forward or backward linear prediction for the estimate. The second type employs a combination of forward and backward linear prediction.

8.5.1 Separate Forward and Backward Linear Prediction Algorithms

Assume the N-point data sequence $x[1], \ldots, x[N]$ is to be used to estimate the pth-order AR parameters. The forward linear predictor $\hat{x}[n]$ for sample $x[n]$ will have the usual form

$$\hat{x}^f[n] = -\sum_{k=1}^{p} a_p^f[k]x[n-k] \quad , \tag{8.18}$$

where the $a_p^f[k]$ are the forward linear prediction coefficients for order p. The prediction is "forward" in the sense that the prediction for the current data sample is a weighted sum of p prior samples. The forward linear prediction error is

$$e_p^f[n] = x[n] - \hat{x}^f[n] = x[n] + \sum_{k=1}^{p} a_p^f[k]x[n-k]. \tag{8.19}$$

This expression is identical in form to the recursion that describes a pth-order autoregressive process, except $e_p^f[n]$ is not a driving white noise process. The linear prediction error derived from a finite data sequence may, or may not, be a white process. For purposes of fitting an autoregressive model, it is *assumed* that the prediction error is a whitened process, permitting one to equate the autoregressive parameters to the linear prediction coefficients.

The forward linear prediction error may be defined over the range from $n = 1$ to $n = N + p$, if one assumes that the data prior to the first sample and after the last sample are zero ($x[n] = 0$ for $n < 1$ and $n > N$). The $N + p$ forward linear prediction error terms represented by Eq. (8.19) may be summarized, using matrix-vector notation, as

$$
\begin{pmatrix}
e_p^f[1] \\
\vdots \\
e_p^f[p+1] \\
\vdots \\
e_p^f[N-p] \\
\vdots \\
e_p^f[N] \\
\vdots \\
e_p^f[N+p]
\end{pmatrix}
=
\underbrace{\begin{pmatrix}
x[1] & \cdots & 0 \\
\vdots & \ddots & \vdots \\
x[p+1] & & x[1] \\
\vdots & \ddots & \vdots \\
x[N-p] & & x[p+1] \\
\vdots & \ddots & \vdots \\
x[N] & & x[N-p] \\
\vdots & \ddots & \vdots \\
0 & \cdots & x[N]
\end{pmatrix}}_{\mathbf{X}_p}
\begin{pmatrix}
1 \\
a_p^f[1] \\
\vdots \\
a_p^f[p]
\end{pmatrix},
\tag{8.20}
$$

in which $\mathbf{X}_p$ is an $(N+p) \times (p+1)$ rectangular Toeplitz data matrix. The upper right and lower left corners of the data matrix are zeros, clearly emphasizing the implied windowing of the data sequence. The data matrix may be partitioned into three components

$$
\mathbf{X}_p = \begin{pmatrix} \mathbf{L}_p \\ \mathbf{T}_p \\ \mathbf{U}_p \end{pmatrix},
\tag{8.21}
$$

where the lower triangular $p \times (p+1)$ matrix $\mathbf{L}_p$, rectangular $(N-p) \times (p+1)$ matrix $\mathbf{T}_p$, and upper triangular $p \times (p+1)$ matrix $\mathbf{U}_p$ are defined as

$$
\mathbf{L}_p = \begin{pmatrix}
x[1] & \cdots & 0 & 0 \\
\vdots & \ddots & \vdots & \vdots \\
x[p] & \cdots & x[1] & 0
\end{pmatrix}
$$

$$
\mathbf{T}_p = \begin{pmatrix}
x[p+1] & \cdots & x[1] \\
\vdots & \ddots & \vdots \\
x[N-p] & & x[p+1] \\
\vdots & \ddots & \vdots \\
x[N] & \cdots & x[N-p]
\end{pmatrix}
\tag{8.22}
$$

$$
\mathbf{U}_p = \begin{pmatrix}
0 & x[N] & \cdots & x[N-p+1] \\
\vdots & \vdots & \ddots & \vdots \\
0 & 0 & \cdots & x[N]
\end{pmatrix}.
$$

The forward linear prediction squared error magnitude to be minimized is simply

$$
\rho_p^f = \sum_n |e_p^f[n]|^2 .
\tag{8.23}
$$

Dividing ρ_p^f by N will yield the sample variance. The summation range for ρ_p^f has purposely not been specified, because there are many possible range cases that one may select. Three cases have been used for spectral estimation. Selecting the full range from $e_p^f[1]$ to $e_p^f[N+p]$ is the *windowed* case, because it involves pre- and postwindowing of the data (i.e., setting unavailable data values to zero). Selecting the range $e_p^f[1]$ to $e_p^f[N]$ is the *prewindowed* case, because it requires data prior to $x[1]$ to be set to zero. Selecting the range $e_p^f[p+1]$ to $e_p^f[N]$ is the *nonwindowed* case, because only available data samples are used. The windowed case has been termed the *autocorrelation* method of linear prediction. The nonwindowed case has been termed the *covariance* method of linear prediction. This terminology is based on historical usage in speech processing [Makhoul, 1975] and is not justified by the standard statistical definitions for these terms (i.e., the covariance is the correlation with the mean removed).

Consider first the least squares linear prediction estimate based on minimization of ρ_p^f for the *autocorrelation* (windowed) method. The relationship between the forward linear prediction errors and the linear prediction coefficients may be succinctly expressed as

$$\mathbf{e}_p^f = \mathbf{X}_p \begin{pmatrix} 1 \\ \mathbf{a}_p^f \end{pmatrix} \quad , \tag{8.24}$$

in which the $(N+p)$-element error vector $\mathbf{e}_p^f$ and p-element linear prediction coefficient vector $\mathbf{a}_p^f$ are defined as

$$\mathbf{e}_p^f = \begin{pmatrix} e_p^f[1] \\ \vdots \\ e_p^f[N+p] \end{pmatrix} \quad , \quad \mathbf{a}_p^f = \begin{pmatrix} a_p^f[1] \\ \vdots \\ a_p^f[p] \end{pmatrix} \tag{8.25}$$

and $\mathbf{X}_p$ is the $(N+p) \times (p+1)$ data matrix of Eq. (8.20). Equation (8.24) has the same form as that of Eq. (3.62), so that the normal equations that minimize the squared error

$$\rho_p^f = \sum_{n=1}^{N+p} |e_p^f[n]|^2 = (\mathbf{e}_p^f)^H \mathbf{e}_p^f \tag{8.26}$$

at order p are determined simply by inspection of Eq. (3.67) to be

$$\mathbf{X}_p^H \mathbf{X}_p \begin{pmatrix} 1 \\ \mathbf{a}_p^f \end{pmatrix} = \begin{pmatrix} \rho_p^f \\ \mathbf{0}_p \end{pmatrix} \quad . \tag{8.27}$$

The product $\mathbf{X}_p^H \mathbf{X}_p$ forms a square $(p+1) \times (p+1)$ Hermitian matrix $\mathbf{R}_p$ of the form

$$\mathbf{R}_p = \mathbf{X}_p^H \mathbf{X}_p = \begin{pmatrix} r_p[0,0] & \cdots & r_p[0,p] \\ \vdots & & \vdots \\ r_p[p,0] & \cdots & r_p[p,p] \end{pmatrix} \quad , \tag{8.28}$$

in which $r_p[i,j] = r_p^*[j,i]$. Elements of $\mathbf{R}_p$ have the lagged-product form

$$r_p[i,j] = \sum_{n=1}^{N+p} x^*[n-i]x[n-j] = \sum_{k=1}^{N-(i-j)} x[k+(i-j)]x^*[k] \qquad (8.29)$$

for $0 \le i-j \le p$. Because $r_p[i,j]$ depends only on the difference $(i-j)$, $\mathbf{X}_p^H\mathbf{X}_p$ forms a Toeplitz matrix [see Eq. (3.35)]. If $r_p[i,j]$ is divided by N, these terms will then be identical to the biased autocorrelation sequence estimate $\check{r}_{xx}[i-j] = r_p[i,j]/N$; in this case, normal equations (8.27) will be identical to the Yule-Walker equations (6.32). Thus, the autocorrelation method of least squares linear prediction analysis is equivalent to the Yule-Walker method of autoregressive parameter estimation in which biased autocorrelation estimates are used. The windowing of the autocorrelation method is responsible for the apparent reduction in resolution relative to the other linear-prediction-based estimation methods to be discussed (see Fig. 8.2 for an example). Thus, this approach is rarely used in practice for short data segments, because better performance is obtained by the other least squares methods.

The relationship between the forward linear prediction errors and the linear prediction coefficients for the *covariance* (nonwindowed) method may be succinctly expressed as

$$\mathbf{e}_p^f = \mathbf{T}_p \begin{pmatrix} 1 \\ \mathbf{a}_p^f \end{pmatrix} \quad, \qquad (8.30)$$

in which the $N \times (p+1)$ Toeplitz data matrix $\mathbf{T}_p$ was defined in Eq. (8.22), the p-element linear prediction coefficient vector $\mathbf{a}_p^f$ was defined in Eq. (8.25), and the $(N-p)$-element error vector $\mathbf{e}_p^f$ now has the structure

$$\mathbf{e}_p^f = \begin{pmatrix} e_p^f[p+1] \\ \vdots \\ e_p^f[N] \end{pmatrix} \quad. \qquad (8.31)$$

The normal equations that minimize the squared error

$$\rho_p^f = \sum_{n=p+1}^{N} |e_p^f[n]|^2 = (\mathbf{e}_p^f)^H \mathbf{e}_p^f \qquad (8.32)$$

at order p are determined, again, simply by inspection of Eq. (3.67) to be

$$\mathbf{T}_p^H \mathbf{T}_p \begin{pmatrix} 1 \\ \mathbf{a}_p^f \end{pmatrix} = \begin{pmatrix} \rho_p^f \\ \mathbf{0}_p \end{pmatrix} \quad. \qquad (8.33)$$

The $(p+1) \times (p+1)$ Hermitian matrix $\mathbf{R}_p = \mathbf{T}_p^H \mathbf{T}_p$ has lagged-product elements of the form

$$r_p[i,j] = \sum_{n=p+1}^{N} x^*[n-i]x[n-j] \qquad (8.34)$$

for $0 \leq i, j \leq p$. The elements of $\mathbf{R}_p$ in the covariance method cannot be expressed as functions of the difference $(i-j)$, which means the product $\mathbf{T}_p^H \mathbf{T}_p$ is not Toeplitz. However, the fact that $\mathbf{R}_p$ is the product of two Toeplitz matrices still makes it possible to develop a fast algorithm similar to that of the Levinson algorithm. Thus, the solution of Eq. (8.33) in the covariance case may be obtained with an algorithm of computational complexity proportional to p^2 operations, as compared to p^3 operations that would be required if the Cholesky algorithm had been used. Appendix 8.C provides the details of this fast algorithm and a computer program (COVAR). A necessary, but not sufficient, condition for $\mathbf{R}_p$ to be a nonsingular matrix is that $N - p \geq p$, or $p \leq N/2$. The selected order must, therefore, be no greater than half the data length. The covariance method will be encountered again in Chap. 11 as part of the Prony method. It can be shown [Kay, 1987] that the covariance method is an approximate maximum likelihood estimate for the AR parameters when the process is Gaussian.

Based on a development similar to that used for the windowed and non-windowed cases, it is simple to show that the normal equation matrix $\mathbf{R}_p$ in the *prewindowed* case may be expressed as the data matrix product

$$\mathbf{R}_p = \begin{pmatrix} \mathbf{L}_p \\ \mathbf{T}_p \end{pmatrix}^H \begin{pmatrix} \mathbf{L}_p \\ \mathbf{T}_p \end{pmatrix} = \mathbf{L}_p^H \mathbf{L}_p + \mathbf{T}_p^H \mathbf{T}_p = \mathbf{X}_p^H \mathbf{X}_p - \mathbf{U}_p^H \mathbf{U}_p \qquad (8.35)$$

with elements of the form

$$r_p[i, j] = \sum_{n=1}^{N} x^*[n - i] x[n - j] \qquad (8.36)$$

for $0 \leq i, j \leq p$. The prewindowed method is of most interest for the sequential least squares linear prediction methods. This method will be treated in more detail in Chap. 9.

The windowed (autocorrelation), nonwindowed (covariance), and prewindowed cases may also be developed for the case of the *backward* linear predictor

$$\hat{x}^b[k] = -\sum_{k=1}^{p} a_p^b[k] x[k + p] \quad , \qquad (8.37)$$

where the $a_p^b[k]$ are the backward linear prediction coefficients for order p. The prediction is "backward" in the sense that the prediction for the current data sample is a weighted sum of p future samples. For a finite data set, the backward linear prediction parameters determined by least squares analysis are not, in general, identical to the forward prediction parameters. The backward linear prediction error is

$$e_p^b[n] = x[n - p] - \hat{x}^b[n - p] = x[n - p] + \sum_{k=1}^{p} a_p^b[k] x[n - p + k] \quad . \qquad (8.38)$$

With the assumption that $x[n] = 0$ for $n < 0$ and $n > N$, the backward linear prediction error terms may be summarized by the matrix-vector product

$$\mathbf{e}_p^b = \mathbf{X}_p \begin{pmatrix} \mathbf{a}_p^b \\ 1 \end{pmatrix} \quad , \tag{8.39}$$

where the backward linear prediction error vector $\mathbf{e}_p^b$ and the backward linear prediction coefficient vector $\mathbf{a}_p^b$ are defined as

$$\mathbf{e}_p^b = \begin{pmatrix} e_p^b[N+p] \\ \vdots \\ e_p^b[1] \end{pmatrix} \qquad \mathbf{a}_p^b = \begin{pmatrix} a_p^b[p] \\ \vdots \\ a_p^b[1] \end{pmatrix} \tag{8.40}$$

and $\mathbf{X}_p$ is the same Toeplitz data matrix defined by Eq. (8.21).

The backward linear prediction squared error is given by

$$\rho_p^b = \sum_n |e_p^b[n]|^2. \tag{8.41}$$

The summation range is 1 to $N + p$ for the windowed (autocorrelation) case, $p + 1$ to N for the nonwindowed (covariance) case, and 1 to N for the prewindowed case. Using the same arguments as used for the forward linear prediction cases, the normal equations for the backward linear prediction cases have the form

$$\mathbf{R}_p \begin{pmatrix} \mathbf{a}_p^b \\ 1 \end{pmatrix} = \begin{pmatrix} \mathbf{0}_p \\ \rho_p^b \end{pmatrix} \quad , \tag{8.42}$$

where $\mathbf{R}_p$ equals $\mathbf{X}_p^H \mathbf{X}_p$ for the windowed case, $\mathbf{T}_p^H \mathbf{T}_p$ for the nonwindowed case, and Eq. (8.35) in the prewindowed case. The solutions for the forward and backward normal equations are coupled because both have the same $\mathbf{R}_p$ matrix. The fast algorithms for both the covariance and prewindowed methods will simultaneously solve the normal equations for both the forward and the backward linear prediction coefficients at all intermediate orders, because the solutions for each are intertwined. Thus, both sets of coefficients are available for analysis at no additional computational cost.

The forward and backward linear prediction coefficients generated by the covariance method do not guarantee a stable filter. This is not generally a problem if the use of the coefficients is only for spectral estimation purposes. In fact, spectral estimates produced with the autoregressive coefficients estimated by the covariance method usually have less distortion [Nuttall, 1976; Lang and McClellan, 1980] than spectral estimates produced by methods that ensure the filter stability, such as the autocorrelation method. If an actual linear prediction filter is synthesized for nonspectral estimation purposes, then the filter stability issue is of concern.

One variation to the covariance method was proposed by Nikias and Scott [1983]. Their method selects the forward and backward linear prediction coefficients based on the weighted squared errors

$$\rho_p^f = \sum_{n=p+1}^{N} w_p[n]|e_p^f[n]|^2 \qquad \rho_p^b = \sum_{n=p+1}^{N} w_p[n]|e_p^b[n]|^2 \quad , \tag{8.43}$$

in which the weights represent the energy of the data used to form the prediction errors within the window,

$$w_p[n] = \sum_{k=n-p+1}^{n} |x[k]|^2.$$

No fast algorithm is known for the general weighted covariance method, so that general matrix solution routines must be used, requiring a number of computations proportional to p^3 in order to solve the associated normal equations.

8.5.2 Combined Forward and Backward Linear Prediction Algorithms

It was shown in Chap. 7 that the forward and backward autoregressive coefficients for a stationary random process are simply complex conjugates of one another, so that the backward linear prediction error may then by expressed as

$$e_p^b[n] = x[n-p] + \sum_{k=1}^{p} a_p^{f\,*}[k]x[n-p+k] \quad . \tag{8.44}$$

Because both directions have similar statistical information, it seems reasonable to combine the linear prediction error statistics of both forward and backward errors in order to generate more error points. The net result should be an improved estimate of the autoregressive parameters. The $(N-p)$ forward and the $(N-p)$ backward linear prediction errors of the nonwindowed case may be summarized concisely by the matrix-vector product

$$\mathbf{e}_p = \begin{pmatrix} \mathbf{e}_p^f \\ \mathbf{e}_p^{b\,*} \end{pmatrix} = \begin{pmatrix} \mathbf{T}_p \\ \mathbf{T}_p^* \mathbf{J} \end{pmatrix} \begin{pmatrix} 1 \\ \mathbf{a}_p^{fb} \end{pmatrix} \quad . \tag{8.45}$$

The error vector $\mathbf{e}_p$ has $2(N-p)$ elements, consisting of $\mathbf{e}_p^f$, an $(N-p)$-element forward linear prediction error vector, and $\mathbf{e}_p^b$, an $(N-p)$-element backward linear prediction error vector, as follows

$$\mathbf{e}_p^f = \begin{pmatrix} e_p^f[p+1] \\ \vdots \\ e_p^f[N] \end{pmatrix} \quad , \quad \mathbf{e}_p^b = \begin{pmatrix} e_p^b[p+1] \\ \vdots \\ e_p^b[N] \end{pmatrix} \quad .$$

The linear prediction coefficient vector $\mathbf{a}_p^{fb}$ in Eq. (8.45) is given by

$$\mathbf{a}_p^{fb} = \begin{pmatrix} a_p[1] \\ \vdots \\ a_p[p] \end{pmatrix} .$$

The $(N - p) \times (p + 1)$ data matrix $\mathbf{T}_p$ in Eq. (8.45) was defined by Eq. (8.22). Noting that $\mathbf{J}$ is an $(p + 1) \times (p + 1)$ reflection matrix, then

$$\mathbf{T}_p^* \mathbf{J} = \begin{pmatrix} x^*[1] & \cdots & x^*[p + 1] \\ \vdots & \cdot^{\cdot^{\cdot}} & \vdots \\ x^*[p + 1] & \cdots & x^*[N - p] \\ \vdots & \cdot^{\cdot^{\cdot}} & \vdots \\ x^*[N - p] & \cdots & x^*[N] \end{pmatrix}$$

forms a Hankel matrix of conjugated data elements. Observe that the superscript f has been omitted from the linear prediction coefficients $a_p[k]$ because these apply now to both forward *and* backward prediction errors.

Minimizing the *average* of the forward *and* backward linear prediction squared errors over the available data

$$\rho_p^{fb} = \frac{1}{2} \left[\sum_{n=p+1}^{N} |e_p^f[n]|^2 + \sum_{n=p+1}^{N} |e_p^b[n]|^2 \right] = \frac{1}{2} \mathbf{e}_p^H \mathbf{e}_p = \frac{1}{2} \left[(\mathbf{e}_p^f)^H \mathbf{e}_p^f + (\mathbf{e}_p^b)^H \mathbf{e}_p^b \right] \tag{8.46}$$

leads to the set of normal equations

$$\mathbf{R}_p \mathbf{a}_p^{fb} = \begin{pmatrix} 2\rho_p^{fb} \\ \mathbf{0}_p \end{pmatrix} , \tag{8.47}$$

in which

$$\mathbf{R}_p = \begin{pmatrix} \mathbf{T}_p \\ \mathbf{T}_p^* \mathbf{J} \end{pmatrix}^H \begin{pmatrix} \mathbf{T}_p \\ \mathbf{T}_p^* \mathbf{J} \end{pmatrix} = \mathbf{T}_p^H \mathbf{T}_p + \mathbf{J} \mathbf{T}_p^T \mathbf{T}_p^* \mathbf{J} \tag{8.48}$$

and $\mathbf{0}_p$ is an p-element all-zeros vector. Equation (8.47) follows by inspection from Eq. (3.67) because the error equation (8.45) is of the same form as Eq. (3.62). Individual elements of $\mathbf{R}_p$ have the form

$$r_p[i, j] = \sum_{n=p+1}^{N} \left(x^*[n - i]x[n - j] + x[n - p + i]x^*[n - p + j] \right) \tag{8.49}$$

for $0 \leq j, k \leq p$. Because the summation range of squared errors in Eq. (8.46) is identical to that of the covariance method, this forward and backward least squares error approach has been called the *modified covariance method*. Burg [1967],

Ulrych and Clayton [1976], and Nuttall [1976] have independently proposed this method. Ulrych and Clayton gave it the name *least squares* (LS) method, even though this is not the only least squares method of linear prediction analysis used for spectral estimation. Other summation ranges for Eq. (8.46) are possible, but are not considered here because they generally do not yield better performance than the modified covariance method.

The modified covariance algorithm and Burg harmonic algorithm are both based on the minimization of the forward and backward squared prediction errors. The modified covariance method is based on minimization with respect to all the prediction coefficients, whereas the Burg method performs a constrained least squares minimization with respect to only a single prediction coefficient $a_p[p]$ (i.e., the reflection coefficient k_p). Several problems with the Burg method, including spectral line splitting and bias of the frequency estimate, appear to be eliminated when the modified covariance method is used. This suggests that the constrained least squares approach creates problems.

Direct solution of Eq. (8.47) by the Cholesky algorithm would require a number of computations proportional to p^3 and element storage proportional to p^2. However, matrix $\mathbf{R}_p$ of Eq. (8.48) has much structure, including centrosymmetry, that can be exploited to develop a fast computational solution of (8.47). The details for this fast algorithm are provided in Appendix 8.D, together with a computer program (MODCOVAR). For a pth-order model and N data samples, the algorithm requires $Np + 6p^2$ computational operations (adds/multiplies) and element storage of $N + 4p$. This is computationally comparable with the Burg algorithm; for $p \ll N$, the modified covariance algorithm is actually more efficient than the Burg algorithm when the same order is used for both algorithms. A necessary, but not sufficient, condition for $\mathbf{R}_p$ to be a nonsingular matrix is that $2(N - p) \geq p$, or $p \leq 2N/3$, so that the selected order must be no greater than two-thirds of the data length.

The modified covariance method, unlike the Burg algorithm, does not guarantee a stable linear prediction filter (poles inside the unit circle of the z-plane), although most of the time it will yield stable poles [Marple, 1980]. This is not a problem for purposes of spectral estimation, but it should be a consideration if the coefficients are to be used for filter synthesis. It is shown in Appendix 8.D that the modified covariance method always yields reflection coefficients with magnitudes less than unity. Thus, stable lattice filters will result from use of the reflection coefficients computed from the modified covariance method.

8.6 ESTIMATOR CHARACTERISTICS

The behavior of spectra produced from many of the autoregressive parameter estimators presented in this chapter has been documented extensively in the literature. Because the Burg method is one of the earliest and most frequently used algorithms, it has also been the most extensively tested and compared. The introduction of new autoregressive estimation schemes has often been the result of a need to improve upon some anomalies in spectral estimates produced by the Burg harmonic algorithm. Anomalies to be discussed include spurious spectral peaks, frequency estimation biases, and spectral line splitting.

If a large model order is selected relative to the number of data samples, AR spectral estimates tend to exhibit spurious peaks. Due to estimation error, the normal equations of most AR methods will generally be full rank, even for high orders, so that solutions for the autoregressive parameters will be obtained even though the true model order may be much lower. The extra poles generated by the additional AR parameters give rise to the spurious peaks. To mitigate against spurious peaks, methods for determining model order should be used. Section 8.7 presents some order selection criteria. Lowering the selected order to prevent spurious peaks also reduces the resolution. Among the methods presented in this chapter, the Burg, covariance, and modified covariance methods tend to have better resolution for a given order than other AR algorithms, as Fig. 8.2 has illustrated. This is primarily due to windowing effects in these other algorithms. The autocorrelation method suffers the most degradation in resolution of all methods for this reason.

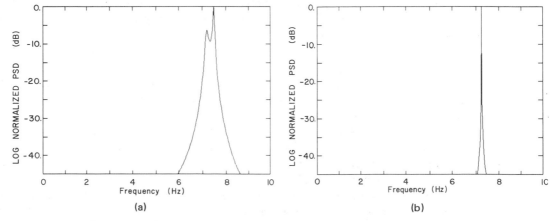

Figure 8.3   Response of two autoregressive spectral estimators to 101 samples of a 7.25-Hz sinusoid in white noise (SNR = 50). The sample rate was 100 IIz and the initial phase was 45°. (a) Burg spectrum with line splitting. (b) Modified covariance spectrum of same data with no line splitting.

It has been observed in the geometric mean, harmonic mean (Burg), and autocorrelation methods that two or more closely spaced peaks in the spectral estimate can occur in certain situations, where only one peak should be present. This phenomenon, known as *spectral line splitting*, is illustrated in Fig. 8.3 with spectral estimates based on the Burg and modified covariance methods. Both spectra are order 25 estimates produced from 101 samples of a process consisting of a unit amplitude sinusoid, of 45° initial phase and frequency 7.25 Hz, with additive noise of variance .01 (SNR = 50 dB). The sample rate was 100 Hz. Figure 8.3(a) exhibits a Burg spectral estimate that has split into two peaks about 7.25 Hz, falsely indicating two sinusoidal frequencies. The modified covariance spectra, based on the same data sequence, yields a single peak at the correct frequency. Spectral line splitting was first documented by Fougere et al. [1976]. They observed that the Burg algorithm would most likely exhibit spectral line splitting when (1) the SNR is high, (2) the initial phase of sinusoidal components is some odd multiple of 45°, (3) the time duration of the data sequence is such that sinusoidal components have an odd number of quarter cycles, and (4) the number of AR parameters estimated is a large percentage of the number of data samples used for the estimation. Both real and complex data sets have been found to produce line splitting. Many spurious spectral peaks often accompany spectra that exhibit line splitting. The phenomenon of line splitting tends to disappear as the data record increases. An analytical discussion of the reasons for line splitting in the Yule-Walker (autocorrelation) method has been presented by Kay and Marple [1979]. By using the unbiased autocorrelation estimate, line splitting in the Yule-Walker method can be reduced, if not eliminated. An analytical discussion of the reasons for line splitting in the Burg method has been presented by Herring [1980]. The use of weighted squared errors [Eq. (8.43)] seems to reduce the occurrence of line splitting in the Burg method, which appears to be caused by bias between positive and negative spectral components of real sinusoids. However, use of the modified covariance method seems to be the best cure, because no evidence of line splitting has ever been observed, especially for those cases for which the Burg algorithm is known to have line splitting.

Chen and Stegen [1974], Ulrych and Clayton [1976], and Thorvaldsen [1981] observed, for a process consisting of one or two sinusoids in white noise, that the spectral peaks of the Burg AR spectral estimate shifted as a function of the initial phases of the sinusoids. In one of the Ulrych and Clayton experiments, Burg and modified covariance spectral estimates were produced from ensembles of 15 data samples of a real-valued unit amplitude 1 Hz sinusoid with 10% additive white noise (the sample interval was .05 sec). Figure 8.4 is a plot of the mean variation of the spectral estimate peak as a function of the initial phase of a sinusoid. Each plotted point represents the mean peak frequency over an ensemble of 50 independent data realizations. It is obvious from Fig. 8.4 that the modified covariance method in the mean is fairly insensitive to the initial phase and is an accurate estimate of the sinusoid frequency. On the other hand, the Burg method has a rather severe sinusoidal-like bias in the frequency estimate as a function of the initial phase. Swingler [1979a, 1980] has demonstrated an analytical basis for the sinusoidal-like variation of the frequency bias; the bias can be as much as 16% of a resolution cell (a resolution cell is $1/NT$ Hz). The use of weighted squared errors, such as Eq. (8.17), has been found to reduce the phase dependence of the Burg method frequency estimate [Swingler, 1979b]. Use of the analytic (complex) signal also reduces the effect of the bias [Jackson et al., 1978].

Nuttall [1976] has made an extensive investigation of the power spectral density variance of many different AR methods, including those presented in this chapter, by use of ensemble averaging over a large number of data sets. He found, of

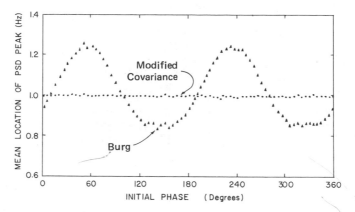

Figure 8.4 Frequency bias of two AR spectral methods. Plot represents the ensemble mean of spectral peak location as a function of initial phase for a cosine signal in white noise (SNR = 10) for Burg and modified covariance methods, using order 9.

all the methods, that the Burg and modified covariance methods tended to have the least PSD variance and the least frequency variance when tested with non-sinusoidal processes. Shon and Mehrotra [1984] also found this to be true. For example, Fig. 8.5 shows the overlapped spectral estimates for 50 data sequences of 40 samples each of the AR(4) process

$$x[k] = 2.7607x[k-1] - 3.8106x[k-2] + 2.6535x[k-3] - 0.9238x[k-4] + w[k],$$

where $w[k]$ is a white Gaussian noise process. The model order for each PSD estimate was preselected to be four. One observation that can be made from Fig. 8.5 is that the spectral estimates of the linear-prediction-based methods tend to have slightly less variability in the skirts, but more spiky estimates near the peaks of the spectra, than that seen in the reflection coefficient estimation methods. That is, the linear prediction methods produce AR spectral estimates with slightly less frequency variance, but more PSD variance, than the reflection coefficient methods. The greater PSD variance may be attributed to the fact that the linear prediction methods do not restrict the poles from moving close to the unit circle, unlike the reflection coefficient methods, which are constrained to be stable (poles within the unit circle only). The Yule-Walker method does the poorest job of estimating the AR(4) spectrum.

Signals that contain large DC levels or a linear trend have been found to corrupt AR spectral estimates [Kane and Trivedi, 1979], particularly at the low-frequency end of the spectrum. These components should be estimated and removed prior to AR spectral estimation.

Although the emphasis in this section has been on short-time-sequence behavior of AR spectral estimates, additional references on the asymptotic statistical behavior of AR spectral estimation may also be found in the literature. Sakai [1979]

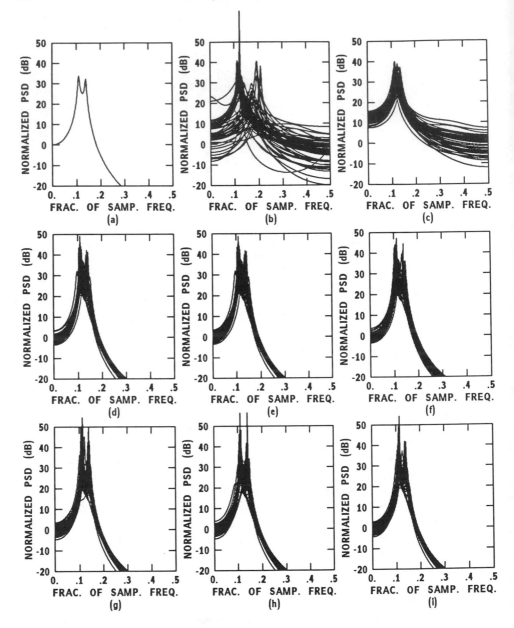

Figure 8.5   Response of five AR spectral estimators to a fourth-order AR process.   Overlapped estimates of 50 realizations of 40-sample records are shown for each method. (a) True spectrum of AR(4) process. (b) Yule-Walker, unbiased autocorrelation estimates. (c) Yule-Walker, biased autocorrelation estimates. (d) Geometric method. (e) Burg method. (f) Kay method. (g) Covariance method, forward prediction coefficients. (h) Covariance method, backward prediction coefficients. (i) Modified covariance method.

has shown empirically that the frequency variance of an AR spectral estimate is inversely proportional to both the data length and the square of the SNR for sinusoids in noise. Keeler [1978] has provided empirical evidence that the variance is proportional to the inverse of both the duration and the SNR (rather than proportional to the square of the SNR) for nonsinusoidal processes. Akaike [1969], Kromer [1970], and Berk [1974] have shown that asymptotic performance of the autoregressive PSD, based on the autocorrelation method, is distributed according to a Gaussian PDF as the number of data points N grows asymptotically; the mean of the AR PSD estimate is the true AR PSD and the variance is proportional to $(4p/N)P^2_{AR}(f)$. Confidence interval results for AR spectra have been given by Baggeroer [1976]. Other performance comparisons may be found in the paper by Kaveh and Cooper [1976].

8.7   MODEL ORDER SELECTION

Because the best choice of filter order p is not generally known a priori, it is usually necessary in practice to postulate several model orders. Based on these, one then computes some error criterion that indicates which model order to choose. Too low a guess for model order results in a highly smoothed spectral estimate. Too high an order increases the resolution and introduces spurious detail into the spectrum. Thus, model order selection represents for AR spectral estimation the classic trade-off of increased resolution and decreased variance. One intuitive approach would be to construct AR models of increasing order until the computed prediction error variance reaches a minimum. However, all the estimation procedures discussed in this chapter have prediction error (residual) variances that decrease monotonically with increasing order p. For example, the Burg, modified covariance, and Yule-Walker autocorrelation methods involve a relationship of the form

$$\rho_p = \rho_{p-1}(1 - |a_p[p]|^2) \quad . \tag{8.50}$$

for the mean square or least squared error. As long as $|a_p[p]|^2$ is nonzero (it must be ≤ 1), the prediction error variance decreases. Thus, the prediction error variance alone is usually not sufficient to indicate when to terminate the search, unless there is some definitive order after which the rate of change in error variance reduction suddenly decreases. Another simple check concerning proper order selection is to perform a periodogram analysis of the prediction error, or residual, sequence. The residuals should be approximately white, so that an approximately flat periodogram estimate should be obtained.

Many criteria have been proposed as allegedly objective functions for selection of the AR model order. Akaike [1969] has provided two criteria. His first criterion is the *final prediction error* (FPE). This criterion selects the order of the AR process so that the average error variance for a one-step prediction is minimized. He considers the error variance to be the sum of the power in the unpredictable part of the process and a quantity representing the inaccuracies in estimating the AR parameters. The FPE for an AR process is defined as

$$\text{FPE}[p] = \hat{\rho}_p \left(\frac{N + (p+1)}{N - (p+1)} \right), \tag{8.51}$$

where N is the number of data samples, p is the order, and $\hat{\rho}_p$ is the estimated white noise variance (the linear prediction error variance will be used for this estimate). Note that Eq. (8.51) assumes that the sample mean has been subtracted from the data. The term in parentheses increases as the order increases, reflecting the increase in the uncertainty of the estimate $\hat{\rho}_p$ of the prediction error variance. The order p selected is the one for which the FPE is minimum. The FPE has been studied for application by Landers and Lacoss [1977], Ulrych and Bishop [1975], and Nuttall [1976]. For a pure AR process, the FPE works fairly well in selecting the correct order. However, when applied against actual signals, the FPE seems to be conservative, often selecting too low an order. For example, in processing geophysical data, both Jones [1976] and Berryman [1978] found that the order selected tended to be too low.

Akaike [1974] also suggested another selection criterion using a maximum likelihood approach to derive a criterion termed the *Akaike information criterion* (AIC). The AIC determines the model order by minimizing an information theoretic function. Assuming the process has Gaussian statistics, the AIC for AR processes has the form

$$\text{AIC}[p] = N \ln(\hat{\rho}_p) + 2p \quad . \tag{8.52}$$

For a development of this criterion, see Kay [1987]. The term $2p$ represents the penalty for the use of extra AR coefficients that do not result in a substantial reduction in the prediction error variance. Again, the order p selected is the one that minimizes the AIC. As $N \to \infty$, the AIC and FPE are asymptotically equivalent. The AIC has been studied for application to pure AR processes by Tong [1975, 1977] and Kaveh and Bruzzone [1979]. As with the FPE, many researchers have found that the order selected by AIC is often too low for practical non-AR data sets. Kaveh and Bruzzone suggest a variant of the AIC that accounts for the initial conditions in the maximum likelihood formulation of the estimator of the AR parameters. Note that Kashyap [1980] has found that the AIC is statistically inconsistent in that the probability of error in choosing the correct order does not tend to zero as $N \to \infty$; the result is a tendency to overestimate the order as the data record length increases. In response to this, Rissanen [1983] developed a variant information theoretic criterion to the AIC with the form

$$\text{MDL}[p] = N \ln(\hat{\rho}_p) + p \ln(N) \quad , \tag{8.53}$$

where MDL stands for *minimum description length*. It is said to be statistically consistent because $p \ln(N)$ increases with N faster than with p.

A third method was proposed by Parzen [1974] and is termed the *criterion autoregressive transfer* (CAT) function. The order p is selected to be the one in which the estimate of the difference between mean square errors of the true prediction error filter (which may be of infinite length) and the estimated filter is a minimum. Parzen showed that this difference can be calculated, without explicitly knowing the true prediction error filter, by

$$\text{CAT}[p] = \left(\frac{1}{N} \sum_{j=1}^{p} \bar{\rho}_j^{-1} \right) - \bar{\rho}_p^{-1} \tag{8.54}$$

where $\bar{\rho}_j = [N/(N-j)]\hat{\rho}_j$. Again, p is chosen to minimize $\text{CAT}[p]$.

The results of spectra using the FPE, AIC, and CAT have been mixed, particularly when applied to actual data rather than simulated AR processes. Ulrych and Clayton [1976] have found that for short data segments, none of the criteria work well. For harmonic processes in noise, the FPE and AIC also tend to underestimate the order, especially if the SNR is high. Ulrych and Ooe [1983] experimentally determined, in the case of short data segments of harmonic processes, that an order selection between $N/3$ to $N/2$ often produced satisfactory results when using the covariance or modified covariance methods. Reinforcement for this experimental observation was given by Lang and McClellan [1980], who showed analytically for the modified covariance method that the spectral peak position variance for one sinusoid or multiple sinusoids well separated in frequency closely approach the Cramer-Rao lower bound when the model order is about 1/3 of the data length. In the final analysis, subjective judgment, rather than science, is still required to select an order for data from actual signals of an unknown process. The criteria presented in this section may be used as guidelines for initial order selection, which are known to work well for computer-generated synthetic AR signals, but may or may not work well with actual data, depending on how well such data is modeled by an AR process.

8.8   AUTOREGRESSIVE PROCESSES WITH OBSERVATION NOISE

In many practical situations, observation noise corrupts the data samples, degrading the performance and resolution of AR spectral estimates [Kay, 1979]. The reason for this degradation is that the all-pole model assumed for the spectral analysis is no longer valid when observation noise is present. Assume $y[k]$ is the noise-corrupted AR process

$$y[k] = x[k] + n[k],$$

where $x[k]$ is the AR(p) process and $n[k]$ is the observation noise. If $n[k]$ is white noise of variance ρ_n and is uncorrelated with $x[k]$, then

$$
\begin{aligned}
\mathsf{P}_{yy}(z) &= \frac{\rho_w}{\mathsf{A}(z)\mathsf{A}^*(1/z^*)} + \rho_n = \frac{[\rho_w + \rho_n \mathsf{A}(z)\mathsf{A}^*(1/z^*)]}{\mathsf{A}(z)\mathsf{A}^*(1/z^*)} \\
&= \frac{\rho[\mathsf{B}(z)\mathsf{B}^*(1/z^*)]}{\mathsf{A}(z)\mathsf{A}^*(1/z^*)}.
\end{aligned}
$$

Thus, the z-transform of the output process autocorrelation is characterized by poles and zeros, i.e., $y[k]$ is an ARMA(p, p) process. Processes of this type should be analyzed, therefore, by the ARMA methods of Chap. 10.

If the observation noise is white, then several concepts have been proposed to reduce the bias effect of this noise through noise power cancellation schemes (e.g., Marple [1978] or Kay [1980]). Noting that the observation noise power affects only the zero-lag autocorrelation term,

$$
r_{yy}[k] = \begin{cases} r_{xx}[0] + \rho_n & \text{for } k = 0 \\ r_{xx}[k] & \text{for } k \neq 0 \end{cases},
$$

then compensating the estimate of the $r_{yy}[0]$ autocorrelation term by removing an estimate of ρ_n serves to remove the effect of the observation noise. The Pisarenko harmonic decomposition method in Chap. 13 provides one such special scheme for estimating ρ_n for the case of sinusoids in white noise. Similar compensation schemes can be developed for the reflection coefficients. In general, the noise cancellation schemes can reduce the bias, but will tend to increase the variance of the spectral estimate. A serious deficiency is that one does not know how much noise power to remove; if the estimate of ρ_n is too large, the estimated AR spectrum will exhibit sharper peaks than the true spectrum.

8.9 APPLICATION TO SUNSPOT NUMBERS

The same filtered sequence of 230 samples of sunspot numbers used in Sec. 5.9 was used to produce autoregressive power spectral density estimates. The AIC expression, Eq. (8.5), was used to attempt an estimate of an appropriate AR model order. Figure 8.6 plots the AIC from order 0 to order 32. No obvious minimum is apparent. The AIC of the Burg method levels out approximately at order 12.

Figure 8.7 has spectral plots of the AR PSD estimates at order 12 by the covariance and Burg methods. The spectra are essentially identical. The detail in the spectra, however, is disappointing. This illustrates the conservative nature of order selection rules like AIC. Figure 8.8(c) illustrates the short-term behavior of autoregressive spectral estimates using the covariance method for order 18. Each spectral estimate represents a segment of 46 filtered sunspot samples, beginning with the year shown on the absissca. A 50-dB range is plotted for each segment spectral estimate. A

Figure 8.6   AIC function of filtered sunspot numbers, normalized to AIC[0]. (a) AIC of covariance method. (b) AIC of Burg method.

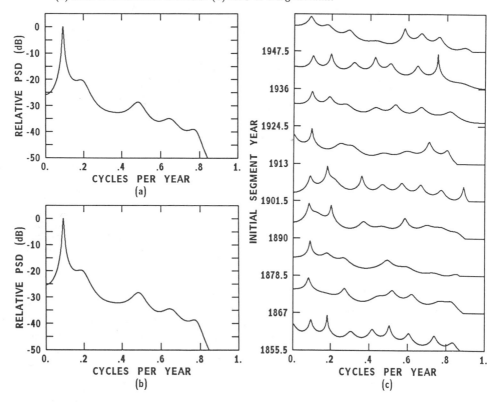

Figure 8.7   Autoregressive spectral estimates of filtered sunspot numbers. Order was $p = 12$. (a) Covariance method (forward coefficients). (b) Burg method. (c) Stack of AR(18) covariance method spectral estimates of sunspot number segments of 46 samples each.

similar nonstationary behavior, as discovered in Fig. 5.12, is also obvious with the AR spectral estimates.

If the order is increased to 36, then the autoregressive spectral estimates of Fig. 8.8 begin to show more detail. Three spectral estimation methods were

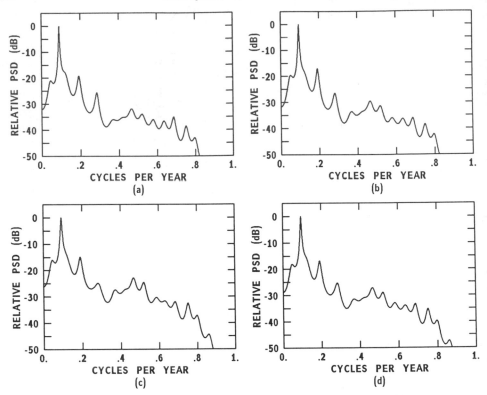

Figure 8.8   Autoregressive spectral estimates of filtered sunspot numbers. Order was $p = 36$. (a) Covariance method (forward coefficients). (b) Burg method. (c) Covariance method (backward coefficients). (d) Modified covariance method.

selected, including spectral estimates made from both the forward and the backward coefficients of the covariance linear prediction method. All four spectral estimates are very similar. A peak at approximately 22 years per cycle is present in all four spectra. The first three peaks of Fig. 8.8(a), converted to units of period, are located at 20.90, 10.72, and 5.20 years per cycle. The first three peaks of Fig. 8.8(b) are located at 19.88, 10.67, and 5.21 years per cycle. The first three peaks of Fig. 8.8(c) are located at 21.33, 10.56, and 5.25 years per cycle. The first three peaks of Fig. 8.8(d) are located at 20.90, 10.67, and 5.21 years per cycle. These sunspot cycle components are very similar to those estimated by Currie [1973].

REFERENCES

Akaike, H., Power Spectrum Estimation through Autoregression Model Fitting, *Ann. Inst. Stat. Math.*, vol. 21, pp. 407–419, 1969.

Akaike, H., A New Look at the Statistical Model Identification, *IEEE Trans. Autom. Control*, vol. AC-19, pp. 716–723, December 1974.

Andersen, N. O., On the Calculation of Filter Coefficients for Maximum Entropy Spectral Analysis, *Geophysics*, vol. 39, pp. 69-72, February 1974.

Andersen, N. O., Comments on the Performance of Maximum Entropy Algorithms, *Proc. IEEE*, vol. 66, pp. 1581-1582, November 1978.

Baggeroer, A. B., Confidence Intervals for Regression (MEM) Spectral Estimates, *IEEE Trans. Inform. Theory*, vol. IT-22, pp. 534–545, September 1976.

Barrodale, I., L. M. Delves, R. E. Erickson, and C. A. Zala, Computational Experience with Marple's Algorithm for Autoregressive Spectrum Analysis, *Geophysics*, vol. 48, pp. 1274–1286, September 1983.

Berk, K. N., Consistent Autoregressive Spectral Estimates, *Ann. Stat.*, vol. 2, pp. 489–502, 1974.

Berryman, J. G., Choice of Operator Length for Maximum Entropy Spectral Analysis, *Geophysics*, vol. 43, pp. 1384–1391, December 1978.

Burg, J. P., Maximum Entropy Spectral Analysis, *Proceedings of the 37th Meeting of the Society of Exploration Geophysicists*, 1967.

Burg, J. P., Maximum Entropy Spectral Analysis, Ph.D. dissertation, Department of Geophysics, Stanford University, Stanford, Calif., May 1975.

Chen, W. Y., and G. R. Stegen, Experiments with Maximum Entropy Power Spectra of Sinusoids, *J. Geophys. Res.*, vol. 79, pp. 3019–3022, 10 July 1974.

Currie, R., Fine Structure in the Sunspot Spectrum—2 to 70 Years, *Astrophys. Space Sci.*, vol. 20, pp. 509–518, 1973.

Datta, A. K., Comments on "The Complex Form of the Maximum Entropy Method for Spectral Estimation," *Proc. IEEE*, vol. 65, PP. 1219–1220, August 1977.

Fougere, P. F., E. J. Zawalick, and H. R. Radoski, Spontaneous Line Splitting in Maximum Entropy Power Spectrum Analysis, *Phys. Earth Planet. Inter.*, vol. 12, pp. 201–207, August 1976.

Haykin, S., and S. Kesler, The Complex Form of the Maximum Entropy Method for Spectral Estimation, *Proc. IEEE*, vol. 64, pp. 822–823, May 1976.

Helme, B., and C. L. Nikias, Improved Spectrum Performance via a Data-Adaptive Weighted Burg Technique, *IEEE Trans. Acoust. Speech Signal Process.*, vol. ASSP-33, pp. 903–910, August 1985.

Herring, R. W., The Cause of Line Splitting in Burg Maximum-Entropy Spectral Analysis, *IEEE Trans. Acoust. Speech Signal Process.*, vol. ASSP-28, pp. 692–701, December 1980.

Jackson, L. B., D. W. Tufts, F. K. Soong, and R. M. Rao, Frequency Estimation by Linear Prediction, *Proceedings of the 1978 IEEE International Conference on Acoustics, Speech, and Signal Processing*, pp. 352–356, 1978.

Jones, R. H., Autoregression Order Selection, *Geophysics*, vol. 41, pp. 771–773, August 1976.

Kane, R. P., and N. B. Trivedi, Effects of Linear Trend and Mean Value on Maximum Entropy Spectral Analysis, *Institute de Pesquisas Espacials, Report INPE-1568-RPE/069*, San Jose dos Compos, Brasil, 1979 (available from NTIS, N79-33949).

Kashyap, R. L., Inconsistency of the AIC Rule for Estimating the Order of Autoregressive Models, *IEEE Trans. Autom. Control*, vol. AC-25, pp. 996–998, October 1980.

Kaveh, M., and S. P. Bruzzone, Order Determination for Autoregressive Spectral Estimation, *Record of the 1979 Rome Air Development Center Spectral Estimation Workshop*, pp. 139–145, 1979.

Kaveh, M., and G. R. Cooper, An Empirical Investigation of the Properties of the Autoregressive Spectral Estimator, *IEEE Trans. Inf. Theory*, vol. IT-22, pp. 313–323, May 1976.

Kaveh, M., and G. A. Lippert, An Optimum Tapered Burg Algorithm for Linear Prediction and Spectral Analysis, *IEEE Trans. Acoust. Speech Signal Process.*, vol. ASSP-31, pp. 438–444, April 1983.

Kay, S. M., The Effect of Noise on the Autoregressive Spectral Estimator, *IEEE Trans. Acoust. Speech Signal Process.*, vol. ASSP-27, pp. 478–485, October 1979.

Kay, S. M., Noise Compensation for Autoregressive Spectral Estimators, *IEEE Trans. Acoust. Speech Signal Process.*, vol. ASSP-28, pp. 292–303, June 1980.

Kay, S. M., Recursive Maximum Likelihood Estimation of Autoregressive Processes, *IEEE Trans. Acoust. Speech Signal Process.*, vol. ASSP-31, pp. 56–65, February 1983.

Kay, S. M., *Modern Spectral Estimation*, Prentice-Hall, Inc., Englewood Cliffs, N. J., 1987.

Kay, S. M., and S. L. Marple, Jr., Sources of and Remedies for Spectral Line Splitting in Autoregressive Spectrum Analysis, *Proceedings of the 1979 IEEE International Conference on Acoustics, Speech, and Signal Processing*, pp. 151–154, 1979.

Keeler, R. J., Uncertainties in Adaptive Maximum Entropy Frequency Estimators, *IEEE Trans. Acoust. Speech Signal Process.*, vol. ASSP-26, pp. 469–471, October 1978.

Kromer, R. E., Asymptotic Properties of the Autoregressive Spectral Estimator, Ph.D. dissertation, Department of Statistics, Stanford University, Stanford, Calif., 1969.

Landers, T. E., and R. T. Lacoss, Some Geophysical Applications of Autoregressive Spectral Estimates, *IEEE Trans. Geosci. Electron.*, vol. GE-15, pp. 26–32, January 1977.

Lang, S. W., and J. H. McClellan, Frequency Estimation with Maximum Entropy Spectral Estimators, *IEEE Trans. Acoust. Speech Signal Process.*, vol. ASSP-28, pp. 716–724, December 1980.

Makhoul, J., Linear Prediction: A Tutorial Review, *Proc. IEEE*, vol. 63, pp. 561-580, April 1975; correction in *Proc. IEEE*, vol. 64, p. 285, February 1976.

Marple, S. L. Jr., A New Autoregressive Spectrum Analysis Algorithm, *IEEE Trans. Acoust. Speech Signal Process.*, vol. ASSP-28, pp. 441-454, August 1980.

Marple, S. L. Jr., High Resolution Autoregressive Spectrum Analysis Using Noise Power Cancellation, *Proceedings of 1978 IEEE International Conference on Acoustics, Speech, and Signal Processing*, Tulsa, Okla., pp. 345–348, April 1978.

Marple, S. L. Jr., Efficient Least Squares FIR System Identification, *IEEE Trans. Acoust. Speech Signal Process.*, vol. ASSP-29, pp. 62–73, February 1981.

Morf, M., B. Dickinson, T. Kailath, and A. Vieira, Efficient Solution of Covariance Equations for Linear Prediction, *IEEE Trans. Acoust. Speech Signal Process.*, vol. ASSP-25, pp. 429–433, October 1977.

Nikias, C. L., and P. D. Scott, The Covariance Least-Squares Algorithm for Spectral Estimation of Processes of Short Data Length, *IEEE Trans. Geosci. Remote Sensing*, vol. GE-21, pp. 180–190, April 1983.

Nuttall, A. H., Spectral Analysis of a Univariate Process with Bad Data Points, via Maximum Entropy and Linear Predictive Techniques, *Naval Underwater Systems Center Technical Report TR-5303*, New London, Conn., March 1976.

Parzen, E., Some Recent Advances in Time Series Modeling, *IEEE Trans. Autom. Control*, vol. AC-19, pp. 723–730, December 1974.

Rissanen, J., A Universal Prior for the Integers and Estimation by Minimum Description Length, *Ann. Stat.*, vol. 11, pp. 417–431, 1983.

Sakai, H., Statistical Properties of AR Spectral Analysis, *IEEE Trans. Acoust. Speech Signal Process.*, vol. ASSP-27, pp. 402–409, August 1979.

Shon, S., and K. Mehrotra, Performance Comparison of Autoregressive Estimation Methods, *Proceedings of the 1984 IEEE International Conference on Acoustics, Speech, and Signal Processing*, pp. 14.3.1–14.3.4, 1984.

Swingler, D. N., A Comparison between Burg's Maximum Entropy Method and a Non-recursive Technique for the Spectral Analysis of Deterministic Signals, *J. Geophys. Res.*, vol. 84, pp. 679–685, 10 February 1979a.

Swingler, D. N., A Modified Burg Algorithm for Maximum Entropy Spectral Analysis, *Proc. IEEE*, vol. 67, pp. 1368–1369, September 1979b.

Swingler, D. N., Frequency Errors in MEM Processing, *IEEE Trans. Acoust. Speech Signal Process.*, vol. ASSP-28, pp. 257–259, April 1980.

Thorvaldsen, T., A Comparison of the Least Squares Method and the Burg Method for Autoregressive Spectral Analysis, *IEEE Trans. Antennas Propag.*, vol. AP-29, pp. 675–679, July 1981.

Tong, H., Autoregressive Model Fitting with Noisy Data by Akaike's Information Criterion, *IEEE Trans. Inf. Theory*, vol. IT-21, pp. 476–480, July 1975; see also the sequel in *IEEE Trans. Inf. Theory*, vol. IT-23, pp. 409–410, May 1977.

Ulrych, T. J., and T. N. Bishop, Maximum Entropy Spectral Analysis and Autoregressive Decomposition, *Rev. Geophys. Space Phys.*, vol. 13, pp. 183–200, February 1975.

Ulrych, T. J., and R. W. Clayton, Time Series Modeling and Maximum Entropy, *Phys. Earth Planet. Inter.*, vol. 12, pp. 188–200, August 1976.

Ulrych, T. J., and M. Ooe, Autoregressive and Mixed ARMA Models and Spectra, Chapter 3 in *Nonlinear Methods of Spectral Analysis*, 2nd ed., S. Haykin, ed., Springer-Verlag, New York, 1983.

Ulrych, T. J., D. E. Smylie, O. G. Jensen, and G. K. C. Clarke, Predictive Filtering and Smoothing of Short Records by Using Maximum Entropy, *J. Geophys. Res.*, vol. 78, pp. 4959–4964, August 1973.

PROBLEMS

1. Incorporate the FPE order selection criterion into the four subroutines shown in Fig. 8.1. Run the 64-point test sequence and note the order selected by each algorithm. How do these compare? Why are there differences? Now incorporate the CAT order selection criterion. What orders are selected by the CAT?

2. Write a program that inplements the geometric-mean AR parameter estimation algorithm. Use subroutine BURG as a model for the structure of this code.

3. Derive a *descending*-order recursion for the Burg algorithm; that is, given the order p solution of the AR coefficients, find the order $p - 1$ solution.

4. Show how to incorporate a correlation lag estimate in the Burg algorithm. Hint: Use Eq. (8.3).

5. Rewrite the Burg algorithm to save only the reflection coefficients; do not evaluate the AR coefficients. From the FPE criteria, find the best order. Then run the Levinson recursion to get the AR coefficients at the best order. Show that this can be done in two steps without additional computational cost.

6. Prove Eq. (8.3).

7. Given the reflection coefficient sequence, find the recursion that yields the correlation sequence.

8. In the Burg algorithm program, why is the statement DEN=P*2 used, rather than DEN=P?

9. In the covariance algorithm, prove the following:

$$\rho_p^f = \mathbf{a}_p^H \mathbf{R}_p \mathbf{a}_p = \rho_{p-1}^{f\prime}(1 - a_p[p]b_p[p])$$

$$\rho_p^b = \mathbf{b}_p^H \mathbf{R}_p \mathbf{b}_p = \rho_{p-1}^{b\prime\prime}(1 - b_[p]a_p[p])$$

$$[e_p^f(p+1)]^* = -\mathbf{r}_p^H \mathbf{d}_{p-1}^{\prime\prime} + x^*(p+1)$$

$$[e_p^b(N)]^* = -\mathbf{s}_p^H \mathbf{c}_{p-1}^{\prime} + x^*(N-p) \quad .$$

10. Prove that $\nabla_p = \Delta_p^*$ in the covariance algorithm.

11. Show that $\delta_p, \gamma_p \to 0$ with increasing order p in the covariance algorithm.

12. Both the Burg algorithm and the modified covariance methods use the sum of the forward and backward linear prediction squared errors. In what sense is the Burg algorithm a constrained least squares problem and the modified covariance method an unconstrained least squares problem?

13. Modify the subroutine COVAR so that, in case an error condition is encountered, the previous order **a** vector and **b** vector coefficients are output, which are assumed to be valid.

14. Use Eqs. (8.C.6) and (8.D.6) to prove that the $\mathbf{R}_p$ matrices of the covariance and modified covariance methods are positive semidefinite.

15. Prove Eq. (8.16).

16. Express $\mathbf{R}_p$ of Eq. (8.28) in terms of $\mathbf{T}_p$, $\mathbf{L}_p$, and $\mathbf{U}_p$.

17. Prove that matrix $\mathbf{R}_p$ in Eq. (8.28) for the autocorrelation method is positive semidefinite.

18. Prove Eq. (8.16).

APPENDIX 8.A
PROGRAM OF YULE–WALKER ALGORITHM

This subroutine produces estimates of the autoregressive parameters and white noise variance based on the Yule-Walker method of Sec. 8.3. It can be converted to process real data using the procedure of Appendix IV at the back of the book. If the 64-point test sequence of Appendix II is processed by this subroutine for $N = 64$, order $IP = 15$, and $L = 1$, then the values produced by the subroutine are

$$P = 0.22833$$

A(1) = (0.277473, -0.707342)	A(9) = (0.051247, 0.158093)
A(2) = (0.336654, -0.536765)	A(10) = (0.157524, 0.075804)
A(3) = (-0.201972, -0.310083)	A(11) = (0.136989, -0.015143)
A(4) = (0.182192, -0.011275)	A(12) = (-0.007077, -0.230838)
A(5) = (-0.146188, -0.147403)	A(13) = (-0.233656, -0.046570)
A(6) = (0.002554, -0.170146)	A(14) = (-0.151503, 0.034726)
A(7) = (-0.216875, -0.044782)	A(15) = (0.018774, 0.093879)
A(8) = (-0.000398, 0.196649) .	

```
      SUBROUTINE YULEWALKER (N,IP,L,X,P,A,ISTAT)
C
C This subroutine determines the autoregressive coefficients by the
C Yule-Walker algorithm.
C
C Input Parameters:
C
C     N    - Number of data samples (integer)
C     IP   - Order of autoregressive process to be fitted (integer)
C     L    - Set this integer to 0 for unbiased lags, or 1 for biased
C     X    - Array of complex data values, X(1) to X(N)
C
C Output Parameters:
C
C     P    - Driving noise variance (real)
C     A    - Array of complex autoregressive coefficients, A(1) to A(IP)
C     ISTAT - Status indicator.  Returns set to 0 for normal exit, else
C             1 if LEVINSON becomes ill-conditioned.
C
C Notes:
C
C     External array X should be dimensioned .GE. N and array A .GE. IP
C     in the calling program.  Internal array R should be dimensioned
C     .GE. IP .  External subroutines used:  CORRELATION (Appendix 5.A)
C     and LEVINSON (Appendix 3.C) .
C
      COMPLEX X(1),A(1),RO,R(100)
      CALL CORRELATION (N,IP,L,X,X,RO,R)
      RZERO=REAL(RO)
      CALL LEVINSON (IP,RZERO,R,P,A,ISTAT)
      RETURN
      END
```

APPENDIX 8.B
PROGRAM OF BURG (HARMONIC) ALGORITHM

The Burg algorithm for estimating the AR parameters and white noise variance from data samples is presented in Sec. 8.4.2. The FORTRAN program of the Burg algorithm is annotated with equation references to the text to enable the reader to follow the program logic. If the 64-point test sequence of Appendix II is processed by this algorithm for N = 64 and order IP = 15, then the following parameters values were computed

$$P = 0.00542$$

A(1) = (2.711213, -0.776930)	A(9) = (-4.678243,-15.089474)
A(2) = (5.179286, -2.737600)	A(10) = (-6.255747,-11.272636)
A(3) = (7.041883, -6.163119)	A(11) = (-6.311070, -6.947133)
A(4) = (7.899391,-10.228625)	A(12) = (-4.916976, -3.253044)
A(5) = (6.848681,-14.106740)	A(13) = (-3.009425, -0.872889)
A(6) = (4.561341,-16.882746)	A(14) = (-1.326651, 0.046931)
A(7) = (1.310846,-18.172159)	A(15) = (-0.356762, 0.148375)
A(8) = (-1.901579,-17.536158) .	

```
      SUBROUTINE BURG (N,IP,X,P,A,ISTAT)
C
C     Program to estimate the complex autoregressive parameters by
C     the Burg algorithm.
C
C     Input Parameters:
C
C        N  - Number of data samples
C        IP - Order of autoregressive process
C        X  - Array of complex data samples X(1) through X(N)
C
C     Output Parameters:
C
C        P  - Real variable representing driving noise variance
C        A  - Array of complex autoregressive parameters A(1) to A(IP)
C        ISTAT - Integer status indicator at time of exit
C                0 for normal exit
C                1 for numerical ill-conditioning (P < 0)
C
C     Notes:
C
C        External array X must be dimensioned .GE. N and array A
C        must be dimensioned .GE. IP in the calling program.
C        Internal arrays EF and EB must be dimensioned .GE. N .
C
      COMPLEX X(1),A(1),EF(300),EB(300),NUM,SAVE1,SAVE2
      REAL P,DEN,TEMP
C
C     Initialization
C
      ISTAT=0
```

```
          P=0.
          DO 10 J=1,N
10          P=P+REAL(X(J))**2+AIMAG(X(J))**2    ! Eq. (8.12)
          DEN=P*2.
          P=P/N
          IF (IP .EQ. 0)  RETURN
          DO 20 J=1,N
            EF(J)=X(J)
20          EB(J)=X(J)                           ! Eq. (8.11)
          TEMP=1.
          K=0
C
C     Main recursion
C
100       K=K+1
          NUM=(0.,0.)
          DO 30 J=K+1,N
30          NUM=NUM+EF(J)*CONJG(EB(J-1))
          DEN=TEMP*DEN-REAL(EF(K))**2-AIMAG(EF(K))**2
     *       -REAL(EB(N))**2-AIMAG(EB(N))**2  ! Eq. (8.10)
          SAVE1=-2.*NUM/DEN                     ! Eq. (8.14)
          TEMP=1.-REAL(SAVE1)**2-AIMAG(SAVE1)**2
          P=P*TEMP                              ! Eq. (8.4)
          IF (TEMP .GT. 0.)  GO TO 40
          ISTAT=1
          RETURN
40        A(K)=SAVE1
          IF (K .EQ. 1)  GO TO 60
          KHALF=K/2
          DO 50 J=1,KHALF
            KJ=K-J
            SAVE2=A(J)
            A(J)=SAVE2+SAVE1*CONJG(A(KJ))        ! Eq. (8.2)
            IF (J .EQ. KJ)  GO TO 50
            A(KJ)=A(KJ)+SAVE1*CONJG(SAVE2)       ! Eq. (8.2)
50          CONTINUE
60        IF (K .EQ. IP)  RETURN
          DO 70 J=N,K+1,-1
            SAVE2=EF(J)
            EF(J)=SAVE2+SAVE1*EB(J-1)            ! Eq. (8.7)
70          EB(J)=EB(J-1)+CONJG(SAVE1)*SAVE2
          GO TO 100
          END
```

APPENDIX 8.C
FAST ALGORITHM AND PROGRAM TO SOLVE COVARIANCE
EQUATIONS OF LINEAR PREDICTION

8.C.1 Introduction

The original fast algorithm to solve the covariance normal equations was developed by Morf et al. [1977]. Further computational reductions were discovered by Marple

[1981]. The presentation here contains further improvements. The algorithm computes all lower-order least squares solutions as part of the recursive structure of the algorithm. The program provided here does not save all of the intermediate lower-order solutions, although the program could be easily modified to do so.

The pth-order forward and backward linear prediction errors may be represented as the vector inner products

$$e_p^f[n] = \mathbf{x}_p^T[n]\mathbf{a}_p^f \tag{8.C.1}$$

$$e_p^b[n] = \mathbf{x}_p^T[n]\mathbf{a}_p^b \tag{8.C.2}$$

where the data vector $\mathbf{x}_p[n]$, forward linear prediction coefficient vector $\mathbf{a}_p^f$, and backward linear prediction coefficient vector $\mathbf{a}_p^b$ have the definitions

$$\mathbf{x}_p[n] = \begin{pmatrix} x[n] \\ x[n-1] \\ \vdots \\ x[n-p] \end{pmatrix} \quad , \quad \mathbf{a}_p^f = \begin{pmatrix} 1 \\ a_p^f[1] \\ \vdots \\ a_p^f[p] \end{pmatrix} \quad , \quad \mathbf{a}_p^b = \begin{pmatrix} a_p^b[p] \\ \vdots \\ a_p^b[1] \\ 1 \end{pmatrix}. \tag{8.C.3}$$

Observe that $\mathbf{a}_p^f$ and $\mathbf{a}_p^b$ as defined here include the unity element, in contrast to definitions (8.25) and (8.40). Based on measured complex data samples $x[1], \dots, x[N]$, the covariance method of linear prediction *separately* minimizes the forward and backward linear prediction squared errors

$$\rho_p^f = \sum_{n=p+1}^{N} |e_p^f[n]|^2 \quad , \quad \rho_p^b = \sum_{n=p+1}^{N} |e_p^b[n]|^2, \tag{8.C.4}$$

resulting in the normal equations

$$\mathbf{R}_p\mathbf{a}_p^f = \begin{pmatrix} \rho_p^f \\ \mathbf{0}_p \end{pmatrix} \quad , \quad \mathbf{R}_p\mathbf{a}_p^b = \begin{pmatrix} \mathbf{0}_p \\ \rho_p^b \end{pmatrix}, \tag{8.C.5}$$

where $\mathbf{0}_p$ is a $p \times 1$ all-zeros vector. Unlike the Levinson algorithm, $\mathbf{a}_p^f \neq \mathbf{a}_p^{b*}$ in general for the covariance algorithm. A vector outer product definition for $\mathbf{R}_p$, equivalent to that given by Eq. (8.32), is

$$\mathbf{R}_p = \sum_{n=p+1}^{N} \mathbf{x}_p^*[n]\mathbf{x}_p^T[n]. \tag{8.C.6}$$

If the error term $e[1]$ is not used, the normal equations that result from considering just the data sequence $x[2], \dots, x[N]$ have the form

$$\mathbf{R}_p'\mathbf{a}_p^{f\prime} = \begin{pmatrix} \rho_p^{f\prime} \\ \mathbf{0}_p \end{pmatrix} \quad , \quad \mathbf{R}_p'\mathbf{a}_p^{b\prime} = \begin{pmatrix} \mathbf{0}_p \\ \rho_p^{b\prime} \end{pmatrix} \quad , \tag{8.C.7}$$

where the prime denotes this as the solution for the reduced data sequence case. In this case

$$\mathbf{R}'_p = \sum_{n=p+2}^{N} \mathbf{x}_p^*[n]\mathbf{x}_p^T[n]. \tag{8.C.8}$$

Similarly, if the error term $e[N]$ is eliminated, the normal equations considering just the data sequence $x[1], \ldots, x[N-1]$ have the form

$$\mathbf{R}''_p \mathbf{a}_p^{f''} = \begin{pmatrix} \rho_p^{f''} \\ \mathbf{0}_p \end{pmatrix} \quad , \quad \mathbf{R}''_p \mathbf{a}_p^{b''} = \begin{pmatrix} \mathbf{0}_p \\ \rho_p^{b''} \end{pmatrix}, \tag{8.C.9}$$

where the double prime denotes each as the solution for this other reduced data sequence case. In this situation

$$\mathbf{R}''_p = \sum_{n=p+1}^{N-1} \mathbf{x}_p^*[n]\mathbf{x}_p^T[n]. \tag{8.C.10}$$

8.C.2   Special Partitions and Auxiliary Parameters

Crucial to the development of a fast algorithm are the following order-index partitions of the $(p+1) \times (p+1)$ matrix $\mathbf{R}_p$,

$$\mathbf{R}_p = \begin{pmatrix} r_p[0,0] & \mathbf{s}_p^H \\ \mathbf{s}_p & \mathbf{R}''_{p-1} \end{pmatrix} \quad , \quad \mathbf{R}_p = \begin{pmatrix} \mathbf{R}'_{p-1} & \mathbf{r}_p \\ \mathbf{r}_p^H & r_p[p,p] \end{pmatrix} \quad , \tag{8.C.11}$$

where the $p \times 1$ column vectors $\mathbf{r}_p$ and $\mathbf{s}_p$ are

$$\mathbf{s}_p = \begin{pmatrix} r_p[1,0] \\ \vdots \\ r_p[p,0] \end{pmatrix} \quad , \quad \mathbf{r}_p = \begin{pmatrix} r_p[0,p] \\ \vdots \\ r_p[p-1,p] \end{pmatrix}. \tag{8.C.12}$$

Partitions (8.C.11) are very similar to partitions (3.124) of the Toeplitz matrix given in Chap. 3.

Also crucial are the following time-index partitions

$$\mathbf{R}'_p = \mathbf{R}_p - \mathbf{x}^*[p+1]\mathbf{x}_p^T[p+1] \tag{8.C.13}$$

$$\mathbf{R}''_p = \mathbf{R}_p - \mathbf{x}_p^*[N]\mathbf{x}_p^T[N]. \tag{8.C.14}$$

These may be considered to be the adjustments necessary to account for the very nearly Toeplitz structure of $\mathbf{R}_p$.

The pair of auxiliary $(p+1) \times 1$ vectors $\mathbf{c}_p$ and $\mathbf{d}_p$ are also needed in the development of a fast algorithm. These are defined by

$$\mathbf{R}_p \mathbf{c}_p = \mathbf{x}_p^*[N] \tag{8.C.15}$$

$$\mathbf{R}_p \mathbf{d}_p = \mathbf{x}_p^*[p+1] \tag{8.C.16}$$

and have the structure

$$\mathbf{c}_p = \begin{pmatrix} c_p[0] \\ \vdots \\ c_p[p] \end{pmatrix} \quad , \quad \mathbf{d}_p = \begin{pmatrix} d_p[0] \\ \vdots \\ d_p[p] \end{pmatrix} . \tag{8.C.17}$$

Similar vectors $\mathbf{c}_p'$ and $\mathbf{d}_p'$ may be defined with the matrix $\mathbf{R}_p'$, as well as vectors $\mathbf{c}_p''$ and $\mathbf{d}_p''$ with the matrix $\mathbf{R}_p''$.

8.C.3 Order Update Recursions

The order update for the forward linear prediction vector is very similar in structure to the Levinson recursion. It is proposed, with hindsight, that the update has the structure

$$\mathbf{a}_p^f = \begin{pmatrix} \mathbf{a}_{p-1}^{f\prime} \\ 0 \end{pmatrix} + a_p^f[p] \begin{pmatrix} 0 \\ \mathbf{a}_{p-1}^{b\prime\prime} \end{pmatrix} , \tag{8.C.18}$$

where $a_p^f[p]$ is given by

$$a_p^f[p] = -\frac{\Delta_p}{\rho_{p-1}^{b\prime\prime}} \tag{8.C.19}$$

in which

$$\Delta_p = \mathbf{r}_p^H \mathbf{a}_{p-1}^{f\prime} \quad .$$

To verify (8.C.18), premultiply both sides by $\mathbf{R}_p$ and substitute the appropriate order partition (8.C.11). This will also yield the relationship for the forward prediction squared error

$$\rho_p^f = \rho_{p-1}^{f\prime} - \Delta_p \nabla_p / \rho_{p-1}^{b\prime\prime} = \rho_{p-1}^{f\prime} - |\Delta_p|^2 / \rho_{p-1}^{b\prime\prime}, \tag{8.C.20}$$

where

$$\nabla_p = \mathbf{s}_p^H \mathbf{a}_{p-1}^{b\prime\prime} \quad .$$

It may be shown (see Problem 11) that $\nabla_p = \Delta_p^*$, thus ensuring that (8.C.20) is real-valued. The order update for the backward linear prediction vector is

$$\mathbf{a}_p^b = \begin{pmatrix} 0 \\ \mathbf{a}_{p-1}^{b\prime\prime} \end{pmatrix} + a_p^b[p] \begin{pmatrix} \mathbf{a}_{p-1}^{f\prime} \\ 0 \end{pmatrix} , \tag{8.C.21}$$

where

$$a_p^b[p] = -\nabla_p / \rho_{p-1}^{f\prime} = -\Delta_p^* / \rho_{p-1}^{f\prime}. \tag{8.C.22}$$

Equation (8.C.21) may be verified by premultiplication of both sides by $\mathbf{R}_p$ and substitution of the appropriate order partitions (8.C.11). This will also yield the relationship for the backward prediction squared error

$$\rho_p^b = \rho_{p-1}^{b\prime\prime} - |\Delta_p|^2 / \rho_{p-1}^{f\prime} = \rho_{p-1}^{b\prime\prime} \left(1 - a_p^f[p] a_p^b[p]\right) \quad . \tag{8.C.23}$$

The vectors $\mathbf{c}_p$ and $\mathbf{d}_p$ obey the following order update recursions

$$\mathbf{c}_p = \begin{pmatrix} \mathbf{c}'_{p-1} \\ 0 \end{pmatrix} + c_p[p]\mathbf{b}_p \qquad (8.\text{C}.24)$$

$$\mathbf{d}_p = \begin{pmatrix} 0 \\ \mathbf{d}''_{p-1} \end{pmatrix} + d_p[0]\mathbf{a}_p \quad , \qquad (8.\text{C}.25)$$

which, again, may be verified by premultiplying both sides by $\mathbf{R}_p$ and using either the partitions (8.C.11) and the expressions (8.C.5). The scalars $c_p[p]$ and $d_p[0]$ may be determined from the following scalar identities (which uses the fact that $\mathbf{R}_p$ is Hermitian)

$$\mathbf{d}_p^H \mathbf{R}_p \mathbf{a}_p^f = (\mathbf{a}_p^{f\,H} \mathbf{R}_p \mathbf{d}_p)^* \quad \Longrightarrow \quad d_p[0] = (e_p^f[p+1])^*/\rho_p^f \qquad (8.\text{C}.26)$$

$$\mathbf{c}_p^H \mathbf{R}_p \mathbf{a}_p^b = (\mathbf{a}_p^{b\,H} \mathbf{R}_p \mathbf{c}_p)^* \quad \Longrightarrow \quad c_p[p] = (e_p^b[N])^*/\rho_p^b. \qquad (8.\text{C}.27)$$

Define the scalars δ_p and γ_p to be

$$\delta_p = 1 - \mathbf{x}_p^T[p+1]\mathbf{d}_p = 1 - \mathbf{x}_p^T[p+1]\mathbf{R}_p^{-1}\mathbf{x}_p^*[p+1] \qquad (8.\text{C}.28)$$

$$\gamma_p = 1 - \mathbf{x}_p^T[N]\mathbf{c}_p = 1 - \mathbf{x}_p^T[N]\mathbf{R}_p^{-1}\mathbf{x}_p^*[N]. \qquad (8.\text{C}.29)$$

These are real-valued due to the manner in which they are defined. Premultiply (8.C.24) by $\mathbf{x}_p^T[N]$ and (8.C.25) by $\mathbf{x}_p^T[p+1]$ in order to yield the order updates for δ_p and γ_p,

$$\delta_p = \delta''_{p-1} - d_p[0]e_p^f[p+1] = \delta''_{p-1} - |e_p^f[p+1]|^2/\rho_p^f \qquad (8.\text{C}.30)$$

$$\gamma_p = \gamma'_{p-1} - c_p[p]e_p^b[N] = \gamma'_{p-1} - |e_p^b[N]|^2/\rho_p^b. \qquad (8.\text{C}.31)$$

One final order recursion is required for the $\mathbf{r}_p$ vector,

$$\mathbf{r}_p = \begin{pmatrix} r_p[0,p] \\ \mathbf{r}_{p-1} - x[N+1-p]\mathbf{x}_{p-2}^*[N] \end{pmatrix} . \qquad (8.\text{C}.32)$$

The proof of the above recursion is obtained by inspection from the definition of $r_p[i,j]$.

8.C.4 Time Update Recursion

The time-index update of the forward linear prediction coefficient vector is given by

$$\mathbf{a}_p^{f\prime} = \mathbf{a}_p^f + \frac{e_p^f[p+1]}{\delta''_{p-1}} \begin{pmatrix} 0 \\ \mathbf{d}''_{p-1} \end{pmatrix} \quad , \qquad (8.\text{C}.33)$$

which may be verified by premultiplying both sides by $\mathbf{R}'_p$ and substituting the time-index partition (8.C.13) and order-index partition (8.C.11) as appropriate. A by-product of this verification is the time-index update for the forward linear prediction squared error

$$
\begin{aligned}
\rho_p^{f'} &= \rho_p^f + \frac{e_p^f[p+1]}{\delta''_{p-1}}\{\mathbf{s}_p^H \mathbf{d}''_{p-1} - x^*[p+1]\} \\
&= \rho_p^f - |e_p^f[p+1]|^2/\delta''_{p-1} \quad .
\end{aligned}
\tag{8.C.34}
$$

Similarly, the backward linear prediction coefficient vector is given by

$$
\mathbf{a}_p^{b''} = \mathbf{a}_p^b + \frac{e_p^b[N]}{\gamma'_{p-1}}\begin{pmatrix} \mathbf{c}'_{p-1} \\ 0 \end{pmatrix} \quad ,
\tag{8.C.35}
$$

which may be verified by premultiplying both sides by $\mathbf{R}''_p$ and substituting the time-index partition (8.C.14) and the order-index partition (8.C.11) as appropriate. A by-product of this verification is the update for the backward linear prediction squared error

$$
\begin{aligned}
\rho_p^{b''} &= \rho_p^b + \frac{e_p^b[N]}{\gamma'_{p-1}}\{\mathbf{r}_p^H \mathbf{c}'_{p-1} - x^*[N-p]\} \\
&= \rho_p^b - |e_p^b[N]|^2/\gamma'_{p-1} \quad .
\end{aligned}
\tag{8.C.36}
$$

The auxiliary vectors $\mathbf{c}_p$ and $\mathbf{d}_p$ satisfy the following time-index update recursions

$$
\mathbf{c}'_p = \mathbf{c}_p + \left(\frac{\theta_p}{\delta_p}\right)\mathbf{d}_p
\tag{8.C.37}
$$

$$
\mathbf{d}''_p = \mathbf{d}_p + \left(\frac{\theta_p^*}{\gamma_p}\right)\mathbf{c}_p \quad ,
\tag{8.C.38}
$$

where the complex scalar θ_p is defined as

$$
\theta_p = \mathbf{x}_p^T[p+1]\mathbf{c}_p = \mathbf{x}_p^T[p+1]\mathbf{R}_p^{-1}\mathbf{x}_p^*[N] = \mathbf{d}_p^H \mathbf{x}_p^*[N] \quad .
\tag{8.C.39}
$$

The update for $\mathbf{c}_p$ may be verified by premultiplying both sides of Eq. (8.C.37) by $\mathbf{R}'_p$ and substituting partition (8.C.13); the update for $\mathbf{d}_p$ may be verified by premultiplying both sides of Eq. (8.C.38) by $\mathbf{R}'_p$ and substituting partition (8.C.14). The time-index recursions of the real scalars δ_p and γ_p may be found simply by forming $\mathbf{x}_p^T[N]\mathbf{c}'_p$ from Eq. (8.C.37) and $\mathbf{x}_p^T[p+1]\mathbf{d}''_p$ from Eq. (8.C.38), yielding

$$
\delta''_p = \delta_p - |\theta_p|^2/\gamma_p
\tag{8.C.40}
$$

$$
\gamma'_p = \gamma_p - |\theta_p|^2/\delta_p .
\tag{8.C.41}
$$

8.C.5 Initial Conditions

The initial conditions needed to commence the recursive solution starting at order zero are

$$r_0[0,0] = \sum_{n=1}^{N} |x[n]|^2$$

$$\rho_0^{f'} = \sum_{n=2}^{N} |x[n]|^2$$

$$\rho_0^{b''} = \sum_{n=1}^{N-1} |x[n]|^2 \qquad (8.C.42) \quad \bullet$$

$$\delta_0 = 1 - |x[1]|^2/r_0[0,0]$$

$$\gamma_0 = 1 - |x[N]|^2/r_0[0,0]$$

$$c_0[0] = x^*[N]/r_0[0,0]$$

$$d_0[0] = x^*[1]/r_0[0,0] \quad .$$

All of these follow directly from the various recursive relationships of the last two subsections.

8.C.6 Simple Checks for Ill-Conditioning

Several simple checks are built into the algorithm for testing for numerical ill-conditioning or singularity of the normal equations. The squared prediction errors ρ^f, ρ^b, $\rho^{f'}$, and $\rho^{b''}$ are, by definition, positive scalars. If these ever become negative, it is due to numerical ill-conditioning. If any become zero, it would indicate a singular normal equation matrix. The scalars δ, γ, δ'', and γ' must be bounded between zero and unity, as will be shown. If any of these scalars fall outside this range, it is indicative of numerical ill-conditioning.

To illustrate the bounds for the δ and γ scalars, consider the matrix inversion lemma, Eq. (3.53), applied to time-index partition equation (8.C.13),

$$\left(\mathbf{R}'_p\right)^{-1} = \mathbf{R}_p^{-1} - \left(1 - \mathbf{x}_p^T[p+1]\mathbf{R}_p^{-1}\mathbf{x}_p^*[p+1]\right)^{-1} \left(\mathbf{R}_p^{-1}\mathbf{x}_p^*[p+1]\right)\left(\mathbf{x}_p^T[p+1]\mathbf{R}_p^{-1}\right)$$

or

$$\left(\mathbf{R}'_p\right)^{-1} = \mathbf{R}_p^{-1} - \mathbf{d}_p\mathbf{d}_p^H/\delta_p \quad .$$

Form the quadratic product

$$\mathbf{x}_p^T[p+1]\left(\mathbf{R}'_p\right)^{-1}\mathbf{x}_p^*[p+1] = \mathbf{x}_p^T[p+1]\mathbf{R}_p^{-1}\mathbf{x}_p^*[p+1] - \mathbf{x}_p^T[p+1]\mathbf{d}_p\mathbf{d}_p^H\mathbf{x}_p^*[p+1]/\delta_p$$
$$= (1 - \delta_p) - (1 - \delta_p)^2/\delta_p = 2\delta_p(1 - \delta_p) \quad .$$

If $\mathbf{R}'_p$ is an invertible positive-definite matrix, then this quadratic product must be positive,

$$2\delta_p(1 - \delta_p) > 0.$$

For this to be true, the real scalar δ_p must satisfy $0 < \delta_p < 1$.

8.C.7 Computation and Storage Requirements

In the main loop, there are $N + 12m$ computational operations (adds or multiplies) per pass that are functions of N or m. For $m = 1$ to $m = M$, this results in a total of $NM + 6M^2$ operations (counting only the quadratic terms). An examination of the vector dimensions in the program indicates memory requirements of $N + 5M$ are needed to store the contents of the vectors. Note that this storage is linear in order, rather than quadratic as would be the case had the entire $\mathbf{R}_p$ matrix been stored. All lower-order solutions are obtained as part of the recursive solution.

If the 64-point complex test sequence of Appendix II is processed by this algorithm for N = 64 and order IP = 15, then the following parameters should be calculated

$$PF = 0.00469$$

```
AF( 1) = (  2.789415,  -0.438349)      AF( 9) = (  3.988581,-10.472203)
AF( 2) = (  5.510542,  -1.506919)      AF(10) = (  2.054187, -8.156341)
AF( 3) = (  8.034858,  -3.420010)      AF(11) = (  0.804809, -5.221524)
AF( 4) = ( 10.026126,  -5.750709)      AF(12) = (  0.295171, -2.585814)
AF( 5) = ( 10.567300,  -8.080594)      AF(13) = (  0.199536, -0.804796)
AF( 6) = (  9.954793,  -9.989690)      AF(14) = (  0.146386, -0.034894)
AF( 7) = (  8.265129,-11.310373)       AF(15) = (  0.078573,  0.090202)
AF( 8) = (  6.184772,-11.547959)  .
```

```
      SUBROUTINE COVAR (N,IP,X,PF,AF,PB,AB,ISTAT)
C
C     Fast algorithm for the solution of the covariance least squares
C     normal equations.
C
C     Input Parameters:
C
C     N    - Number of data samples (integer)
C     IP   - Order of linear prediction model (integer)
C     X    - Array of complex data samples X(1) to X(N)
C
C     Output Parameters:
C
C     PF    - Real forward linear prediction variance at order IP
C     AF    - Array of complex forward linear prediction coefficients
C     PB    - Real backward linear prediction variance at order IP
C     AB    - Array of complex backward linear prediction coefficients
C     ISTAT - Integer indicating status of algorithm at time of exit:
C               0 for normal exit if no numerical ill-conditioning
C               1 if PF and PB are not positive values
C               2 if DELTA'' and GAMMA' do not lie in the range 0 to 1
```

```
C                  3 if PF' and PB'' are not positive values
C                  4 if DELTA and GAMMA do not lie in the range 0 to 1
C
C    Notes:
C
C       External arrays AF,AB must be dimensioned .GE. IP and array X must
C       be dimensioned .GE. N in the calling program.  Internal array  R
C       must be dimensioned .GE. IP and arrays  C,D  must be dimensioned
C       .GE. IP+1.  Program elements C(k+1) and D(k+1) correspond to text
C       elements c(k) and d(k), for k=0 to IP .
C
         COMPLEX X(1),AF(1),AB(1)
         COMPLEX C(101),D(101),R(100),EF,EB,THETA,TEMP,SAVE,C1,C2,C3,C4
C
C    Initialization
C
         R1=0.
         DO 10 K=2,N-1
10          R1=R1+REAL(X(K))**2+AIMAG(X(K))**2
         R2=REAL(X(1))**2+AIMAG(X(1))**2
         R3=REAL(X(N))**2+AIMAG(X(N))**2
         PF=R1+R3
         PB=R1+R2
         R4=R1+R2+R3
         R5=1./R4
         DELTA=1.-R2*R5
         GAMMA=1.-R3*R5
         C(1)=CONJG(X(N))*R5
         D(1)=CONJG(X(1))*R5
         ISTAT=0
         M=0
         IF (IP .NE. 0)  GO TO 1000
         PF=R4/FLOAT(N)
         PB=PF
         RETURN
C
C    MAIN LOOP
C
1000     M=M+1
         R1=1./PF
         R2=1./PB
         R3=1./DELTA
         R4=1./GAMMA
C
C    Order update: AF and AB vectors ; time update: C and D vectors
C
         TEMP=(0.,0.)
         DO 20 K=M+1,N
20          TEMP=TEMP+X(K)*CONJG(X(K-M))
         R(M)=CONJG(TEMP)
         THETA=X(1)*C(M)
         IF (M .EQ. 1)  GO TO 40
         DO 30 K=1,M-1
            THETA=THETA+X(M+1-K)*C(K)              ! Eq. (8.C.39)
            R(K)=R(K)-X(N+1-M)*CONJG(X(N+1-M+K))   ! Eq. (8.C.32)
30          TEMP=TEMP+CONJG(R(K))*AF(M-K)
40       C1=-TEMP*R2
         C2=-CONJG(TEMP)*R1
```

```
          C3=THETA*R3
          C4=CONJG(THETA)*R4
          AF(M)=C1                                    ! Eq. (8.C.19)
          AB(M)=C2                                    ! Eq. (8.C.22)
          SAVE=C(M)
          C(M)=SAVE+C3*D(M)
          D(M)=D(M)+C4*SAVE
          IF (M .EQ. 1)  GO TO 60
          DO 50 K=1,M-1
            SAVE=AF(K)
            AF(K)=SAVE+C1*AB(M-K)                     ! Eq. (8.C.18)
            AB(M-K)=AB(M-K)+C2*SAVE                   ! Eq. (8.C.21)
            SAVE=C(K)
            C(K)=SAVE+C3*D(K)                         ! Eq. (8.C.37)
50          D(K)=D(K)+C4*SAVE                         ! Eq. (8.C.38)
60        R5=REAL(TEMP)**2+AIMAG(TEMP)**2
          PF=PF-R5*R2                                 ! Eq. (8.C.20)
          PB=PB-R5*R1                                 ! Eq. (8.C.23)
          R5=REAL(THETA)**2+AIMAG(THETA)**2
          DELTA=DELTA-R5*R4                           ! Eq. (8.C.39)
          GAMMA=GAMMA-R5*R3                           ! Eq. (8.C.40)
          IF (M .NE. IP)  GO TO 65
          PF=PF/FLOAT(N-M)
          PB=PB/FLOAT(N-M)
          RETURN
65        IF (PF .GT. 0. .AND. PB .GT. 0.)  GO TO 70
          ISTAT=1
          RETURN
70        IF (DELTA .GT. 0. .AND. DELTA .LE. 1. .AND. GAMMA .GT. 0.
       *     .AND. GAMMA .LE. 1)  GO TO 80
          ISTAT=2
          RETURN
C
C    Time update:  AF and AB vectors; order update:  C and D vectors
C
80        R1=1./PF
          R2=1./PB
          R3=1./DELTA
          R4=1./GAMMA
          EF=X(M+1)
          EB=X(N-M)
          DO 90 K=1,M
            EF=EF+AF(K)*X(M+1-K)                      ! Eq. (8.C.1)
90          EB=EB+AB(K)*X(N-M+K)                      ! Eq. (8.C.2)
          C1=EF*R3
          C2=EB*R4
          C3=CONJG(EB)*R2
          C4=CONJG(EF)*R1
          DO 100 K=M,1,-1
            SAVE=AF(K)
            AF(K)=SAVE+C1*D(K)                        ! Eq. (8.C.33)
            D(K+1)=D(K)+C4*SAVE                       ! Eq. (8.C.25)
            SAVE=AB(K)
            AB(K)=SAVE+C2*C(M+1-K)                    ! Eq. (8.C.35)
100         C(M+1-K)=C(M+1-K)+C3*SAVE                 ! Eq. (8.C.24)
          C(M+1)=C3
          D(1)=C4
          R5=REAL(EF)**2+AIMAG(EF)**2
```

```
      PF=PF-R5*R3                          ! Eq. (8.C.34)
      DELTA=DELTA-R5*R1                    ! Eq. (8.C.30)
      R5=REAL(EB)**2+AIMAG(EB)**2
      PB=PB-R5*R4                          ! Eq. (8.C.36)
      GAMMA=GAMMA-R5*R2                    ! Eq. (8.C.31)
      IF (PF .GT. 0. .AND. PB .GT. 0.)  GO TO 110
      ISTAT=3
      RETURN
110   IF (DELTA .GT. 0. .AND. DELTA .LE. 1. .AND. GAMMA .GT. 0.
     *    .AND. GAMMA .LE. 1.)  GO TO 1000
      ISTAT=4
      RETURN
      END
```

APPENDIX 8.D
FAST ALGORITHM AND PROGRAM TO SOLVE THE MODIFIED
COVARIANCE EQUATIONS OF LINEAR PREDICTION

8.D.1 Introduction

The original fast algorithm for the solution of the modified covariance normal
equations was published by Marple [1980]. The presentation here contains further computational reductions over the original algorithm. The pth-order forward
and backward linear prediction errors for the modified covariance method may be
represented as the vector inner products

$$e_p^f[n] = \mathbf{x}_p^T[n]\mathbf{a}_p^{fb} \tag{8.D.1}$$

$$e_p^b[n] = \mathbf{x}_p^T[n]\mathbf{J}\mathbf{a}_p^{fb*}, \tag{8.D.2}$$

where the data vector $\mathbf{x}_p[n]$ and linear prediction coefficient vector $\mathbf{a}_p^{fb}$ are defined
as

$$\mathbf{x}_p[n] = \begin{pmatrix} x[n] \\ x[n-1] \\ \vdots \\ x[n-p] \end{pmatrix} \quad , \quad \mathbf{a}_p^{fb} = \begin{pmatrix} 1 \\ a_p[1] \\ \vdots \\ a_p[p] \end{pmatrix}, \tag{8.D.3}$$

and $\mathbf{J}$ is a $(p+1) \times (p+1)$ reflection matrix. Based on measured complex data
samples $x[1], \ldots, x[N]$, the modified covariance method minimizes the average of
the forward and backward linear prediction squared errors

$$\rho_p^{fb} = \frac{1}{2}\left[\sum_{n=p+1}^{N} \left[|e_p^f[n]|^2 + |e_p^b[n]|^2 \right] \right], \tag{8.D.4}$$

resulting in the normal equations

$$\mathbf{R}_p \mathbf{a}_p^{fb} = \begin{pmatrix} 2\rho_p^{fb} \\ \mathbf{0}_p \end{pmatrix} \quad , \tag{8.D.5}$$

where $\mathbf{0}_p$ is a $p \times 1$ all-zero vector. An equivalent dyadic vector definition for $\mathbf{R}_p$ to that given by Eq. (8.47) is

$$\mathbf{R}_p = \sum_{n=p+1}^{N} \left[\mathbf{x}_p^*[n]\mathbf{x}_p^T[n] + \mathbf{J}\mathbf{x}_p[n]\mathbf{x}_p^H[n]\mathbf{J} \right]. \tag{8.D.6}$$

Note that $\mathbf{R}_p$ is persymmetric, because $\mathbf{J}\mathbf{R}_p^*\mathbf{J} = \mathbf{R}_p$, and also Hermitian, because $\mathbf{R}_p^H = \mathbf{R}_p$. These properties are the result of the assumption that $\mathbf{a}_p$ is the forward linear prediction vector and the conjugated and inverted vector $\mathbf{J}\mathbf{a}_p^*$ is the backward linear prediction coefficient vector (these were different in the covariance method).

If the forward prediction error term $e_p^f[p+1]$ and the backward prediction error term $e_p^b[N]$ are both not used, the resulting squared error

$$\rho_p^{fb\prime} = \frac{1}{2} \left[\sum_{n=p+2}^{N} \left(|e_p^{f\prime}[n]|^2 + |e_p^{b\prime}[n-1]|^2 \right) \right] \tag{8.D.7}$$

is minimized; then the linear prediction coefficients satisfy the normal equations

$$\mathbf{R}_p' \mathbf{a}_p^{fb\prime} = \begin{pmatrix} 2\rho_p^{fb\prime} \\ \mathbf{0}_p \end{pmatrix} \quad , \tag{8.D.8}$$

where the prime denotes the solution for this case of omitted error terms. The matrix $\mathbf{R}_p'$ may be expressed as

$$\mathbf{R}_p' = \sum_{n=p+2}^{N} \left(\mathbf{x}_p^*[n]\mathbf{x}_p^T[n] + \mathbf{J}\mathbf{x}_p[n-1]\mathbf{x}_p^H[n-1]\mathbf{J} \right). \tag{8.D.9}$$

8.D.2 Special Partitions and Auxiliary Parameters

Crucial to the development of a fast algorithm are the following order-index partitions of the $(p+1) \times (p+1)$ matrix $\mathbf{R}_p$,

$$\mathbf{R}_p = \begin{pmatrix} \mathbf{R}_{p-1}' & \mathbf{r}_p \\ \mathbf{r}_p^H & r_p[p,p] \end{pmatrix} = \begin{pmatrix} r_p[0,0] & \mathbf{r}_p^T\mathbf{J} \\ \mathbf{J}\mathbf{r}_p^* & \mathbf{J}\mathbf{R}_{p-1}'^*\mathbf{J} \end{pmatrix}, \tag{8.D.10}$$

where the $p \times 1$ column vector $\mathbf{r}_p$ is

$$\mathbf{r}_p = \begin{pmatrix} r_p[0, p] \\ \vdots \\ r_p[p-1, p] \end{pmatrix} \tag{8.D.11}$$

and $\mathbf{J}$ is a $p \times p$ reflection matrix. Note also that

$$r_p[0, 0] = r_p^*[p, p] = \sum_{n=p+1}^{N} \left(|x[n]|^2 + |x[n-p]|^2 \right).$$

This is very similar to the partition equation (3.124) of the Toeplitz matrix in Chap. 3. Also crucial is the following time-index partition

$$\mathbf{R}_p = \mathbf{R}'_p + \mathbf{x}_p^*[p+1]\mathbf{x}_p^T[p+1] + \mathbf{J}\mathbf{x}_p[N]\mathbf{x}_p^H[N]\mathbf{J} \tag{8.D.12}$$

and its centrosymmetric variant

$$\mathbf{R}_p = \mathbf{J}\mathbf{R}'^*_p\mathbf{J} + \mathbf{J}\mathbf{x}_p[p+1]\mathbf{x}_p^H[p+1]\mathbf{J} + \mathbf{x}_p^*[N]\mathbf{x}_p^T[N] \quad . \tag{8.D.13}$$

The pair of $(p+1) \times 1$ auxiliary vectors $\mathbf{c}_p$ and $\mathbf{d}_p$ are also needed in the development of this fast algorithm, defined by the matrix equations

$$\mathbf{R}_p\mathbf{c}_p = \mathbf{J}\mathbf{x}_p[N] \tag{8.D.14}$$

$$\mathbf{R}_p\mathbf{d}_p = \mathbf{x}_p^*[p+1] \quad , \tag{8.D.15}$$

where

$$\mathbf{c}_p = \begin{pmatrix} c_p[0] \\ \vdots \\ c_p[p] \end{pmatrix} \quad , \quad \mathbf{d}_p = \begin{pmatrix} d_p[0] \\ \vdots \\ d_p[p] \end{pmatrix}. \tag{8.D.16}$$

Due to the Hermitian persymmetry of $\mathbf{R}_p$, it may easily be shown that

$$\mathbf{J}\mathbf{R}_p^*\mathbf{a}_p^{fb*} = \mathbf{R}_p\mathbf{J}\mathbf{a}_p^{fb*} = \begin{pmatrix} \mathbf{0}_p \\ \rho_p^{fb} \end{pmatrix} \tag{8.D.17}$$

$$\mathbf{R}_p\mathbf{J}\mathbf{c}_p^* = \mathbf{x}_p^*[N] \tag{8.D.18}$$

$$\mathbf{R}_p\mathbf{J}\mathbf{d}_p^* = \mathbf{J}\mathbf{x}_p[p+1] \quad . \tag{8.D.19}$$

Vectors $\mathbf{c}'_p$ and $\mathbf{d}'_p$ are defined for the matrix $\mathbf{R}'_p$ in a similar manner

$$\left(\mathbf{J}\mathbf{R}'^*_p\mathbf{J} \right) \mathbf{c}'_p = \mathbf{J}\mathbf{x}_p[N] \tag{8.D.20}$$

$$\left(\mathbf{J}\mathbf{R}'^*_p\mathbf{J} \right) \mathbf{d}'_p = \mathbf{x}_p^*[p+1] \tag{8.D.21}$$

and simply use inverted and conjugated $\mathbf{x}_p$ vectors.

8.D.3 Order Update Recursions

The order update for the linear prediction coefficient vector is very similar to that found in the Levinson algorithm,

$$\mathbf{a}_p^{fb} = \begin{pmatrix} \mathbf{a}_{p-1}^{fb\prime} \\ 0 \end{pmatrix} + a_p[p] \begin{pmatrix} 0 \\ \mathbf{J}\mathbf{a}_{p-1}^{fb\prime*} \end{pmatrix} \quad, \tag{8.D.22}$$

where $a_p[p]$ is given by

$$a_p[p] = -\Delta_p / \rho_{p-1}^{fb\prime} \tag{8.D.23}$$

and

$$\Delta_p = \mathbf{r}_p^H \mathbf{a}_{p-1}^{fb\prime} \quad. \tag{8.D.24}$$

To verify Eq. (8.D.22), premultiply both sides by $\mathbf{R}_p$ and substitute the appropriate order partition given in Eq. (8.D.10). Property (8.D.17) has also been used. The verification will also yield the order update relationship for the linear prediction squared error

$$\rho_p^{fb} = \rho_{p-1}^{fb\prime} - |\Delta_p|^2 / \rho_{p-1}^{fb\prime} = \rho_{p-1}^{fb\prime} \left(1 - |a_p[p]|^2 \right). \tag{8.D.25}$$

Observe that in order for ρ_p^{fb} to be positive and real, as it must be because it is a squared error, then it must be true that $|a_p[p]|^2 < 1$. Thus, the reflection coefficient of the modified covariance method has *magnitude less than unity*.

The vectors $\mathbf{c}_p$ and $\mathbf{d}_p$ obey the following order update recursions

$$\mathbf{c}_p = \begin{pmatrix} 0 \\ \mathbf{c}_{p-1}' \end{pmatrix} + c_p[0]\mathbf{a}_p \tag{8.D.26}$$

$$\mathbf{d}_p = \begin{pmatrix} 0 \\ \mathbf{d}_{p-1}' \end{pmatrix} + d_p[0]\mathbf{a}_p \quad, \tag{8.D.27}$$

which again may be verified by premultiplying both sides by $\mathbf{R}_p$ and substituting the appropriate order partitions from Eq. (8.D.10). The scalar terms $c_p[0]$ and $d_p[0]$ may be determined from the following scalar identities (which use the Hermitian property $\mathbf{R}_p^H = \mathbf{R}_p$):

$$\mathbf{c}_p^H \mathbf{R}_p \mathbf{a}_p^{fb} = \left(\mathbf{a}_p^{fbH} \mathbf{R}_p \mathbf{c}_p \right)^* \quad \Longrightarrow \quad c_p[0] = e_p^b[N]/\rho_p^{fb} \tag{8.D.28}$$

$$\mathbf{d}_p^H \mathbf{R}_p \mathbf{a}_p^{fb} = \left(\mathbf{a}_p^{fbH} \mathbf{R}_p \mathbf{d}_p \right)^* \quad \Longrightarrow \quad d_p[0] = e_p^{f*}[p+1]/\rho_p^{fb} \quad. \tag{8.D.29}$$

Define the scalars δ_p and γ_p to be

$$\gamma_p = 1 - \mathbf{x}_p^H[N]\mathbf{J}\mathbf{c}_p = 1 - \mathbf{x}_p^H[N]\mathbf{J}\mathbf{R}_p^{-1}\mathbf{J}\mathbf{x}_p[N] \tag{8.D.30}$$

$$\delta_p = 1 - \mathbf{x}_p^T[p+1]\mathbf{d}_p = 1 - \mathbf{x}_p^T[p+1]\mathbf{R}_p^{-1}\mathbf{x}_p^*[p+1]. \tag{8.D.31}$$

These are real-valued due to the quadratic product definitions. Premultiply equation (8.D.26) by $\mathbf{x}_p^H[N]\mathbf{J}$ and equation (8.D.27) by $\mathbf{x}_p^T[p+1]$. The order update for δ_p and γ_p are, thus, easily determined to be

$$\gamma_p = \gamma'_{p-1} - c_p[0]e_p^{b*}[N] = \gamma'_{p-1} - |e_p^b[N]|^2/\rho_p^{fb} \tag{8.D.32}$$

$$\delta_p = \delta'_{p-1} - d_p[0]e_p^f[p+1] = \delta'_{p-1} - |e_p^f[p+1]|^2/\rho_p^{fb}. \tag{8.D.33}$$

Another scalar parameter required by the fast algorithm is defined as

$$\lambda_p = \mathbf{x}_p^H[N]\mathbf{J}\mathbf{d}_p. \tag{8.D.34}$$

Premultiply (8.D.27) by $\mathbf{x}_p^H[N]\mathbf{J}$ to yield the order update for this scalar,

$$\lambda_p = \lambda'_{p-1} + \left(e_p^f[p+1]e_p^b[N]\right)^* /\rho_p^{fb} \quad . \tag{8.D.35}$$

Note that λ_p is a complex-valued parameter. The identity $\mathbf{d}_p^H\mathbf{R}_p\mathbf{c}_p = (\mathbf{c}_p^H\mathbf{R}_p\mathbf{d}_p)^*$ leads to the conclusion that

$$\lambda_p^* = \mathbf{x}_p^T[p+1]\mathbf{c}_p. \tag{8.D.36}$$

One final order recursion is required for the $\mathbf{r}_p$ vector,

$$\mathbf{r}_p = \begin{pmatrix} r_p[0,p] \\ \mathbf{r}_{p-1} - x[N+1-p]\mathbf{x}_{p-2}^*[N] - x^*[p]\mathbf{J}\mathbf{x}_{p-2}[p-1] \end{pmatrix} . \tag{8.D.37}$$

The proof of this recursion is obtained by inspection of the definition of $r_p[i,j]$.

8.D.4   Time Update Recursions

The time-index update of the linear prediction coefficient vector is given by

$$\mathbf{a}_p^{fb\prime} = \mathbf{a}_p^{fb} + \alpha_1 \begin{pmatrix} 0 \\ \mathbf{c}'_{p-1} \end{pmatrix} + \beta_1 \begin{pmatrix} 0 \\ \mathbf{d}'_{p-1} \end{pmatrix} , \tag{8.D.38}$$

where

$$\alpha_1 = \left(e_p^{b*}[N]\delta'_{p-1} + e_p^f[p+1]\lambda'_{p-1}\right)/\text{DEN}'_{p-1} \tag{8.D.39}$$

$$\beta_1 = \left(e_p^f[p+1]\gamma'_{p-1} + e_p^{b*}[N]\lambda'^*_{p-1}\right)/\text{DEN}'_{p-1} \tag{8.D.40}$$

$$\text{DEN}'_{p-1} = \gamma'_{p-1}\delta'_{p-1} - |\lambda'_{p-1}|^2 \quad . \tag{8.D.41}$$

Equation (8.D.38) may be verified by premultiplying both sides by $\mathbf{R}'_p$ and substituting the time-index partition (8.D.12) and order-index partition (8.D.10), as appropriate. A by-product of this verification is the update for the linear prediction squared error

$$\rho_p^{fb\prime} = \rho_p^{fb} - \frac{|e_p^b[N]|^2 \delta_{p-1}' + |e_p^f[p+1]|^2 \gamma_{p-1}' + 2\operatorname{Re}\left\{e_p^f[p+1]e_p^b[N]\lambda_{p-1}'\right\}}{\mathrm{DEN}_{p-1}'}.$$

(8.D.42)

The auxiliary vectors $\mathbf{c}_p$ and $\mathbf{d}_p$ satisfy the following time-index recursions

$$\mathbf{c}_p' = \mathbf{c}_p + \alpha_2 \mathbf{J}\mathbf{c}_p^* + \beta_2 \mathbf{J}\mathbf{d}_p^* \tag{8.D.43}$$

$$\mathbf{d}_p' = \mathbf{d}_p + \alpha_3 \mathbf{J}\mathbf{c}_p^* + \beta_3 \mathbf{J}\mathbf{d}_p^* \quad, \tag{8.D.44}$$

where

$$\begin{aligned}
\alpha_2 &= \left(\theta_p \lambda_p^* + \phi_p \delta_p\right)/\mathrm{DEN}_p \\
\beta_2 &= \left(\phi_p \lambda_p + \theta_p \gamma_p\right)/\mathrm{DEN}_p \\
\alpha_3 &= \left(\Xi_p \lambda_p^* + \theta_p \delta_p\right)/\mathrm{DEN}_p \\
\beta_3 &= \left(\theta_p \lambda_p + \Xi_p \gamma_p\right)/\mathrm{DEN}_p \\
\mathrm{DEN}_p &= \gamma_p \delta_p - |\lambda_p|^2 \\
\theta_p &= \mathbf{x}_p^T[N]\mathbf{d}_p \\
\phi_p &= \mathbf{x}_p^T[N]\mathbf{c}_p \\
\Xi_p &= \mathbf{x}_p^H[p+1]\mathbf{J}\mathbf{d}_p \quad.
\end{aligned}$$

(8.D.45)

Equations (8.D.43) and (8.D.44) may be verified by premultiplying both sides of these equations by $\mathbf{J}\mathbf{R}_p^{\prime*}\mathbf{J}$ and substituting time-index partition (8.D.13). The identity $\theta_p = \mathbf{x}_p^H[p+1]\mathbf{J}\mathbf{c}_p$ has been used to obtain recursions (8.D.43) and (8.D.44). This identity follows from the property $\mathbf{c}_p^H \mathbf{J}\mathbf{R}_p \mathbf{d}_p^* = \left(\mathbf{d}_p^H \mathbf{R}_p \mathbf{J}\mathbf{c}_p^*\right)^*$.

The time-index recursions of the real scalars γ_p and δ_p may be obtained by forming $\mathbf{x}_p^H[N]\mathbf{J}\mathbf{c}_p'$ from (8.D.43) and $\mathbf{x}_p^T[p+1]\mathbf{d}_p'$ from (8.D.42), to yield

$$\gamma_p' = \gamma_p - \left(|\phi_p|^2 \delta_p + |\theta_p|^2 \gamma_p + 2\operatorname{Re}[\phi_p \lambda_p \theta_p^*]\right)/\mathrm{DEN}_p \tag{8.D.46}$$

$$\delta_p' = \delta_p - \left(|\theta_p|^2 \delta_p + |\Xi_p|^2 \gamma_p + 2\operatorname{Re}[\theta_p \lambda_p \Xi_p^*]\right)/\mathrm{DEN}_p \quad. \tag{8.D.47}$$

The time-index recursion for scalar λ_p is obtained by forming $\mathbf{x}_p^H[N]\mathbf{J}\mathbf{d}_p'$ from (8.D.44),

$$\lambda_p' = \lambda_p + \alpha_3 \phi_p^* + \beta_3 \theta_p^* \quad. \tag{8.D.48}$$

8.D.5 Initial Conditions

The initial conditions needed to start this recursive algorithm at order zero are

$$r_0[0,0] = 2\sum_{n=1}^{N} |x[n]|^2$$
$$\rho_0^{fbi} = r_0[0,0] - |x[1]|^2 - |x[N]|^2$$
$$c_0[0] = x[N]/r_0[0,0]$$
$$d_0[0] = x^*[1]/r_0[0,0] \qquad\qquad\qquad (8.D.49)$$
$$\lambda_0 = x^*[1]x^*[N]/r_0[0,0]$$
$$\delta_0 = 1 - |x[1]|^2/r_0[0,0]$$
$$\gamma_0 = 1 - |x[n]|^2/r_0[0,0] \quad .$$

8.D.6 Simple Checks for Numerical Ill-Conditioning

As with the covariance algorithm it can be shown that $0 < \text{DEN} \le 1$ and $0 < \text{DEN}' \le 1$. Also, it can be shown using techniques presented in Sec. 8.C.6 that $0 < \gamma, \delta \le 1$. These are checked, as well as the positivity of the squared error terms, at each stage of the algorithm. Barrodale et al. [1983] have provided some improvements to the basic algorithm for both the high-SNR and the high-order cases.

8.D.7 Computation and Storage Count

In the main loop, there are $N + 12p$ computational operations (adds or multiplies) that are functions of N or p. For $p = 1$ to $p = M$, this yields a total of $NM + 6M^2$ operations (counting only the quadratic terms). An examination of the vector dimensions in the program listing reveals that memory requirements of $N + 4M$ are needed.

If the 64-point complex test sequence of Appendix II is processed by this algorithm for N = 64 and order IP = 15, then the following parameter should be calculated

$$P = 0.00395$$

```
A( 1) = (  2.878987, -0.474820)      A( 9) = (  3.204673,-14.283307)
A( 2) = (  5.847520, -1.795236)      A(10) = (  0.854681,-11.484167)
A( 3) = (  8.693661, -4.219615)      A(11) = ( -0.582791, -7.833453)
A( 4) = ( 10.966792, -7.316369)      A(12) = ( -0.968658, -4.332430)
A( 5) = ( 11.597926,-10.521787)      A(13) = ( -0.732152, -1.757008)
A( 6) = ( 10.831415,-13.236135)      A(14) = ( -0.341911, -0.416644)
A( 7) = (  8.699289,-15.097140)      A(15) = ( -0.084096, -0.002586)
A( 8) = (  6.027758,-15.518534)    .
```

```
      SUBROUTINE MODCOVAR (N,IP,X,P,A,ISTAT)
C
C     Fast algorithm for the solution of the modified covariance least
C     squares normal equations.
C
C     Input Parameters:
C
C       N    - Number of data samples (integer)
C       IP   - Order of linear prediction model (integer)
C       X    - Array of complex data samples X(1) through X(N)
C
C     Output Parameters:
C
C       P    - Real linear prediction variance at order IP
C       A    - Array of complex linear prediction coefficients
C       ISTAT - Integer status indicator at time of exit
C               0 for normal exit (no numerical ill-conditioning)
C               1 if P is not a positive value
C               2 if DELTA' and GAMMA' do not lie in the range 0 to 1
C               3 if P' is not a positive value
C               4 if DELTA and GAMMA do not lie in the range 0 to 1
C
C     Notes:
C
C       External array X must be dimensioned .GE. N and array A must be
C       dimensioned .GE. IP in the calling program.   Internal array  R
C       must be dimensioned .GE. IP  and arrays C,D must be dimensioned
C       .GE. IP+1 .
C
      COMPLEX X(1),A(1),C(101),D(101),R(100),LAMBDA,THETA,PSI,XI
      COMPLEX EF,EB,C1,C2,C3,C4,SAVE1,SAVE2,SAVE3,SAVE4
C
C     Initialization
C
      R1=0.
      DO 10 K=2,N-1
10      R1=R1+2.*(REAL(X(K))**2+AIMAG(X(K))**2)
      R2=REAL(X(1))**2+AIMAG(X(1))**2
      R3=REAL(X(N))**2+AIMAG(X(N))**2
      R4=1./(R1+2.*(R2+R3))
      P=R1+R2+R3
      DELTA=1.-R2*R4
      GAMMA=1.-R3*R4
      LAMBDA=CONJG(X(1)*X(N))*R4
      C(1)=X(N)*R4
      D(1)=CONJG(X(1))*R4
      ISTAT=0
      M=0
      IF (IP .NE. 0)  GO TO 1000
      P=(.5*R1+R2+R3)/FLOAT(N)
      RETURN
C
C     Main loop
C
1000  M=M+1
      SAVE1=(0.,0.)
      DO 20 K=M+1,N
20      SAVE1=SAVE1+X(K)*CONJG(X(K-M))
```

```
           SAVE1=2.*SAVE1
           R(M)=CONJG(SAVE1)
           THETA=X(N)*D(1)
           PSI=X(N)*C(1)
           XI=CONJG(X(1))*D(1)
           IF (M .EQ. 1)  GO TO 40
           DO 30 K=1,M-1
              THETA=THETA+X(N-K)*D(K+1)              ! Eq. (8.D.45)
              PSI=PSI+X(N-K)*C(K+1)                  ! Eq. (8.D.45)
              XI=XI+CONJG(X(K+1))*D(K+1)             ! Eq. (8.D.45)
              R(K)=R(K)-X(N+1-M)*CONJG(X(N+1-M+K))
        *              -CONJG(X(M))*X(M-K)           ! Eq. (8.D.37)
30            SAVE1=SAVE1+CONJG(R(K))*A(M-K)         ! Eq. (8.D.24)
C
C   Order update of A vector
C
40         C1=-SAVE1/P
           A(M)=C1                                   ! Eq. (8.D.23)
           P=P*(1.-REAL(C1)**2-AIMAG(C1)**2)         ! Eq. (8.D.25)
           IF (M .EQ. 1)  GO TO 60
           DO 50 K=1,M/2
              MK=M-K
              SAVE1=A(K)
              A(K)=SAVE1+C1*CONJG(A(MK))             ! Eq. (8.D.22)
              IF (K .EQ. MK)  GO TO 50
              A(MK)=A(MK)+C1*CONJG(SAVE1)            ! Eq. (8.D.22)
50         CONTINUE
60         IF (M .NE. IP)  GO TO 65
           P=.5*P/FLOAT(N-M)
           RETURN
C
C   Time update of C,D vectors and GAMMA,DELTA,LAMBDA scalars
C
65         R1=1./(DELTA*GAMMA-REAL(LAMBDA)**2-AIMAG(LAMBDA)**2)
           C1=(THETA*CONJG(LAMBDA)+PSI*DELTA)*R1
           C2=(PSI*LAMBDA+THETA*GAMMA)*R1
           C3=(XI*CONJG(LAMBDA)+THETA*DELTA)*R1
           C4=(THETA*LAMBDA+XI*GAMMA)*R1
           DO 70 K=1,(M-1)/2+1
              MK=M+1-K
              SAVE1=CONJG(C(K))
              SAVE2=CONJG(D(K))
              SAVE3=CONJG(C(MK))
              SAVE4=CONJG(D(MK))
              C(K)=C(K)+C1*SAVE3+C2*SAVE4            ! Eq. (8.D.43)
              D(K)=D(K)+C3*SAVE3+C4*SAVE4            ! Eq. (8.D.44)
              IF (K .EQ. MK)  GO TO 70
              C(MK)=C(MK)+C1*SAVE1+C2*SAVE2          ! Eq. (8.D.43)
              D(MK)=D(MK)+C3*SAVE1+C4*SAVE2          ! Eq. (8.D.44)
70         CONTINUE
           R2=REAL(PSI)**2+AIMAG(PSI)**2
           R3=REAL(THETA)**2+AIMAG(THETA)**2
           R4=REAL(XI)**2+AIMAG(XI)**2
           R5=GAMMA-(R2*DELTA+R3*GAMMA+2.*REAL(PSI*LAMBDA*CONJG(THETA)))*R1
           R2=DELTA-(R3*DELTA+R4*GAMMA+2.*REAL(THETA*LAMBDA*CONJG(XI)))*R1
           GAMMA=R5                                  ! Eq. (8.D.46)
           DELTA=R2                                  ! Eq. (8.D.47)
           LAMBDA=LAMBDA+C3*CONJG(PSI)+C4*CONJG(THETA) ! Eq. (8.D.48)
```

```
         IF (P .GT. 0.)  GO TO 80
         ISTAT=1
         RETURN
80       IF (DELTA .GT. 0. .AND. DELTA .LE. 1. .AND. GAMMA .GT. 0.
        *      .AND. GAMMA .LE. 1.)  GO TO 90
         ISTAT=2
         RETURN
C
C   Time update of A vector; order updates of C,D vectors aand GAMMA,
C   DELTA,LAMBDA scalars
C
90       R1=1./P
         R2=1./(DELTA*GAMMA-REAL(LAMBDA)**2-AIMAG(LAMBDA)**2) ! Eq. (8.D.41)
         EF=X(M+1)
         EB=X(N-M)
         DO 100 K=1,M
           EF=EF+A(K)*X(M+1-K)                             ! Eq. (8.D.1)
100        EB=EB+CONJG(A(K))*X(N-M+K)                      ! Eq. (8.D.2)
         C1=EB*R1                                          ! Eq. (8.D.28)
         C2=CONJG(EF)*R1                                   ! Eq. (8.D.29)
         C3=(CONJG(EB)*DELTA+EF*LAMBDA)*R2
         C4=(EF*GAMMA+CONJG(EB*LAMBDA))*R2
         DO 110 K=M,1,-1
           SAVE1=A(K)
           A(K)=SAVE1+C3*C(K)+C4*D(K)                      ! Eq. (8.D.38)
           C(K+1)=C(K)+C1*SAVE1                            ! Eq. (8.D.26)
110        D(K+1)=D(K)+C2*SAVE1                            ! Eq. (8.D.27)
         C(1)=C1
         D(1)=C2
         R3=REAL(EB)**2+AIMAG(EB)**2
         R4=REAL(EF)**2+AIMAG(EF)**2
         P=P-(R3*DELTA+R4*GAMMA+2.*REAL(EF*EB*LAMBDA))*R2  ! Eq. (8.D.42)
         DELTA=DELTA-R4*R1                                 ! Eq. (8.D.32)
         GAMMA=GAMMA-R3*R1                                 ! Eq. (8.D.33)
         LAMBDA=LAMBDA+CONJG(EF*EB)*R1                     ! Eq. (8.D.35)
         IF (P .GT. 0.)  GO TO 120
         ISTAT=3
         RETURN
120      IF (DELTA .GT. 0. .AND. DELTA .LE. 1. .AND. GAMMA .GT. 0.
        *      .AND. GAMMA .LE. 1.)  GO TO 1000
         ISTAT=4
         RETURN
         END
```

9

AUTOREGRESSIVE SPECTRAL ESTIMATION: SEQUENTIAL DATA ALGORITHMS

9.1 INTRODUCTION

Block estimation methods are appropriate for applications where data is very limited and the best possible performance with the available data is desired. For longer data sets, a variety of sequential estimation techniques are available for updating the autoregressive parameter estimates as each new data sample is received from a real-time data acquisition system. A new spectral density plot can then be made from these updated parameters as frequently as desired. These techniques are especially useful for tracking signals with slowly time varying characteristics. An example would be the doppler tone frequency of a sonar signal from a moving target. Time-sequential estimation methods have sometimes been called *adaptive* algorithms because they constantly adapt to the characteristics of the signal, even as it changes. This concept of adaptive should not be confused with the terminology *data adaptive* that has often appeared in the spectral estimation literature. Data adaptive is used to distinguish parametric methods of spectral estimation from nonparametric methods. Parametric methods are said to "adapt" their parameters to the nature of the data, whereas nonparametric methods have no parameters to adjust.

The sequential algorithms for adaptive AR parameter estimation fall into two categories. The simplest algorithms are based on a gradient approximation approach and include the well-known least-mean-square (LMS) algorithm. Recursive least squares (RLS) algorithms form a second category. The RLS algorithms provide better performance than the LMS algorithm, but at some additional computational expense. Both types of algorithms are presented in this chapter.

Algorithms for the sequential update of the parameters of a lattice filter are also available in the literature. Because the lattice filter parameters represent the reflection coefficients of an AR process, the Levinson algorithm must be used each time to convert the reflection coefficient sequence to an autoregressive parameter sequence for subsequent use in the AR PSD formula. The sequential algorithms presented in this chapter directly update the AR parameters, rather than the reflection coefficients, thereby avoiding the need to use the Levinson algorithm and saving on computations. For those readers interested in sequential lattice algorithms, consult the tutorial papers by Friedlander [1982a, 1982b].

- **SELECT PARAMETERS**
  Model order IP
  U adaptive time constant (LMS only)
  OMEGA decay factor (FASTRLS only)

- **INITIALIZE DATA SHIFT REGISTER**
  Set SAMPLE = 0 and call subroutine
  SHIFT a total of IP times

- **ACQUIRE NEXT DATA SAMPLE**

- **UPDATE DATA SHIFT REGISTER**
  Subroutine SHIFT (Appendix 9.A)

- **UPDATE ESTIMATE OF AR PARAMETERS**
  Select one of the following:
  — Gradient adaptive method
    (Subroutine LMS, Appendix 9.B)
  — Recursive least squares adaptive method
    (Subroutine FASTRLS, Appendix 9.C)

- **COMPUTE AR PSD ESTIMATE** (optional)
  Subroutine ARMAPSD, Appendix 6.B

Figure 9.1   Flowchart for two time-sequential algorithms for the estimation of the autoregressive PSD.

9.2 SUMMARY

Three computer programs have been provided in this chapter to enable the reader to produce two possible time-sequential estimates (one gradient and one RLS) of

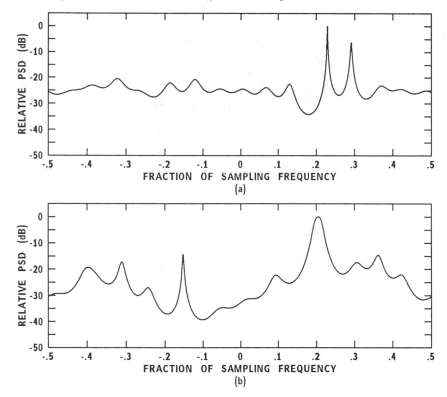

Figure 9.2   Examples of time-sequential AR spectral estimates made from the 64-point test data sequence. (a) LMS method. (b) Fast RLS method.

the AR parameters, which may then be used after any time update operation to compute an AR PSD estimate

$$\hat{P}_{\text{AR}}(f) = \frac{T\hat{\rho}_w}{\left|1 + \sum_{n=1}^{p} \hat{a}[n]\exp(-j2\pi fnT)\right|^2} . \tag{9.1}$$

Figure 9.1 is a flowchart of the steps required to compute the AR PSD with the two sequential algorithms. The subroutine names that compute the function of a given step are shown, as well as the appendix where the program listings may be found. Note that the model order must be provided as an input parameter. The adaptive time constant μ must also be provided if the LMS algorithm is selected, or decay factor ω if the RLS algorithm is selected. The model order must remain fixed once it is selected.

Figure 9.2 illustrates the relative performance of the two algorithms using the 64-point test data set of Appendix II. A 15th-order AR model was selected. The fast RLS algorithm has produced the reasonable spectral estimate of Fig. 9.2(b) after just 64 time updates using $\omega = 1$, which is to be expected because it is a fast-converging exact least squares method. Sections 9.4 and 9.5 discuss this method. The gradient LMS algorithm has done poorly, but this is to be expected because it is a slowly converging sequential algorithm and 64 time updates is not a sufficient record length for convergence. A time constant of $\mu = .02$ was selected for the LMS algorithm, based on a procedure given in Sec. 9.3.

9.3   GRADIENT ADAPTIVE AUTOREGRESSIVE METHODS

The gradient steepest descent adaptive procedure recursively estimates the p component AR parameter vector $\mathbf{a}_p^T = (a_p[1], \ldots, a_p[p])$ at time index $N + 1$ from the previous estimate at time index N

$$\hat{\mathbf{a}}_{p,N+1} = \hat{\mathbf{a}}_{p,N} - \mu \nabla \mathcal{E}\{|e_{p,N}^f[N+1]|^2\} \quad , \tag{9.2}$$

where μ is a positive scalar adaptive step size that controls the adaptive time constant and other properties of the algorithm, ∇ denotes the gradient, and $e_{p,N}^f[N+1]$ is the forward linear prediction *filter residual*

$$\begin{aligned} e_{p,N}^f[N+1] &= x[N+1] + \sum_{k=1}^{p} \hat{a}_{p,N}[k]x[N+1-k] \\ &= x[N+1] + \mathbf{x}_{p-1}^T[N]\hat{\mathbf{a}}_{p,N} \quad . \end{aligned} \tag{9.3}$$

The data vector is defined as $\mathbf{x}_{p-1}[N] = (x[N], \ldots, x[N-p+1])^T$. The filter residual $e_{p,N}^f[N+1]$ in Eq. (9.3) is not a prediction *error* because it is defined using the vector $\hat{\mathbf{a}}_{p,N}$ rather than the vector $\hat{\mathbf{a}}_{p,N+1}$. The mean value of $|e_{p,N}[N+1]|^2$ is given by

$$\mathcal{E}\left\{\left|e_{p,N}^f[N+1]\right|^2\right\} = r[0] + \hat{\mathbf{a}}_{p,N}^H \mathbf{R}_{p-1}\hat{\mathbf{a}}_{p,N} + 2\text{Real}(\hat{\mathbf{a}}_{p,N}^H \mathbf{r}_p) \quad , \tag{9.4}$$

where

$$r[0] = \mathcal{E}\{x[N+1]x^*[N+1]\},$$

$$\mathbf{r}_p = \mathcal{E}\{x[N+1]\mathbf{x}_{p-1}^*[N]\},$$

and

$$\mathbf{R}_{p-1} = \mathcal{E}\{\mathbf{x}_{p-1}^*[N]\mathbf{x}_{p-1}^T[N]\}$$

are an autocorrelation element, vector, and matrix, respectively. The gradient is then

$$\nabla \mathcal{E}\left\{\left|e_{p,N}^f[N+1]\right|^2\right\} = 2\mathbf{r}_p + 2\mathbf{R}_{p-1}\hat{\mathbf{a}}_{p,N} \quad . \tag{9.5}$$

When the gradient adaptive procedure converges, $\nabla \mathcal{E}\left\{\left|e_{p,N}^f[N+1]\right|^2\right\} = 0$ and, therefore, $\hat{\mathbf{a}}_{p,N} = \mathbf{a}_p$, yielding

$$\mathbf{R}_{p-1}\mathbf{a}_p = -\mathbf{r}_p \quad , \tag{9.6}$$

which is identical to the Yule-Walker equation (6.32).

   In practice, the autocorrelation sequence is not available, so the instantaneous estimates

$$\hat{\mathbf{r}}_p = x[N+1]\mathbf{x}_{p-1}^*[N] \quad , \quad \hat{\mathbf{R}}_{p-1} = \mathbf{x}_{p-1}^*\mathbf{x}_{p-1}^T \tag{9.7}$$

are substituted. This yields

$$\hat{\mathbf{a}}_{p,N+1} = \hat{\mathbf{a}}_{p,N} - e_{p,N}^f[N+1]2\mu\mathbf{x}_{p-1}^*[N] \quad . \tag{9.8}$$

Expressions (9.3) and (9.8) together form the classic *least mean square* (LMS) adaptive algorithm [Widrow and Stearns, 1985]. Each time update then takes roughly $2p$ add or multiply computations.

   Rules for selecting appropriate values of μ involve difficult analyses. Assuming the input process is a zero-mean Gaussian process, convergence of the mean of $\hat{\mathbf{a}}_p$ to $\mathbf{a}_p$ is guaranteed as long as μ is selected as a positive value between 0 and $1/\lambda_{max}$, where λ_{max} is the maximum eigenvalue of the matrix $\mathbf{R}_{p-1}$. The trace of a matrix was shown by Eq. (3.81) to be equal to the sum of the eigenvalues of the same matrix. Therefore, $\lambda_{max} \leq \operatorname{tr}\mathbf{R}_{p-1}$ and a more restrictive bound for the adaptive time constant is $0 < \mu < 1/\operatorname{tr}\mathbf{R}_{p-1}$. This bound is easier to apply because $\mathbf{R}_{p-1}$ is Toeplitz and, therefore, $\operatorname{tr}\mathbf{R}_{p-1} = pr[0]$. An estimate of $r[0]$, representing the sample signal power, is obtained simply from N samples of the data,

$$\hat{r}_{xx}[0] = \frac{1}{N}\sum_{k=1}^{N}|x[k]|^2 \quad .$$

   The mean convergence rate, or exponential convergence time constant τ_k along the kth eigenvector λ_k of $\mathbf{R}_p$, is roughly [Widrow and Stearns, 1985, p. 107]

$$\tau_k \approx \frac{1}{4\mu\lambda_k} \quad . \tag{9.9}$$

The convergence rate is seen to be a function of both the adaptive factor μ and the spread in eigenvalues of the autocorrelation matrix. The convergence behavior thus depends on the combined effects of all the modes associated with the eigenvalues of $\mathbf{R}_p$. The convergence time is dominated by the smallest eigenvalue. For a large spread $\lambda_{max}/\lambda_{min} \gg 1$, such as that characteristic of a narrowband process in noise, the convergence time may be quite slow.

   Because a gradient *estimate* is used, this has the effect of introducing self-noise into the adaptive process. This self-noise manifests itself as a steady-state variance or excess mean square error of the $\hat{\mathbf{a}}_p$ parameters about their means once convergence is achieved. This variance may be made arbitrarily small by choice of a sufficiently small μ, which will unfortunately cause a slow convergence. Selecting the value of μ therefore involves a trade-off between the rate of convergence and the accuracy of the AR parameter estimates (level of self-noise to be tolerated).

The LMS adaptive algorithm is able to track time variations of the input AR parameter signal statistics, provided they are sufficiently slowly varying with respect to the convergence rate of the adaptive algorithm. A time average of the error sequence generated by the LMS algorithm provides an estimate of the white noise variance needed by the AR PSD formula. Griffiths [1975] was an early proponent of this method of AR spectral estimation.

As illustrated by the example of Fig. 9.2, the gradient LMS adaptive algorithm has inferior performance and convergence rate on relatively short data records when compared to the RLS algorithms to be presented in the next section. However, the LMS is more robust in its behavior and less sensitive to numerical ill-conditioning and finite-word-length effects than the RLS algorithms. For applications in which data is plentiful and slower convergence is tolerable, the LMS method may be the more prudent choice of sequential algorithms.

9.4 RECURSIVE LEAST SQUARES (RLS) AUTOREGRESSIVE METHODS

The N-point data sequence $x[1], \ldots, x[N]$ can be used to estimate the pth-order AR parameters by forming the forward linear prediction error

$$e_{p,N}^f[n] = x[n] + \sum_{k=1}^{p} a_{p,N}[k]x[n-k] \tag{9.10}$$

and solving for the set of $a_{p,N}[k]$ parameters that minimize the exponentially weighted squared error, given all available measured data up to time index N,

$$\rho_{p,N}^f = \sum_{n=1}^{N} \omega^{N-n} |e_{p,N}^f[n]|^2 \quad , \tag{9.11}$$

where ω is a positive real scalar satisfying $0 < \omega \leq 1$. This exponential window moves with the data, giving least reduction to current errors and most reduction to older error terms, thus permitting tracking of slowly varying signal parameters (nonstationary processes). The summation range in Eq. (9.11) for selection $\omega = 1$ was called the prewindowed case in Sec. 8.5, because it made the assumption $x[n] = 0$ for $n \leq 0$. Following the same minimization procedure used in Sec. 8.5 and Appendix 8.C, it may be shown that the linear prediction/autoregressive coefficients that minimize ρ_p^f satisfy the $(p+1) \times (p+1)$ matrix normal equation

$$\mathbf{R}_{p,N}\bar{\mathbf{a}}_{p,N} = \begin{pmatrix} \rho_{p,N}^f \\ \mathbf{0}_p \end{pmatrix} \quad , \tag{9.12}$$

where

$$\mathbf{R}_{p,N} = \sum_{n=1}^{N} \omega^{N-n} \mathbf{x}_p^*[n] \mathbf{x}_p^T[n] \tag{9.13}$$

and

$$\mathbf{x}_p[n] = \begin{pmatrix} x[n] \\ \vdots \\ x[n-p] \end{pmatrix} \quad , \quad \bar{\mathbf{a}}_{p,N} = \begin{pmatrix} 1 \\ a_{p,N}[1] \\ \vdots \\ a_{p,N}[p] \end{pmatrix} = \begin{pmatrix} 1 \\ \mathbf{a}_{p,N} \end{pmatrix}$$

and $\mathbf{0}_p$ is an all-zero $p \times 1$ vector. Solution of Eq. (9.12) yields the linear predictor vector $\mathbf{a}_{p,N}$ and the least squared error $\rho_{p,N}^f$. The matrix $\mathbf{R}_{p,N}$ and parameter vector $\bar{\mathbf{a}}_{p,N}$ are indexed by N to indicate they are based on all data samples up to time index N. It can be shown (see the Problems) that the elements of $\bar{\mathbf{a}}_{p,N}$ give rise to a stable prediction filter.

If a new sample $x[N+1]$ is acquired, then the least squares fit to the entire set of $N+1$ samples may be expressed as the matrix normal equation

$$\mathbf{R}_{p,N+1} \bar{\mathbf{a}}_{p,N+1} = \begin{pmatrix} \rho_{p,N+1}^f \\ \mathbf{0}_p \end{pmatrix} \quad , \tag{9.14}$$

where

$$\mathbf{R}_{p,N+1} = \sum_{n=1}^{N+1} \omega^{N+1-n} \mathbf{x}_p^*[n] \mathbf{x}_p^T[n]. \tag{9.15}$$

An algorithm that, upon acquisition of a new sample $x[N+1]$, can update $\mathbf{a}_{p,N}$ to $\mathbf{a}_{p,N+1}$ without explicitly solving Eq. (9.14) is termed a *recursive least squares* procedure. Two RLS algorithms will be discussed. The traditional RLS algorithm requires a number of computations proportional to p^2 per time update. A new fast RLS algorithm exploits the structure in the normal equations to yield the identical solution with a procedure that only requires a number of computations proportional to p, a significant reduction in the computational load. The fast RLS algorithm is the sequential counterpart to the fast block-processing algorithms presented in Chap. 8.

9.4.1 Classical Recursive Least Squares Algorithm

The traditional RLS algorithm [Ljung and Söderström, 1983] provides an exact least squares recursive solution for the linear prediction coefficients as each data sample is made available. Noting that matrix $\mathbf{R}_{p,N}$ can be factored as

$$\mathbf{R}_{p,N} \bar{\mathbf{a}}_{p,N} = \begin{pmatrix} r_{p,N}[0,0] & \mathbf{r}_{p,N}^H \\ \mathbf{r}_{p,N} & \mathbf{R}_{p-1,N-1} \end{pmatrix} \begin{pmatrix} 1 \\ \mathbf{a}_{p,N} \end{pmatrix} = \begin{pmatrix} \rho_{p,N}^f \\ \mathbf{0}_p \end{pmatrix} \quad , \tag{9.16}$$

where

$$\mathbf{R}_{p-1,N-1} = \sum_{n=1}^{N} \omega^{N-n} \mathbf{x}_{p-1}^*[n-1]\mathbf{x}_{p-1}^T[n-1]$$

$$= \sum_{n=1}^{N-1} \omega^{N-1-n} \mathbf{x}_{p-1}^*[n]\mathbf{x}_{p-1}^T[n]$$

$$\mathbf{r}_{p,N} = \sum_{n=1}^{N} \omega^{N-n} \mathbf{x}_{p-1}^*[n-1]x[n]$$

$$r_{p,N}[0,0] = \sum_{n=1}^{N} \omega^{N-n} |x[n]|^2 \quad ,$$

(9.17)

the equations for $\rho_{p,N}^f$ and $\mathbf{a}_{p,N}$ may then be written separately as

$$\mathbf{R}_{p-1,N-1}\mathbf{a}_{p,N} = -\mathbf{r}_{p,N}$$

(9.18)

$$\rho_{p,N}^f = r_{p,N}[0,0] + \mathbf{r}_{p,N}^H \mathbf{a}_{p,N} \quad .$$

(9.19)

Using the definition

$$\mathbf{P}_{N-1} = \mathbf{R}_{p-1,N-1}^{-1} \quad ,$$

(9.20)

the least squares solution at time index $N+1$ for $\mathbf{a}_{p,N+1}$ then has the form

$$\mathbf{a}_{p,N+1} = -\mathbf{P}_N \mathbf{r}_{p,N+1} \quad .$$

(9.21)

Noting the identity

$$\mathbf{r}_{p,N+1} = \omega \mathbf{r}_{p,N} + \mathbf{x}_{p-1}^*[N]x[N+1] \quad ,$$

(9.22)

which may be proved by inspection of definition (9.17), then

$$\mathbf{a}_{p,N+1} = -\mathbf{P}_N(\omega \mathbf{r}_{p,N} + \mathbf{x}_{p-1}^*[N]x[N+1])$$

$$= -\mathbf{P}_N(\omega \mathbf{P}_{N-1}^{-1}\mathbf{P}_{N-1}\mathbf{r}_{p,N} + \mathbf{x}_{p-1}^*[N]x[N+1]) \qquad (9.23)$$

$$= \mathbf{P}_N(\omega \mathbf{P}_{N-1}^{-1}\mathbf{a}_{p,N} - \mathbf{x}_{p-1}^*[N]x[N+1]) \quad .$$

Using the identity

$$\omega \mathbf{P}_{N-1}^{-1} = \mathbf{P}_N^{-1} - \mathbf{x}_{p-1}^*\mathbf{x}_{p-1}^T[N] \quad ,$$

(9.24)

which is easily proved using the definition of $\mathbf{R}_{p-1,N-1}$ in Eq. (9.17), then substituting into Eq. (9.23) yields

$$\mathbf{a}_{p,N+1} = \mathbf{a}_{p,N} - \mathbf{P}_N\mathbf{x}_{p-1}^*[N](\mathbf{x}_{p-1}^T[N]\mathbf{a}_{p,N} + x[N+1])$$

$$= \mathbf{a}_{p,N} - e_{p,N}^f[N+1]\mathbf{P}_N\mathbf{x}_{p-1}^*[N] \qquad (9.25)$$

$$= \mathbf{a}_{p,N} - e_{p,N}^f[N+1]\mathbf{c}_{p-1,N} \quad , \qquad (9.26)$$

where the vector $c_{p-1,N}$ has the definition

$$c_{p-1,N} = P_N x_{p-1}^*[N] \quad . \tag{9.27}$$

The scalar $e_{p,N}^f[N+1]$ is a *filtered residual*, rather than a *prediction error*, because the $a_{p,N}$ parameter vector is used, rather than the $a_{p,N+1}$ vector.

The distinction between the RLS and LMS adaptive algorithms may be seen by comparing the parameter update Eqs. (9.8) and (9.25). They are identical, except for the adaptive gains. In the LMS algorithm, the adaptive gain 2μ is a *constant scalar*. In the RLS algorithm, the adaptive gain P_N is a *time-varying matrix*. The time update for P_N may be determined by applying the matrix inversion lemma, Eq. (3.53), to expression (9.24), yielding

$$
\begin{aligned}
P_N &= (\omega P_{N-1}^{-1} + x_{p-1}^*[N] x_{p-1}^T[N])^{-1} \\
&= \omega^{-1} \left[P_{N-1} - \frac{P_{N-1} x_{p-1}^*[N] x_{p-1}^T[N] P_{N-1}}{(\omega + x_{p-1}^T[N] P_{N-1} x_{p-1}^*[N])} \right] .
\end{aligned}
\tag{9.28}
$$

It is simple to show from Eq. (9.28) that

$$c_{p-1,N} = P_{N-1} x_{p-1}^*[N] / (\omega + x_{p-1}^T[N] P_{N-1} x_{p-1}^*[N]) \quad , \tag{9.29}$$

so that Eq. (9.28) may be simplified to

$$P_N = \omega^{-1}(I - c_{p-1,N} x_{p-1}^T[N]) P_{N-1} \quad . \tag{9.30}$$

To complete the RLS algorithm, the update for $\rho_{p,N+1}^f$ is obtained by combining Eq. (9.19) with Eq. (9.22).

Equations (9.26), (9.29), and (9.30) form the basic RLS algorithm. They are similar in structure to the Kalman filter equations of random control theory. The vector $x_{p-1}[N]$ and matrix P_{N-1}, which are composed of data elements, are analogous to the correlation vector and correlation matrix of the Kalman formulation. The vector $c_{p-1,N}$ is analogous to the *Kalman gain vector*. The RLS algorithm requires a number of computations per time update proportional to p^2 due to the matrix updates (9.29) and (9.30). This is in contrast to the LMS algorithm, which has computational complexity proportional to p.

Initial values must be assigned to AR parameter vector a_0 and gain matrix P_0 in order to start the recursion. The choice of a_0 must be made carefully to avoid biases in a_N, the AR parameter vector after N samples. Setting $R_{p,0}$ to a diagonal matrix ϵI with small positive constant ϵ will ensure that it is invertible, so that $P_0 = 1/\epsilon I$. The effect of ϵ diminishes as N becomes large. The RLS algorithm is sensitive to numerical ill-conditioning caused by round-off noise that accumulates during the recursive computations. To partly remedy this instability, square root factorization algorithms based on triangular decomposition of the symmetric matrix $\mathbf{P}_N$ have been devised [Bierman, 1977].

9.4.2 Fast Recursive Least Squares Algorithm

The classical RLS algorithm was developed to handle general linear least squares minimization problems. Equation (9.16) has additional structure that may be exploited to yield a more efficient algorithm and still be able to yield the exact least squares solution. This structure is similar to that used to develop the fast block algorithms of Chap. 8. The fast block algorithms were recursive in order, but fixed in time (a block of N data samples). Using similar principles devised to create the fast block algorithms, a fast RLS algorithm can be developed. In contrast to the fast block algorithms, the fast RLS algorithm is recursive in time, but fixed in order. Appendix 9.C provides development details of the fast algorithm, as well as a computer program. The key to a fast algorithm is an updating procedure for the gain vector $\mathbf{c}_{p-1,N}$ in Eq. (9.26) that uses only vector operations rather than matrix operations such as Eqs. (9.29) and (9.30). The computational complexity of the entire RLS algorithm is reduced from p^2 to exactly $5p$ complex operations (multiplies/adds) per time update. This is two and one-half times the complexity of the LMS algorithm, which requires $2p$ operations per time update. Thus, the fast RLS algorithm is computationally competitive with the LMS algorithm. There has been a tendency to call the fast RLS algorithm a "fast Kalman" algorithm, but this seems inappropriate due to the nonrandom nature of the deterministic least squares solution.

The fast RLS algorithm has two additional virtues not obtained with the classical RLS algorithm. The backward linear prediction coefficients $a^b_{p,N}[k]$ that minimize the sum of squared backward linear prediction errors

$$\rho^b_{p,N} = \sum_{n=1}^{N} \omega^{N-n} |e^b_{p,N}[n]|^2,$$

where

$$e^b_{p,N}[n] = x[n-p] + \sum_{k=1}^{p} a^b_{p,N}[k] x[n-p+k] \quad,$$

are also computed and updated as part of the fast RLS algorithm, along with $\rho^b_{p,N}$. This may be useful for exponential determination methods such as those described in Sec. 11.9.

The matrix $\mathbf{R}_{p,N}$ requires at least $p+1$ data samples before it becomes nonsingular (has rank $p+1$). The classical RLS algorithm handles this initialization difficulty by assigning arbitrary initial values to $\mathbf{P}_0$ and $\mathbf{a}_{p,0}$. This adds a bias to the exact least squares solution. The fast RLS algorithm in Appendix 9.C has been provided with a simultaneous order and time updating routine for initialization. This routine processes the first $p+1$ samples such that, at time update $N = p+1$, all parameters are set to their *exact* least squares solution values for those first $p+1$ data samples. Thus, the initialization bias of the classical RLS procedure is avoided with the fast RLS algorithm.

The fast RLS algorithm appears to have poor long-term numerical stability, but is quite accurate for short- to medium-length data records. The performance of RLS algorithms have been observed to diverge in long-term operation of the adaptive algorithm [Cioffi and Kailath, 1984]. This is due to error accumulation from finite-precision computations, especially when the $\mathbf{R}_{p,N}$ matrix is nearly singular, as it can be for narrowband inputs. One solution is to add low-level white noise to the input. Lin [1984] has introduced a rescue solution based upon reinitialization of the gain vector. Square-root-normalized versions of the fast RLS algorithm can increase dynamic range for limited-precision machines and improve performance [Fabre and Gueguen, 1986]. The normalized algorithms basically double the computational complexity in exchange for a halving of the required precision to store and compute the algorithm quantities. Setting $\omega \ll 1$ appears to introduce significant self-noise into the algorithm [Ling and Proakis, 1984a]. The RLS converges exponentially and uniformly, regardless of the eigenvalue spread of the signal autocorrelation matrix; convergence depends only on the weighting factor ω after a change in the input (the initial convergence does not depend on ω).

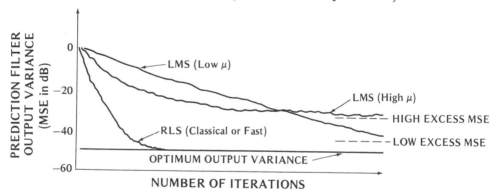

Figure 9.3   Typical convergence performance of gradient LMS algorithm and exact least squares RLS algorithm.

9.4.3 Comparison of RLS and LMS Performance

Typical convergence performance plots for RLS and LMS algorithms are depicted in Fig. 9.3. The RLS algorithm generally converges to steady state faster than the LMS algorithm, but it is never slower than LMS. In high noise, or where the eigenvalue disparity is low, the RLS and LMS have comparable convergence rates. The self-noise generated by the gradient estimate of the LMS algorithm manifests itself as a bias in the filter output variance and as misadjusted prediction filter parameters. The level of bias and misadjustment can be decreased by decreasing the value of the adaptive time constant μ. This, however, is at the expense of an increased convergence time for the LMS algorithm, as Fig. 9.3 illustrates. Convergence rate and misadjustment noise are interdependent in the LMS algorithm, and one cannot be improved without adversely affecting the other.

If the LMS and RLS algorithms are implemented in hardware for real-time spectral estimation, the performance of the two adaptive algorithms will be affected by quantization error and round-off error due to small word lengths and fixed-point arithmetic [Lawrence and Tewksbury, 1983]. The round-off error may accumulate and increase with time, until it destroys the normal operation of the algorithm. Selecting $\omega < 1$ in the RLS algorithm will bound this error accumulation and keep the filter stable, although prediction parameter numerical accuracy will be affected. Ling and Proakis [1984b] found in one experiment that the fast RLS algorithm needed at least 10 bits to work properly, whereas the LMS algorithm could operate properly with as few as 7 bits. Both algorithms gave comparable steady-state behavior when at least 12 bits were used.

9.5 FAST LATTICE AUTOREGRESSIVE METHODS

An AR(p) process was shown in Chap. 7 to have an equivalent parameterization as either p prediction parameters or as p reflection coefficients. If parameterized by the prediction parameters, the autoregressive process is generated by passing white noise through a tapped delay line (transversal) filter with the prediction parameters forming the filter weights. If parameterized by the reflection coefficients, the equivalent autoregressive process is generated by passing white noise through a lattice filter with the reflection coefficients forming the lattice filter weights. The fast RLS algorithm may be reformulated into a mathematically equivalent fast lattice algorithm. This algorithm also yields the exact least squares solution as the transversal filter, but only in terms of the reflection coefficients rather than in terms of the linear prediction (AR) parameters. The fast lattice algorithm takes about twice the number of operations of the fast RLS algorithm. Interested readers may consult the papers of Friedlander [1982a, 1982b] or Satorius and Pack [1981] or the book by Honig and Messerschmitt [1984] for details of fast least squares lattice algorithms.

The prediction parameters from the fast RLS algorithm may be directly (instantaneously) used after any time update to evaluate the AR PSD function. However, the reflection coefficients from the fast least squares lattice algorithm must be converted by a Levinson-like recursion to the equivalent prediction parameters before the AR PSD function can be evaluated. This roughly requires an additional p^2 computational operations at any time step for which a spectral function evaluation is desired. This two-stage procedure and additional computational burden is a disadvantage of the lattice algorithm for AR spectral estimation, especially for frequent updating of the AR spectral estimate. However, the fast lattice algorithms have better numerical properties than the related fast RLS algorithms, which may be useful for hardware implementation. The performance of lattice algorithms is less sensitive to round-off noise and coefficient quantization than the fast RLS algorithm. The fast lattice algorithms also yield all lower-order least squares solutions, so that the filter order may be adjusted at any time step.

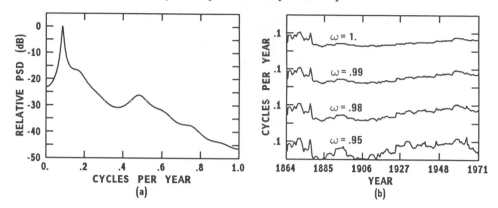

Figure 9.4   Demonstration of capability of the fast RLS algorithm to track the dominant sunspot cycle. (a) Typical AR(16) spectral estimate after 115 samples with $\omega = .98$. (b) Location of highest peak in spectrum as a function of year for four weighting factors. Each division along the vertical axis represents .02 cycle per year.

9.6   APPLICATION TO SUNSPOT NUMBERS

The 230 samples of the filtered sunspot data set are too few to achieve convergence with the LMS adaptive algorithm. Therefore, only the RLS algorithm is considered in this section. Figure 9.4 illustrates the tracking behavior of the fast RLS algorithm for various selections of the exponential weighting factor ω. A typical order 15 autoregressive spectral estimate is shown in Fig. 9.4(a). This spectrum is the result of sequentially processing the first 115 samples from year 1855.5 to year 1913.0 for the selection $\omega = .98$. Figure 9.4(b) depicts the sequential frequency location of the dominant peak in the spectrum, obtained by searching the AR spectral response after each data point update. Tracking behavior for four choices of ω are shown. A rough estimate of the effective exponential window duration in samples is given by $1/(1 - \omega)$. The effective window durations used in Fig. 9.4(b) are therefore 20, 50, 100, and ∞ samples. The nonstationary behavior of the dominant sunspot cycle, previously detected in stacked periodogram plots, is clearly indicated by the variations in Fig. 9.4(b).

REFERENCES

Bierman, G. J., *Factorization Methods for Discrete Sequential Estimation*, Academic Press, Inc., New York, 1977.

Carayannis, G., D. G. Manolakis, and N. Kalouptsidis, A Fast Sequential Algorithm for Least Squares Filtering and Prediction, *IEEE Trans. Acoust. Speech Signal Process.*, vol. ASSP-31, pp. 1394–1402, December 1983.

Cioffi, J. M., and T. Kailath, Fast, Recursive-Least-Squares, Transversal Filters for Adaptive Filtering, *IEEE Trans. Acoust. Speech Signal Process.*, vol. ASSP-32, pp. 304–337, April 1984.

Fabre, P., and C. Gueguen, Improvement of the Fast Recursive Least-Squares Algorithms via Normalization: A Comparative Study, *IEEE Trans. Acoust. Speech Signal Process.*, vol. ASSP-34, pp. 296–308, April 1986.

Falconer, D. D., and L. Ljung, Application of Fast-Kalman Estimation to Adaptive Equalization, *IEEE Trans. Commun.*, vol. COM-26, pp. 1439–1446, October 1978.

Friedlander, B., Lattice Filters for Adaptive Processing, *Proc. IEEE*, vol. 70, pp. 829–867, August 1982a.

Friedlander, B., Recursive Lattice Forms for Spectral Estimation, *IEEE Trans. Acoust. Speech Signal Process.*, vol. ASSP-30, pp. 920–930, December 1982b.

Griffiths, L. J., Rapid Measurements of Digital Instantaneous Frequency, *IEEE Trans. Acoust. Speech Signal Process.*, vol. ASSP-23, pp. 207–222, April 1975.

Honig, M., and D. Messerschmitt, *Adaptive Filters: Structures, Algorithms, and Applications*, Kluwer Academic Publishers, Hingham, Mass., 1984.

Lawrence, V. B., and S. K. Tewksbury, Microprocessor Implementation of Adaptive Digital Filters, *IEEE Trans. Commun.*, vol. COM-31, pp. 826–835, June 1983.

Lin, D. W., On Digital Implementation of the Fast Kalman Algorithm, *IEEE Trans. Acoust. Speech Signal Process.*, vol. ASSP-32, pp. 998–1006, October 1984.

Ling, F., and J. G. Proakis, Nonstationary Learning Characteristics of Least Squares Adaptive Estimation Algorithms, *Proceedings 1984 International Conference on Acoustics, Speech, and Signal Processing*, paper 3.7, 1984a.

Ling, F., and J. G. Proakis, Numerical Accuracy and Stability: Two Problems of Adaptive Estimation Algorithms Caused by Round-off Error, *Proceedings 1984 International Conference on Acoustics, Speech, and Signal Processing*, paper 30.3, 1984b.

Ljung, L., and T. Söderström, *Theory and Practice of Recursive Identification*, The MIT Press, Cambridge, Mass., 1983.

Ljung, L., M. Morf, and D. Falconer, Fast Calculation of Gain Matrices for Recursive Estimation Schemes, *Int. J. Control*, vol. 27, pp. 1–19, January 1978.

Satorius, E. H., and J. D. Pack, Application of Least Squares Lattice Algorithms to Adaptive Equalization, *IEEE Trans. Commun.*, vol. COM-29, pp. 136–142, February 1981.

Widrow, B., and S. D. Stearns, *Adaptive Signal Processing*, Prentice-Hall, Inc., Englewood Cliffs, N. J., 1985.

PROBLEMS

1. Prove Eq. (9.29).
2. Prove that prewindowed method yields a stable filter, so long as $\mathbf{R}_{p,N}$ is invertible.
3. Prove that $0 \leq \gamma_{p,N} \leq 1$ in the fast RLS algorithm, and that $\gamma_{p,N}$ is real. Also show that similar results hold for $\gamma_{p,N-1}$ and $\gamma_{p-1,N+1}$.
4. Prove that

$$\gamma_{p,N+1} = \frac{\det \mathbf{R}_{p,N+1}}{\det \mathbf{R}_{p,N}}, \rho_{p,N+1}^f = \frac{\det \mathbf{R}_{p+1,N+1}}{\det \mathbf{R}_{p,N}}, \rho_{p,N+1}^b = \frac{\det \mathbf{R}_{p+1,N+1}}{\det \mathbf{R}_{p,N+1}}.$$

This means $\gamma, \rho^f, \rho^b > 0$ guarantee the invertibility of $\mathbf{R}_{p,N}$.

5. Incorporate the numerical ill-conditioning checks comparable to subroutine COVAR into subroutine FASTRLS based on testing the γ variables and testing for positive squared prediction errors.

6. Define $\psi_{p,N} = \gamma_{p,N}^{-1}$. Then show that alternative updates to Eqs. (9.B.28) and (9.B.30) have the form

$$\psi_{p,N+1} = \left(\frac{\omega \rho_{p,N}^f}{\rho_{p,N+1}^f} \right) \psi_{p-1,N}$$

$$\psi_{p-1,N+1} = \psi_{p,N+1} \left(1 - \psi_{p,N+1} c_{p,N+1}[p] e_{p,N}^b[N+1] \right)^{-1}$$

$$= \psi_{p,N+1} \left(2 - \frac{\rho_{p,N+1}^b}{\omega \rho_{p,N}^b} \right) \quad .$$

Show how to change the implementation of subroutine FASTRLS to use PSI rather than GAMMA.

APPENDIX 9.A
PROGRAM OF SHIFT REGISTER

```
      SUBROUTINE SHIFT (X,IP,SAMPLE)
C
C     This subroutine updates the data in the shift register
C
C     Parameters:
C
C         X       - Complex array of data samples X(1) [most current
C                   sample] to X(IP) [oldest sample]
C         IP      - Integer scalar of data vector length
C         SAMPLE  - Complex scalar of newest time sample
C
C     External array X must be dimensioned .GE. IP+1 in calling program
C
      COMPLEX X(1),SAMPLE
```

```
      DO 10 K=IP+1,2,-1
10      X(K)=X(K-1)
      X(1)=SAMPLE
      RETURN
      END
```

APPENDIX 9.B
PROGRAM OF LMS ADAPTIVE ALGORITHM

This subroutine implements the LMS adaptive algorithm described in Sec. 9.3. The subroutine is called once after each call to subroutine SHIFT that updates the contents of the data shift register.

```
      SUBROUTINE LMS (IP,U,X,A)
C
C  This subroutine is the LMS sequential adaptive algorithm
C
C  Input Parameters:
C
C    IP - Integer scalar of filter length
C    U  - Real scalar representing the adaptive step size
C    X  - Complex array of contents of input data shift register
C
C  Output Parameters:
C
C    A  - Complex array of AR parameters (adaptive weights)
C
C  Notes:
C
C    External array X must be dimensioned .GE. IP+1 and array A must
C    be dimensioned .GE. IP in the calling program.
C
      COMPLEX X(1),A(1),EF
      EF=X(1)
      DO 10 K=1,IP
10      EF=EF+A(K)*X(K+1)          ! Eq. (9.3)
      DO 20 K=1,IP
20      A(K)=A(K)-2.*U*EF*X(K+1)    ! Eq. (9.8)
      RETURN
      END
```

APPENDIX 9.C
FAST RLS ALGORITHM AND PROGRAM TO SOLVE EXPONENTIALLY WINDOWED EQUATIONS OF LINEAR PREDICTION

9.C.1 Introduction

This algorithm is based on the fast recursive least squares adaptive filter developed by Ljung et al. [1978], Falconer and Ljung [1978], Carayannis et al. [1983], and Cioffi and Kailath [1984].

The pth-order forward and backward linear prediction errors based on all the data available up to time N may be represented as the vector inner products

$$e^f_{p,N}[n] = \mathbf{x}^T_p[n]\mathbf{a}^f_{p,N} \tag{9.C.1}$$

$$e^b_{p,N}[n] = \mathbf{x}^T_p[n]\mathbf{a}^b_{p,N} \quad , \tag{9.C.2}$$

where the data vector $\mathbf{x}_p[n]$, forward linear prediction coefficient vector $\mathbf{a}^f_{p,N}$, and backward linear prediction coefficient vector $\mathbf{a}^b_{p,N}$ have the definitions

$$\mathbf{x}_p[n] = \begin{pmatrix} x[n] \\ x[n-1] \\ \vdots \\ x[n-p] \end{pmatrix} , \mathbf{a}^f_{p,N} = \begin{pmatrix} 1 \\ a^f_{p,N}[1] \\ \vdots \\ a^f_{p,N}[p] \end{pmatrix} , \mathbf{a}^b_{p,N} = \begin{pmatrix} a^b_{p,N}[p] \\ \vdots \\ a^b_{p,N}[1] \\ 1 \end{pmatrix} . \tag{9.C.3}$$

Based on observed complex data samples $x[1], \ldots, x[N]$, the prewindowed method separately minimizes the forward and backward exponentially weighted linear prediction squared errors

$$\rho^f_{p,N} = \sum_{n=1}^{N} \omega^{N-n} |e^f_{p,N}[n]|^2 \quad , \quad \rho^b_{p,N} = \sum_{n=1}^{N} \omega^{N-n} |e^b_{p,N}[n]|^2 \quad , \tag{9.C.4}$$

resulting in the normal equations

$$\mathbf{R}_{p,N}\mathbf{a}^f_{p,N} = \begin{pmatrix} \rho^f_{p,N} \\ \mathbf{0}_p \end{pmatrix} \quad , \quad \mathbf{R}_{p,N}\mathbf{a}^b_{p,N} = \begin{pmatrix} \mathbf{0}_p \\ \rho^b_{p,N} \end{pmatrix} \quad , \tag{9.C.5}$$

where $\mathbf{0}_p$ is a $p \times 1$ all-zero vector. The effective window length is approximately $1/(1-\omega)$. An equivalent dyadic vector definition for $\mathbf{R}_{p,N}$ is given by

$$\mathbf{R}_{p,N} = \sum_{n=1}^{N} \omega^{N-n} \mathbf{x}^*_p[n]\mathbf{x}^T_p[n] \tag{9.C.6}$$

and individual elements by

$$r_{p,N}[j,k] = \sum_{n=1}^{N} \omega^{N-n} x[n-k]x^*[n-j] \tag{9.C.7}$$

for $0 \le j, k \le p$.

9.C.2 Special Partitions and Auxiliary Parameters

Crucial to the development of a fast RLS algorithm are the following order-index partitions of the $(p+1) \times (p+1)$ matrix $\mathbf{R}_{p,N}$,

$$\mathbf{R}_{p,N} = \begin{pmatrix} \mathbf{R}_{p-1,N} & \mathbf{s}_{p,N} \\ \mathbf{s}_{p,N}^H & r_{p,N}[p,p] \end{pmatrix} = \begin{pmatrix} r_{p,N}[0,0] & \mathbf{r}_{p,N}^H \\ \mathbf{r}_{p,N} & \mathbf{R}_{p-1,N-1} \end{pmatrix} \quad , \qquad (9.\text{C}.7)$$

where the $p \times 1$ column vectors $\mathbf{r}_{p,N}$ and $\mathbf{s}_{p,N}$ are

$$\mathbf{r}_{p,N} = \begin{pmatrix} r_{p,N}[1,0] \\ \vdots \\ r_{p,N}[p,0] \end{pmatrix} \quad , \quad \mathbf{s}_{p,N} = \begin{pmatrix} r_{p,N}[0,p] \\ \vdots \\ r_{p,N}[p-1,p] \end{pmatrix} . \qquad (9.\text{C}.8)$$

Also crucial is the following time-index partition

$$\mathbf{R}_{p,N} = \omega \mathbf{R}_{p,N-1} + \mathbf{x}_p^*[N]\mathbf{x}_p^T[N] \quad , \qquad (9.\text{C}.9)$$

obtained by inspection of Eq. (9.C.6).

    The application of the matrix inversion lemma (3.53) to the two order partitions of Eq. (9.C.7) will yield, after some considerable matrix algebra,

$$\mathbf{R}_{p,N}^{-1} = \begin{pmatrix} \mathbf{R}_{p-1,N}^{-1} & \mathbf{0}_p \\ \mathbf{0}_p^H & 0 \end{pmatrix} + \mathbf{a}_{p,N}^b \mathbf{a}_{p,N}^{b\,H}/\rho_{p,N}^b \qquad (9.\text{C}.10)$$

$$\mathbf{R}_{p,N}^{-1} = \begin{pmatrix} 0 & \mathbf{0}_p^H \\ \mathbf{0}_p & \mathbf{R}_{p-1,N-1}^{-1} \end{pmatrix} + \mathbf{a}_{p,N}^f \mathbf{a}_{p,N}^{f\,H}/\rho_{p,N}^f. \qquad (9.\text{C}.11)$$

A $(p+1) \times 1$ gain vector $\mathbf{c}_{p,N}$, defined as

$$\mathbf{R}_{p,N-1}\mathbf{c}_{p,N} = \omega^{-1}\mathbf{x}_p^*[N] \quad , \qquad (9.\text{C}.12)$$

is also required by the fast algorithm. Note that $\mathbf{c}_{p,N}$ is defined in a different manner than the auxiliary vector required in the fast block algorithms of Chap. 8 because $\mathbf{R}_{p,N-1}$, rather than $\mathbf{R}_{p,N}$, is used. The column vector $\mathbf{c}_{p,N}$ has the structure

$$\mathbf{c}_{p,N} = \begin{pmatrix} c_{p,N}[0] \\ \vdots \\ c_{p,N}[p] \end{pmatrix} .$$

9.C.3 Time Update Recursions

The time-index update of the forward linear prediction coefficient vector is given by

$$\mathbf{a}_{p,N+1}^f = \mathbf{a}_{p,N}^f - e_{p,N+1}^f[N+1]\begin{pmatrix} 0 \\ \mathbf{c}_{p-1,N} \end{pmatrix}, \tag{9.C.13}$$

which may be verified by premultiplying both sides by $\mathbf{R}_{p,N+1}$ and substituting either the time-index partition (9.C.9) or order-index partitions (9.C.7) as appropriate. A by-product of this verification is the time update of the real forward linear prediction squared error

$$\begin{aligned} \rho_{p,N+1}^f &= \omega\rho_{p,N}^f + e_{p,N+1}^f[N+1](x^*[N+1] - \mathbf{r}_{p,N}^H \mathbf{c}_{p-1,N}) \\ &= \omega\rho_{p,N}^f + c_{p,N+1}^f[N+1]c_{p,N}^{f*}[N+1]. \end{aligned} \tag{9.C.14}$$

Multiplying both sides of Eq. (9.C.13) by $\mathbf{x}_p^T[N+1]$ to give the result

$$e_{p,N+1}^f[N+1] = e_{p,N}^f[N+1] - e_{p,N+1}^f[N+1](\mathbf{x}_{p-1}^T[N]\mathbf{c}_{p-1,N}) \,, \tag{9.C.15}$$

or more concisely (relates filter residuals to prediction error)

$$e_{p,N+1}^f[N+1] = e_{p,N}^f[N+1]/\gamma_{p-1,N} \,, \tag{9.C.16}$$

where, by definition, $\gamma_{p-1,N}$ is a real, positive scalar

$$\gamma_{p-1,N} = 1 + \mathbf{x}_{p-1}^T[N]\mathbf{c}_{p-1,N} = 1 + \omega^{-1}\mathbf{x}_{p-1}^T[N]\mathbf{R}_{p-1,N-1}^{-1}\mathbf{x}_{p-1}^*[N]. \tag{9.C.17}$$

Substituting Eq. (9.C.16) into (9.C.14) yields

$$\rho_{p,N+1}^f = \omega\rho_{p,N}^f + |e_{p,N}^f[N+1]|^2/\gamma_{p-1,N} \,, \tag{9.C.18}$$

which upholds the real and positive nature of the squared error.

The time-index update of the backward linear prediction coefficient vector is given by

$$\mathbf{a}_{p,N+1}^b = \mathbf{a}_{p,N}^b - e_{p,N+1}^b[N+1]\begin{pmatrix} \mathbf{c}_{p-1,N+1} \\ 0 \end{pmatrix}, \tag{9.C.19}$$

which may be verified by premultiplying both sides by $\mathbf{R}_{p,N+1}$ and substituting either the time-index partition (9.C.9) or the appropriate order-index partition of Eq. (9.C.7). A by-product of this verification is the time update of the real-valued backward linear prediction squared error

$$\begin{aligned} \rho_{p,N+1}^b &= \omega\rho_{p,N}^b + e_{p,N+1}^b[N+1](x^*[N-p+1] - \mathbf{s}_{p,N}^H\mathbf{c}_{p-1,N+1}) \\ &= \omega\rho_{p,N}^b + e_{p,N+1}^b[N+1]e_{p,N}^{b*}[N+1] \,. \end{aligned} \tag{9.C.20}$$

Multiply both sides of Eq. (9.C.19) by $\mathbf{x}_p^T[N+1]$ to give the result

$$e_{p,N+1}^b[N+1] = e_{p,N}^b[N+1] - e_{p,N+1}^b[N+1](\mathbf{x}_{p-1}^T[N+1]\mathbf{c}_{p-1,N+1}) \tag{9.C.21}$$

or, more concisely,

$$e^b_{p,N+1}[N+1] = e^b_{p,N}[N+1]/\gamma_{p-1,N+1} \quad , \qquad (9.C.22)$$

where, by definition, $\gamma_{p-1,N+1}$ is the real, positive scalar

$$\begin{aligned} \gamma_{p-1,N+1} &= 1 + \mathbf{x}^T_{p-1}[N+1]\mathbf{c}_{p-1,N+1} \\ &= 1 + \omega^{-1}\mathbf{x}^T_{p-1}[N+1]\mathbf{R}^{-1}_{p-1,N}\mathbf{x}^*_{p-1}[N+1] \quad . \end{aligned} \qquad (9.C.23)$$

Substituting Eq. (9.C.22) into (9.C.20) yields

$$\rho^b_{p,N+1} = \rho^b_{p,N} + |e^b_{p,N}[N+1]|^2/\gamma_{p-1,N+1} \quad , \qquad (9.C.24)$$

which upholds the real and positive properties of the squared error.

A useful scalar relationship is obtained from the quadratic product

$$\mathbf{c}^H_{p,N+1}\mathbf{R}_{p,N}\mathbf{a}^b_{p,N} = (\mathbf{a}^b_{p,N}{}^H\mathbf{R}_{p,N}\mathbf{c}_{p,N+1})^* .$$

This reduces to

$$\mathbf{c}^H_{p,N+1}\begin{pmatrix} \mathbf{0}_p \\ \rho^b_{p,N} \end{pmatrix} = \mathbf{a}^b_{p,N}{}^T\omega^{-1}\mathbf{x}_p[N+1] \quad ,$$

and this in turn reduces to

$$e^b_{p,N}[N+1] = \omega c^*_{p,N+1}[p]\rho^b_{p,N} \quad . \qquad (9.C.25)$$

9.C.4 Order Update Recursions

If the substitution (9.C.11) for $\mathbf{R}^{-1}_{p,N}$ in

$$\mathbf{c}_{p,N+1} = \omega^{-1}\mathbf{R}^{-1}_{p,N}\mathbf{x}^*_p[N+1] \qquad (9.C.26)$$

is made, then the result is

$$\mathbf{c}_{p,N+1} = \omega^{-1}\begin{pmatrix} 0 & \mathbf{0}^H_p \\ \mathbf{0}_p & \mathbf{R}^{-1}_{p-1,N-1} \end{pmatrix}\mathbf{x}^*_p[N+1] + (\omega\rho^f_{p,N})^{-1}\mathbf{a}^f_{p,N}\mathbf{a}^f_{p,N}{}^H\mathbf{x}^*_p[N+1]$$

or

$$\mathbf{c}_{p,N+1} = \begin{pmatrix} 0 \\ \mathbf{c}_{p-1,N} \end{pmatrix} + (\omega\rho^f_{p,N})^{-1}e^{f*}_{p,N}[N+1]\mathbf{a}^f_{p,N} \quad . \qquad (9.C.27)$$

This forms a *step-up recursion* for $\mathbf{c}_{p,N+1}$ in the sense that the recursion is from order $p-1$ to order p. Premultiplying both sides of Eq. (9.C.27) by $\mathbf{x}^T_p[N+1]$, and then adding one to each side, yields the scalar order update

$$\gamma_{p,N+1} = \gamma_{p-1,N} + |e^f_{p,N}[N+1]|^2/(\omega\rho^f_{p,N}) \quad . \qquad (9.C.28)$$

If the substitution (9.C.10) for $\mathbf{R}_{p,N}^{-1}$ in Eq. (9.C.26) is made, then

$$\mathbf{c}_{p,N+1} = \omega^{-1} \begin{pmatrix} \mathbf{R}_{p-1,N}^{-1} & \mathbf{0}_p \\ \mathbf{0}_p^H & 0 \end{pmatrix} \mathbf{x}_p^*[N+1] + (\omega\rho_{p,N}^b)^{-1} \mathbf{a}_{p,N}^b \mathbf{a}_{p,N}^{b\ H} \mathbf{x}_p^*[N+1]$$

or

$$\begin{pmatrix} \mathbf{c}_{p-1,N+1} \\ 0 \end{pmatrix} = \mathbf{c}_{p,N+1} - (\omega\rho_{p,N}^b)^{-1} e_{p,N}^{b*}[N+1]\mathbf{b}_{p,N} \quad . \tag{9.C.29}$$

This forms a *step-down recursion* for $\mathbf{c}_{p-1,N+1}$ in the sense that the recursion is from order p to order $p-1$. Premultiplying both sides of Eq. (9.C.29) by $\mathbf{x}_p^T[N+1]$ and then adding one to each side yields the scalar order update

$$\begin{aligned} \gamma_{p-1,N+1} &= \gamma_{p,N+1} - |e_{p,N}^b[N+1]|^2/(\omega\rho_{p,N}^b) \\ &= \gamma_{p,N+1} - c_{p,N+1}[p]e_{p,N}^b[N+1]. \end{aligned} \tag{9.C.30}$$

9.C.5 Initialization

The steady-state fast RLS algorithm for a fixed-order p filter applies only when $N > p$; otherwise, the least squares normal equations are underdetermined. During the interval $1 \leq N \leq p$, *simultaneous order and time updating* can be developed to provide a $(N-1)$-order exact least squares solution to the available N data samples. With the arrival of time sample $x[p+1]$, a switch from the initialization *order and time* updating procedure to the steady-state *fixed-order time-update* RLS algorithm is made in order to continue the exact RLS solution for $N > p$.

Upon acquisition of the first time sample $x[1]$, the following parameters are initialized

$$\mathbf{a}_{0,1}^f = \mathbf{a}_{0,1}^b = 1$$
$$\gamma_{-1,1} = 1 \tag{9.C.31}$$
$$\rho_{0,1}^f = |x[1]|^2 \quad .$$

For data samples in the range $2 \leq N \leq p+1$, the following order and time relationships hold

$$\begin{aligned} e_{N-2,N-1}^f[N] &= \mathbf{a}_{N-2,N-1}^{f\ T}\mathbf{x}_{N-2}[N] \\ e_{N-2,N}^f[N] &= e_{N-2,N-1}^f[N]/\gamma_{N-3,N-1} \\ \rho_{N-1,N}^f &= \omega\rho_{N-2,N-1}^f \\ \gamma_{N-2,N} &= \gamma_{N-3,N-1} + |e_{N-2,N-1}^f[N]|^2/\rho_{N-1,N}^f \\ \mathbf{a}_{N-1,N}^f &= \begin{pmatrix} \mathbf{a}_{N-2,N-1}^f \\ -e_{N-2,N-1}^f[N]/x[1] \end{pmatrix} \\ \mathbf{c}_{N-2,N} &= \begin{pmatrix} 0 \\ \mathbf{c}_{N-3,N-1} \end{pmatrix} + \frac{e_{N-2,N}^{f*}[N]}{\rho_{N-1,N}^f}\mathbf{a}_{N-2,N-1}^f \quad . \end{aligned} \tag{9.C.32}$$

The values for $\mathbf{a}_{N-1,N}^b$ and $\rho_{N-1,N}^b$ need to be initialized *only* at time $N = p+1$,

$$\mathbf{a}_{p,p+1}^b = \begin{pmatrix} -x[1]\mathbf{c}_{p-1,p+1}/\gamma_{p-1,p+1} \\ 1 \end{pmatrix}$$

$$\rho_{p,p+1}^b = |x[1]|^2/\gamma_{p+1,p} \quad . \qquad (9.C.33)$$

9.C.6 Checks for Ill-Conditioning

The invertibility of $\mathbf{R}_{p,N}$ and $\mathbf{R}_{p,N+1}$ is guaranteed as long as $\gamma_{p,N}$ and $\gamma_{p,N+1}$ are both positive and bounded between 0 and 1, and also that the squared errors $\rho_{p,N}^f$ and $\rho_{p,N}^b$ are positive. Violation of these positivity properties in the implementation given by subroutine FASTRLS is related to the numerical deterioration of the algorithm due to round-off and finite-precision effects. The matrix $\mathbf{R}_{p,N}$ is positive definite, as is easily proved.

If the 64-point complex test sequence of Appendix II is processed by this algorithm for OMEGA = 1. and order IP = 15, then the following parameters should be obtained after processing the 64th data sample:

PF = 12.47651

```
AF( 1) = (  0.367824, -0.741921)      AF( 9) = (  0.105724,  0.253750)
AF( 2) = (  0.369765, -0.660722)      AF(10) = (  0.257914,  0.106587)
AF( 3) = ( -0.245683, -0.445400)      AF(11) = (  0.246466, -0.067043)
AF( 4) = (  0.075830, -0.056228)      AF(12) = (  0.004733, -0.322168)
AF( 5) = ( -0.228449, -0.135792)      AF(13) = ( -0.283299, -0.098737)
AF( 6) = ( -0.056229, -0.146420)      AF(14) = ( -0.212917,  0.020704)
AF( 7) = ( -0.263949, -0.024513)      AF(15) = (  0.015728,  0.124406)
AF( 8) = ( -0.033696,  0.260718)
```

Note that PF will become an estimator of the error variance if divided by the number of data samples processed.

```
      SUBROUTINE FASTRLS (INIT,OMEGA,IP,X,PF,AF,PB,AB,GAMMA,C)
C
C  This subroutine is the fast RLS sequential adaptive algorithm
C
C  Input Parameters:
C
C      INIT  - Integer set to 0 whenever the algorithm is to be
C              re-initialized; program will set it > 0 after first
C              pass
C      OMEGA - Real exponential weighting factor ( 0 < Omega <= 1)
C      IP    - Integer scalar of filter length
C      X     - Complex array of contents of input data shift register
C
C  Output Parameters:
C
C      PF    - Real scalar of forward linear prediction squared error
C      AF    - Complex array of forward linear prediction parameters
C      PB    - Real scalar of backward linear prediction squared error
```

```
C     AB    - Complex array of backward linear prediction parameters
C     GAMMA - Real scalar gain factor
C     C     - Complex array of gain parameters
C
C   Notes:
C
C     External arrays X,C must be dimensioned .GE. IP+1 and arrays AF,AB
C     must be dimensioned  .GE. IP  in the calling program.   Program
C     element C(k+1) corresponds to text element c(k), for k=0 to k=IP.
C
      COMPLEX SAMPLE,X(1),AF(1),AB(1),C(1),EF,EPF,EB,EPB,TEMP,HOLD
      REAL PF,PB,GAMMA,OMEGA,SAVE
      INTEGER IP,INIT,K,MK
C
C   Initialization section              ! Eqs. (9.C.31),(9.C.32),(9.C.33)
C
      IF (INIT .GT. IP)  GO TO 100
      IF (INIT .NE. 0)    GO TO  20
      GAMMA=1.
      PF=REAL(X(1))**2+AIMAG(X(1))**2
      GO TO 70
20    EF=X(1)
      IF (INIT .EQ. 1)  GO TO 40
      DO 30 K=1,INIT-1
30       EF=EF+AF(K)*X(K+1)
40    EPF=EF/GAMMA
      PF=OMEGA*PF
      HOLD=CONJG(EF)/PF
      GAMMA=GAMMA+REAL(EF)*REAL(HOLD)-AIMAG(EF)*AIMAG(HOLD)
      TEMP=X(INIT+1)
      AF(INIT)=-EF/TEMP
      IF (INIT .EQ. 1)  GO TO 55
      DO 50 K=INIT-1,1,-1
50       C(K+1)=C(K)+HOLD*AF(K)
55    C(1)=HOLD
      IF (INIT .LT. IP)  GO TO 70
      HOLD=-TEMP/GAMMA                             !
      PB=(REAL(TEMP)**2+AIMAG(TEMP)**2)/GAMMA      ! Eq. (9.C.31)
      DO 60 K=1,INIT                               !
60       AB(K)=HOLD*C(INIT+1-K)                    !
70    INIT=INIT+1
      RETURN
C
C-----------------------------------------------------------------------
C
C   Forward prediction update section
C
100   SAVE=OMEGA*PF
      EF=X(1)
      DO 110 K=1,IP
110      EF=EF+AF(K)*X(K+1)                          ! Eq. (9.C.1)
      EPF=EF/GAMMA                                   ! Eq. (9.C.16)
      HOLD=CONJG(EF)/SAVE
      PF=SAVE+REAL(EPF)*REAL(EF)+AIMAG(EPF)*AIMAG(EF)   ! Eq. (9.C.14)
C            Test that PF > 0 could be placed here
      GAMMA=GAMMA+REAL(EF)*REAL(HOLD)-AIMAG(EF)*AIMAG(HOLD) ! Eq. (9.C.28)
C            Test that 0 < GAMMA < 1 could be placed here
      DO 120 K=IP,1,-1
```

```
         TEMP=C(K)
         C(K+1)=TEMP+HOLD*AF(K)                        ! Eq. (9.C.27)
120      AF(K)=AF(K)-EPF*TEMP                          ! Eq. (9.C.13)
         C(1)=HOLD
C
C------------------------------------------------------------------------
C
C   Backward predictor update section
C
         SAVE=OMEGA*PB
         EB=SAVE*CONJG(C(IP+1))                        ! Eq. (9.C.25)
         HOLD=C(IP+1)
         GAMMA=GAMMA-REAL(EB)*REAL(HOLD)+AIMAG(EB)*AIMAG(HOLD)  ! Eq. (9.C.30)
C                  Test that 0 < GAMMA < 1 could be placed here
         EPB=EB/GAMMA                                  ! Eq. (9.C.22)
         PB=SAVE+REAL(EPB)*REAL(EB)+AIMAG(EPB)*AIMAG(EB)        ! Eq. (9.C.20)
C                  Test that PB > 0 could be placed here
         DO 130 K=1,IP
           MK=IP+1-K
           TEMP=C(K)-HOLD*AB(MK)                       ! Eq. (9.C.29)
           C(K)=TEMP
130      AB(MK)=AB(MK)-EPB*TEMP                        ! Eq. (9.C.19)
C
C------------------------------------------------------------------------
C
         RETURN
         END
```

10

AUTOREGRESSIVE–MOVING AVERAGE SPECTRAL ESTIMATION

10.1 INTRODUCTION

The autoregressive–moving average (ARMA) model has more degrees of freedom than the autoregressive model (AR). A greater latitude in its ability to generate diverse spectral shapes is therefore expected of ARMA PSD estimators. Unlike the extensive repertoire of linear algorithms available to produce AR PSD estimators, there have been few algorithms produced for ARMA PSD estimators. This is due primarily to the nonlinear nature required of algorithms that must *simultaneously* estimate the MA and AR parameters of the ARMA model. The nonlinear equation (6.29) demonstrates the difficulty of estimating the ARMA parameters, even when the autocorrelation sequence is exactly known. Iterative optimization techniques based on maximum likelihood estimation (MLE) and related concepts are often used to solve the nonlinear techniques [Kay, 1987]. These techniques involve significant computations and are not guaranteed to converge, or they may converge to the wrong solution, and are, therefore, not as practical for real-time processing as are AR algorithms. Suboptimum techniques have been developed to significantly reduce the computational complexity. These techniques are usually based on a least squares criterion and require solution of linear equations. These methods generally estimate the AR and the MA parameters *separately*, rather than *jointly*, as required for optimal parameter estimation. The AR parameters are typically estimated first, independently of the MA parameters, by some variant of the modified Yule-Walker equation (6.30). The MA parameters are then estimated assuming the AR parameters are known or have been previously estimated.

Very little statistical characterization of ARMA spectral estimators for finite data records is available. Most characterizations have been made on empirical evidence of a few simulations. Some asymptotic results with MLE estimates of the ARMA parameters are available, but these do not lend much insight into the finite data record estimation behavior.

Section 10.3 is devoted to moving average parameter estimation. The methods of this section can then be used to generate a MA PSD estimate from the data or to develop the MA component of an ARMA model, as described in Sec. 10.4. A suboptimum technique for separate estimation of the AR and MA parameters is developed in Sec. 10.4. Simultaneous estimation of the AR and MA parameters is discussed in Sec. 10.5. Sequential estimation methods are summarized in Sec. 10.6. A special ARMA model that fits a process consisting of sinusoids in white noise is described in Sec. 10.7.

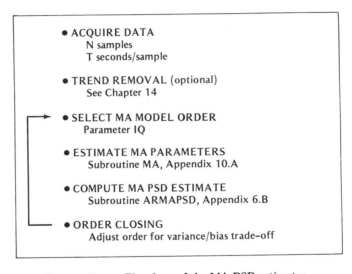

Figure 10.1   Flowchart of the MA PSD estimator.

10.2 SUMMARY

A flowchart of an algorithm to estimate the MA parameters from a sample sequence is illustrated in Fig. 10.1. The main computer program, called MA, is located in

Figure 10.2 MA(15) spectral estimate of the 64-point test sequence using a long AR(30).

Appendix 10.A. The MA parameter array B and white noise variance estimate RHO from this program are used to compute the MA spectral estimate

$$\hat{P}_{\mathrm{MA}}(f) = T\hat{\rho}_w \left| 1 + \sum_{l=1}^{p} \hat{b}[l] \exp(-j2\pi flT) \right|^2 \tag{10.1}$$

by calling subroutine ARMAPSD. Figure 10.2 illustrates a typical MA(15) spectral plot made from the 64-point test sequence of Appendix II. As with the AR methods, the order selected controls the trade-off between resolution bias and PSD variance. The spectral estimate is similar to the correlogram method PSD of Fig. 5.4.

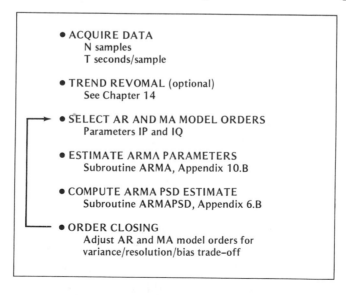

Figure 10.3 Flowchart of the ARMA PSD estimator.

Figure 10.4   ARMA(15,15) spectral estimate of the 64-point test sequence using 30 autocorrelation lag estimates ($M = 30$).

A flowchart of an algorithm to estimate the ARMA parameters from a sample sequence, based on a method that separately estimates the AR and the MA parameters, is illustrated in Fig. 10.3. The main computer program, called ARMA, is located in Appendix 10.B. The AR parameter array A, the MA parameter array B, and the white noise variance estimate RHO from this program are input to subroutine ARMAPSD in order to evaluate the ARMA PSD estimate

$$\hat{P}_{\text{ARMA}}(f) = T\hat{\rho}_w \left| \frac{1 + \sum\limits_{k=1}^{q} \hat{b}[k] \exp(-j2\pi fkT)}{1 + \sum\limits_{l=1}^{p} \hat{a}[l] \exp(-j2\pi flT)} \right|^2 . \qquad (10.2)$$

Figure 10.4 illustrates a typical ARMA(15,15) spectral estimate made from the 64-point test sequence of Appendix II. Order selection will effect the resolution versus variance trade-off.

Few guidelines exist for the selection of the ARMA model orders p and q, or for the MA model order q. Most often, it is assumed that $p = q$, although there is no reason for them to be the same. The AIC rule of AR processes has often been applied. Checking the rank of the modified Yule-Walker equations (6.30) can also give some indication of the AR model order p.

10.3 MOVING AVERAGE PARAMETER ESTIMATION

This section is generally applicable to all data sequences for which estimates of moving average parameters are desired, be it an original measured time sequence or the filtered residual sequence of the ARMA method described in Sec. 10.4. Recall that MA models are appropriate for processes that have broad peaks or sharp nulls in their spectra. The MA PSD does not model narrowband spectra well and is not, therefore, a "high-resolution" spectral estimator. This has tended to limit the research for means to estimate the MA parameters to be used in a MA power spectral density estimator.

The most obvious approach to estimate the MA parameters would be to solve the nonlinear equation (6.35) using autocorrelation estimates made from the data. Solutions of Eq. (6.35) often involve difficult spectral factorizations techniques [Box and Jenkins, 1970]. There is, however, an alternative approach based on a high-order AR approximation to the MA process that uses only linear operations. As the linear approach can yield satisfactory MA spectral estimates, it shall be the preferred algorithm for MA parameter estimation in this text.

Let

$$B(z) = 1 + \sum_{k=1}^{q} b[k]z^{-k} \tag{10.3}$$

denote the system function of a MA(q) process. Let $1/A_\infty(z)$, where

$$A_\infty(z) = 1 + \sum_{k=1}^{\infty} a[k]z^{-k} \quad , \tag{10.4}$$

be the system function of an AR(∞) process that is equivalent to the MA(q) process, that is,

$$B(z) = \frac{1}{A_\infty(z)} \quad , \tag{10.5}$$

or $B(z)A_\infty(z) = 1$. The inverse z-transform of the transform product $B(z)A_\infty(z)$ is the convolution of the MA parameters with the AR parameters, which may be deduced from Table 2.1. The inverse z-transform of the constant 1 is the sample function $\delta[m]$. The net result is

$$a[m] + \sum_{n=1}^{q} b[n]a[m-n] = \delta[m] = \begin{cases} 1 & \text{if } m = 0 \\ 0 & \text{if } m \neq 0 \end{cases} \quad , \tag{10.6}$$

where, by definition, $a[0] = 1$ and $a[k] = 0$ for $k < 0$. Thus, the moving average parameters can be determined from the parameters of an equivalent infinite-order autoregressive model by solving any subset of q equations formed from Eq. (10.6). In practice, one can calculate a high-order AR(M) estimate, such that $M \gg q$. Based on the high-order autoregressive parameter estimates $1, \hat{a}_M[1], \ldots, \hat{a}_M[M]$, a set of equations of the form

$$e_{\text{MA}}[m] = \hat{a}_M[m] + \sum_{n=1}^{q} b[n]\hat{a}_M[m-n] \tag{10.7}$$

can be formed. Ideally, the error $e_{\text{MA}}[m]$ should be zero for all m except $m = 0$, as suggested by Eq. (10.6). Practically, the error will not be zero when dealing with finite data records, so estimates of the MA parameters are obtained by the minimization of the squared error variance

$$\hat{\rho}_q = \sum_m |e_{\mathrm{MA}}[m]|^2 / M \quad . \tag{10.8}$$

where the index range will be defined. This estimation procedure can be shown [Kay, 1987] to be an approximate maximum likelihood estimate under the assumption that the process is Gaussian. Equation (10.7) is structurally identical to a forward linear prediction error, with the $\hat{a}[k]$ parameters taking the place of data samples. Two possible summation ranges for Eq. (10.8) are $0 \leq m \leq M + q$, corresponding to the *autocorrelation* method of linear prediction, and $q \leq m \leq M$, corresponding to the *covariance* method of linear prediction. Fast computational algorithms were presented in Chap. 8 for the solution of these two linear prediction methods. Subroutine YULEWALKER will solve the normal equations of the autocorrelation method. Subroutine COVAR will solve the normal equations of the covariance method. Appendix 10.A provides a listing of subroutine MA for the estimation of the MA parameters by least squares linear prediction from a high-order AR parameter estimate. The autocorrelation method was selected for subroutine MA in order to guarantee a minimum-phase estimate of the moving average parameters, i.e., the zeros of $B(z)$ will fall inside the unit circle. Simple substitution, however, of subroutine COVAR for subroutine YULEWALKER will yield a solution in terms of the covariance method. Note that an estimate of the driving noise variance of the MA process is simply the $AR(M)$ least squares variance estimate.

Several methods may be used to determine an appropriate MA model order q. The AIC criterion for MA models has the same form as in the AR case

$$\mathrm{AIC}\,[q] = N \ln(\hat{\rho}_q) + 2q$$

where $\hat{\rho}_q$ is an estimate of the white noise variance (use the least squares error variance for this). One could also filter the original data with the inverse MA filter and test for whiteness of the filtered residuals. [Chow, 1972a]. The residuals are white if the estimated autocorrelation sequence made from the residuals is approximately zero for all lags except lag zero.

10.4   SEPARATE AUTOREGRESSIVE AND MOVING AVERAGE PARAMETER ESTIMATION

Suboptimum procedures are most often used to produce ARMA parameter and PSD estimates. Most of these procedures make separate estimates of the AR parameters and the MA parameters. Typically, the AR parameters are estimated first, and then used to construct an inverse filter to apply to the original data. The residuals out of this filter should be representative of a moving average process, to which an MA parameter estimator can then be applied. This section describes one such ARMA algorithm involving three main steps.

It was shown in Chap. 6 [Eq. (6.29)] that the autocorrelation sequence for an ARMA(p, q) satisfies the relationship

$$r_{xx}[n] = -\sum_{k=1}^{p} a_p[k] r_{xx}[n - k] \tag{10.9}$$

for $n > q$. If the autocorrelation sequence were known exactly, then the p relations for $q + 1 \leq n \leq q + p$ can be set up as a set of simultaneous equations to solve for the AR parameters. These were called the modified Yule-Walker equations, as formulated by Eq. (6.30). In a practical situation, only data samples are available, so that autocorrelation estimates must be substituted for the unknown autocorrelation sequence. Estimates of the AR parameters using the modified Yule-Walker equations are generally of poor quality (large variance) where the ARMA PSD normally has small values [Sakai and Tokumura, 1980] because the autocorrelation estimates are inaccurate, or the selected order is not correct, or both [Kay, 1987, Sec. 10.4].

An alternative approach examined by Mehra [1971], Cadzow [1981, 1982], and Porat and Friedlander [1985] is to use more than p equations for lags greater than q and minimize a squared error to fit p AR parameters. Such a procedure then becomes a *least squares modified Yule-Walker* technique. Assuming autocorrelation estimates $\hat{r}_{xx}[n]$ from lag 0 to lag M have been calculated, where M is the highest lag index that can be accurately estimated, the $M - q$ equations (such that $M - q > p$)

$$\hat{r}_{xx}[n] = -\sum_{k=1}^{p} a[k] \hat{r}_{xx}[n - k] + \epsilon[n] \tag{10.10}$$

for $q + 1 \leq n \leq M$ are formed, where $\epsilon[n]$ is the estimation error. The *unbiased* autocorrelation estimates must be used to ensure that the bias of $\epsilon[n]$ will be zero. The sum of squared errors

$$\rho = \sum_{n=q+1}^{M} |\epsilon[n]|^2 \tag{10.11}$$

is minimized with respect to the p autoregressive parameters $a[k]$. The normal equations that result are identical to the covariance method of linear prediction presented in Sec. 8.5.1, namely,

$$\left(\mathbf{T}_p^H \mathbf{T}_p \right) \begin{pmatrix} 1 \\ a[1] \\ \vdots \\ a[p] \end{pmatrix} = \begin{pmatrix} \rho \\ 0 \\ \vdots \\ 0 \end{pmatrix} , \tag{10.12}$$

where $\mathbf{T}_p$ is a rectangular Toeplitz matrix of autocorrelation estimates

$$
\mathbf{T}_p = \begin{pmatrix}
\hat{r}_{xx}[q+1] & \cdots & \hat{r}_{xx}[q-p+1] \\
\vdots & \ddots & \vdots \\
\hat{r}_{xx}[M-p] & & \hat{r}_{xx}[q+1] \\
\vdots & \ddots & \vdots \\
\hat{r}_{xx}[M] & \cdots & \hat{r}_{xx}[M-p]
\end{pmatrix} , \tag{10.13}
$$

rather than data elements as used in Chap. 8. Subroutine COVAR is a fast algorithm that may be used to solve Eq. (10.12), using $\hat{r}_{xx}[q-p+1]$, ..., $\hat{r}_{xx}[M]$ as the input sequence, rather than the data values $x[1]$, ..., $x[N]$ as used in the covariance linear prediction method of Chap. 8.

A weighted squared error

$$
\rho = \sum_{n=q+1}^{M} w[n]|\epsilon[n]|^2 \tag{10.14}
$$

of decreasing weight sequence $w[n]$ with increasing n has been proposed by Friedlander and Sharman [1985] to reduce the effect of the increased estimation variance associated with the autocorrelation estimates that are used to compute the higher-indexed error terms. As the lag index of the autocorrelation estimate increases, fewer data samples are used than at the lower lag indices, increasing the estimation variance. Cadzow [1982] has proposed a similar scheme, except errors are averaged in a neighborhood of error values.

The AR parameters estimated by the least squares modified Yule-Walker technique will not yield, in general, a minimum-phase autoregression. Spectral factorization may be used to create a minimum-phase autoregression by reflecting the poles outside the unit circle to the inside. No statistical results for finite data records are available for this technique. Kaveh and Bruzzone [1983] have made empirical observations that the performance is highly dependent upon the pole locations, giving the best results when the AR poles are close to the unit circle and the worst results when the MA zeros are near the unit circle and the AR poles are farther from the unit circle. Both Izraelevitz and Lim [1985] and Friedlander and Sharman [1985] have provided some asymptotic analytical results of the least squares modified Yule-Walker techniques as functions of the number of error terms used, the signal-to-noise ratio, and the spectral bandwidth of features in the ARMA spectra.

Selection of the order of the AR portion of the ARMA process can be based on similar order selection methods discused in Chap. 8 for pure AR processes. A high AR order will be required if there are sharp narrowband features in the ARMA spectra. Bruzzone and Kaveh [1980] have even shown overdetermination of the actual AR order in the ARMA model can improve the overall ARMA spectral estimate. One can also test the rank of $\mathbf{T}_p$ in Eq. (10.13) based on SVD analysis as an indicator of order [Cadzow, 1982].

Once the AR parameters have been determined, a residual time series that is approximately an MA process can be created by filtering the original data sequence with the filter that has the system function

$$\hat{\mathsf{A}}(z) = 1 + \sum_{k=1}^{p} \hat{a}[k]z^{-k} \quad , \tag{10.15}$$

in which $\hat{a}[k]$ are the estimated AR parameters determined by the least squares modified Yule-Walker technique. The system function of the ARMA process is $\mathsf{B}(z)/\mathsf{A}(z)$, so that

$$\frac{\mathsf{B}(z)}{\mathsf{A}(z)}\hat{\mathsf{A}}(z) \approx \mathsf{B}(z) \quad . \tag{10.16}$$

Therefore, passing the measured data record through the filter with system function $\hat{\mathsf{A}}(z)$ will yield an approximate moving average process at the filter output. The procedure of Sec. 10.3 may then be used to estimate the MA parameters. The filtered sequence of length $N - p$ is given by the convolution

$$z[n] = x[n] + \sum_{m=1}^{p} \hat{a}[m]x[n-m] \tag{10.17}$$

for $p + 1 \leq n \leq N$. Appendix 10.B contains program ARMA that estimates the ARMA parameters based on the three step process: (1) Estimate the AR parameters by the least squares modified Yule-Walker method, (2) filter the original data, and (3) estimate the MA parameters from the filter residuals.

Although the MA parameters are needed for estimating the ARMA time-series model, the ARMA PSD estimator only needs an estimate of $T\rho_w|\hat{B}(f)|^2$. Explicit estimation of the MA parameters is not required [Kaveh, 1979]. The correlogram method PSD estimator could also be used to directly estimate the numerator function of the ARMA PSD estimator,

$$T\rho_w|\hat{B}(f)|^2 = T \sum_{m=-q}^{q} \hat{r}_{zz}[m]\exp(-j2\pi fmT) \quad , \tag{10.18}$$

in which $\hat{r}_{zz}[m]$ is the autocorrelation estimate produced from the filtered sequence $z[n]$. Spectral factorization can be used, if desired, to ensure a minimum-phase MA process.

Selecting the AR and MA orders of an ARMA time series model is not a simple procedure. There is not much in the literature on order selection except for simple cases. The AIC criterion for an ARMA has been one of the most used techniques. It has the form

$$\mathrm{AIC}\,[p,q] = N\ln(\hat{\rho}_{pq}) + 2(p+q)$$

in which $\hat{\rho}_{pq}$ is an estimate of the input white noise variance of the assumed ARMA(p, q) model. The actual value used is typically the squared error variance from the techniques described in this section or the next section. The minimum of the AIC $[p, q]$ over all orders p and q represents the appropriate order to use. One could also test the whiteness of the residual out of the inverse filter with systems function $\hat{B}(z)/\hat{A}(z)$ that uses the estimated AR and MA parameters. The estimated autocorrelation of the residual sequence should be approximately zero except at lag zero [Chow, 1972b].

10.5 SIMULTANEOUS AUTOREGRESSIVE AND MOVING AVERAGE PARAMETER ESTIMATION

A suboptimum method that makes a simultaneous estimate of both the autoregressive and the moving average parameters is motivated by a variant of the iterative prefiltering concept of Steiglitz and McBride [1965], one of a class of techniques that attempt to set up a linear problem by estimating the unknown white noise input to the ARMA filter. Other methods from this class of techniques have been described by Kay [1987]. The method to be described here is based on the improvement of a linear problem by a succession of these linear problems that iteratively refine the AR and MA parameter estimates.

Assuming for the moment that the input to the ARMA filter has been estimated as the sequence $\hat{u}[n]$, then this makes it possible to form the approximation error equations for an ARMA(p, q) process

$$e[n] = x[n] + \sum_{k=1}^{p} \hat{a}[k]x[n-k] + \sum_{k=1}^{q} \hat{b}[k]\hat{u}[n-k] \quad , \qquad (10.19)$$

in which the estimates of $\hat{u}[n]$ have been used in place of the unknown driving noise sequence values $u[n]$. The error becomes, therefore, linear in the unknown $a[k]$ and $b[k]$ parameters. The range for the time index is $1 \leq \alpha \leq n \leq \beta \leq N$, assuming data samples $x[n]$ from 1 to N are available. The actual values for α and β will depend on the specific algorithm used to estimate $u[n]$, to be discussed later. The set of $\beta - \alpha + 1$ error equations represented by (10.19) can be expressed in matrix form as

$$\mathbf{e} = \mathbf{X}\hat{\mathbf{a}} + \hat{\mathbf{U}}\hat{\mathbf{b}} \quad , \qquad (10.20)$$

in which

$$\mathbf{e} = \begin{pmatrix} e[\alpha] \\ \vdots \\ e[\beta] \end{pmatrix}, \quad \mathbf{X} = \begin{pmatrix} x[\alpha] & \dots & x[\alpha-p] \\ \vdots & & \vdots \\ x[\beta] & \dots & x[\beta-p] \end{pmatrix}, \quad \hat{\mathbf{a}} = \begin{pmatrix} 1 \\ \hat{a}[1] \\ \vdots \\ \hat{a}[p] \end{pmatrix}$$

and

$$\hat{\mathbf{U}} = \begin{pmatrix} \hat{u}[\alpha - 1] & \cdots & \hat{u}[\alpha - q] \\ \vdots & & \vdots \\ \hat{u}[\beta - 1] & \cdots & \hat{u}[\beta - q] \end{pmatrix}, \hat{\mathbf{b}} = \begin{pmatrix} \hat{b}[1] \\ \vdots \\ \hat{b}[q] \end{pmatrix}.$$

Using the least squares solution described in Sec. 3.4 that minimizes

$$\rho_{\mathrm{ARMA}} = \sum_{n=\alpha}^{\beta} |e[n]|^2 \quad,$$

the set of linear simultaneous equations, to be solved for the AR parameter estimates $\hat{\mathbf{a}}$ and the MA parameter estimates $\hat{\mathbf{b}}$, may easily be seen to take the form

$$\begin{pmatrix} \mathbf{X}^H \mathbf{X} & \mathbf{X}^H \hat{\mathbf{U}} \\ \hat{\mathbf{U}}^H \mathbf{X} & \hat{\mathbf{U}}^H \hat{\mathbf{U}} \end{pmatrix} \begin{pmatrix} \hat{\mathbf{a}} \\ \hat{\mathbf{b}} \end{pmatrix} = \begin{pmatrix} \rho_{\mathrm{ARMA}} \\ \mathbf{0}_{p+q} \end{pmatrix} \quad. \tag{10.21}$$

Once Eq. (10.21) has been solved, the new estimates of $\hat{\mathbf{a}}$ and $\hat{\mathbf{b}}$ may be used to filter the original time series $x[n]$ with the inverse ARMA filter $\hat{A}(z)/\hat{B}(z)$ to yield an updated estimate of the input sequence, $\hat{u}[n]$. The normal equations (10.21) are then solved iteratively in this fashion until convergence is achieved. The impulse response $h[k]$ of the filter $1/\hat{B}(z)$ will, in general, be infinite in duration and must be truncated to a finite interval in order to operate on the finite data sequence $x[n]$. This will be one source of error in this estimation procedure. The truncation interval selected and the accounting for the filter end effects will determine the index values α and β that can be used. The whole iterative process is started by making an estimate of $u[n]$ based on a long-order AR approximation using any AR algorithm from Chap. 8.

   This iterative procedure is not guaranteed to converge and may, in fact, diverge. Conditions for convergence are not generally known. The inverse filter $\hat{A}(z)/\hat{B}(z)$ formed from the AR and MA parameter estimates is not guaranteed to be minimum phase, so the filter could be unstable. This usually requires some modification of the iterative algorithm to yield a minimum phase inverse filter, such as reflecting the poles/zeros outside of the unit z-plane circle to the inside. A modified version of this algorithm that uses a single five-step iteration has been implemented as program MAYNE in the text by Kay [1987].

10.6   SEQUENTIAL APPROACH TO ARMA ESTIMATION

Time-sequential AR parameter estimation algorithms were introduced in Chap. 9. The ARMA process may be expressed in a form that permits similar time-sequential algorithms to be applied for the *simultaneous* estimation of the AR and MA parameters. The ARMA process may be set up by embedding it into a two-channel autoregressive process

$$\mathbf{e}[n] = \mathbf{y}[n] + \sum_{k=1}^{p} \mathbf{A}[k]\mathbf{y}[n - k] \quad , \tag{10.22}$$

in which the two-element vectors $\mathbf{e}[n]$ and $\mathbf{y}[n]$ and 2×2 parameter matrix $\mathbf{A}[k]$ are defined as

$$\mathbf{e}[n] = \begin{pmatrix} e_x[n] \\ e_u[n] \end{pmatrix} \quad , \quad \mathbf{y}[n] = \begin{pmatrix} x[n] \\ u[n] \end{pmatrix} \quad , \quad \mathbf{A}[k] = \begin{pmatrix} a[k] & -b[k] \\ 0 & 0 \end{pmatrix}. \tag{10.23}$$

The parameter matrix $\mathbf{A}[k]$ is half zeros, reflecting the assumed white statistics of $u[n]$. Techniques of multichannel autoregressive analysis are presented in Chap. 15. A multichannel version of the single-channel fast RLS algorithm is available in the literature [Cioffi, 1984]. Assumptions have been made in Eq. (10.22) that the input driving noise sequence $u[n]$ is available, which is not the case, and that the MA order is identical to the AR order $(p = q)$. Embedding methods can be modified to account for nonequal AR and MA orders [Lee et al.,1982; Friedlander, 1982]. The unknown process $u[n]$ is replaced in practice by the estimate

$$\hat{u}[n] = e_x[n] \tag{10.24}$$

after each time update with a new data sample and treating the $\hat{u}[n]$ as "known" data for the next update, permitting the sequential algorithm to operate by "bootstrapping" to its own two-channel prediction error sequence. Some convergence conditions for this two-step method [Eqs. (10.22) and (10.24)] have been conjectured by Friedlander [1982], although detailed analysis still remains to be performed.

10.7   A SPECIAL ARMA PROCESS FOR SINUSOIDS IN WHITE NOISE

The sinusoids in additive white noise process can be modeled as a special ARMA process. It is shown in Chap. 11 on the Prony method that a sample sequence consisting of M real sinusoids of arbitrary frequencies within the range $0 \leq f \leq 1/2T$ (T is the sample interval) may be generated by a symmetric $2M$-order linear difference equation of the form

$$\sum_{k=0}^{2M} a[k]x[n - k] = 0 \tag{10.25}$$

such that $a[0] = a[2M] = 1$ and $a[2M - k] = a[k]$ for $0 \le k \le 2M$. The initial conditions $x[1]$, $\ldots$, $x[2M]$ determine the amplitude and initial phase of the M sinusoids. Adding white noise $w[n]$ produces the sinusoids in noise process

$$y[n] = x[n] + w[n] \quad . \tag{10.26}$$

Substituting $x[n - k] = y[n - k] - w[n - k]$ into Eq. (10.25) yields

$$y[n] = -\sum_{k=1}^{2M} a[k]y[n - k] + \sum_{k=0}^{2M} a[k]w[n - k] \quad . \tag{10.27}$$

This has the structure of an ARMA($2M, 2M$) process in which the AR and MA parameters are identical and the poles and zeros are on the unit circle [Ulrych and Clayton, 1976]. This forms an all-pass filter for which the system function $B(z)/A(z) = 0/0$ when evaluated at the sinusoidal frequencies, i.e., it is undefined. Impulses may then be inserted into the PSD at the locations of the sinusoidal frequencies, yielding the spectrum of Fig. 10.4. Equation (10.27) will be useful in the discussion on the Pisarenko harmonic decomposition technique in Chap. 13.

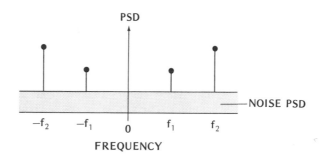

Figure 10.5   Spectrum of special ARMA PSD for sinusoids in white noise.

10.8   APPLICATION TO SUNSPOT NUMBERS

Figure 10.5 illustrates MA and ARMA PSD estimates made from the filtered sunspot numbers using the programs of Appendix 10.A and 10.B.. A long AR model of 50 was used to make the ARMA(25,25) estimate. The first two peaks in the ARMA spectrum are located at .0938 and .2012 cycle per year (10.67 and 4.97 years per cycle). A long AR model of 64 was used to make the MA(32) estimate.

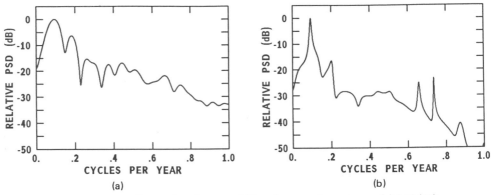

Figure 10.6   Spectral estimates of filtered sunspot numbers. (a) MA(25). (b) ARMA(32,32).

The first two peaks in the MA spectrum are located at .0923 and .181 cycle per year (10.84 and 5.52 years per cycle).

REFERENCES

Box, G. E. P., and G. M. Jenkins, *Time Series Analysis, Forecasting and Control*, Holden-Day, Inc., San Francisco, 1970.

Bruzzone, S. P., and M. Kaveh, On Some Suboptimum ARMA Spectral Estimators, *IEEE Trans. Acoust. Speech Signal Process.*, vol. ASSP-28, pp. 753–755, December 1980.

Bruzzone, S. P., and M. Kaveh, Information Tradeoffs in Using the Sample Autocorrelation Function in ARMA Parameter Estimation, *IEEE Trans. Acoust. Speech Signal Process.*, vol. ASSP-32, pp. 701–715, August 1984.

Cadzow, J. A., Autoregressive Moving Average Spectral Estimation: A Model Equation Error Procedure, *IEEE Trans. Geosci. Remote Sensing*, vol. GE-19, pp. 24–28, January 1981.

Cadzow, J. A., Spectral Estimation: An Overdetermined Rational Model Equation Approach, *Proc. IEEE*, vol. 70, pp. 907–938, September 1982.

Chow, J. C., On the Estimation of the Order of a Moving Average Process, *IEEE Trans. Autom. Control*, vol. AC-17, pp. 386–387, June 1972a.

Chow, J. C., On Estimating the Orders of an Autoregressive-Moving Average Process with Uncertain Observations, *IEEE Trans. Autom. Control*, vol. AC-17, pp. 707–709, October 1972b.

Cioffi, J. M., and T. Kailath, Fast, Recursive-Least-Squares Transversal Filters for Adaptive Filtering, *IEEE Trans. Acoust. Speech Signal Process.*, vol. ASSP-32, pp. 304–337, April 1984.

Friedlander, B., Recursive Lattice Forms for Spectral Estimation, *IEEE Trans. Acoust. Speech Signal Process.*, vol. ASSP-30, pp. 920–930, December 1982.

Friedlander, B., and K. C. Sharman, Performance Evaluation of the Modified Yule-Walker Estimator, *IEEE Trans. Acoust. Speech Signal Process.*, vol. ASSP-33, pp. 719–725, June 1985.

Graupe, D., D. J. Krause, and J. B. Moore, Identification of Autoregressive Moving Average Parameters of Time Series, *IEEE Trans. Autom. Control*, vol. AC-20, pp. 104–107, February 1975.

Izraelevitz, D., and J. S. Lim, Properties of the Overdetermined Normal Equation Method for Spectral Estimation When Applied to Sinusoids in Noise, *IEEE Trans. Acoust. Speech Signal Process.*, vol. ASSP-33, pp. 406–412, April 1985.

Kaveh, M., High Resolution Spectral Estimation for Noisy Signals, *IEEE Trans. Acoust. Speech Signal Process.*, vol. ASSP-27, pp. 286–287, June 1979.

Kaveh, M., and S. P. Bruzzone, Statistical Efficiency of Correlation-Based Methods for ARMA Spectral Estimation, *IEE Proc.*, Part F, vol. 130, pp. 211–217, April 1983.

Kay, S. M., *Modern Spectral Estimation*, Prentice-Hall, Inc., Englewood Cliffs, N. J., 1987.

Lee, D.T.L., B. Friedlander, and M. Morf, Recursive Ladder Algorithms for ARMA Modeling, *IEEE Trans. Autom. Control*, vol. AC-27, pp. 753–764, August 1982.

Mehra, R. K., On-Line Identification of Linear Dynamic Systems with Applications to Kalman Filtering, *IEEE Trans. Autom. Control*, vol. AC-16, pp. 12–22, February 1971.

Porat, B., and B. Friedlander, Asymptotic Analysis of the Bias of the Modified Yule-Walker Estimator, *IEEE Trans. Autom. Control*, vol. AC-30, pp. 765–767, August 1985.

Sakai, H., and H. Tokumaru, Statistical Analysis of a Spectral Estimator for ARMA Processes, *IEEE Trans. Autom. Control*, vol. AC-25, pp. 122–124, February 1980.

Steiglitz, K., and L. E. McBride, A Technique for the Identification of Linear Systems, *IEEE Trans. Autom. Control*, vol. AC-10, pp. 461–464, October 1965.

Ulrych, T. J., and R. W. Clayton, Time Series Modeling and Maximum Entropy, *Phys. Earth Planet. Inter.*, vol. 12, pp. 188–200, August 1976.

PROBLEMS

1. Prove Eq. (10.6).

2. How is a MA PSD estimator like the correlogram method PSD estimator of Chap. 5?

3. Show by counterexample that the modified Yule-Walker equations do not generally produce minimum phase AR parameter sequences, even when the ACS is exactly known.

4. Compute the AIC$[p,q]$ for $0 \leq p,q \leq 20$ using subroutine ARMA and the test sequence of Appendix II. Where is the AIC minimum? Plot the ARMA spectrum for the orders (p,q) at the minimum.

5. Substitute subroutine COVAR for subroutine YULEWALKER in program MA. Compute and plot an MA(15) using the test data of Appendix II. What differences are found between the spectral estimate of Fig. 10.2 and the plot made using subroutine COVAR in program MA? Why are there differences?

APPENDIX 10.A
PROGRAM FOR ESTIMATING THE PARAMETERS
OF AN MA MODEL

This subroutine computes estimates of the moving average parameter array B and
the white noise variance RHO of an MA process based on an algorithm described in
Sec. 10.3. The program can be converted to process real-valued data by the scheme
of Appendix IV. Selection of the parameters N = 64, IQ = 15, and M = 30 will
yield the following parameter estimates when used with the 64-point test sequence
of Appendix II

$$RHO = 0.21432$$

```
B( 1) = ( -0.251507,  0.672468)    B( 9) = (  0.260140, -0.161014)
B( 2) = ( -0.686121,  0.145718)    B(10) = (  0.251199,  0.167119)
B( 3) = (  0.020615, -0.522469)    B(11) = ( -0.134490,  0.212024)
B( 4) = (  0.114441, -0.191581)    B(12) = ( -0.161253,  0.108043)
B( 5) = (  0.365925,  0.098857)    B(13) = ( -0.034023, -0.180158)
B( 6) = (  0.005570,  0.433081)    B(14) = (  0.087808, -0.114639)
B( 7) = ( -0.406348,  0.048549)    B(15) = (  0.022949,  0.084114)
B( 8) = ( -0.100927, -0.428140)  .
```

```
      SUBROUTINE MA (N,IQ,M,X,RHO,B,ISTAT)
C
C     This program provides an estimate of the moving average parameters
C     and driving noise variance for a complex data sequence based on  a
C     long AR model and a least squares fit.
C
C     Input Parameters:
C
C     N    - Number of complex data samples
C     IQ   - Desired MA model order
C     M    - Order of "long" AR model (suggest at least 2*IQ )
C     X    - Array of complex data samples X(1) to X(N)
C
C     Output Parameters:
C
C     RHO  - Real scalar of white noise variance estimate
C     B    - Array of complex MA parameter estimates B(1) to B(IQ)
C     ISTAT - Integer error indicator:
C                0 for normal exit (no errors)
C                1 if error in subroutine YULEWALKER
C                2 if IQ is out of bounds (must be > 0 and < M
C
C     Notes:
C
C     External arrays should be dimensioned in the calling program as
C     follows:  X .GE. N, B .GE. IQ . Internal array should be
C     dimensioned as follows: A .GE. M+1 . External subroutines
C     used:  YULEWALKER (Appendix 8.A)
C
      COMPLEX X(1),B(1),A(100)
      IF (IQ .GT. 0 .AND. IQ .LT. M)  GO TO 10
      ISTAT=2
```

```
      RETURN
C   Fit a high-order AR to the data
10    CALL YULEWALKER (N,M,1,X,RHO,A,ISTAT)       ! Eq. (10.5)
      IF (ISTAT .NE. 0) RETURN
      DO 20 K=M,1,-1
20      A(K+1)=A(K)
      A(1)=(1.,0.)
C   Find MA parameters from autocorrelations by Yule-Walker method
      CALL YULEWALKER (M+1,IQ,1,A,P,B,ISTAT)     ! Eq. (10.7)
      RETURN
      END
```

APPENDIX 10.B
PROGRAM FOR ESTIMATING THE PARAMETERS
OF AN ARMA MODEL

This subroutine computes estimates of the autoregressive and moving average parameter arrays A and B and the white noise variance RHO of an ARMA process based on a three-step algorithm described in Sec. 10.4. The program can be converted to process real-valued data by the scheme of Appendix IV. Selection of the parameters $N = 64$, $IP = IQ = 15$, and $M = 30$ will yield the following parameter estimates when used with the 64-point test sequence of Appendix II

```
                         RHO = 0.18861

A( 1) = (   1.878354,  -1.612764)     A( 9) = (   3.159017,   1.981841)
A( 2) = (   2.336005,  -1.779042)     A(10) = (   2.585279,   2.064622)
A( 3) = (   1.746248,  -0.553477)     A(11) = (   1.235883,   3.146405)
A( 4) = (   3.711644,   0.331686)     A(12) = (   1.411187,   2.564941)
A( 5) = (   3.825539,   0.710195)     A(13) = (  -0.103888,   2.140406)
A( 6) = (   2.638773,   0.365052)     A(14) = (  -0.581367,   1.333906)
A( 7) = (   2.368238,   2.086531)     A(15) = (  -1.053285,   1.504694)
A( 8) = (   2.144489,   1.935402)

B( 1) = (  -0.916489,  -0.005500)     B( 9) = (  -0.461919,   0.010084)
B( 2) = (  -0.143437,  -0.245983)     B(10) = (   0.094423,  -0.021009)
B( 3) = (   0.689553,   0.668978)     B(11) = (   0.131542,   0.280898)
B( 4) = (  -0.478825,  -0.385360)     B(12) = (  -0.052980,  -0.183776)
B( 5) = (   0.265910,  -0.418730)     B(13) = (  -0.009754,  -0.058460)
B( 6) = (  -0.396341,   0.562510)     B(14) = (  -0.121936,   0.132263)
B( 7) = (   0.140056,  -0.119093)     B(15) = (   0.103597,  -0.061122)
B( 8) = (   0.452928,  -0.159134)
```

```
      SUBROUTINE ARMA (N,IP,IQ,M,X,RHO,A,B,ISTAT)
C
C   This program provides an estimate of the autoregressive parameters, the
C   moving average parameters,  and the driving white noise variance of  an
C   ARMA(IP,IQ) for a complex data sequence.   The parameters are estimated
C   using three steps:    estimate the AR parameters from the original data
C   based on a least squares modified Yule-Walker technique,  produce a re-
C   sidual time sequence by filtering the original data with a filter based
```

```
C   on the AR parameters, estimate the MA parameters from the residual time
C   sequence.
C
C   Input Parameters:
C
C       N      - Number of complex data samples
C       IP     - Desired number of AR parameters
C       IQ     - Desired number of MA parameters
C       M      - Maximum lag to use for autocorrelation estimates
C       X      - Array of complex data samples X(1) to X(N)
C
C   Output Parameters:
C
C       RHO    - Real scalar of white noise variance estimate
C       A      - Array of complex AR parameter estimates A(1) to A(IP)
C       B      - Array of complex MA parameter estimates B(1) to B(IQ)
C       ISTAT  - Integer status indicator:  0 for normal exit (no errors)
C                                           1-4 if error in COVAR
C                                           5 if error in subroutine MA
C                                           6 if IP < 1
C
C   Notes:
C
C       External arrays should be dimensioned in the calling program as
C       follows: X .GE. N, A .GE. IP, B .GE. IQ .  Internal arrays should
C       be dimensioned as follows: R .GE. M, Y .GE. max of N-IP,M+IP-IQ .
C       External subroutines used:  CORRELATION (Appendix 5.B),
C       COVAR (Appendix 8.C), MA (Appendix 10.B)
C
        COMPLEX X(1),A(1),B(1),RO,R(100),Y(300),SUM
        IF (IP .GT. 0)  GO TO 5
        ISTAT=6
        RETURN
5       CALL CORRELATION (N,M,0,X,X,RO,R)
C   Estimate the AR parameters (no error weighting is used).
C   Number of equation errors is M-IQ .
        MPQ=M-IQ+IP
        DO 10 K=1,MPQ
          KPQ=K+IQ-IP
          IF (KPQ .LT. 0)  Y(K)=CONJG(R(-KPQ))
          IF (KPQ .EQ. 0)  Y(K)=RO
10        IF (KPQ .GT. 0)  Y(K)=R(KPQ)
        CALL COVAR (MPQ,IP,Y,PF,A,PB,R,ISTAT)          ! Eq. (10.12)
        IF (ISTAT .NE. 0)  RETURN
C   Filter the original time series
        DO 30 K=IP+1,N
          SUM=X(K)
          DO 20 J=1,IP
20          SUM=SUM+A(J)*X(K-J)                        ! Eq. (10.17)
30        Y(K-IP)=SUM
C   Estimate the MA parameters (a "long" AR of order at least 2*IQ
C   is suggested)
        CALL MA (N-IP,IQ,2*IQ,Y,RHO,B,JSTAT)          ! Eq. (10.3)
        IF (JSTAT .NE. 0)  ISTAT=5
        RETURN
        END
```

11

PRONY'S METHOD

11.1 INTRODUCTION

Prony's method is a technique for modeling sampled data as a linear combination of exponentials. Although it is not a spectral estimation technique, Prony's method has a close relationship to the least squares linear prediction algorithms used for AR and ARMA parameter estimation. This relationship yields additional insight into spectral estimation methods that use AR and ARMA models. Prony's method seeks to fit a *deterministic* exponential model to the data, in contrast to AR and ARMA methods that seek to fit a *random* model to the second-order data statistics. A spectral interpretation of Prony's method may be obtained by computing the energy spectral density (ESD) of the deterministic exponential model.

Gaspard Riche, Baron de Prony [1795], was led to believe that laws governing expansion of various gases could be represented by sums of damped exponentials. He proposed a method for interpolating data points in his measurements by fitting an exponential model to a few equally spaced measured data points, and then computing the additional values by evaluation of the exponential model at intermediate points. The modern least squares version of the exponential modeling method has evolved significantly from Prony's original procedure. Prony's paper presented a method of *exactly* fitting as many purely *damped* exponentials as needed to fit the N available data points. The modern version of Prony's method generalizes to damped sinusoidal models. It also makes use of least squares analysis to *approximately* fit an exponential model for cases where there are more data points than needed to fit to the assumed number of exponential terms. A modification of the modern Prony method can fit a purely sinusoidal model with no damped components. The original and modified least squares Prony methods are presented in this chapter.

There are three basic steps in the Prony method. Step one determines the linear prediction parameters that fit the available data. In step two, the roots of a polynomial formed from the linear prediction coefficients will yield the estimates of damping and sinusoidal frequencies of each of the exponential terms. Step three involves the solution of a second set of linear equations to yield the estimates of the exponential amplitude and sinusoidal initial phase. The relationship of the linear prediction and autoregressive parameters explored in Chap. 7 leads to an interpretation of steps one and two as solving for the *poles* of an AR process. Thus, any AR or ARMA spectral analysis that involves a study of the pole locations could loosely be termed a Prony procedure.

11.2 SUMMARY

Assuming one has the N complex data samples $x[1], \ldots, x[N]$, the Prony method will estimate $x[n]$ with a p-term complex exponential model

$$\hat{x}[n] = \sum_{k=1}^{p} A_k \exp\big[(\alpha_k + j2\pi f_k)(n-1)T + j\theta_k\big] \tag{11.1}$$

for $1 \leq n \leq N$, where T is the sample interval in seconds, A_k is the amplitude of the complex exponential, α_k is the damping factor in seconds^{-1}, f_k is the sinusoidal frequency in Hz, and θ_k is the sinusoidal initial phase in radians. The parameters are completely arbitrary. In the case of real data samples, the complex exponentials must occur in complex conjugate pairs of equal amplitude, thus reducing the exponential representation to

$$\hat{x}[n] = \sum_{k=1}^{p/2} 2A_k \exp[\alpha_k(n-1)T] \cos[2\pi f_k(n-1)T + \theta_k] \tag{11.2}$$

for $1 \leq n \leq N$. If the number of complex exponentials p is even, then there are $p/2$ damped cosines. If p is odd, then there are $(p-1)/2$ damped cosines plus a single purely damped exponential. The periodogram is shown in the Problems to have the interpretation as modeling a time series as a harmonic sinusoidal model. The distinction between the periodogram model and the Prony approach is the method

- ● ACQUIRE DATA
    N samples
    T seconds/sample

- ● SELECT INPUT PARAMETERS
    Number of complex exponentials, IP
    Select METHOD = 1 for damped exponentials
    Select METHOD = 2 for undamped sinusoids
    (Note: IP must be even if METHOD = 2)

- ● ESTIMATE COMPLEX EXPONENTIAL
    PARAMETERS
    Subroutine PRONY, Appendix 11.C

- ● COMPUTE REAL EXPONENTIAL PARAMETERS
    (Amplitude , phase, damping factor, frequency)
    Subroutine EXPARAMS, Appendix 11.D

- ● COMPUTE PRONY ENERGY SPECTRAL
    DENSITY (optional)
    Subroutine ESD, Appendix 11.E

Figure 11.1   Flowchart of Prony exponential estimation method and Prony ESD.

by which frequencies are selected. The periodogram *preselects* a harmonic set of frequencies. The Prony method *estimates* the frequencies from the data.

Figure 11.1 is a block diagram of the program steps that will yield the Prony amplitude, damping factor, frequency, and initial phase estimates. Two variations are possible. If a general damped sinusoidal model is required, set the parameter METHOD = 1. If specialization to the undamped sinusoidal model is desired, set parameter METHOD = 2. The output of PRONY contains the estimates of two complex exponential parameter arrays associated with the p complex exponentials (see Sec. 11.3). These parameters may then optionally be input to subroutine EXPARAMS, which yields the four real exponential parameters, or to subroutine ESD, which yields a Prony "spectral" estimate.

Figure 11.2 depicts the Prony energy spectral density (ESD) estimates, based on the 64-point test data sequence, for the two Prony methods of Figure 11.1. The estimated exponential parameter values are included in Appendix 11.D. The modified Prony method produces a line spectrum because of its sinusoidal model assumption. This results in very good estimates for the four actual sinusoids in the process, but is inaccurate in its representation of the colored noise process within the spectrum.

Figure 11.2   Examples of two Prony spectral estimates made from the 64-point test data sequence. (a) Extended Prony method, order 15. (b) Modified Prony method, order 16.

11.3 SIMULTANEOUS EXPONENTIAL PARAMETER ESTIMATION

The p-exponent discrete-time function of Eq. (11.1) may be concisely expressed in the form

$$\hat{x}[n] = \sum_{k=1}^{p} h_k z_k^{n-1} \quad , \tag{11.3}$$

where the complex constants h_k and z_k are defined as

$$h_k = A_k \exp(j\theta_k) \tag{11.4}$$

$$z_k = \exp\left[(\alpha_k + j2\pi f_k)T\right] \quad . \tag{11.5}$$

Note that h_k is a complex amplitude that represents a time-*independent* parameter, whereas z_k is a complex exponent that represents a time-*dependent* parameter. Ideally, one would like to minimize the squared error over the N data values

$$\rho = \sum_{n=1}^{N} \left| \epsilon[n] \right|^2 \quad , \tag{11.6}$$

where

$$\epsilon[n] = x[n] - \hat{x}[n] = x[n] - \sum_{k=1}^{p} h_k z_k^{n-1} \quad , \tag{11.7}$$

with respect to the h_k parameters, the z_k parameters, and the number of exponents p simultaneously. This turns out to be a difficult nonlinear problem, even if the value of p is known. This difficulty can be demonstrated by the single-exponent case. Minimization of the squared error ρ using the damped exponential model

$$\hat{x}[n] = A \exp(\alpha[n-1]T)$$

is obtained by setting to zero the derivatives with respect to A and α

$$\begin{aligned}
\frac{\partial \rho}{\partial A} &= c_1 - c_2 A = 0 \\
\frac{\partial \rho}{\partial \alpha} &= c_3 - c_4 A = 0 \quad ,
\end{aligned} \tag{11.8}$$

where

$$\begin{aligned}
c_1 &= \sum_{n=1}^{N} x[n] \exp(\alpha[n-1]T) \\
c_2 &= \sum_{n=1}^{N} \exp(\alpha[n-1]T) \\
c_3 &= \sum_{n=1}^{N} n\, x[n] \exp(\alpha[n-1]T) \\
c_4 &= \sum_{n=1}^{N} n \exp(\alpha[n-1]T) \quad .
\end{aligned} \tag{11.9}$$

It has been assumed for simplicity that $x[n]$, A, and α are real. From the first equation of (11.8) one obtains $A = c_1/c_2$; substituting this into the second equation of (11.8) yields

$$c_2 c_3 = c_2 c_4 \quad . \tag{11.10}$$

This is a highly nonlinear expression in terms of sums involving $\exp(\alpha[n-1]T)$ which must be solved for α. No analytic solution is available.

Iterative algorithms, such as gradient descent procedures or Newton's method, have been devised to minimize Eq. (11.6) simultaneously with respect to all the exponential parameters [McDonough, 1963; McDonough and Huggins, 1968; Evans and Fischl, 1973]. These algorithms are very computationally expensive, sometimes requiring at each step the inversion of matrices of dimension as large as the number of data samples. Gradient descent algorithms for multimodal equations also may not converge to the global minimum. This computational difficulty led to the development of a suboptimum minimization of ρ, known as the least-squares Prony method, that utilizes linear equation solutions. The Prony method embeds the nonlinear aspects of the exponential model into a polynomial factoring, for which reasonably fast solution algorithms are available.

11.4   ORIGINAL PRONY CONCEPT

If as many data samples are used as there are exponential parameters, then an exact exponential fit to the data may be made. Consider the p-exponent discrete-time function

$$x[n] = \sum_{k=1}^{p} h_k z_k^{n-1} \ . \tag{11.11}$$

Note that $x[n]$, rather than $\hat{x}[n]$, has been used because exactly $2p$ complex samples $x[1], \ldots, x[2p]$ are used to fit an exact exponential model to the $2p$ complex parameters $h_1, \ldots, h_p, z_1, \ldots, z_p$. The p equations of Eq. (11.11) for $1 \leq n \leq p$ may be expressed in matrix form as

$$\begin{pmatrix} z_1^0 & z_2^0 & \cdots & z_p^0 \\ z_1^1 & z_2^1 & \cdots & z_p^1 \\ \vdots & \vdots & & \vdots \\ z_1^{p-1} & z_2^{p-1} & \cdots & z_p^{p-1} \end{pmatrix} \begin{pmatrix} h_1 \\ h_2 \\ \vdots \\ h_p \end{pmatrix} = \begin{pmatrix} x[1] \\ x[2] \\ \vdots \\ x[p] \end{pmatrix} \ . \tag{11.12}$$

The matrix of time-indexed z elements has a Vandermonde structure. If a method can be found to separately determine the z elements, then Eq. (11.12) represents a set of linear simultaneous equations that can be solved for the unknown vector of complex amplitudes. Prony's contribution was the discovery of such a method.

The key to the separation is to recognize that Eq. (11.11) is the solution to some homogeneous linear constant-coefficient difference equation. In order to find the form of this difference equation, first define the polynomial $\phi(z)$ that has the z_k exponents as its roots,

$$\phi(z) = \prod_{k=1}^{p} (z - z_k) \ . \tag{11.13}$$

If the products of Eq. (11.13) are expanded into a power series, then the polynomial may be represented as the summation

$$\phi(z) = \sum_{m=0}^{p} a[m] z^{p-m} \ , \tag{11.14}$$

with complex coefficients $a[m]$ such that $a[0] = 1$. Shifting the index on Eq. (11.11) from n to $n - m$ and multiplying by the parameter $a[m]$ yields

$$a[m]x[n-m] = a[m] \sum_{k=1}^{p} h_k z_k^{n-m-1} \ . \tag{11.15}$$

Forming similar products $a[0]x[n], \ldots, a[m-1]x[n-m+1]$ and summing produces

$$\sum_{m=0}^{p} a[m]x[n-m] = \sum_{i=0}^{p} h_i \sum_{m=0}^{p} a[m]z_i^{n-m-1} \quad , \tag{11.16}$$

which is valid for $p+1 \le n \le 2p$. Making the substitution $z_i^{n-m-1} = z_i^{n-p}z_i^{p-m-1}$, then

$$\sum_{m=0}^{p} a[m]x[n-m] = \sum_{i=0}^{p} h_i z_i^{n-p} \sum_{m=0}^{p} a[m]z_i^{p-m-1} = 0 \quad . \tag{11.17}$$

The right-hand summation in Eq. (11.17) may be recognized as the polynomial defined by Eq. (11.14), evaluated at each of its roots z_i, yielding the zero result indicated. Equation (11.17) is the linear difference equation whose homogeneous solution is given by Eq. (11.11). The polynomial (11.14) is the *characteristic equation* associated with this linear difference equation.

The p equations representing the valid values of $a[n]$ that satisfy Eq. (11.17) may be expressed as the $p \times p$ matrix equation

$$\begin{pmatrix} x[p] & x[p-1] & \cdots & x[1] \\ x[p+1] & x[p] & \cdots & x[2] \\ \vdots & \vdots & \ddots & \vdots \\ x[2p-1] & x[2p-2] & \cdots & x[p] \end{pmatrix} \begin{pmatrix} a[1] \\ a[2] \\ \vdots \\ a[p] \end{pmatrix} = - \begin{pmatrix} x[p+1] \\ x[p+2] \\ \vdots \\ x[2p] \end{pmatrix} \quad . \tag{11.18}$$

Equation (11.18) demonstrates that, with $2p$ complex data samples, it is possible to decouple the h_k and z_k parameters. The complex polynomial coefficients $a[1], \ldots, a[p]$, which are functions of only the time-dependent components z_k of the exponential model, form a linear predictive relationship among the time samples. The matrix of Eq. (11.18) has a Toeplitz structure, so that the solution may be obtained with subroutine TOEPLITZ in Chap. 3.

The Prony procedure to fit p exponentials to $2p$ data samples may now be summarized in three steps. First, solution of Eq. (11.18) for the polynomial coefficients is obtained. Second, the roots of the polynomial defined by Eq. (11.14) are calculated. A polynomial factoring program, CPOLY, may be found in Appendix 11.B to perform this. The damping α_i and sinusoidal frequency f_i may be determined from the root z_i using the relationships

$$\alpha_i = \ln|z_i|/T \quad \sec^{-1} \tag{11.19}$$
$$f_i = \tan^{-1}\left[\mathrm{Im}\{z_i\}/\mathrm{Re}\{z_i\}\right]/2\pi T \quad \mathrm{Hz} \quad . \tag{11.20}$$

To complete the Prony procedure, the roots computed in the second step are used to construct the matrix elements of Eq. (11.12), which is then solved for the p

complex parameters $h[1], \ldots, h[p]$. The amplitude A_i and initial phase θ_i may be determined from each h_i parameter with the relationships

$$A_i = |h_i| \tag{11.21}$$

$$\theta_i = \tan^{-1}\left[\text{Im}\{h_i\}/\text{Re}\{h_i\}\right] \quad \text{radians.} \tag{11.22}$$

Subroutine EXPARAMS in Appendix 11.D makes the appropriate conversions given by Eqs. (11.19)–(11.22).

11.5 LEAST SQUARES PRONY METHOD

For practical situations, the number of data points N usually exceeds the minimum number needed to fit a model of p exponentials, i.e., $N > 2p$. In this overdetermined case, the data sequence can only be approximated as an exponential sequence,

$$\hat{x}[n[= \sum_{k=1}^{p} h_k z_k^{n-1} \tag{11.23}$$

for $1 \leq n \leq N$. Denote the approximation error as $\epsilon[n] = x[n] - \hat{x}[n]$. Simultaneously finding the order p and the parameters $\{h_k, z_k\}$ for $k = 1$ to $k = p$ that minimizes the total squared error

$$\rho = \sum_{n=1}^{N} \left|\epsilon[n]\right|^2 \tag{11.24}$$

was shown in Sec. 11.3 to be a difficult nonlinear problem. A suboptimum solution that provides satisfactory results may be obtained with a variant of the Prony method presented in Sec. 11.4. Substitution of appropriate linear least squares procedures for the first and third steps of the three-step Prony method yields an exponential modeling procedure that has sometimes been called the *extended Prony method* [Householder, 1950; McDonough, 1963]. This suboptimum approach effectively concentrates the nonlinearity of the exponential fitting problem into a polynomial factoring.

In the overdetermined data case, the linear difference Eq. (11.17) must be modified to

$$\sum_{m=1}^{p} a[m]x[n-m] = e[n] \tag{11.25}$$

for $p + 1 \leq n \leq N$. The term $e[n]$ represents the *linear prediction* approximation error, in contrast to error $\epsilon[n]$, which represents the *exponential* approximation error. Expression (11.25) is identical to the forward linear prediction error equation, making each $a[m]$ term a linear prediction parameter. In lieu of Eq. (11.17), the $a[m]$ parameters may be selected as those that minimize the linear prediction squared error $\sum_{n=p+1}^{N} |e[n]|^2$, rather than the exponential approximation squared error ρ of Eq. (11.24). This is simply the covariance method of linear prediction. Program COVAR in Appendix 8.C provided the solution of the covariance linear prediction normal equations. The number of exponentials p (also called the number of poles in deference to AR processing) may be estimated using the same order selection rules established in Chap. 8. Alternatively, singular value decomposition (SVD) analysis similar to that covered in Sec. 11.9 may be used. In either case, the maximum order is limited to $p \le N/2$. The roots of the polynomial constructed from the linear prediction coefficients will yield, using Eqs. (11.19) and (11.20), the estimates of damping and frequency for each exponent.

If $z_1, \ldots, z_p$ have been determined by least squares linear prediction analysis and polynomial factoring, then the exponential approximation $\hat{x}[n]$ of Eq. (11.23) becomes linear in the remaining unknown parameters $h_1, \ldots, h_p$. Minimizing the squared error with respect to each of the h_k parameters yields the complex-valued $p \times p$ matrix normal equation (see Sec. 3.4 for derivation details)

$$\left(\mathbf{Z}^H \mathbf{Z} \right) \mathbf{h} = \left(\mathbf{Z}^H \mathbf{x} \right) \quad , \tag{11.26}$$

where the $N \times p$ matrix $\mathbf{Z}$, the $p \times 1$ vector $\mathbf{b}$, and $N \times 1$ data vector $\mathbf{x}$ are defined as

$$\mathbf{Z} = \begin{pmatrix} 1 & 1 & \cdots & 1 \\ z_1 & z_2 & \cdots & z_p \\ \vdots & \vdots & & \vdots \\ z_1^{N-1} & z_2^{N-1} & \cdots & z_p^{N-1} \end{pmatrix} \quad , \quad \mathbf{h} = \begin{pmatrix} h_1 \\ h_2 \\ \vdots \\ h_p \end{pmatrix} \quad , \quad \mathbf{x} = \begin{pmatrix} x[1] \\ x[2] \\ \vdots \\ x[N] \end{pmatrix} \quad . \tag{11.27}$$

The $p \times p$ Hermitian matrix $\mathbf{Z}^H \mathbf{Z}$ has the form

$$\mathbf{Z}^H \mathbf{Z} = \begin{pmatrix} \gamma_{11} & \cdots & \gamma_{1p} \\ \vdots & & \vdots \\ \gamma_{p1} & \cdots & \gamma_{pp} \end{pmatrix} \quad , \tag{11.28}$$

where

$$\gamma_{jk} = \sum_{n=0}^{N-1} (z_j^* z_k)^n = \gamma_{kj}^* \quad . \tag{11.29}$$

A useful relationship that avoids the summation of Eq. (11.29) is

$$\gamma_{jk} = \begin{cases} \dfrac{(z_j^* z_k)^N - 1}{(z_j^* z_k) - 1} & \text{if } z_j^* z_k \ne 1 \\ N & \text{if } z_j^* z_k = 1 \end{cases} \quad . \tag{11.30}$$

Subroutine CHOLESKY in Chap. 3 may then be used to solve Eq. (11.26) for the unknown $h[k]$ parameters.

The Prony method will also fit exponentials to any additive noise present in the data because the exponential model does not make a separate estimate of the noise process. An exponential model incorporating additive noise would have the form

$$x[n] = \sum_{k=1}^{p} h_k z_k^{n-1} + \epsilon[n] \quad .$$ (11.31)

The function $\epsilon[n]$ has also been used to represent the approximation error of the exponential model. If $x[n] - \epsilon[n]$ is used in place of $x[n]$ in the analysis of Sec. 11.4, then the linear difference equation that describes the process consisting of a sum of exponentials plus white noise becomes

$$x[n] = -\sum_{k=1}^{p} a[m]x[n-m] + \sum_{k=0}^{p} a[m]\epsilon[n-m] \quad .$$ (11.32)

This is an ARMA(p,p) with identical AR and MA coefficients and a driving noise process $\epsilon[n]$. The first step of the Prony method uses the linear prediction

$$x[n] = -\sum_{k=1}^{p} a[m]x[n-m] + e[n]$$ (11.33)

and attempts to whiten $e[n]$. Comparing Eq. (11.33) with (11.32), the whitened process $e[n]$ does not correspond well to the nonwhite MA process represented by $\sum_{k=0}^{p} a[m]\epsilon[n-m]$. It is for this reason that the Prony method does not often perform well in the presence of significant additive noise; it fails to account for nonwhite noise in the process. When the Prony estimation method is performed in the presence of significant additive noise, the damping terms are significantly misestimated, often being estimated to be much greater than they actually are [McDonough, 1963; Van Blaricum and Mittra, 1975, 1978; Poggio et al., 1978]. Using p larger than the actual number of poles helps to model and account for the noise (see Sec. 11.9).

11.6 MODIFIED LEAST SQUARES PRONY METHOD

The normal least squares Prony method can be modified to approximate a *complex* data sequence by a model consisting of *undamped* ($\alpha = 0$) complex sinusoids [Marple, 1979; Korn and Korn, 1961]. Only the case of an even number of complex exponentials shall be considered here. The $2p$ component model similar to Eq. (11.1) then has the form

$$\hat{x}[n] = \sum_{k=1}^{2p} A_k \exp(j2\pi f_k[n-1]T + j\theta_k) = \sum_{k=1}^{2p} h_k z_k^{n-1}$$ (11.34)

for $1 \leq n \leq N$, with $h_k = A_k \exp(j\theta_k)$ and $z_k = \exp(j2\pi f_k T)$. Note that the z_k are of unit modulus, that is, $|z_k| = 1$. If the h_k and z_k occur in complex conjugate pairs and $f_k \neq 0$ or $f_k \neq 1/2T$, then a *real* data sequence may be approximated by a model consisting of p even or odd real undamped sinusoids

$$\hat{x}[n] = \sum_{k=1}^{p} 2A_k \cos(2\pi f_k[n-1]T + \theta_k) = \sum_{k=1}^{p} \left(h_k z_k^{n-1} + h_k^*(z_k^*)^{n-1} \right) \quad (11.35)$$

for $1 \leq n \leq N$. The polynomial constructed with roots that are the z_k of either Eq. (11.34) or (11.35) has the form

$$\phi(z) = \prod_{k=1}^{2p} (z - z_k) = \sum_{k=0}^{2p} a[k] z^{2p-k} \quad , \quad (11.36)$$

where $a[0] = 1$ by definition and the remaining $a[k]$ parameters will be, in general, complex, unless the real sinusoid case of Eq. (11.35) is considered. In the latter situation, the $a[k]$ are all real. It is simple to establish that coefficient $a[2p]$ is given by

$$a[2p] = \prod_{k=1}^{2p} z_k \quad , \quad (11.37)$$

which follows from the definition of $\phi(z)$. Due to the unit modulus property $z_k^{-1} = z_k^*$, it is simple to show that $|a[2p]| = 1$ and that the polynomial

$$a[2p] z^{2p} \phi^*(z) \quad (11.38)$$

has the same roots as $\phi(z)$. Because the polynomial

$$a[2p] z^{2p} \phi^*(z) = \sum_{k=0}^{2p} a[2p] a^*[2p-k] z^{2p-k} \quad (11.39)$$

must yield the same roots, one is led to conclude that the conjugate property $a[k] = a[2p] a^*[2p-k]$ for $k = 0$ to $k = 2p$ must exist between the coefficients. Thus, the homogeneous linear difference equation that has Eq. (11.35) as its solution is

$$a[p] x[n-p] + \sum_{k=1}^{p} \left(a[p-k] x[n-p+k] + a[p+k] x[n-p-k] \right) = 0 \quad (11.40)$$

for $2p + 1 \leq n \leq N$. A more convenient form of Eq. (11.40), obtained by dividing by the value of the center element $a[p]$, yields the conjugate symmetric difference equation

$$x[n-p] + \sum_{k=1}^{p} \left(g_p[k] x[n-p+k] + g_p^*[k] x[n-p-k] \right) = 0 \quad , \quad (11.41)$$

where $g_p[k] = a[p-k]/a[p]$. The conjugate symmetry is due to the property $a[p] = a[2p]a^*[p]$. A similar symmetric difference equation for real sinusoids was presented by Hildebrand [1956].

The modified Prony method replaces in step one the linear prediction error of Eq. (11.33) with the conjugate symmetric linear smoothing error (uses both past and future sample values)

$$e_p^s[n] = x[n] + \sum_{k=1}^{p} \Big(g_p[k]x[n+k] + g_p^*[k]x[n-k] \Big) \quad , \tag{11.42}$$

defined over the interval $p + 1 \le n \le N - p$ (uses only the available data), and minimizes the squared smoothing error

$$\rho_p^s = \sum_{n=p+1}^{N-p} \Big| e_p^s[n] \Big|^2 \quad , \tag{11.43}$$

rather than the squared linear prediction error given by Eq. (11.24). Setting the complex derivatives of ρ_p^s with respect to $g_p[1]$ through $g_p[p]$ to zero yields the normal equations expressed succintly by the matrix representation

$$\mathbf{R}_{2p}\mathbf{g}_{2p} = \begin{pmatrix} \mathbf{0}_p \\ 2\rho_p^s \\ \mathbf{0}_p \end{pmatrix} \quad , \tag{11.44}$$

where centrosymmetric matrix $\mathbf{R}_{2p}$ and conjugate symmetric vector $\mathbf{g}_{2p}$ are

$$\mathbf{R}_{2p} = \begin{pmatrix} r_{2p}[0,0] & \cdots & r_{2p}[0,2p] \\ \vdots & & \vdots \\ r_{2p}[2p,0] & \cdots & r_{2p}[2p,2p] \end{pmatrix} \quad , \quad \mathbf{g}_{2p} = \begin{pmatrix} g_p[p] \\ \vdots \\ g_p[1] \\ 1 \\ g_p^*[1] \\ \vdots \\ g_p^*[p] \end{pmatrix} \quad . \tag{11.45}$$

Elements of $\mathbf{R}_{2p}$ are

$$r_{2p}[j,k] = \sum_{n=2p+1}^{N} \Big(x^*[n-j]x[n-k] + x[n-p+j]x^*[n-p+k] \Big) \quad . \tag{11.46}$$

The astute reader will have made the observation that $\mathbf{R}_{2p}$ in Eq. (11.45) is identical to the matrix of the modified covariance method, given by Eq. (8.48) in Chap. 8. A fast algorithm was presented in Chap. 8 for the solution of the modified covariance normal equations. The fast algorithm that solves Eq. (11.44) can be developed (see Appendix 11.A) by a simple extension of the modified covariance algorithm. The resulting fast algorithm requires $Np + 18p^2$ computations to solve Eq. (11.44). In addition, all lower-order least squares solutions of Eq. (11.44) are solved as part of the fast algorithm solution with no additional computations required. In situations where the number of sinusoids is not known, this provides an ability to check all models from one sinusoid up to p sinusoids. Appendix 11.A contains computer program SYMCOVAR to solve Eq. (11.44) that uses the fast algorithm.

Although complex roots of unit modulus produce polynomials with conjugate symmetric coefficients, the converse is not necessarily true. A conjugate symmetric polynomial only guarantees that if z_i is a root, then its reciprocal z_i^{-1} will also be a root. The root need not be of unit modulus, a requirement if an undamped sinusoidal is to be generated. In practice, the order $2p$ polynomials formed from the vector $\mathbf{g}_{2p}$ of linear smoothing parameters

$$g[p]z^{2p} + \cdots + g[1]z^{p+1} + z^p + g^*[1]z^{p-1} + \cdots + g^*[p] = 0 \quad , \qquad (11.47)$$

rarely exhibit reciprocal roots of nonunit modulus. When such roots occur, they often correspond to frequencies of 0 Hz or $1/2T$ Hz. The modified Prony method is completed with the same method as used by the unmodified Prony method to determine the sinusoid amplitudes and initial phases.

11.7 PRONY SPECTRUM

The Prony procedure normally terminates with the computation of the amplitude, damping, frequency, and phase parameter estimates. However, it is possible to carry the processing one further step to yield a Prony "spectrum" [Marple, 1980]. Many possible spectra may be defined, depending on the assumptions made concerning the waveform outside of the observed interval. The Prony spectrum is defined in terms of the exponential approximation $\hat{x}[n]$, rather than in terms of the original time sequence $x[n]$.

One assumption is that the discrete-time exponential sum in Eq. (11.3) is defined over the interval $-\infty < n < \infty$ as the one-sided function

$$\hat{x}_1[n+1] = \begin{cases} \displaystyle\sum_{k=1}^{p} h_k z_k^n & n \geq 0 \\ 0 & n < 0 \quad , \end{cases} \qquad (11.48)$$

as depicted in Fig. 11.3(a). If the signal $x[n]$ is real, the exponentials will occur in complex conjugate pairs $\exp(\pm j[2\pi f_k + \theta_k])$ to form a single cosine term $\cos(2\pi f_k + \theta_k)$. The z-transform of Eq. (11.48) is

$$\hat{X}_1(z) = \sum_{k=1}^{p} \left(\frac{h_k}{1 - z_k z^{-1}} \right) \quad , \qquad (11.49)$$

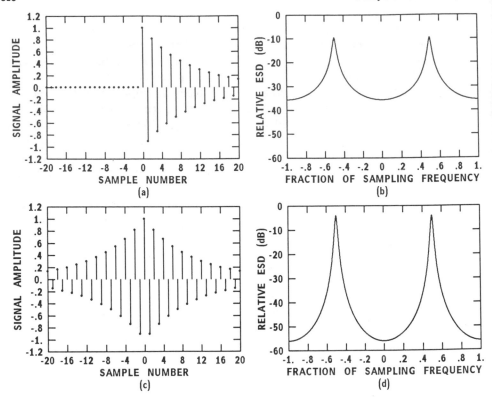

Figure 11.3 Exponential models and associated energy spectral density.
(a) One-sided exponential model. (b) ESD of one-sided model. (c) Two-sided
model. (d) ESD of two-sided model.

which converges for $|z_k| < |z|$. It is also assumed that $|z_k| < 1$, that is, all
damping parameters are negative, yielding decaying exponentials. If this is so,
then substitution of $z = \exp(j2\pi fT)$ into Eq. (11.49) will yield the discrete-time
Fourier transform of the deterministic, finite-energy sequence $\hat{x}_1[n]$. Therefore, the
Prony energy spectral density (ESD) for this one-sided exponential model is

$$\hat{S}_1(f) = \left| T\,\hat{X}_1(\exp[j2\pi fT]) \right|^2 \quad , \tag{11.50}$$

defined over the frequency interval $-1/2T \le f \le 1/2T$. This spectrum is appropriate for transient signals. A typical spectrum is shown in Fig. 11.3(b).

An alternative interpretation of the exponential model is the two-sided function

$$\hat{x}_2[n] = \begin{cases} \sum_{k=1}^{p} h_k z_k^n & n \ge 0 \\ \sum_{k=1}^{p} h_k (z_k^*)^{-n} & n < 0 \quad , \end{cases} \tag{11.51}$$

where $z_k = \exp(\alpha_k T + j2\pi f_k T)$ and $(z_k^*)^{-1} = \exp(-\alpha_k T + j2\pi f_k T)$. This definition forces the damped portion of the exponential to be symmetrical about the origin, as depicted in Fig. 11.3(c). The z-transform of Eq. (11.51) is

$$\hat{X}_2(z) = \sum_{k=1}^{p} h_k \left(\frac{1}{1 - z_k z^{-1}} - \frac{1}{1 - (z_k^* z)^{-1}} \right)$$

$$= \sum_{k=1}^{p} h_k \left(\frac{(z_k - 1/z_k^*) z^{-1}}{1 - (z_k + 1/z_k^*) z^{-1} + (z_k/z_k^*) z^{-2}} \right) \quad , \tag{11.52}$$

which converges for $|z_k| < |z| < |z_k^{-1}|$. If one also assumes that $|z_k| < 1$ and substitutes $z = \exp(j2\pi fT)$ into Eq. (11.52), then the discrete-time Fourier transform of the two-sided exponential model will be

$$\hat{X}_2(f) = T \hat{X}_2\left(\exp[j2\pi fT]\right)$$

$$= \sum_{k=1}^{p} h_k \left(\frac{T(\exp[\alpha_k T] - \exp[-\alpha_k T]) \exp(j2\pi[f_k - f]T)}{1 - (\exp[\alpha_k T] + \exp[-\alpha_k T]) \exp(j2\pi[f_k - f]T) + \exp(j4\pi[f_k - f]T)} \right) \tag{11.53}$$

and the resulting Prony ESD is

$$\hat{S}_2(f) = \left| \hat{X}_2(f) \right|^2 \quad . \tag{11.54}$$

In general, $\hat{S}_2(f)$ provides a sharper spectral response than $\hat{S}_1(f)$, as depicted in Fig. 11.3(d). The author prefers this second definition because an undamped sinusoid ($\alpha = 0$) is defined over the infinite time interval. The ESD function $\hat{S}_2(f)$ has in this case an infinite response at the sinusoidal frequency, behaving like a discrete impulse function.

Either of the two possible Prony spectra has the ability to produce both narrowband and wideband spectral shapes. The response widths are a function of the magnitude of the damping factor, as illustrated by Fig. 11.3. The bell-shaped responses have peak ESD magnitudes of $(2A_k/\alpha_k)^2$ and bandwidths (to the 6-dB points) of α/π Hz, so resolution varies as a function of damping. If α is large, the response is broadband. If α is small, then a sharp narrowband response is produced.

Another possible Prony spectrum incorporates all information in the entire data sample sequence. If the exponential approximation residuals

$$\epsilon[n] = x[n] - \sum_{k=1}^{p} h_k z_k^{n-1} \tag{11.55}$$

are computed, then a conventional periodogram analysis may be performed on the residuals and the periodogram spectrum combined with either of the two suggested Prony spectra.

11.8 ACCOUNTING FOR KNOWN EXPONENTIAL COMPONENTS

There are applications in which some of the exponential modes (either the poles or the damping and frequency components) may be known *a priori*, due to the availability of prior measurements or due to the physical or electrical properties of the source generating the signal under analysis. The associated amplitude and phase components of these exponential modes may, however, not be known. The first step of the Prony method can be modified to account for these known poles [Trivett and Robinson, 1981]. Suppose the q exponential components $z_1, \ldots, z_q$ are known. The characteristic polynomial associated with these q known components is

$$\prod_{i=0}^{q} (z - z_k) = \sum_{k=0}^{q} c[k] z^k \quad , \tag{11.56}$$

where $c[q] = 1$. The characteristic polynomial for all p components [Eq. (11.14)] may then be factored as

$$\sum_{m=0}^{p} a[m] z^m = \left(\sum_{k=0}^{q} c[k] z^k \right) \left(\sum_{i=0}^{p-q} \alpha[i] z^i \right) \quad , \tag{11.57}$$

where $\alpha[p - q] = 1$. Equating similar powers of z yields

$$a[m] = \sum_{k=0}^{q} c[k] \alpha[m - k] \quad , \tag{11.58}$$

where $\alpha[i] = 0$ for $i > p - q + 1$ or $i < 0$. Substituting Eq. (11.58) for $a[m]$ in Eq. (11.16) yields

$$\sum_{m=0}^{p} a[m] x[n - m] = \sum_{m=0}^{p} \left(\sum_{k=0}^{q} c[k] \alpha[m - k] \right) x[n - m] = 0 \tag{11.59}$$

defined for $p + 1 \leq n \leq 2p$. Equation (11.59) may be reorganized as

$$\sum_{m=0}^{p-q} \alpha[m] y[n - m] = 0 \tag{11.60}$$

for $p + 1 \leq n \leq 2p$, where the new sequence $y[n]$ is defined as

$$y[n] = \sum_{k=0}^{q} c[k] x[n - k] \quad . \tag{11.61}$$

This represents a convolution operation, that is, filtering of the original time sequence $x[n]$ to produce the new sequence $y[n]$.

The Prony method with some components known proceeds as follows. First, the original data is filtered [Eq. (11.61)] using a filter with coefficients determined by the known poles [Eq. (11.58)]. The filtered data samples are then processed as usual by the least squares covariance linear prediction algorithm to yield estimates of the parameters $\alpha[m]$. The roots of the reduced-order polynomial

$$\sum_{i=0}^{p-q} \alpha[i]z^i \tag{11.62}$$

produce estimates of the unknown poles. These $p - q$ poles and the q known poles are then combined for the least squares operation that will yield the amplitudes and phases of all p components.

11.9   IDENTIFICATION OF EXPONENTIALS IN NOISE

The least squares Prony method has been shown to require the solution of the identical covariance linear prediction normal equations as encountered for AR spectral analysis in Chap. 8. This common heritage with the AR spectral method suggests use of the AR order selection criteria, as developed in Sec. 8.10, for the determination of the number of exponentials present in the data. In situations where the noise level is low, these criteria are often satisfactory. However, in higher noise levels, the frequency and damping component estimates are usually inaccurate and biased due to the effect of noise. Distinguishing roots of the Prony characteristic polynomial due to the weak exponentials from roots due to noise is often difficult. Three methods may be used to enhance identification of actual exponential signals in the data and to improve the accuracy of the frequency and damping component estimates. These methods involve the use of both forward and backward linear prediction polynomial zeros, high prediction orders, and singular value decomposition (SVD).

In the absence of additive noise, it was shown in Sec. 11.4 that p exponentials are generated by the forward linear prediction

$$\sum_{m=0}^{p} a[m]x[n - m] = 0 \quad , \tag{11.63}$$

in which $a[0] = 1$ and the characteristic polynomial

$$\mathsf{A}(z) = \sum_{m=0}^{p} a[m]z^{p-m} \tag{11.64}$$

has roots at $z_k = \exp(s_k)$ for $k = 1$ to $k = p$, where $s_k = (\alpha_k + j2\pi f_k)T$ contains the damping factor and frequency of the kth exponential. The same p exponentials may also be generated in reverse time by the backward linear prediction

$$\sum_{m=0}^{p} b[m]x[n - p + m] = 0 \quad , \tag{11.65}$$

in which $b[0] = 1$. The characteristic polynomial

$$B(z) = \sum_{m=0}^{p} b^*[m]z^{p-m} \tag{11.66}$$

formed from the conjugated backward linear prediction coefficients has roots at $z_k = \exp(-s_k^*) = \exp([-\alpha_k + j2\pi f_k]T)$ for $k = 1$ to $k = p$. See the Problems for a proof of this property. For a decaying damping factor ($\alpha_k < 0$), the roots of the forward linear prediction characteristic polynomial $A(z)$ fall *inside* the unit z-plane circle, whereas the roots of the backward linear prediction characteristic polynomial $B(z)$ fall *outside* the unit circle due to the reciprocal damping factor $\exp(-\alpha_k T)$, which is a growing exponential. These characteristics of the root locations of polynomials $A(z)$ and $B(z)$ are properties of deterministic exponentials.

Consider the process consisting of two complex exponentials in complex additive white Gaussian noise

$$x[n] = A_1 \exp(s_1 n) + A_2 \exp(s_2 n) + w[n] \quad , \tag{11.67}$$

in which $s_1 = -0.1 + j2\pi(0.52)$, $s_2 = -0.2 + j2\pi(0.42)$, $A_1 = 1$, $A_2 = 1$, and the noise variance is ρ. With no noise, the second-order characteristic polynomials $A(z)$ and $B(z)$ for the two exponentials will have roots located at the positions indicated in Fig. 11.4(a) and (b). Fifty epochs, each of 25 data points indexed from $n = 0$ to $n = 24$, were generated by using different $w[n]$ sequences at a signal-to-noise ratio of $10\log_{10}(1/\rho) = 20$ dB. Each epoch was processed by the covariance least squares linear prediction algorithm (subroutine COVAR) using order $p = 2$ and the roots (zeros) of $A(z)$ and $B(z)$ were plotted. The backward linear prediction coefficients are obtained simultaneously with the forward linear prediction coefficients by the fast algorithm of Appendix 8.C. Therefore, no additional computations are required in order to get the backward linear prediction coefficients. Figure 11.4(c) and (d), respectively, show the zero locations of the forward and backward characteristic polynomials for all 50 epochs. For comparison, the true zero locations for the two exponentials are also indicated. The additive noise has caused a bias in the estimates of the zeros, which means a bias in the damping and frequency terms. The bias is more severe for the exponential with the larger damping factor.

The bias may be reduced significantly by selecting a linear prediction order much higher than the number of exponentials actually present in the signal, an empirical observation made frequently in the literature (e.g., see Van Blaricum and

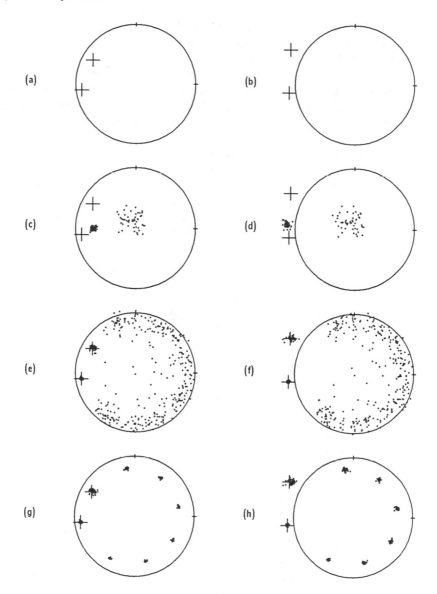

Figure 11.4   Zero locations of forward linear prediction filter polynomial
$A(z)$ and backward linear prediction filter polynomial $B(z)$ for 50 independent
data realizations of 25 samples each. The unit radius circle of the z-plane is
shown for reference. The circled x symbols show the true location of the two
exponential signals. For $A(z)$, these correspond to $\exp(s_1)$ and $\exp(s_2)$ inside
the unit circle. For $B(z)$, these correspond to $\exp(-s_1^*)$ and $\exp(-s_2^*)$ outside
the unit circle. (a) $A(z)$, $p = 2$, no noise. (b) $B(z)$, $p = 2$, no noise. (c) $A(z)$,
$p = 2$, noise. (d) $B(z)$, $p = 2$, noise. (e) $A(z)$, $p = 8$, noise. (f) $B(z)$, $p = 8$,
noisc. (g) $A(z)$, $p = 8$, SVD with two principal eigenvectors. (h) $B(z)$, $p = 8$,
SVD with two principal eigenvectors.

Mittra [1975] and Kumaresan and Tufts [1982]). Figure 11.4(e) and (f) illustrate the positions of the zeros when the covariance algorithm for order $p = 8$ is selected. The zeros related to the true exponentials in the signal now cluster closer to the correct positions, but the extraneous zeros due to noise fluctuate widely. However, the selection of a higher linear prediction order has a negative effect in that extraneous zeros are introduced, making it difficult to separate the zeros due to the actual exponential signals from the zeros due to noise, at least when examining only the $A(z)$ polynomial roots. The separation is obvious in the $B(z)$ zero locations of Fig. 11.4(f) only due to the clustering effect of 50 independent data sets. The zeros from a single polynomial would not be so obvious. By examining the zeros of *both* $A(z)$ and $B(z)$, one then has a means to distinguish the true signal zeros from the noise zeros. The statistics of a stationary random process do not change when the process is time reversed. Thus, the noise zeros of both $A(z)$ and $B(z)$ tend predominantly to stay within the unit circle, as illustrated by the test ensemble results in Fig. 11.4(e) and (f). The true exponential signal zeros will occur in reciprocal positions along a common radius when examining the zeros of $A(z)$ and $B(z)$ [Kumaresan, 1983].

The application of singular value decomposition (SVD) can provide further improvement. The forward and backward linear prediction errors of Sec. 8.5.1 may be expressed succintly as

$$\mathbf{X}_p^f \mathbf{a}_p^f = -\mathbf{x}_p^f + \mathbf{e}_p^f \qquad \mathbf{X}_p^b \mathbf{a}_p^b = -\mathbf{x}_p^b + \mathbf{e}_p^b \quad , \tag{11.68}$$

in which the Toeplitz data matrices $\mathbf{X}_p^f, \mathbf{X}_p^b$ and data vectors $\mathbf{x}_p^f, \mathbf{x}_p^b$ are defined as

$$\mathbf{X}_p^f = \begin{pmatrix} x[p] & \cdots & x[1] \\ \vdots & & \vdots \\ x[N-1] & \cdots & x[N-p] \end{pmatrix}, \quad \mathbf{x}_p^f = \begin{pmatrix} x[p+1] \\ \vdots \\ x[N] \end{pmatrix},$$

$$\mathbf{X}_p^b = \begin{pmatrix} x[p+1] & \cdots & x[2] \\ \vdots & & \vdots \\ x[N] & \cdots & x[N-p+1] \end{pmatrix}, \quad \mathbf{x}_p^b = \begin{pmatrix} x[1] \\ \vdots \\ x[N-p] \end{pmatrix}, \tag{11.69}$$

and the forward linear prediction coefficient vector $\mathbf{a}_p^f$, forward linear prediction error vector $\mathbf{e}_p^f$, backward linear prediction coefficient vector $\mathbf{a}_p^b$, and backward linear prediction error vector $\mathbf{e}_p^b$ are defined as

$$\mathbf{a}_p^f = \begin{pmatrix} a^f[1] \\ \vdots \\ a^f[p] \end{pmatrix}, \quad \mathbf{e}_p^f = \begin{pmatrix} e^f[p+1] \\ \vdots \\ e^f[N] \end{pmatrix}, \quad \mathbf{a}_p^b = \begin{pmatrix} a^b[p] \\ \vdots \\ a^b[1] \end{pmatrix}, \quad \mathbf{e}_p^b = \begin{pmatrix} e^b[p+1] \\ \vdots \\ e^b[N] \end{pmatrix}.$$

$$\tag{11.70}$$

Based on Eq. (3.96), the data matrices have the following singular value decompositions

$$\mathbf{X}_p^f = \sum_{n=1}^{p} \sigma_n^f \mathbf{u}_n^f (\mathbf{v}_n^f)^H \qquad \mathbf{X}_p^b = \sum_{n=1}^{p} \sigma_n^b \mathbf{u}_n^b (\mathbf{v}_n^b)^H \quad , \qquad (11.71)$$

in which the σ_n^f are positive singular values of $\mathbf{X}_p^f$ and the σ_n^b are positive singular values of $\mathbf{X}_p^b$. The $\mathbf{u}_n$ and $\mathbf{v}_n$ are eigenvectors of the respective data matrix. If a signal consists of m exponentials in additive noise, then the m eigenvectors associated with the m largest singular values primarily span the m exponential components. The $p - m$ eigenvectors of the remaining smaller singular values primarily span the noise components. Chapter 13 will provide more details of this procedure. Assuming the singular values have been ordered by decreasing value, e.g., $\sigma_1^f > \sigma_2^f > \ldots > \sigma_p^f$, then a *reduced rank approximation* to each data matrix may be formed by truncating the SVD relationships of Eq. (11.71) to the m principal singular values

$$\hat{\mathbf{X}}_p^f = \sum_{n=1}^{m} \sigma_n^f \mathbf{u}_n^f (\mathbf{v}_n^f)^H \qquad \hat{\mathbf{X}}_p^b = \sum_{n=1}^{m} \sigma_n^b \mathbf{u}_n^f (\mathbf{v}_n^f)^H \quad . \qquad (11.72)$$

This will reduce the noise contribution to the data matrix, effectively enhancing the SNR [Holt and Antill, 1977; Kumaresan and Tufts, 1982; Tufts and Kumaresan, 1982]. Minimizing the norms $\|\mathbf{a}_p^f\|_2$ and $\|\mathbf{a}_p^b\|_2$ with respect to the reduced rank data matrices will yield the solutions

$$\mathbf{a}_p^f = -\left(\hat{\mathbf{X}}_p^f\right)^{\#} \mathbf{x}_p^f \qquad \mathbf{a}_p^b = -\left(\hat{\mathbf{X}}_p^b\right)^{\#} \mathbf{x}_p^b \qquad (11.73)$$

in which the pseudoinverse data matrices are defined as

$$\left(\hat{\mathbf{X}}_p^f\right)^{\#} = \sum_{n=1}^{m} (\sigma_n^f)^{-1} \mathbf{v}_n^f (\mathbf{u}_n^f)^H \qquad \left(\hat{\mathbf{X}}_p^b\right)^{\#} = \sum_{n=1}^{m} (\sigma_n^b)^{-1} \mathbf{v}_n^b (\mathbf{u}_n^b)^H \quad . \qquad (11.74)$$

The order p must lie in the range $m \leq p \leq N - m$ in order to keep the rank of $\mathbf{X}_p^f$ amd $\mathbf{X}_p^b$ greater than or equal to m, the assumed number of exponentials. If the number of exponentials is not known, it may be estimated by comparing the relative magnitudes of the singular values. The signal-related singular values tend to be larger than the noise-related singular values. Once the forward and backward linear prediction coefficients have been computed, as indicated by Eq. (11.73), the roots computed as indicated by Eqs. (11.64) and (11.66) will yield the exponential estimates. The data vectors $\mathbf{x}_p^f$ and $\mathbf{x}_p^b$ are not considered for noise effects, even though they are themselves noisy. In order to reduce the effect of noise from both data matrices and data vectors, the total least squares method [Rahman and Yu, 1986] can be applied to give slightly better results than shown here.

Using the SVD approach with a reduced-order approximation produced the results shown in Fig. 11.4(g) and (h) for the 50 data epochs. Selection of $p = 8$ and $m = 2$ was used in this truncated SVD result. The extraneous zeros are much less perturbed and form a uniform pattern around the inside of the unit circle, which is representative of an exponential model approximation to white noise. The zeros due to the actual pair of damped exponentials stand out distinctly in Fig. 11.4(g) and (h). Application of reduced rank SVD in cases of highly damped exponentials or in cases of low SNR may only be of limited success. In both of these situations, the signal singular values are comparable in magnitude to the noise singular values, making it difficult to separate the singular values based strictly on relative magnitude.

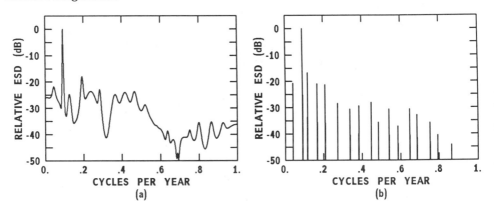

Figure 11.5   Prony ESD estimates of the filtered sunspot numbers.   (a) Extended Prony. (b) Modified Prony (undamped sinusoids).

11.10 APPLICATION TO SUNSPOT NUMBERS

Figure 11.5 illustrates the energy spectral density estimates of the filtered sunspot numbers when processed by the Prony method. A model order of 36 complex exponentials was fitted. This corresponds to 18 real sinusoids in the modified Prony case. The usual least squares Prony algorithm yielded periods for the four lowest-frequency peaks of 22.71, 10.78, 7.92, and 5.19 years per cycle with an estimated amplitude of 58.78 and an estimated damping of $-.0057$ for the 10.78-year component. The modified Prony algorithm yielded periods for the four lowest-frequency peaks of 24.84, 10.96, 8.60, and 5.96 years per cycle with an estimated amplitude of 37.69 for the 10.78-year component, which was the strongest.

Other applications of Prony's method that the reader may find interesting include bearing estimation [Bucker, 1977] and radar target resonances [Chuang and Moffatt, 1977].

REFERENCES

Bucker, H. P., Comparison of FFT and Prony Algorithms for Bearing Estimation of Narrow-Band Signals in Realistic Ocean Environment, *J. Acoust. Soc. Am.*, vol. 61, pp. 756–762, March 1977.

Chuang, C. W., and D. L. Moffatt, Natural Resonances of Radar Targets via Prony's Method and Target Discrimination, *IEEE Trans. Aerosp. Electron. Syst.*, vol. AES-12, pp. 583–589, September 1976.

Evans, A. G., and R. Fischl, Optimal Least-Squares Time-Domain Synthesis of Recursive Digital Filters, *IEEE Trans. Audio Electoacoust.*, vol. AU-21, pp. 61–65, February 1973.

Hildebrand, F. B., *Introduction to Numerical Analysis*, McGraw-Hill Book Company, New York, 1956, Chapter 9.

Holt, J. N., and R. J. Antill, Determining the Number of Terms in a Prony Algorithm Exponential Fit, *Math. Biosci.*, vol. 36, pp. 319–332, 1977.

Householder, A. S., On Prony's Method of Fitting Exponential Decay Curves and Multiple-Hit Survival Curves, *Oak Ridge National Laboratory Report ORNL-455*, Oak Ridge, Tenn., February 1950.

Jenkins, M. A., and J. F. Traub, Algorithm 419: Zeros of a Complex Polynomial, *Commun. ACM*, vol. 15, pp. 97–99, February 1972.

Korn, G. A., and T. M. Korn, *Mathematical Handbook for Scientists and Engineers*, McGraw-Hill Book Company, New York, p. 660, 1961.

Kulp, R. W., An Optimum Sampling Procedure for Use with the Prony Method, *IEEE Trans. Electromagn. Compat.*, vol. EMC-23, pp. 67–71, May 1981.

Kumaresan, R., On the Zeros of the Linear Prediction-Error Filter for Deterministic Signals, *IEEE Trans. Acoust. Speech Signal Process.*, vol. ASSP-31, pp. 217–220, February 1983.

Kumaresan, R., and D. W. Tufts, Estimating the Parameters of Exponentially Damped Sinusoids and Pole-Zero Modeling in Noise, *IEEE Trans. Acoust. Speech Signal Process.*, vol. ASSP-30, pp. 833–840, December 1982.

Marple, S. L., Jr., Spectral Line Analysis by Pisarenko and Prony Methods, *Proceedings of the 1979 IEEE International Conference on Acoustics, Speech, and Signal Processing*, Washington, D.C., pp. 159–161.

Marple, S. L., Jr., Exponential Energy Spectral Density Estimation, *Proceedings of the 1980 IEEE International Conference on Acoustics, Speech, and Signal Processing*, Denver, Colo., pp. 588–591.

Marple, S. L., Jr., Spectral Line Analysis via a Fast Prony Algorithm, *Proceedings of the 1982 IEEE International Conference on Acoustics, Speech, and Signal Processing*, Paris, France, pp. 1375–1378, 1982a

Marple, S. L., Jr., Fast Algorithms for Linear Prediction and System Identification Filters with Linear Phase, *IEEE Trans. Acoust. Speech Signal Process.*, vol. ASSP-30, pp. 942–953, December 1982b.

McDonough, R. N., Representations and Analysis of Signals. Part XV. Matched Exponents for the Representation of Signals, Ph.D. dissertation, Department of Electrical Engineering, John Hopkins University, Baltimore, Md., April 1963.

McDonough, R. N., and W. H. Huggins, Best Least-Squares Representation of Signals by Exponentials, *IEEE Trans. Autom. Control*, vol. AC-13, pp. 408–412, August 1968.

Poggio, A. J., M. L. Van Blaricum, E. K. Miller, and R. Mittra, Evaluation for a Processing Technique for Transient Data, *IEEE Trans. Antennas Propag.*, vol. AP-26, pp. 165–173, January 1978.

de Prony, Baron (Gaspard Riche), Essai expérimental et analytique: sur les lois de la dilatabilité de fluides élastiques et sur celles de la force expansive de la vapeur de l'eau et de la vapeur de l'alkool, à différentes températures, *J. E. Polytech.*, vol. 1, no. 2, pp. 24–76, 1795.

Rahman, M. A., and Kai-Bor Yu, Improved Frequency Estimation Using Total Least Squares Approach, *Proceedings of the 1986 IEEE International Conference on Acoustics, Speech, and Signal Processing*, Tokyo, Japan, pp. 1397–1400, April 1986.

Trivett, D. H., and A. Z. Robinson, Modified Prony Method Approach to Echo-Reduction Measurements, *J. Acoust. Soc. Am.*, vol. 70, pp. 1166–1175, October 1981.

Tufts, D. W., and R. Kumaresan, Estimation of Frequencies of Multiple Sinusoids: Making Linear Prediction Perform Like Maximum Likelihood, *Proc. IEEE*, vol. 70, pp. 975–989, September 1982.

Van Blaricum, M. L., and R. Mittra, A Technique for Extracting the Poles and Residues of a System Directly from Its Transient Response, *IEEE Trans. Antennas Propag.*, vol. AP-23, pp. 777–781, November 1975.

Van Blaricum, M. L., and R. Mittra, Problems and Solutions Associated with Prony's Method for Processing Transient Data, *IEEE Trans. Antennas Propag.*, vol. AP-26, pp. 174–182, January 1978; correction in vol. AP-28, p. 949, November 1980.

PROBLEMS

1. Prove that $\mathbf{Z}^H\mathbf{Z}$ in Eq. (11.26) is positive semidefinite.

2. If a multiple zero is encountered when factoring the polynomial, this gives rise to the product of a polynomial with the exponential. How can the Prony method be adjusted to handle this?

3. Show that the AR and ARMA processes have autocorrelation sequences that are representable as sums of damped exponentials. Show how to apply Prony's method to the *autocorrelation sequence* (not the data sequence) to get the MA and AR coefficients.

4. Prove that the sum of p exponentials may also be generated using backward linear prediction if the time direction is reversed. How do the roots of the characteristic polynomial relate to the exponents of the p exponentials?

5. Define the exponential signal $x[n] = \exp(-.2nT)\sin(2\pi.05nT)$. Let $T = 1$. and choose 20 samples for $0 \le n \le 19$. Compute the least squares Prony estimate of the damping. Now let $T = .5$ and choose 40 samples for $0 \le n \le 39$. Recompute the Prony estimate. How do the two estimates differ? Why? (see Kulp [1981] for more details of the effect of sampling rate on the accuracy of Prony's method).

6. Using Eq. (11.49), show that the inverse transform of $\hat{\mathbf{X}}_1(z)$ is an ARMA model with order $p = q$.

7. Prove matrix expression (11.44) is true.

8. Let $\hat{x}[n] = a\exp[sn]$ be a single-exponential approximation for a real a and a real $s = \alpha T$, such that $\alpha < 0$, and defined over the index range 0 to $N-1$. Form $e[n] = x[n] - \hat{x}[n]$. Minimize

$$\sum_{n=0}^{N-1} e^2[n]$$

by setting the derivative with respect to a and s to zero. Find an analytic solution for both a and s. (This example shows how nonlinear and difficult the general minimization problem is, even for a real case.)

9. Show that for real data, Eq. (11.A.17) reduces to two linear equations in two real unknowns α_2 and α_3. Find explicit solutions for α_2 and α_3.

10. In this problem, the periodogram method of spectral estimation will be viewed as a special case of the Prony method in which a harmonic model of preselected frequencies is used to fit to the data. Assume that the time-series model is

$$\hat{x}(nT) = \hat{x}[n] = \sum_{m=0}^{M-1} a_m \exp(j2\pi f_m nT)$$

for the data samples $n = 0, \ldots, N-1$, such that $M < N$. Using the preselected harmonic frequencies $f_m = m/NT$ for $0 \le m \le M-1$ and Eq. (11.26), show that the least squares solution for the complex sinusoidal amplitudes a_m is given by

$$a_m = \frac{1}{N} \sum_{n=0}^{N-1} x[n]\exp(-j2\pi mn/N)$$

for $m = 0, \ldots, M-1$. This, of course, is the usual discrete-time Fourier series when $M = N$ and $T = 1$.

APPENDIX 11.A
FAST ALGORITHM AND PROGRAM TO SOLVE SYMMETRIC COVARIANCE NORMAL EQUATIONS

11.A.1   Introduction

The fast algorithm to solve the symmetric covariance normal equations [Eq. (11.44)] was developed by Marple [1982a, 1982b]. The $2p$th-order complex linear smoothing error may be represented as

$$e_{2p}^s[n] = \mathbf{x}_{2p}^T[n+p]\mathbf{g}_{2p} \quad , \tag{11.A.1}$$

where the data vector $\mathbf{x}_{2p}[n+p]$ and symmetric linear smoothing vector $\mathbf{g}_{2p}$ are defined as

$$
\mathbf{x}_{2p}[n+p] = \begin{pmatrix} x[n+p] \\ \vdots \\ x[n+1] \\ x[n] \\ x[n-1] \\ \vdots \\ x[n-p] \end{pmatrix} \quad , \quad \mathbf{g}_{2p} = \begin{pmatrix} g_{2p}[p] \\ \vdots \\ g_{2p}[1] \\ 1 \\ g^*_{2p}[1] \\ \vdots \\ g^*_{2p}[p] \end{pmatrix} \quad . \tag{11.A.2}
$$

Note that $\mathbf{g}_{2p} = \mathbf{J}\mathbf{g}^*_{2p}$, where $\mathbf{J}$ is a $(2p+1) \times (2p+1)$ reflection matrix. Based on measured complex data samples $x[1], \ldots, x[N]$, the symmetric covariance method minimizes the sum of squared linear smoothing errors

$$
\rho^s_{2p} = \sum_{n=p+1}^{N-p} \left| e^s_{2p}[n] \right|^2 \quad , \tag{11.A.3}
$$

resulting in the normal equation

$$
\mathbf{R}_{2p}\mathbf{g}_{2p} = \begin{pmatrix} \mathbf{0}_p \\ 2\rho^s_{2p} \\ \mathbf{0}_p \end{pmatrix} \quad , \tag{11.A.4}
$$

where $\mathbf{0}_p$ is a $p \times 1$ all-zero vector. The centrosymmetric matrix $\mathbf{R}_{2p}$ may be expressed as

$$
\mathbf{R}_{2p} = \sum_{n=2p+1}^{N} \left[\mathbf{x}^*_{2p}[n]\mathbf{x}^T_{2p}[n] + \mathbf{J}\mathbf{x}_{2p}[n]\mathbf{x}^H_{2p}[n]\mathbf{J} \right] \quad . \tag{11.A.5}
$$

If the smoothing error terms $e^s_{2p}[N-p]$ and $e^s_{2p}[p+1]$ are not used, and the resulting squared error

$$
\rho^{s\prime\prime}_{2p} = \sum_{n=p+2}^{N-p-1} \left| e^s_{2p}[n] \right|^2 \tag{11.A.6}
$$

is minimized, then the following normal equations are the result

$$
\mathbf{R}''_{2p}\mathbf{g}''_{2p} = \begin{pmatrix} \mathbf{0}_p \\ 2\rho^{s\prime\prime}_{2p} \\ \mathbf{0}_p \end{pmatrix} \quad , \tag{11.A.7}
$$

where the double prime denotes the solution for this case of omitted error terms. The matrix $\mathbf{R}_{2p}''$ is defined by

$$\mathbf{R}_{2p}'' = \sum_{n=2p+2}^{N-1} \left(\mathbf{x}_{2p}^*[n]\mathbf{x}_{2p}^T[n] + \mathbf{J}\mathbf{x}_{2p}[n]\mathbf{x}_{2p}^H[n]\mathbf{J} \right) \quad . \tag{11.A.8}$$

The fast algorithm developed embeds additional recursive relationships into the modified covariance algorithm of Appendix 8.D. The algorithms run concurrently.

11.A.2 Special Partitions and Auxiliary Parameters

Crucial to the development of a fast algorithm is the following order-index partition of the $(2p+1) \times (2p+1)$ matrix $\mathbf{R}_{2p}$,

$$\mathbf{R}_{2p} = \begin{pmatrix} r_{2p}[0,0] & \mathbf{r}_{2p}^T\mathbf{J} & r_{2p}[0,2p] \\ \mathbf{J}\mathbf{r}_{2p}^* & \mathbf{R}_{2p-2}'' & \mathbf{r}_{2p} \\ r_{2p}[2p,0] & \mathbf{r}_{2p}^H & r_{2p}[2p,2p] \end{pmatrix} \quad , \tag{11.A.9}$$

where the $(2p-1) \times 1$ column vector $\mathbf{r}_{2p}$ is

$$\mathbf{r}_{2p} = \begin{pmatrix} r_{2p}[1,2p] \\ \vdots \\ r_{2p}[2p-1,2p] \end{pmatrix} \tag{11.A.10}$$

and $\mathbf{J}$ is a $(2p-1) \times (2p-1)$ reflection matrix. The elements $r_{2p}[i,j]$ are defined by Eq. (8.49). Note also that $r_{2p}[0,0] = r_{2p}[2p,2p]$ and $r_{2p}[0,2p] = r_{2p}^*[2p,0]$. Also crucial is the following time-index partition,

$$\begin{aligned} \mathbf{R}_{2p} =&\mathbf{R}_{2p}'' + \mathbf{x}_{2p}^*[2p+1]\mathbf{x}_{2p}^T[2p+1] + \mathbf{J}\mathbf{x}_{2p}[2p+1]\mathbf{x}_{2p}^H[2p+1]\mathbf{J} \\ &+ \mathbf{x}_{2p}^*[N]\mathbf{x}_{2p}^T[N] + \mathbf{J}\mathbf{x}_{2p}[N]\mathbf{x}_{2p}^H[N]\mathbf{J} \quad . \end{aligned} \tag{11.A.11}$$

11.A.3 Order Update Recursions

The order update for the linear smoothing coefficient vector $\mathbf{g}_{2p}$ has the form

$$\mathbf{g}_{2p} = \beta_1 \left\{ \begin{pmatrix} 0 \\ \mathbf{g}_{2p-2}'' \\ 0 \end{pmatrix} + \alpha_1\mathbf{a}_{2p} + \alpha_1^*\mathbf{J}\mathbf{a}_{2p}^* \right\} \quad , \tag{11.A.12}$$

for which the complex scalar α_1 and real scalar β_1 are defined as

$$\alpha_1 = -\mathbf{r}_{2p}^T\mathbf{g}_{2p-2}''^* / \rho_{2p} \tag{11.A.13}$$

$$\beta_1 = \left(1 + 2\text{Re}\{\alpha_1 a_{2p}[p]\}\right)^{-1}. \tag{11.A.14}$$

The vector $\mathbf{a}_{2p}$ is obtained from the modified covariance fast algorithm. To verify Eq. (11.A.12), premultiply both sides by $\mathbf{R}_{2p}$ and substitute the order partition (11.A.9) or (8.D.10) as appropriate. This will also yield the order update for the linear smoothing squared error

$$\rho_{2p}^s = \beta_1 \rho_{2p-2}^{s''} \quad . \tag{11.A.15}$$

Observe that the order update $\mathbf{g}_{2p}$ only takes place coincident with the even-order update of the linear prediction coefficient vector $\mathbf{a}_{2p}$, that is, only on alternate order updates of $\mathbf{a}_{2p}$. Also observe that $\beta_1 > 0$ to ensure that ρ_{2p}^s is positive, as it must be because it is a squared error.

11.A.4 Time Update Recursions

The time-index update of the linear smoothing coefficient vector is given by

$$\mathbf{g}_{2p}'' = \beta_2 \left[\mathbf{g}_{2p} + \alpha_2 \mathbf{c}_{2p} + \alpha_2^* \mathbf{Jc}_{2p}^* + \alpha_3 \mathbf{d}_{2p} + \alpha_3^* \mathbf{Jd}_{2p}^*\right] \quad , \tag{11.A.16}$$

where the complex scalars α_2 and α_3 are found as the solution of the 4×4 complex matrix

$$\begin{pmatrix} \delta_{2p} & -\xi_{2p}^* & -\lambda_{2p}^* & -\theta_{2p}^* \\ -\xi_{2p} & \delta_{2p} & -\theta_{2p} & -\lambda_{2p} \\ -\lambda_{2p} & -\theta_{2p}^* & \gamma_{2p} & -\phi_{2p}^* \\ -\theta_{2p} & -\lambda_{2p}^* & -\phi_{2p} & \gamma_{2p} \end{pmatrix} \begin{pmatrix} \alpha_3 \\ \alpha_3^* \\ \alpha_2 \\ \alpha_2^* \end{pmatrix} = \begin{pmatrix} e_{2p}^s[p+1] \\ (e_{2p}^s[p+1])^* \\ (e_{2p}^s[N-p])^* \\ e_{2p}^s[N-p] \end{pmatrix} . \tag{11.A.17}$$

This matrix is Hermitian, so that subroutine CHOLESKY may be used to solve it. The real scalar β_2 is given simply by

$$\beta_2 = \left[1 + 2\text{Re}\{\alpha_2 c_{2p}[p]\} + 2\text{Re}\{\alpha_3 d_{2p}[p]\}\right]^{-1} \quad . \tag{11.A.18}$$

The complex vectors $\mathbf{c}_{2p}, \mathbf{d}_{2p}$, real scalars δ_{2p}, γ_{2p}, and complex scalars $\lambda_{2p}, \theta_{2p}, \xi_{2p}$, ϕ_{2p} are available from the modified covariance algorithm of Appendix 8.D. To verify Eq. (11.A.16), premultiply both sides by $\mathbf{R}_{2p}''$ and substitute the time partition (11.A.11) as appropriate. This will also yield the time update for the squared linear smoothing error

$$\rho_{2p}^{s''} = \beta_2 \rho_{2p}^s \quad . \tag{11.A.19}$$

11.A.5 Initial Conditions

Only one initial condition is required, namely the adjusted smoothing squared error

$$\rho_0^{s''} = \sum_{n=2}^{N-1} |x[n]|^2 \quad . \tag{11.A.20}$$

11.A.6 Operation Count

The symmetric covariance algorithm requires $3Np + 40p^2$ multiplications, $12p$ real divides, and storage of $N + 10p + 12$ elements. Going from order $2p + 1$ to $2p + 3$ requires a number of computations proportional to $2N + 36p$ at each iteration. Using the 64-point sample sequence from Appendix II and selecting N = 64 and order IP = 16, then the following values should be obtained from the program

$$PS = 0.000397$$

$$
\begin{aligned}
G[1] &= (\ 0.954512,\ 0.151396) \\
G[2] &= (\ 0.823844,\ 0.266706) \\
G[3] &= (\ 0.632592,\ 0.317878) \\
G[4] &= (\ 0.418971,\ 0.298189) \\
G[5] &= (\ 0.229737,\ 0.223792) \\
G[6] &= (\ 0.097085,\ 0.132041) \\
G[7] &= (\ 0.027857,\ 0.055635) \\
G[8] &= (\ 0.003689,\ 0.013973)\quad .
\end{aligned}
$$

```
      SUBROUTINE SYMCOVAR (N,IP,X,PS,G,ISTAT)
C
C     Fast algorithm for the solution of the Hermitian symmetric covariance
C     least squares normal equations.
C
C     Input Parameters:
C
C        N     - Number of data samples (integer)
C        IP    - Order of linear prediction model (must be an even integer)
C        X     - Array of complex data samples X(1) through X(N)
C
C     Output Parameters:
C
C        PS    - Real linear smoothing squared error at order IP; note that PF
C                must be scaled by 1/(N-IP) to make it a variance estimate
C        G     - Array of IP/2 complex linear smoothing coefficients
C        ISTAT - Integer status indicator at time of exit
C                0 for normal exit (no numerical ill-conditioning)
C                1 if P is not a positive value
C                2 if DELTA' and GAMMA' are not in the range 0 to 1
C                3 if P' is not a positive value
C                4 if DELTA and GAMMA are not in the range 0 to 1
C                5 if IP is not an even number
C                6 if PS is not a positive value
C                7 if PS" is not a positive value
C                8 if error in subroutine CHOLESKY
C
C     Notes:
C
C        External array G must be dimensioned .GE. IP/2 .  External array X
C        must be dimensioned .GE. N and array A must be dimensioned .GE. IP
C        in the calling program.   Internal array R must be dimensioned .GE.
C        IP  and arrays C,D must be dimensioned .GE. IP+1.  Internal arrays
C        AA and BB are fixed at the indicated dimensions.
C
```

```
      COMPLEX X(1),AF(100),C(101),D(101),R(100),LAMBDA,THETA,PSI,XI
      COMPLEX EF,EB,C1,C2,C3,C4,SAVE1,SAVE2,SAVE3,SAVE4
      COMPLEX G(1),AA(10),BB(4),ESP,ESN
      REAL PS,DELTA,GAMMA,P,R1,R2,R3,R4,R5,EPS
C
C   Initialization
C
      EPS=1.E-15
      IF (MOD(IP,2) .EQ. 0)  GO TO 5
      ISTAT=5
      RETURN
5     R1=0.
      DO 10 K=2,N-1
10      R1=R1+REAL(X(K))**2+AIMAG(X(K))**2
      R2=REAL(X(1))**2+AIMAG(X(1))**2
      R3=REAL(X(N))**2+AIMAG(X(N))**2
      R4=1./(2.*(R1+R2+R3))
      P=2.*R1+R2+R3
      PS=R1                                     ! Eq. (11.A.20)
      DELTA=1.-R2*R4
      GAMMA=1.-R3*R4
      LAMBDA=CONJG(X(1)*X(N))*R4
      C(1)=X(N)*R4
      D(1)=CONJG(X(1))*R4
      ISTAT=0
      M=0
      IF (IP .EQ. 0)  RETURN
C
C   Main loop
C
1000  M=M+1
      SAVE1=(0.,0.)
      DO 20 K=M+1,N
20      SAVE1=SAVE1+X(K)*CONJG(X(K-M))
      SAVE1=2.*SAVE1
      R(M)=CONJG(SAVE1)
      THETA=X(N)*D(1)
      PSI=X(N)*C(1)
      XI=CONJG(X(1))*D(1)
      IF (M .EQ. 1)  GO TO 40
      DO 30 K=1,M-1
        THETA=THETA+X(N-K)*D(K+1)              ! Eq. (8.D.45)
        PSI=PSI+X(N-K)*C(K+1)                  ! Eq. (8.D.45)
        XI=XI+CONJG(X(K+1))*D(K+1)             ! Eq. (8.D.45)
        R(K)=R(K)-X(N+1-M)*CONJG(X(N+1-M+K))
     *            -CONJG(X(M))*X(M-K)          ! Eq. (8.D.37)
30      SAVE1=SAVE1+CONJG(R(K))*AF(M-K)        ! Eq. (8.D.24)
C
C   Order update of AF vector
C
40    C1=-SAVE1/P
      AF(M)=C1                                 ! Eq. (8.D.23)
      P=P*(1.-REAL(C1)**2-AIMAG(C1)**2)        ! Eq. (8.D.25)
      IF (M .EQ. 1)  GO TO 60
C
      IF (MOD(M,2) .EQ. 0)  GO TO 46
      MH=(M-1)/2
      MH1=MH+1
```

```
              BB(1)=ESP
              BB(2)=CONJG(ESP)
              BB(3)=CONJG(ESN)
              BB(4)=ESN
              AA(1)=CMPLX(DELTA,0.)
              AA(2)=-CONJG(XI)
              AA(3)=CMPLX(DELTA,0.)
              AA(4)=-CONJG(LAMBDA)
              AA(5)=-THETA
              AA(6)=CMPLX(GAMMA,0.)
              AA(7)=-CONJG(THETA)
              AA(8)=-LAMBDA
              AA(9)=-CONJG(PSI)
              AA(10)=CMPLX(GAMMA,0.)
              CALL CHOLESKY (4,EPS,AA,BB,JSTAT)                  ! Eq. (11.A.17)
              IF (JSTAT .EQ. 0)  GO TO 42
              ISTAT=8
              RETURN
      42      R5=1./(1.+2.*REAL(BB(3)*C(MH1))+2.*REAL(BB(1)*D(MH1)))  !(11.A.18)
              DO 44 K=1,MH
      44        G(K)=R5*(G(K)+BB(4)*CONJG(C(MH1+K))+BB(3)*C(MH1-K) ! (11.A.16)
           *       +BB(2)*CONJG(D(MH1+K))+BB(1)*D(MH1-K))  ! Eq. (11.A.19)
              PS=R5*PS
              IF (PS .GT. 0)  GO TO 46
              ISTAT=7
              RETURN
      C
      46      DO 50 K=1,M/2
                MK=M-K
                SAVE1=AF(K)
                AF(K)=SAVE1+C1*CONJG(AF(MK))                   ! Eq. (8.D.22)
                IF (K .EQ. MK)  GO TO 50
                AF(MK)=AF(MK)+C1*CONJG(SAVE1)                  ! Eq. (8.D.22)
      50        CONTINUE
      C
              IF (MOD(M,2) .NE. 0)  GO TO 60
              MH=M/2
              MH1=MH+1
              SAVE1=R(MH)
              DO 54 K=1,MH-1
      54        SAVE1=SAVE1+CONJG(G(K))*R(MH+K)+G(K)*R(MH-K)
              C1=-SAVE1/P                                     ! Eq. (11.A.13)
              R5=1./(1.+2.*REAL(C1*AF(MH)))                   ! Eq. (11.A.14)
              G(MH)=R5*(C1+CONJG(C1*AF(M)))
              ESP=X(MH1)+G(MH)*X(M+1)+CONJG(G(MH))*X(1)
              ESN=X(N-MH)+G(MH)*X(N)+CONJG(G(MH))*X(N-M)
              DO 56 K=1,MH-1
                G(K)=R5*(G(K)+C1*AF(MH-K)+CONJG(C1*AF(MH+K))) ! Eq. (11.A.12)
                ESP=ESP+G(K)*X(MH1+K)+CONJG(G(K))*X(MH1-K) ! Eq. (11.A.1)
      56        ESN=ESN+G(K)*X(N-MH+K)+CONJG(G(K))*X(N-MH-K) ! Eq. (11.A.1)
              PS=R5*PS                                        ! Eq. (11.A.15)
              IF (PS .GT. 0.)  GO TO 60
              ISTAT=6
              RETURN
      C
      60      IF (M .EQ. IP)  RETURN
      C
      C   Time update of C,D vectors and GAMMA,DELTA,LAMBDA scalars
```

```
C
65      R1=1./(DELTA*GAMMA-REAL(LAMBDA)**2-AIMAG(LAMBDA)**2)
        C1=(THETA*CONJG(LAMBDA)+PSI*DELTA)*R1
        C2=(PSI*LAMBDA+THETA*GAMMA)*R1
        C3=(XI*CONJG(LAMBDA)+THETA*DELTA)*R1
        C4=(THETA*LAMBDA+XI*GAMMA)*R1
        DO 70 K=1,(M-1)/2+1
          MK=M+1-K
          SAVE1=CONJG(C(K))
          SAVE2=CONJG(D(K))
          SAVE3=CONJG(C(MK))
          SAVE4=CONJG(D(MK))
          C(K)=C(K)+C1*SAVE3+C2*SAVE4                   ! Eq. (8.D.43)
          D(K)=D(K)+C3*SAVE3+C4*SAVE4                   ! Eq. (8.D.44)
          IF (K .EQ. MK)  GO TO 70
          C(MK)=C(MK)+C1*SAVE1+C2*SAVE2                 ! Eq. (8.D.43)
          D(MK)=D(MK)+C3*SAVE1+C4*SAVE2                 ! Eq. (8.D.44)
70        CONTINUE
        R2=REAL(PSI)**2+AIMAG(PSI)**2
        R3=REAL(THETA)**2+AIMAG(THETA)**2
        R4=REAL(XI)**2+AIMAG(XI)**2
        R5=GAMMA-(R2*DELTA+R3*GAMMA+2.*REAL(PSI*LAMBDA*CONJG(THETA)))*R1
        R2=DELTA-(R3*DELTA+R4*GAMMA+2.*REAL(THETA*LAMBDA*CONJG(XI)))*R1
        GAMMA=R5                                        ! Eq. (8.D.46)
        DELTA=R2                                        ! Eq. (8.D.47)
        LAMBDA=LAMBDA+C3*CONJG(PSI)+C4*CONJG(THETA)     ! Eq. (8.D.48)
        IF (P .GT. 0.)  GO TO 80
        ISTAT=1
        RETURN
80      IF (DELTA .GT. 0. .AND. DELTA .LT. 1. .AND. GAMMA .GT. 0.
      *    .AND. GAMMA .LT. 1.)  GO TO 90
        ISTAT=2
        RETURN
C
C    Time update of AF vector; order updates of C,D vectors and GAMMA,
C    DELTA,LAMBDA scalars
C
90      R1=1./P
        R2=1./(DELTA*GAMMA-REAL(LAMBDA)**2-AIMAG(LAMBDA)**2) ! Eq. (8.D.41)
        EF=X(M+1)
        EB=X(N-M)
        DO 100 K=1,M
          EF=EF+AF(K)*X(M+1-K)                          ! Eq. (8.D.1)
100       EB=EB+CONJG(AF(K))*X(N-M+K)                   ! Eq. (8.D.2)
        C1=EB*R1                                        ! Eq. (8.D.28)
        C2=CONJG(EF)*R1                                 ! Eq. (8.D.29)
        C3=(CONJG(EB)*DELTA+EF*LAMBDA)*R2
        C4=(EF*GAMMA+CONJG(EB*LAMBDA))*R2
        DO 110 K=M,1,-1
          SAVE1=AF(K)
          AF(K)=SAVE1+C3*C(K)+C4*D(K)                   ! Eq. (8.D.38)
          C(K+1)=C(K)+C1*SAVE1                          ! Eq. (8.D.26)
110       D(K+1)=D(K)+C2*SAVE1                          ! Eq. (8.D.27)
        C(1)=C1
        D(1)=C2
        R3=REAL(EB)**2+AIMAG(EB)**2
        R4=REAL(EF)**2+AIMAG(EF)**2
        P=P-(R3*DELTA+R4*GAMMA+2.*REAL(EF*EB*LAMBDA))*R2  ! Eq. (8.D.42)
```

```
        DELTA=DELTA-R4*R1                          ! Eq. (8.D.32)
        GAMMA=GAMMA-R3*R1                          ! Eq. (8.D.33)
        LAMBDA=LAMBDA+CONJG(EF*EB)*R1              ! Eq. (8.D.35)
        IF (P .GT. 0.) GO TO 120
        ISTAT=3
        RETURN
120     IF (DELTA .GT. 0. .AND. DELTA .LT. 1. .AND. GAMMA .GT. 0.
       *     .AND. GAMMA .LT. 1.)  GO TO 1000
        ISTAT=4
        RETURN
        END
```

APPENDIX 11.B
PROGRAM FOR FACTORING A COMPLEX POLYNOMIAL

The following polynomial factoring algorithm is taken from a routine by Jenkins and Traub [1972]. A three-stage complex algorithm is used. The program finds the zeros one at a time in roughly increasing order of modulus and deflates the polynomial to one of lower degreee. Maximal degree is fixed internal to the subroutine at 99.

```
        SUBROUTINE CPOLY (OPR,OPI,DEGREE,ZEROR,ZEROI,FAIL)
C
C       Copyright 1972, Association for Computing Machinery.  Reprinted
C       with permission.
C
C       This program from M.A. Jenkins and J.F. Traub, "Zeros of a Complex
C       Polynomial," Communications of the ACM, vol.15, pp. 97-99, Feb. 1972.
C
C       Note that subroutine MCON sets up four variables for the precision
C       and floating-point arithmetic range of the VAX 11/780.
C
C       Finds the zeros of a complex polynomial.
C
C       OPR,OPI    - Double-precision vectors of real and imaginary parts
C                    of the coefficients in order of decreasing powers
C       DEGREE     - Integer degree of the polynomial
C       ZEROR,ZEROI - Output double-precision vectors of real and imaginary
C                    parts of the zeros
C       FAIL       - Output logical parameter; .TRUE. only if leading
C                    coefficient is zero or if CPOLY has found fewer than
C                    DEGREE zeros
C
C       The program has been written to reduce the chance of overflow
C       occurring.  If it does occur, there is still a possibility that the
C       zerofinder will work provided the overflowed quantity is replaced
C       by a large number.
C
        COMMON /GLOBAL/PR,PI,HR,HI,QPR,QPI,QHR,QHI,SHR,SHI,SR,SI,TR,TI,
       *             PVR,PVI,ARE,MRE,ETA,INFIN,NN
        REAL*8 SR,SI,TR,TI,PVR,PVI,ARE,MRE,ETA,INFIN
        REAL*8 PR(100),PI(100),HR(100),HI(100),QPR(100),QPI(100)
        REAL*8 QHR(100),QHI(100),SHR(100),SHI(100)
```

```
C    To change the size of the polynomials which can be solved, replace
C    the dimension of the array in the COMMON area.
     REAL*8 XX,YY,COSR,SINR,SMALNO,BASE,XXX,ZR,ZI,BND
     REAL*8 OPR(1),OPI(1),ZEROR(1),ZEROI(1),CMOD,SCALE,CAUCHY,DSQRT
     LOGICAL*4 FAIL,CONV
     INTEGER*4 DEGREE,CNT1,CNT2
C    Initialization of constants
     CALL MCON (ETA,INFIN,SMALNO,BASE)
     ARE = ETA
     MRE = 2.D0*DSQRT(2.D0)*ETA
     XX = .70710678D0
     YY = -XX
     COSR = -.069756474D0
     SINR = .99756405D0
     FAIL = .FALSE.
     NN=DEGREE+1
C    Algorithm fails if the leading coefficient is zero
     IF (OPR(1) .NE. 0.D0 .OR. OPI(1) .NE. 0.D0)  GO TO 10
          FAIL = .TRUE.
          RETURN
C    Remove the zeros at the origin, if any
10   IF (OPR(NN) .NE. 0.D0 .OR. OPI(NN) .NE. 0.D0)  GO TO 20
          IDNN2 = DEGREE-NN+2
          ZEROR(IDNN2) = 0.D0
          ZEROI(IDNN2) = 0.D0
          NN = NN-1
          GO TO 10
C    Make a copy of the coefficients
20   DO 30 I=1,NN
          PR(I) = OPR(I)
          PI(I) = OPI(I)
          SHR(I) = CMOD(PR(I),PI(I))
30        CONTINUE
C    Scale the polynomial
     BND = SCALE(NN,SHR,ETA,INFIN,SMALNO,BASE)
     IF (BND .EQ. 1.D0)  GO TO 40
     DO 35 I=1,NN
          PR(I) = BND*PR(I)
          PI(I) = BND*PI(I)
35        CONTINUE
C    Start the algorithm for one zero
40   IF (NN .GT. 2)  GO TO 50
     IF (NN .EQ. 1)  RETURN
C    Calculate the final zero and return
          CALL CDIVID (-PR(2),-PI(2),PR(1),PI(1),ZEROR(DEGREE),
     *                 ZEROI(DEGREE))
          RETURN
C    Calculate BND, a lower bound on the modulus of the zeros
50   DO 60 I=1,NN
          SHR(I) = CMOD(PR(I),PI(I))
60        CONTINUE
     BND = CAUCHY(NN,SHR,SHI)
C    Outer loop to control two major passes with different sequences
C    of shifts
     DO 100 CNT1=1,2
C    First stage calculation, no shift
          CALL NOSHFT (5)
C    Inner loop to select a shift
```

```
            DO 90 CNT2=1,9
C    Shift is chosen with modulus BND and amplitude rotated by 94 degrees
C    from the previous shift
                XXX = COSR*XX-SINR*YY
                YY = SINR*XX+COSR*YY
                XX = XXX
                SR = BND*XX
                SI = BND*YY
C    Second stage calculation, fixed shift
                CALL FXSHFT (10*CNT2,ZR,ZI,CONV)
                IF (.NOT. CONV)  GO TO 80
C    The second stage jumps directly to the third-stage iteration; if
C    successful, the zero is stored and the polynomial deflated.
                IDNN2 = DEGREE-NN+2
                ZEROR(IDNN2) = ZR
                ZEROI(IDNN2) = ZI
                NN = NN-1
                DO 70 I=1,NN
                  PR(I) = QPR(I)
                  PI(I) = QPI(I)
70              CONTINUE
                GO TO 40
80          CONTINUE
C    If the iteration is unsuccessful, another shift is chosen
90        CONTINUE
C    If nine shifts fail, the outer loop is repeated with another
C    sequence of shifts
100   CONTINUE
C    The zerofinder has failed on two major passes; return empty-handed
        FAIL = .TRUE.
        RETURN
        END



        SUBROUTINE NOSHFT (L1)
C    Computes the derivative polynomial as the initial H
C    polynomial and computes L1 no-shift H polynomials
C
        COMMON /GLOBAL/PR,PI,HR,HI,QPR,QPI,QHR,QHI,SHR,SHI,
       *              SR,SI,TR,TI,PVR,PVI,ARE,MRE,ETA,INFIN,NN
        REAL*8 SR,SI,TR,TI,PVR,PVI,ARE,MRE,ETA,INFIN
        REAL*8 PR(100),PI(100),HR(100),HI(100),QPR(100),QPI(100)
        REAL*8 QHR(100),QHI(100),SHR(100),SHI(100)
        REAL*8 XNI,T1,T2,CMOD
        N = NN-1
        NM1 = N-1
        DO 10 I=1,N
          XNI = NN-I
          HR(I) = XNI*PR(I)/FLOAT(N)
          HI(I) = XNI*PI(I)/FLOAT(N)
10      CONTINUE
        DO 50 JJ=1,L1
          IF (CMOD(HR(N),HI(N)) .LE. ETA*10.D0*CMOD(PR(N),PI(N)))
       *                GO TO 30
          CALL CDIVID (-PR(NN),-PI(NN),HR(N),HI(N),TR,TI)
          DO 20 I=1,NM1
            J = NN-I
            T1 = HR(J-1)
```

```
             T2 = HI(J-1)
             HR(J) = TR*T1-TI*T2+PR(J)
             HI(J) = TR*T2+TI*T1+PI(J)
20           CONTINUE
         HR(1) = PR(1)
         HI(1) = PI(1)
         GO TO 50
C    If the constant term is essentially zero, shift H coefficients
30       DO 40 I=1,NM1
             J = NN-I
             HR(J) = HR(J-1)
             HI(J) = HI(J-1)
40           CONTINUE
         HR(1) = 0.D0
         HI(1) = 0.D0
50       CONTINUE
      RETURN
      END



      SUBROUTINE FXSHFT (L2,ZR,ZI,CONV)
C    Computes L2 fixed-shift H polynomials and tests for convergence.
C    Initiates a variable-shift iteration and returns with the
C    approximate zero if successful.
C
C    L2    - Limit of fixed-shift steps
C    ZR,ZI - Approximate zero if CONV is .TRUE.
C    CONV  - Logical indicating convergence of stage three iteration
C
      COMMON /GLOBAL/PR,PI,HR,HI,QPR,QPI,QHR,QHI,SHR,SHI,SR,SI,
     *              TR,TI,PVR,PVI,ARE,MRE,ETA,INFIN,NN
      REAL*8 SR,SI,TR,TI,PVR,PVI,ARE,MRE,ETA,INFIN
      REAL*8 PR(100),PI(100),HR(100),HI(100),QPR(100),QPI(100)
      REAL*8 QHR(100),QHI(100),SHR(100),SHI(100)
      REAL*8 ZR,ZI,OTR,OTI,SVSR,SVSI,CMOD
      LOGICAL*4 CONV,TEST,PASD,BOOL
      N = NN-1
C    Evaluate P at S
      CALL POLYEV (NN,SR,SI,PR,PI,QPR,QPI,PVR,PVI)
      TEST = .TRUE.
      PASD = .FALSE.
C    Calculate first T = -P(S)/H(S)
      CALL CALCT (BOOL)
C    Main loop for one second-stage step
      DO 50 J=1,L2
         OTR = TR
         OTI = TI
C    Compute next H polynomial and new T
         CALL NEXTH (BOOL)
         CALL CALCT (BOOL)
         ZR = SR+TR
         ZI = SI+TI
C    Test for convergence, unless stage three has failed once or this
C    is the last H polynomial
         IF (BOOL .OR. .NOT. TEST .OR. J .EQ. L2)  GO TO 50
         IF (CMOD(TR-OTR,TI-OTI) .GE. .5D0*CMOD(ZR,ZI))  GO TO 40
            IF (.NOT. PASD)  GO TO 30
C    The weak convergence test has been passed twice; start the third-
```

```
C    stage iteration, after saving the current H polynomial and shift
              DO 10 I=1,N
                 SHR(I) = HR(I)
                 SHI(I) = HI(I)
10               CONTINUE
              SVSR = SR
              SVSI = SI
              CALL VRSHFT (10,ZR,ZI,CONV)
              IF (CONV) RETURN
C    The iteration failed to converge.  Turn off testing and restore H,
C    S,PV, and T
              TEST = .FALSE.
              DO 20 I=1,N
                 HR(I) = SHR(I)
                 HI(I) = SHI(I)
20               CONTINUE
              SR = SVSR
              SI = SVSI
              CALL POLYEV (NN,SR,SI,PR,PI,QPR,QPI,PVR,PVI)
              CALL CALCT (BOOL)
              GO TO 50
30        PASD = .TRUE.
          GO TO 50
40        PASD = .FALSE.
50     CONTINUE
C    Attempt an iteration with final H polynomial from second stage
       CALL VRSHFT (10,ZR,ZI,CONV)
       RETURN
       END



       SUBROUTINE VRSHFT (L3,ZR,ZI,CONV)
C    Carries out the third-stage iteration
C
C    L3    - Limit of steps in stage three
C    ZR,ZI - On entry contains the initial iterate; if the iteration
C            converges, it contains the final iterate on exit
C    CONV  - .TRUE. if iteration converges
C
       COMMON /GLOBAL/PR,PI,HR,HI,QPR,QPI,QHR,QHI,SHR,SHI,SR,SI,
      *              TR,TI,PVR,PVI,ARE,MRE,ETA,INFIN,NN
       REAL*8 SR,SI,TR,TI,PVR,PVI,ARE,MRE,ETA,INFIN
       REAL*8 PR(100),PI(100),HR(100),HI(100),QPR(100),QPI(100)
       REAL*8 QHR(100),QHI(100),SHR(100),SHI(100)
       REAL*8 ZR,ZI,MP,MS,OMP,RELSTP,R1,R2,CMOD,DSQRT,ERREV,TP
       LOGICAL*4 CONV,B,BOOL
       CONV = .FALSE.
       B = .FALSE.
       SR = ZR
       SI = ZI
C    Main loop for stage three
       DO 60 I=1,L3
C    Evaluate P at S and test for convergence
          CALL POLYEV (NN,SR,SI,PR,PI,QPR,QPI,PVR,PVI)
          MP = CMOD(PVR,PVI)
          MS = CMOD(SR,SI)
          IF (MP .GT. 20.DO*ERREV(NN,QPR,QPI,MS,MP,ARE,MRE)) GO TO 10
C    Polynomial value is smaller in value than a bound on the error
```

```
C    in evaluating P; terminate the iteration
              CONV = .TRUE.
              ZR = SR
              ZI = SI
              RETURN
10        IF (I .EQ. 1)  GO TO 40
          IF (B .OR. MP .LT. OMP .OR. RELSTP .GE. .05D0)  GO TO 30
C    Iteration has stalled.  Probably a cluster of zeros.  Do five
C    fixed-shift steps into the cluster to force one zero to dominate.
              TP = RELSTP
              B = .TRUE.
              IF (RELSTP .LT. ETA)  TP = ETA
              R1 = DSQRT(TP)
              R2 = SR*(1.D0+R1)-SI*R1
              SI = SR*R1+SI*(1.D0+R1)
              SR = R2
              CALL POLYEV (NN,SR,SI,PR,PI,QPR,QPI,PVR,PVI)
              DO 20 J=1,5
                  CALL CALCT (BOOL)
                  CALL NEXTH (BOOL)
20                CONTINUE
              OMP = INFIN
              GO TO 50
C    Exit if the polynomial value increases significantly
30        IF (MP*.1D0 .GT. OMP)  RETURN
40     OMP =MP
C    Calculate next iterate
50     CALL CALCT (BOOL)
       CALL NEXTH (BOOL)
       CALL CALCT (BOOL)
       IF (BOOL)  GO TO 60
       RELSTP = CMOD(TR,TI)/CMOD(SR,SI)
       SR = SR+TR
       SI = SI+TI
60     CONTINUE
       RETURN
       END


       SUBROUTINE CALCT (BOOL)
C    Computes T = -P(S)/H(S)
C
C    BOOL - Logical, set .TRUE. if H(S) is essentially zero
       COMMON /GLOBAL/PR,PI,HR,HI,QPR,QPI,QHR,QHI,SHR,SHI,SR,SI,
      *              TR,TI,PVR,PVI,ARE,MRE,ETA,INFIN,NN
       REAL*8 SR,SI,TR,TI,PVR,PVI,ARE,MRE,ETA,INFIN
       REAL*8 PR(100),PI(100),HR(100),HI(100),QPR(100),QPI(100)
       REAL*8 QHR(100),QHI(100),SHR(100),SHI(100)
       REAL*8 HVR,HVI,CMOD
       LOGICAL*4 BOOL
       N = NN-1
C    Evaluate H(S)
       CALL POLYEV (N,SR,SI,HR,HI,QHR,QHI,HVR,HVI)
       BOOL = CMOD(HVR,HVI) .LE. ARE*10.D0*CMOD(HR(N),HI(N))
       IF (BOOL)  GO TO 10
          CALL CDIVID (-PVR,-PVI,HVR,HVI,TR,TI)
          RETURN
10     TR = 0.D0
```

```
        TI = 0.D0
        RETURN
        END



        SUBROUTINE NEXTH (BOOL)
C    Calculates the next shifted H polynomial
C
C    BOOL - Logical, if .TRUE. H(S) is essentially zero
        COMMON /GLOBAL/PR,PI,HR,HI,QPR,QPI,QHR,QHI,SHR,SHI,SR,SI,
     *                 TR,TI,PVR,PVI,ARE,MRE,ETA,INFIN,NN
        REAL*8 SR,SI,TR,TI,PVR,PVI,ARE,MRE,ETA,INFIN
        REAL*8 PR(100),PI(100),HR(100),HI(100),QPR(100),QPI(100)
        REAL*8  QHR(100),QHI(100),SHR(100),SHI(100),T1,T2
        LOGICAL*4 BOOL
        N = NN-1
        IF (BOOL)  GO TO 20
          DO 10 J=2,N
            T1 = QHR(J-1)
            T2 = QHI(J-1)
            HR(J) = TR*T1-TI*T2+QPR(J)
            HI(J) = TR*T2+TI*T1+QPI(J)
10        CONTINUE
          HR(1) = QPR(1)
          HI(1) = QPI(1)
          RETURN
C    If H(S) is zero, replace H with QH
20      DO 30 J=2,N
          HR(J) = QHR(J-1)
          HI(J) = QHI(J-1)
30      CONTINUE
        HR(1) = 0.D0
        HI(1) = 0.D0
        RETURN
        END



        SUBROUTINE POLYEV (NN,SR,SI,PR,PI,QR,QI,PVR,PVI)
C    Evaluates a polynomial P at S by the Horner recurrence,
C    placing the partial sums in Q and the computed value in PV
        REAL*8 PR(NN),PI(NN),QR(NN),QI(NN),SR,SI,PVR,PVI,T
        QR(1) = PR(1)
        QI(1) = PI(1)
        PVR = QR(1)
        PVI = QI(1)
        DO 10 I=2,NN
          T = PVR*SR-PVI*SI+PR(I)
          PVI = PVR*SI+PVI*SR+PI(I)
          PVR = T
          QR(I) = PVR
          QI(I) = PVI
10      CONTINUE
        RETURN
        END



        REAL*8 FUNCTION ERREV(NN,QR,QI,MS,MP,ARE,MRE)
C    Bounds the error in evaluating the polynomial by the Horner recurrence
```

```
C
C     QR,QI   - The partial sums
C     MS      - Modulus of the point
C     MP      - Modulus of the polynomial value
C     ARE,MRE - Error bounds on complex addition and multiplication
        REAL*8 QR(NN),QI(NN),MS,MP,ARE,MRE,E,CMOD
        E = CMOD(QR(1),QI(1))*MRE/(ARE+MRE)
        DO 10 I=1,NN
          E = E*MS+CMOD(QR(I),QI(I))
10      CONTINUE
        ERREV = E*(ARE+MRE)-MP*MRE
        RETURN
        END


        REAL*8 FUNCTION CAUCHY(NN,PT,Q)
C     Cauchy computes a lower bound on the moduli of the zeros of a
C     polynomial - PT is the modulus of the coefficients
        REAL*8 Q(NN),PT(NN),X,XM,F,DX,DF,DABS,DEXP,DLOG
        PT(NN) = -PT(NN)
C     Compute upper estimate of bound
        N = NN-1
        X = DEXP((DLOG(-PT(NN))-DLOG(PT(1)))/FLOAT(N))
        IF (PT(N) .EQ. 0.D0)  GO TO 20
C     If Newton step at the origin is better, use it
        XM = -PT(NN)/PT(N)
        IF (XM .LT. X)  X = XM
C     Chop the interval (0,X) until F<=0
20      XM = X*.1D0
        F = PT(1)
        DO 30 I=2,NN
          F = F*XM+PT(I)
30      CONTINUE
        IF (F .LE. 0.D0)  GO TO 40
        X = XM
        GO TO 20
40      DX = X
C     Do Newton iteration until X converges to two decimal places
50      IF (DABS(DX/X) .LE. .005D0)  GO TO 70
        Q(1) = PT(1)
        DO 60 I=2,NN
          Q(I) = Q(I-1)*X+PT(I)
60      CONTINUE
        F = Q(NN)
        DF = Q(1)
        DO 65 I=2,N
          DF = DF*X+Q(I)
65      CONTINUE
        DX = F/DF
        X = X-DX
        GO TO 50
70      CAUCHY = X
        RETURN
        END


        REAL*8 FUNCTION SCALE(NN,PT,ETA,INFIN,SMALNO,BASE)
C     Returns a scale factor to multiply the coefficients of the
```

```
C     polynomial.  The scaling is done to avoid overflow and to
C     avoid undetected underflow interfering with the convergence
C     criterion.  The factor is a power of the base.
C
C     PT - Modulus of the coefficients of P
C     ETA,INFIN,SMALNO,BASE - Constants describing the floating-
C                             point arithmetic
      REAL*8 PT(NN),ETA,INFIN,SMALNO,BASE,HI,LO,MAX,MIN,X,SC
      REAL*8 DSQRT,DLOG
C     Find largest and smallest moduli of coefficients
      HI = DSQRT(INFIN)
      LO = SMALNO/ETA
      MAX = 0.D0
      MIN = INFIN
      DO 10 I=1,NN
        X = PT(I)
        IF (X .GT. MAX)  MAX = X
        IF (X .NE. 0.D0 .AND. X .LT. MIN)  MIN = X
10      CONTINUE
C     Scale only if there are very large or very small components.
      SCALE = 1.D0
      IF (MIN .GE. LO .AND. MAX .LE. HI)  RETURN
      X = LO/MIN
      IF (X .GT. 1.D0)  GO TO 20
        SC = 1.D0/(DSQRT(MAX)*DSQRT(MIN))
        GO TO 30
20    SC = X
      IF (INFIN/SC .GT. MAX)  SC = 1.D0
30    L = DLOG(SC)/DLOG(BASE)+.5D0
      SCALE = BASE**L
      RETURN
      END



      SUBROUTINE CDIVID (AR,AI,BR,BI,CR,CI)
C     Complex division C=A/B, avoiding overflow.
      REAL*8 AR,AI,BR,BI,CR,CI,R,D,T,INFIN,DABS
      IF (BR .NE. 0.D0 .OR. BI .NE. 0.D0)  GO TO 10
C     Division by zero, C=infinity
      CALL MCON (T,INFIN,T,T)
      CR = INFIN
      CI = INFIN
      RETURN
10    IF (DABS(BR) .GE. DABS(BI))  GO TO 20
      R = BR/BI
      D = BI+R*BR
      CR = (AR*R+AI)/D
      CI = (AI*R-AR)/D
      RETURN
20    R = BI/BR
      D = BR+R*BI
      CR = (AR+AI*R)/D
      CI = (AI-AR*R)/D
      RETURN
      END



      REAL*8 FUNCTION CMOD(R,I)
```

```
C     Modulus of a complex number avoiding overflow
      REAL*8 R,I,AR,AI,DABS,DSQRT
      AR = DABS(R)
      AI = DABS(I)
      IF (AR .GE. AI)  GO TO 10
        CMOD = AI*DSQRT(1.D0+(AR/AI)**2)
        RETURN
10    IF (AR .LE. AI)  GO TO 20
        CMOD = AR*DSQRT(1.D0+(AI/AR)**2)
        RETURN
20    CMOD = AR*DSQRT(2.D0)
      RETURN
      END



      SUBROUTINE MCON (ETA,INFINY,SMALNO,BASE)
C     MCON provides machine constants used in various parts of the program.
C     The user may either set them directly or use the statements below to
C     compute them.  The meaning of the four constants are:
C
C     ETA     - Maximum relative representation error which can be described
C               as the smallest positive floating-point number such that
C               1.D0+ETA is greater than 1.D0
C     INFINY  - The largest floating-point number
C     SMALNO  - The smallest positive floating-point number
C     BASE    - The base of the floating-point number system used
C
C     Let T be the number of base digits in each floating-point number
C     (double precision).  Then ETA is either .5*B**(1-T) or B**(1-T)
C     depending on whether rounding or truncation is used.
C     Let M be the largest exponent and N the smallest exponent in the
C     number system.  Then INFINY is (1-BASE**(-T))*BASE**M and SMALNO
C     is BASE**N.
C     The values for BASE,T,M,N below correspond to VAX 11/780
      REAL*8 ETA,INFINY,SMALNO,BASE
      INTEGER*4 M,N,T
      BASE = 2.D0
      T = 56
      M = 127
      N = -127
      ETA = BASE**(1-T)
      INFINY = BASE*(1.D0-BASE**(-T))*BASE**(M-1)
      SMALNO = (BASE**(N+3))/BASE**3
      RETURN
      END
```

APPENDIX 11.C
PROGRAM OF PRONY METHOD

This subroutine computes estimates of the complex exponential parameters h_k and z_k of Eq. (11.3). The usual least squares (METHOD = 1) Prony of Sec. 11.5 or the modified least squares (METHOD = 2) of Sec. 11.6 may be selected. To operate with real data, simply set the imaginary component of each input array element (X) to zero.

```
      SUBROUTINE PRONY (METHOD,N,IP,X,H,Z,ISTAT)
C
C     Solves for the exponential model parameters by the Prony method
C
C     Input parameters:
C
C       METHOD - Indicates desired method: 1 for regular Prony or 2
C                for modified Prony (integer)
C       N      - Number of data samples (integer)
C       IP     - Order of exponential model (integer); must be even
C                if METHOD=2
C       X      - Array of complex data samples X(1) through X(N)
C
C     Output parameters:
C
C       H      - Array of exponential model complex amplitudes
C       Z      - Array of exponential model complex exponents
C       ISTAT  - Integer status indicator at time of exit
C                0 - normal exit with no errors
C                1 - error exists in routine COVAR
C                2 - error exists in routine SYMCOVAR
C                3 - error exists in routine CPOLY
C                4 - error exists in routine CHOLESKY
C
C     Notes:
C
C       External arrays H,Z must be dimensioned  .GE. IP  and array  X
C       must be dimensioned .GE. N in calling program.  Internal array
C       B must be dimensioned .GE. IP(IP+1)/2 ; arrays A, ROOTR, ROOTI
C       must be dimensioned .GE. IP ; arrays PR,PI must be dimensioned
C       .GE. IP+1 .  Array G must be dimensioned .GE. IP/2 .
C
C       Subroutines COVAR (Appendix 8.B), SYMCOVAR (Appendix 14.A),
C       CPOLY (Appendix 14.B), and CHOLESKY (Appendix 3.A) are required
C
      COMPLEX X(1),H(1),Z(1),A(100),B(5050),G(100)
      REAL*4 PF,PB,PS,EPS
      REAL*8 PR(101),PI(101),ROOTR(100),ROOTI(100)
      REAL*8 C1,C2,C3,C4,C5,C6,SUMR,SUMI,SUM
      LOGICAL*4 FAIL
      ISTAT=0
      EPS=1.E-15
C     ****************************************************************
C     *    FIRST STEP:  Covariance or symmetric covariance method    *
C     ****************************************************************
      IF (METHOD .EQ. 2)  GO TO 20
      CALL COVAR (N,IP,X,PF,A,PB,B,JSTAT)
      IF (JSTAT .EQ. 0)  GO TO 5
        ISTAT=1
        RETURN
5     PR(1)=1.D0
      PI(1)=0.D0
      DO 10 K=1,IP
        PR(K+1)=REAL(A(K))
```

```
10      PI(K+1)=AIMAG(A(K))
        GO TO 50
C
20      CALL SYMCOVAR (N,IP,X,PS,G,JSTAT)
        IF (JSTAT .EQ. 0)  GO TO 30
        ISTAT=2
        RETURN
30      MHALF=IP/2
        M1=MHALF+1
        PR(M1)=1.DO
        PI(M1)=0.DO
        DO 40 K=1,MHALF
          PR(M1+K)=REAL(G(K))
          PI(M1+K)=-AIMAG(G(K))
          PR(M1-K)=REAL(G(K))
40        PI(M1-K)=AIMAG(G(K))
C     ****************************************************************
C     *    SECOND STEP:  Polynomial rooting for complex exponential   *
C     *                  parameters                                   *
C     ****************************************************************
50      CALL CPOLY (PR,PI,IP,ROOTR,ROOTI,FAIL)
        IF (FAIL .NE. .TRUE.)  GO TO 55
        ISTAT=3
        RETURN
55      DO 60 K=1,IP
60      Z(K)=CMPLX(SNGL(ROOTR(K)),SNGL(ROOTI(K)))
C     ****************************************************************
C     *    THIRD STEP:  Complex amplitude parameter estimates         *
C     ****************************************************************
        I=0
        DO 100 K=1,IP
          C1=ROOTR(K)
          C2=ROOTI(K)
          DO 80 J=1,K
            SUMR=C1*ROOTR(J)+C2*ROOTI(J)
            SUMI=C2*ROOTR(J)-C1*ROOTI(J)
            I=I+1
            C3=SUMR*SUMR+SUMI*SUMI
            SUM=C3-2.DO*SUMR+1.DO
            IF (SUM .EQ. 0.DO)  GO TO 70
            C3=C3**N
            C3=DSQRT(C3)
            C4=DATAN2(SUMI,SUMR)*N
            C5=C3*DCOS(C4)-1.DO
            C6=C3*DSIN(C4)
            SUMR=SUMR-1.DO
            SUMI=-SUMI
            C3=(SUMR*C5-SUMI*C6)/SUM
            C4=(SUMR*C6+SUMI*C5)/SUM
            B(I)=CMPLX(SNGL(C3),SNGL(C4))
            GO TO 80
70          B(I)=CMPLX(FLOAT(N),0.)
80          CONTINUE
          SUMR=REAL(X(1))
          SUMI=AIMAG(X(1))
          C2=-C2
          C3=1.DO
          C4=0.DO
```

```
         DO 90 J=2,N
           SUM=C3
           C3=SUM*C1-C4*C2
           C4=SUM*C2+C4*C1
           SUMR=SUMR+C3*REAL(X(J))-C4*AIMAG(X(J))
90         SUMI=SUMI+C4*REAL(X(J))+C3*AIMAG(X(J))
100     H(K)=CMPLX(SNGL(SUMR),SNGL(SUMI))
        CALL CHOLESKY (IP,EPS,B,H,JSTAT)
        IF (JSTAT .NE. 0) ISTAT=4
C    **************************************************************
C    *      Computation of residue could go here                 *
C    **************************************************************
        RETURN
        END
```

APPENDIX 11.D
PROGRAM FOR COMPUTING THE EXPONENTIAL PARAMETERS

The amplitudes, damping factors, frequencies, and phases estimated from the 64-point test data sequence obtained from subroutines PRONY and EXPARAMS for selection of the regular least squares Prony method (METHOD = 1), order IP = 15, and T = 1. second are:

FREQUENCY	DAMPING	AMPLITUDE	PHASE(rad)
-0.49163	-0.17371	0.13521	1.30373
-0.41007	-0.10256	0.59115	0.79553
-0.38589	-0.05828	0.51430	3.11306
-0.31345	-0.03573	0.23348	0.62037
-0.27254	-0.11726	0.26078	-2.61130
-0.23315	-0.00972	0.02494	0.27368
-0.15001	-0.00008	0.09466	-0.98327
-0.06426	-1.34236	1.00616	-1.33355
0.10001	-0.00009	0.10869	0.61524
0.20100	-0.00024	1.21926	1.03794
0.20914	0.00592	0.91410	1.64492
0.30043	-0.03858	0.38163	0.19629
0.33765	-0.06556	0.50696	1.65248
0.38231	-0.06997	0.20830	-1.50325
0.42640	-0.11518	0.20499	0.95396

The modified least squares Prony method (METHOD = 2) for order IP = 16 and T = 1. second will yield the following parameters:

FREQUENCY	DAMPING	AMPLITUDE	PHASE(rad)
-0.42996	0.00000	0.04092	0.30816
-0.39495	0.00000	0.12822	-1.81738
-0.35502	0.00000	0.02274	-0.10270
-0.31035	0.00000	0.12497	-0.11989
-0.26485	0.00000	0.05410	-0.93568

-0.22608	0.00000	0.03279	-1.13157
-0.15003	0.00000	0.10509	-0.91128
0.10002	0.00000	0.10017	0.59811
0.20021	0.00000	0.98100	1.23697
0.21014	0.00000	0.98191	1.30105
0.24917	0.00000	0.03746	-0.29225
0.30629	0.00000	0.15687	-0.44691
0.34351	0.00000	0.19537	0.73366
0.38368	0.00000	0.09891	0.00492
0.43086	0.00000	0.04702	1.38147
0.48952	0.00000	0.02784	1.76092 .

The listing of subroutine EXPARAMS follows.

```
      SUBROUTINE EXPARAMS (IP,T,H,Z,AMP,DAMP,FREQ,PHASE)
C
C   Routine that produces the real amplitude, damping, frequency, and
C   phase from the complex amplitude and exponential parameter arrays.
C
C   Input Parameters:
C
C     IP    - Order of exponential model (integer)
C     T     - Real variable representing the sample interval (sec.)
C     H     - Array of complex amplitude parameters, H(1) to H(IP)
C     Z     - Array of complex exponential parameters, Z(1) to Z(IP)
C
C   Output Parameters:
C
C     AMP   - Array of real amplitudes (arbitrary units)
C     DAMP  - Array of real damping factors (1/sec)
C     FREQ  - Array of real frequencies (Hz)
C     PHASE - Array of real phase (radians)
C
C   Notes:
C
C     External arrays H,Z,AMP,DAMP,FREQ,PHASE must be dimensioned
C     .GE. IP in the calling program.   If the original data was
C     data was real, the phase reported represents that of a
C     cosine waveform.
C
      COMPLEX H(1),Z(1)
      REAL AMP(1),DAMP(1),FREQ(1),PHASE(1)
      TWOPI=8.*ATAN(1.)
      DO 10 K=1,IP
        FREQ(K)=ATAN2(AIMAG(Z(K)),REAL(Z(K)))/(TWOPI*T)
        DAMP(K)=LOG(CABS(Z(K)))/T
        AMP(K)=CABS(H(K))
10      PHASE(K)=ATAN2(AIMAG(H(K)),REAL(H(K)))
      RETURN
      END
```

APPENDIX 11.E
PROGRAM FOR PRONY ENERGY SPECTRAL DENSITY

This subroutine computes the one-sided (set METHOD $= 1$) or two-sided (set METHOD $= 2$) Prony energy spectral density based on equations (11.50) and (11.54). The program returns one ESD value for each fractional frequency F input to the subroutine. Note that F must lie in the range $-.5 \leq F \leq .5$.

```
      SUBROUTINE ESD (METHOD,IP,T,F,H,Z,SD)
C
C     Routine to compute the one-sided or two-sided energy spectral
C     density of the exponential model at a given frequency F .
C
C     Input Parameters:
C
C       METHOD - Indicates desired ESD:  1 for one-sided or 2 for
C                two-sided (integer)
C       IP     - Order of the exponential model (integer)
C       T      - Real variable representing the sample interval (sec.)
C       F      - Real variable representing the fraction of the
C                sampling frequency (ranges from -.5 to .5)
C       H      - Array of complex amplitude parameters, H(1) to H(IP)
C       Z      - Array of complex exponential parameters, Z(1) to Z(IP)
C
C     Output Parameters:
C
C       SD     - Real energy spectral density value at frequency F
C
C     Notes:
C
C       External arrays H and Z must be dimensioned .GE. IP in the
C       calling program.
C
      COMPLEX H(1),Z(1),ZK,ZKC,ZI,SUM
      TWOPI=8.*ATAN(1.)
      ZI=CEXP(CMPLX(0.,-TWOPI*F))
      SUM=(0.,0.)
      IF (METHOD .EQ. 2)  GO TO 20
      DO 10 K=1,IP
10    SUM=SUM+H(K)/(1.-Z(K)*ZI)
      GO TO 40
20    DO 30 K=1,IP
      ZK=Z(K)
      ZKC=1./CONJG(ZK)
30    SUM=SUM+(H(K)*(ZK-ZKC)*ZI)/(1.-(ZK+ZKC)*ZI+ZK*ZKC*ZI*ZI)
40    SD=T*(REAL(SUM)**2+AIMAG(SUM)**2)
      RETURN
      END
```

12

MINIMUM VARIANCE
SPECTRAL ESTIMATION

12.1 INTRODUCTION

The minimum variance (MV) spectral estimator was originally introduced by Capon [1969, 1983] for use in multi-dimensional seismic array frequency-wavenumber analysis. Capon promoted the method as a high-resolution spectral analysis technique, although its resolution is actually between that of the AR spectral estimator and that of the classical spectral estimators. Lacoss [1971] reformulated Capon's original space-time analysis for application to one-dimensional time-series analysis and renamed the technique as the *maximum likelihood method* (MLM) of spectral estimation, due to the maximum likelihood and Gaussian process context used by Capon in his 1969 paper. MLM is not an accurate description because it is not a maximum likelihood estimate of a power spectral density (PSD) function. In fact, the MV spectral estimator is not a true PSD function because the area under the MV estimate does not represent the total power in the measured process, which should be a characteristic of a true PSD. The inverse transform of the MV estimator also does not match the autocorrelation sequence that is used to create the MV estimate, unlike AR methods that do match. Thus, MV will be a spectral estimate in that it describes relative component strengths over frequency, but it is not a true PSD estimator. It does have the virtue of yielding peak heights that are linearly proportional to the power of sinusoids present in the process. *Minimum variance* is more descriptive of the origin of the estimator, which is created by minimizing the

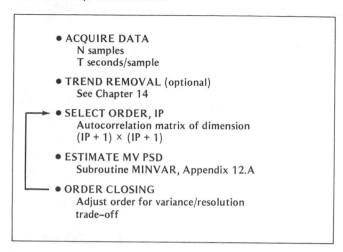

Figure 12.1   Flowchart of the minimum variance spectral estimator.

variance of the output of a narrowband filter that adapts to the spectral content of the input process at each frequency of interest.

12.2   SUMMARY

The MV spectral estimator is given by

$$P_{\text{MV}}(f) = \frac{T}{\mathbf{e}^H(f)\mathbf{R}_p^{-1}\mathbf{e}(f)} \quad , \tag{12.1}$$

in which $\mathbf{R}_p^{-1}$ is the inverse of the known or estimated autocorrelation matrix of dimension $(p+1) \times (p+1)$, $\mathbf{e}(f)$ is the complex sinusoid vector

$$\mathbf{e}(f) = \begin{pmatrix} 1 \\ \exp(j2\pi fT) \\ \vdots \\ \exp(j2\pi fpT) \end{pmatrix} \quad , \tag{12.2}$$

and T is the sample interval. Figure 12.1 is a flowchart of the MV spectral estimator. The key program is MINVAR, included in Appendix 12.A. MINVAR is based on a fast algorithm suggested by Musicus [1985] which incorporates the autocorrelation estimate implied by the Burg algorithm. The minimum variance spectral estimate of the 64-point test case for order $p = 15$ is shown in Fig. 12.2. It may be seen that the apparent resolution is poorer than that of the autoregressive spectral estimator of Chap. 8, but better than that of the classical correlogram method of Chap. 5. An order closing procedure can be used to trade-off resolution for spectral variance,

Figure 12.2 Minimum variance spectral estimate of the 64-point test sequence for $p = 15$.

as indicated in Fig. 12.1. Cox [1973] has quantified the resolution capability of the MV method.

12.3 DERIVATION OF THE MINIMUM VARIANCE SPECTRAL ESTIMATOR

Consider a transversal filter with $p + 1$ coefficients $a[0]$, $a[1]$,..., $a[p]$. The filter output $y[n]$ to the input $x[n]$ is given by the convolution

$$y[n] = \sum_{k=0}^{p} a[k]x[n-k] = \mathbf{x}^T[n]\mathbf{a} \quad , \tag{12.3}$$

in which the vectors $\mathbf{x}[n]$ and $\mathbf{a}$ of dimension $p + 1$ are defined as

$$\mathbf{x}[n] = \begin{pmatrix} x[n] \\ x[n-1] \\ \vdots \\ x[n-p] \end{pmatrix} \quad , \quad \mathbf{a} = \begin{pmatrix} a[0] \\ a[1] \\ \vdots \\ a[p] \end{pmatrix} \quad . \tag{12.4}$$

The filter output variance is simply

$$\rho = \mathcal{E}\{|y[n]|^2\} = \mathcal{E}\{\mathbf{a}^H\mathbf{x}^*[n]\mathbf{x}^T[n]\mathbf{a}\} = \mathbf{a}^H\mathcal{E}\{\mathbf{x}^*[n]\mathbf{x}^T[n]\}\mathbf{a} = \mathbf{a}^H\mathbf{R}_p\mathbf{a} \quad , \tag{12.5}$$

in which the $(p+1) \times (p+1)$ Toeplitz autocorrelation matrix is

$$\mathbf{R}_p = \begin{pmatrix} r_{xx}[0] & \cdots & r_{xx}^*[p] \\ \vdots & \ddots & \vdots \\ r_{xx}[p] & \cdots & r_{xx}[0] \end{pmatrix} \quad . \tag{12.6}$$

The output variance of Eq. (12.5) is similar to the linear prediction error filter variance of Eq. (7.4), except that $a[0]$ is arbitrary here rather than constrained to be unity. The coefficients are to be selected so that, at a frequency f_0 under consideration, the frequency response of the filter has unit gain. This constraint can be represented as

$$\sum_{k=0}^{p} a[k] \exp(-j2\pi f_0 pT) = \mathbf{e}^H(f_0)\mathbf{a} = 1 \quad , \tag{12.7}$$

in which the vector $\mathbf{e}(f_0)$ of dimension $p+1$ was defined by Eq. (12.2). A sinusoid of frequency f_0 that is input to the filter would, therefore, be undistorted at the filter output. In order to reject components of the spectrum not near f_0, simply minimize the output variance, Eq. (12.5), subject to the unity frequency response constraint, Eq. (12.7). The constrained minimum variance solution for the filter coefficients can be shown [McDonough, 1983] to satisfy

$$\mathbf{a}_{\mathrm{MV}} = \frac{\mathbf{R}_p^{-1}\mathbf{e}(f_0)}{\mathbf{e}^H(f_0)\mathbf{R}_p^{-1}\mathbf{e}(f_0)} \quad . \tag{12.8}$$

Substitution of Eq. (12.8) into Eq. (12.5) yields the minimum variance

$$\rho_{\mathrm{MV}} = \frac{1}{\mathbf{e}^H(f_0)\mathbf{R}_p^{-1}\mathbf{e}(f_0)} \quad . \tag{12.9}$$

The output variance serves as a good indicator of power in the input spectrum in the vicinity of f_0. A different optimum variance is obtained for each f_0 selected. The filter adapts its shape across the frequency range to the process autocorrelation function.

An appropriate *minimum variance* (MV) *spectral estimator* that may be deduced from Eq. (12.9) is

$$P_{\mathrm{MV}}(f) = T\rho_{\mathrm{MV}} = \frac{T}{\mathbf{e}^H(f)\mathbf{R}_p^{-1}\mathbf{e}(f)} \tag{12.10}$$

defined for $-1/2T \leq f \leq 1/2T$. The sample interval T gives Eq. (12.10) units of power per Hz, appropriate for a power spectral density. The MV spectral estimator is not a true PSD, however. Consider a white noise process of variance ρ_w. It can be shown (see the Problems) that the MV spectral estimate of a white noise process is

$$P_{\mathrm{MV}}(f) = \frac{T\rho_w}{p+1} \quad , \tag{12.11}$$

where $p+1$ is the dimension of the autocorrelation matrix of Eq. (12.6). The true PSD is, of course, $T\rho_w$. Other interpretations and modifications of the MV spectral estimator have been provided by Barnard [1969], Marzetta [1983], Lagunas and Gasull [1984], and Marzetta and Lang [1983, 1984]. Marzetta and Lang [1983] have shown, for example, that the MV relationship (12.10) can be interpreted as providing an upper bound on the weighted power spectral density of an unknown random process, some of whose correlations have been measured.

It can be shown (see the Problems and Lacoss [1971]) that a complex sinusoid in white noise with autocorrelation

$$r_{xx}[k] = P \exp(j2\pi f_0 kT) + \rho_w \delta[k] \tag{12.12}$$

has a MV spectral estimator value at $f = f_0$ of

$$P_{\mathrm{MV}}(f_0) = \frac{T\rho_w}{P}(1 + pP/\rho_w) \quad . \tag{12.13}$$

If the signal-to-noise ratio P/ρ_w is very high, then

$$P_{\mathrm{MV}}(f_0) \approx PT \quad , \tag{12.14}$$

which is the power of the sinusoid scaled by T. Peaks in the MV spectral estimator will be,therefore, approximately *linearly* proportional to power when the signal-to-noise ratio is high and the spectral lines are sufficiently separated, unlike the AR PSD estimator that was proportional to the *square* of the power. However, the area under the MV PSD curve is proportional to the square root of the sinusoid power, an indicator that the MV PSD is not a true PSD. Capon and Goodman [1971] have shown that the MV PSD has a mean and a variance that behaves much like the averaged periodogram (i.e., the variance is reduced linearly as the number of data segments averaged increases).

In practice, an estimate of the autocorrelation matrix, $\hat{\mathbf{R}}_p$, must be used when only data samples are available. A better approach, using the Burg algorithm in lieu of the autocorrelation matrix estimate, is discussed in the next section.

12.4   RELATIONSHIP OF MV AND AR SPECTRAL ESTIMATORS

An explicit relationship exists between the MV and AR spectral estimators when the autocorrelation sequence is known. The inverse of the Toeplitz autocorrelation matrix was shown in Chap. 3 [Eq. (3.166)] to be expressible as

$$\mathbf{R}_p^{-1} = \mathbf{A}_p \mathbf{P}_p^{-1} \mathbf{A}_p^H \quad , \tag{12.15}$$

in which $\mathbf{A}_p$ is a $(p+1) \times (p+1)$ matrix of the AR parameters from order 0 to order p

$$\mathbf{A}_p = \begin{pmatrix} 1 & 0 & \cdots & 0 \\ a_p[1] & 1 & \cdots & 0 \\ a_p[2] & a_{p-1}[1] & \cdots & 0 \\ \vdots & \vdots & \ddots & \vdots \\ a_p[p] & a_{p-1}[p-1] & \cdots & 1 \end{pmatrix} \tag{12.16}$$

and $\mathbf{P}_p^{-1}$ is a $(p+1) \times (p+1)$ diagonal matrix of inverted white noise variances for the corresponding orders

$$\mathbf{P}_p^{-1} = \begin{pmatrix} 1/\rho_p & 0 & \cdots & 0 \\ 0 & 1/\rho_{p-1} & \cdots & 0 \\ \vdots & \vdots & \ddots & \vdots \\ 0 & 0 & \cdots & 1/\rho_0 \end{pmatrix} . \tag{12.17}$$

Substituting Eq. (12.15) into the reciprocal MV spectral function (12.1) yields

$$\frac{1}{P_{\mathrm{MV}}(p,f)} = \frac{1}{T}\mathbf{e}^H(f)\mathbf{R}_{xx}^{-1}\mathbf{e}(f) = \frac{1}{T}\mathbf{e}^H(f)\mathbf{A}_p\mathbf{P}_p^{-1}\mathbf{A}_p^H\mathbf{e}(f)$$

$$= \frac{1}{T}\sum_{k=0}^{p}\frac{1}{\rho_k}\left|\sum_{m=0}^{k}a_k[m]\exp(-j2\pi fmT)\right|^2 = \sum_{k=0}^{p}\frac{1}{P_{\mathrm{AR}}(k,f)} ,$$

$$\tag{12.18}$$

where notation $P(k,f)$ is used to indicate a PSD of order k with frequency f [Burg, 1972]. The assumption $a_k[0] = 1$ is made for all orders $0 \leq k \leq p$. Thus, the reciprocal of the minimum variance spectral estimator is equal to the average of the reciprocals of the autoregressive spectral estimators from order 0 to order p. The lower resolution of the MV spectral estimate relative to the AR estimate observed in practice is, therefore, due to the averaging effect of low-order AR spectra of least resolution mixed with high-order AR spectra of highest resolution. The MV method, though, still has greater resolution than classical PSD estimators in higher signal-to-noise-level conditions. The variance of the MV spectral estimator has been observed empirically for large data records to be less than an AR PSD estimator of identical order p [Lacoss, 1971]. The variance reduction may also be attributed to the averaging effect of Eq. (12.18).

Equation (12.18) represents a *frequency*-domain relationship between the MV and AR spectral estimators. A *time*-domain relationship can also be developed [Musicus, 1985]. The pth order AR PSD estimator may alternatively be expressed as

$$P_{\mathrm{AR}}(f) = \frac{T\rho_p}{\left|1 + \sum_{k=1}^{p}a_p[k]\exp(-j2\pi fkT)\right|^2} = \frac{T}{\sum_{k=-p}^{p}\psi_{\mathrm{AR}}[k]\exp(-j2\pi fkT)} \tag{12.19}$$

by expanding its denominator. The $\psi_{\mathrm{AR}}[k]$ coefficients are calculated from the correlation of the AR parameters

$$\psi_{\mathrm{AR}}[k] = \begin{cases} \dfrac{1}{\rho_p}\displaystyle\sum_{i=0}^{p-k}a_p[k+i]a_p^*[i] & \text{for } 0 \leq k \leq p \\ \psi_{\mathrm{AR}}^*[-k] & \text{for } -1 \geq k \geq -p , \end{cases} \tag{12.20}$$

in which $a_p[0] = 1$ is assumed, by definition.

The MV spectral estimator may be expressed in a similar fashion by first recalling the form of the inverse of a Hermitian Toeplitz matrix $\mathbf{R}_p$ is [see Eq. (3.160)]

$$\mathbf{R}_p^{-1} = \frac{1}{\rho_p}\mathbf{T}_p\mathbf{T}_p^H - \frac{1}{\rho_p}\mathbf{S}_p\mathbf{S}_p^H \quad , \tag{12.21}$$

in which the triangular Toeplitz matrix $\mathbf{T}_p$ is

$$\mathbf{T}_p = \begin{pmatrix} 1 & 0 & \cdots & 0 & 0 \\ a_p[1] & 1 & \cdots & 0 & 0 \\ \vdots & \vdots & \ddots & \vdots & \vdots \\ a_p[p-1] & a_p[p-2] & \cdots & 1 & 0 \\ a_p[p] & a_p[p-1] & \cdots & a_p[1] & 1 \end{pmatrix} \tag{12.22}$$

and the triangular Toeplitz matrix $\mathbf{S}_p$ is

$$\mathbf{S}_p = \begin{pmatrix} 0 & 0 & \cdots & 0 & 0 \\ a_p^*[p] & 0 & \cdots & 0 & 0 \\ \vdots & \vdots & \ddots & \vdots & \vdots \\ a_p^*[2] & a_p^*[3] & \cdots & 0 & 0 \\ a_p^*[1] & a_p^*[2] & \cdots & a_p^*[p] & 0 \end{pmatrix} . \tag{12.23}$$

Substituting Eq. (12.21) into Eq. (12.10) for the inverse $\mathbf{R}_p^{-1}$ will yield, after extensive algebra,

$$P_{\mathrm{MV}}(f) = \frac{T}{\displaystyle\sum_{k=-p}^{p} \psi_{\mathrm{MV}}[k]\exp(-j2\pi fkT)} . \tag{12.24}$$

The $\psi_{\mathrm{MV}}[k]$ coefficients are calculated as a linearly weighted (windowed) correlation of AR parameters

$$\psi_{\mathrm{MV}}[k] = \begin{cases} \dfrac{1}{\rho_p}\displaystyle\sum_{i=0}^{p-k}(p+1-k-2i)a_p[k+i]a_p^*[i] & \text{for } 0 \le k \le p \\[2mm] \psi_{\mathrm{MV}}^*[-k] & \text{for } -1 \ge k \ge -p. \end{cases} \tag{12.25}$$

Computations proportional to p^2 are required to calculate the set of $\psi_{\mathrm{MV}}[k]$ coefficients once. An FFT, such as that in Appendix 2.A, may then be used to evaluate the alternative representation (12.25) of the MV spectral estimator over a range of frequencies. This is more computationally efficient than direct evaluation of the original MV spectral estimator function (12.10), which requires p^3 operations to invert $\mathbf{R}_p$ and p^2 operations for each frequency to be evaluated.

12.5   IMPLEMENTATION OF THE MINIMUM VARIANCE SPECTRAL ESTIMATOR

The most computationally efficient approach to implement the MV spectral estimator uses the four steps

- Compute a sequence of autocorrelation estimates from the data.
- Solve the Yule-Walker equations for the AR parameters using the Levinson algorithm.
- Correlate the AR parameters to yield the $\psi_{MV}[k]$ coefficients; make use of Eq. (12.25).
- Evaluate the MV spectral estimator over frequency using Eq. (12.24) and an FFT algorithm.

Better results can be obtained in practice by replacing the first two steps above with any of the AR parameter estimators of Chap. 8. For example, the first two steps can be replaced with

- Estimate the AR coefficients with the Burg algorithm.

The use of the Burg algorithm means that the implied autocorrelation function is derived from a Toeplitz matrix. Appendix 12.A contains subroutine MINVAR to compute the MV spectral estimate from a set of complex data samples using the procedure above. It uses the Burg algorithm for the first step.

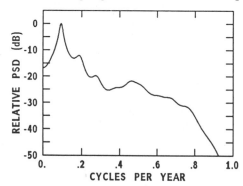

Figure 12.3   Minimum variance spectral estimate of the filtered sunspot numbers, using $p = 32$.

12.6   APPLICATION TO SUNSPOT NUMBERS

Figure 12.3 is a spectral estimate produced from PSD values generated by subroutine MINVAR using the filtered sunspot number sequence as input. An order of $p = 32$ was selected, comparable to the autoregressive spectral estimates of Chap. 8. The two highest peaks are located at .0938 cycle per year (10.67 years per cycle) and .1870 cycle per year (5.35 years per cycle).

REFERENCES

Barnard, T. E., Analytical Studies of Techniques for the Computation of High-Resolution Wavenumber Spectra, Special Report No. 9 prepared by *Texas Instruments, Inc.* for the Advanced Research Projects Agency under contract F33657-68-C-0867, May 1969.

Burg, J. P., The Relationship between Maximum Entropy and Maximum Likelihood Spectra, *Geophysics*, vol. 37, pp. 375–376, April 1972.

Capon, J., High-Resolution Frequency-Wavenumber Spectrum Analysis, *Proc. IEEE*, vol. 57, pp. 1408–1418, August 1969.

Capon, J., Maximum-Likelihood Spectral Estimation, Chapter 5 in *Nonlinear Methods of Spectral Analysis*, 2nd ed., S. Haykin, ed., Springer-Verlag, New York, 1983.

Capon, J., and N. R. Goodman, Probability Distribution for Estimators of the Frequency-Wavenumber Spectrum, *Proc. IEEE*, vol. 58, pp. 1785–1786, October 1970; corrections in vol. 59, p. 112, January 1971.

Cox, H., Resolving Power and Sensitivity to Mismatch of Optimum (Line) Array Processors, *J. Acoust. Soc. Am.*, vol. 54, pp. 771–785, 1973.

Lacoss, R. T., Data Adaptive Spectral Analysis Methods, *Geophysics*, vol. 36, pp. 661–675, August 1971.

Lagunas, M. A., and A. Gasull, Measuring True Spectral Density from ML Filters, *Proceedings of the 1984 IEEE International Conference on Acoustics, Speech, and Signal Processing*, San Diego, Calif., pp. 14.10.1–14.10.4, March 1984.

Marzetta, T. L., A New Interpretation for Capon's Maximum Likelihood Method of Frequency-Wavenumber Spectral Estimation, *IEEE Trans. Acoust. Speech Signal Process.*, vol. ASSP-31, pp. 445–449, April 1983.

Marzetta, T. L., and S. W. Lang, New Interpretations for the MLM and DASE Spectral Estimators, *Proceedings of the 1983 IEEE International Conference on Acoustics, Speech, and Signal Processing*, Boston, Mass., pp. 844–846, April 1983.

Marzetta, T. L., and S. W. Lang, Power Spectral Density Bounds, *IEEE Trans. Inform. Theory*, vol. IT-30, pp. 117–122, January 1984.

McDonough, R. N., Application of the Maximum-Likelihood Method and the Maximum-Entropy Method to Array Processing, Chapter 6 in *Nonlinear Methods of Spectral Analysis*, 2nd ed., S. Haykin, ed., Springer-Verlag, New York, 1983.

Musicus, B., Fast MLM Power Spectrum Estimation from Uniformly Spaced Correlations, *IEEE Trans. Acoust. Speech Signal Process.*, vol. ASSP-33, pp. 1333–1335, October 1985.

PROBLEMS

1. Prove Eqs. (12.20) and (12.25).

2. Prove that

$$\frac{1}{P_{AR}(p, f)} = \frac{1}{P_{MV}(p, f)} - \frac{1}{P_{MV}(p-1, f)} \quad .$$

3. Substitute subroutine YULEWALKER for subroutine BURG in program MINVAR. Compute a spectral estimate with the modified MINVAR program using the test

sequence of Appendix II. How does the resulting spectral plot compare with that of Fig. 12.2? Account for any differences.

4. Using the analytic form of the autocorrelation sequence up to lag p for a single sinusoid in white noise [Eq. (12.12)], develop the analytic form of the solution for (12.8) for the minimum variance filter coefficients. Plot the filter response for the case $p = 10$. Note the sidelobes. How could a weighting of the autocorrelation sequence be used to suppress the sidelobes?

APPENDIX 12.A
PROGRAM OF MINIMUM VARIANCE SPECTRAL ESTIMATOR

This subroutine implements the minimum variance spectral estimator using the algorithm of Sec. 12.5. Using N = 64, order IP = 15, and T = 1. second, the following selected PSD values were produced by MINVAR when processing the test sequence of Appendix II

$$
\begin{aligned}
\text{PSD}(1) &= 0.170584\text{E-}06 \\
\text{PSD}(1000) &= 0.101236\text{E-}01 \\
\text{PSD}(2000) &= 0.139269\text{E-}02 \\
\text{PSD}(3000) &= 0.418217\text{E-}02 \\
\text{PSD}(4000) &= 0.128422\text{E-}06 \\
\text{PSD}(4096) &= 0.169758\text{E-}06
\end{aligned}
$$

```
      SUBROUTINE MINVAR (N,IP,T,X,PSD,ISTAT)
C
C     This subroutine computes the minimum variance spectral estimate using
C     the Musicus procedure.   The Burg algorithm is used for estimation of
C     the autoregressive parameters.
C
C     Input Parameters:
C
C     N    - Number of data samples
C     IP   - Dimension of correlation matrix (AR model order is 1 less)
C     T    - Sample interval
C     X    - Array of complex data samples X(1) to X(N)
C
C     Output Parameters:
C
C     PSD   - Array of real power spectral density values
C     ISTAT - Status indicator
C
C     Notes:
C
C     External array X must be dimensioned .GE. N and array PSD must be
C     dimensioned .GE. NPSD in the calling program.   Internal array A
C     must be dimensioned .GE. IP-1 and arrays PSI,W must be dimensioned
C     .GE. NPSD.   External subroutines used:   BURG (Appendix 8.B), PREFFT
C     and FFT (Appendix 2.C)
C
      PARAMETER NPSD=4096    ! No. of PSD values (must be a power of two)
```

```
        COMPLEX X(1),A(50),PSI(NPSD),W(NPSD),SUM
        REAL PSD(1)
        M=IP-1
        CALL BURG (N,M,X,P,A,ISTAT)   ! Compute AR coefficients
        IF (ISTAT .NE. 0)  RETURN
        DO 10 K=M,1,-1
10        A(K+1)=A(K)
        A(1)=(1.,0.)
        DO 30 K=0,M            ! Compute the psi coefficients
          SUM=(0.,0.)
          MK=M+1-K
C   Correlate the autoregressive parameters
        DO 20 I=0,M-K
20          SUM=SUM+FLOAT(MK-2*I)*CONJG(A(I+1))*A(I+1+K)   ! Eq. (12.25)
          SUM=SUM/P
          IF (K .NE. 0)  PSI(NPSD+1-K)=CONJG(SUM)
30        PSI(K+1)=SUM
C   Zero pad the remaining PSI terms
        DO 40 K=M+2,NPSD-M
40        PSI(K)=(0.,0.)
        CALL PREFFT (NPSD,0,NEXP,W)
        CALL FFT (NPSD,0,1.,NEXP,W,PSI)                    ! Compute FFT of denominator
C   Invert the psi terms at this point to get PSD values
        DO 50 K=1,NPSD
50        PSD(K)=T/REAL(PSI(K))                            ! Eq. (12.24)
        RETURN
        END
```

13

EIGENANALYSIS-BASED
FREQUENCY ESTIMATION

13.1 INTRODUCTION

A class of spectral techniques based on an eigenanalysis of an autocorrelation matrix or one of the data matrices of Chap. 8 have been promoted in the research literature as having better resolution and better frequency-estimation characteristics than spectral techniques such as autoregressive or Prony, especially at lower signal-to-noise ratios, where these latter techniques often fail to resolve close sinusoids or other narrowband spectral components. Some support for this claim has previously been demonstrated in Sec. 11.9. Singular value decomposition was used there to provide more accurate estimates of the frequency and damping factors for a process consisting of two damped exponentials in noise. The basis for the improved performance of the eigenanalysis techniques is presented in this chapter. Key to the performance is the division of the information in the autocorrelation matrix or the data matrix into two vector subspaces, one a *signal* subspace and the other a *noise* subspace.

Functions of the vectors in either the signal or noise subspaces can be used to create *frequency estimators* that, when plotted, show sharp peaks at the frequency locations of sinusoids or other narrowband spectral components. These are not true PSD estimators because they do not preserve the measured process power nor can the autocorrelation sequence be recovered by Fourier transforming the frequency estimators. Included in this class of eigenanalysis-based frequency estimators are

- ● ACQUIRE DATA
  N samples
  T samples/second

- ● TREND REMOVAL (optional)
  See Chapter 14

- ● SELECT INPUT PARAMETERS
  Order of data matrix, IP
  Number of signal components, NSIG

- ● COMPUTE FREQUENCY ESTIMATOR
  Subroutine EIGENFREQ, Appendix 13.A
  Make one of the following selections:
  — MUSIC algorithm (METHOD = 0)
  — EV algorithm (METHOD = 1)

Figure 13.1   Flowchart of two eigenanalysis-based frequency estimators.

the Pisarenko harmonic decomposition (PHD) and the multiple signal classification (MUSIC) algorithms.

13.2 SUMMARY

Figure 13.1 is a flowchart of the processing steps needed to generate two types of eigenfrequency estimators: the MUSIC and EV algorithms, for which a computer program is included. Figure 13.2 illustrates the eigenvector (EV) algorithm response to the 64-point test case. Figure 13.3 illustrates the MUSIC algorithm response to the same test signal. Both algorithms require as inputs the autocorrelation matrix order IP and an estimate of the number of signal components NSIG. Note that NSIG < IP. These figures do not show the ultimate performance of these methods, which work best for processes consisting of narrowband signals in white noise; the colored noise of the test case causes a degradation in the performance because these methods were not designed to handle this case. The Pisarenko harmonic decompostion technique is summarized in Sec. 13.6.

13.3 EIGENANALYIS OF AUTOCORRELATION MATRIX FOR SINUSOIDS IN WHITE NOISE

It was shown in Chap. 4 that the ACS for the wide-sense stationary process consisting of M *complex* sinusoids of random phase in additive complex white noise is

$$r_{xx}[k] = \sum_{i=1}^{M} P_i \exp(j2\pi f_i kT) + \rho_w \delta[k] \quad , \tag{13.1}$$

Figure 13.2   EigenVector method (EV) frequency estimate of the 64-point test sequence using an order IP = 15 data matrix and NSIG = 11 (4 noise subspace eigenvectors).

Figure 13.3   MUltiple SIgnal Classification method (MUSIC) frequency estimate of the 64-point test sequence using an order IP = 15 data matrix and NSIG = 11 (4 noise subspace eigenvectors).

in which P_i is the power of the ith sinusoid and ρ_w is the noise variance. If the process consists of M *real* sinusoids in additive real white noise, the ACS is

$$
\begin{aligned}
r_{xx}[k] &= \sum_{i=1}^{M} P_i \cos(2\pi f_i kT) + \rho_w \delta[k] \\
&= \sum_{i=1}^{M} \frac{P_i}{2} \left[\exp(j2\pi f_i kT) + \exp(-j2\pi f_i kT) \right] + \rho_w \delta[k] \quad .
\end{aligned}
\tag{13.2}
$$

The pth-order Toeplitz autocorrelation matrix of dimension $(p+1) \times (p+1)$ is

$$
\mathbf{R}_p = \begin{pmatrix} r_{xx}[0] & \cdots & r_{xx}^*[p] \\ \vdots & \ddots & \vdots \\ r_{xx}[p] & \cdots & r_{xx}[0] \end{pmatrix}
\tag{13.3}
$$

for the case of complex sinusoids in white noise has the structure

$$\mathbf{R}_p = \sum_{i=1}^{M} P_i \mathbf{s}_i \mathbf{s}_i^H + \rho_w \mathbf{I} \quad , \tag{13.4}$$

in which $\mathbf{I}$ is a $(p+1) \times (p+1)$ identity matrix and $\mathbf{s}_i$ is a signal vector of dimension $p+1$ carrying the frequency information of the ith sinusoid

$$\mathbf{s}_i = \begin{pmatrix} 1 \\ \exp(j2\pi f_i T) \\ \vdots \\ \exp(j2\pi f_i pT) \end{pmatrix} . \tag{13.5}$$

Matrix $\mathbf{R}_p$ can be expressed as the sum of a signal autocorrelation matrix and a noise autocorrelation matrix

$$\mathbf{R}_p = \mathbf{S}_p + \mathbf{W}_p \quad , \tag{13.6}$$

in which

$$\mathbf{S}_p = \sum_{i=1}^{M} P_i \mathbf{s}_i \mathbf{s}_i^H \tag{13.7}$$

$$\mathbf{W}_p = \rho_w \mathbf{I} \tag{13.8}$$

are $(p+1) \times (p+1)$ matrices. If an autocorrelation matrix has an order greater than the number of complex sinusoids $(p > M)$, then the signal matrix $\mathbf{S}_p$ will have rank M (because each vector outer product $\mathbf{s}_i \mathbf{s}_i^H$ is a rank 1 matrix). The noise matrix will have the full rank $p+1$.

In an analogous manner, the pth-order autocorrelation matrix for the case of M real sinusoids in white noise has the structure

$$\mathbf{R}_p = \sum_{i=1}^{M} \frac{P_i}{2} \left[\mathbf{s}_i \mathbf{s}_i^H + \mathbf{s}_i^* \mathbf{s}_i^T \right] + \rho_w \mathbf{I} \quad . \tag{13.9}$$

The signal matrix $\mathbf{S}_p$ in this case will have rank $2M$. Discussions from this point will concentrate on the complex case; the real case is generally a simple extension of the complex case with a change in rank from M to $2M$.

The signal matrix will have the eigendecomposition

$$\mathbf{S}_p = \sum_{i=1}^{p+1} \lambda_i \mathbf{v}_i \mathbf{v}_i^H \tag{13.10}$$

in which the eigenvalues have been ordered in decreasing value $\lambda_1 \geq \lambda_2 \geq \ldots \geq \lambda_{p+1}$ and the eigenvectors are orthonormal ($\mathbf{v}_i^H \mathbf{v}_j = 0$ if $i \neq j$ or 1 if $i = j$). It can be shown [Noble and Daniell, 1977] that a matrix of dimension $p + 1$ with rank $M < p + 1$ will have $p - M + 1$ zero eigenvalues. The eigendecomposition of Eq. (13.10) can then be written as

$$\mathbf{S}_p = \sum_{i=1}^{M} \lambda_i \mathbf{v}_i \mathbf{v}_i^H \quad . \tag{13.11}$$

The eigenvectors $\mathbf{v}_1, \ldots, \mathbf{v}_M$, known as the *principal eigenvectors*, span the same *signal subspace* as the signal vectors $\mathbf{s}_1, \ldots, \mathbf{s}_M$. This means that any principal eigenvector must be expressible as a linear combination of the signal vectors

$$\mathbf{v}_i = \sum_{k=1}^{M} \beta_{ik} \mathbf{s}_k \tag{13.12}$$

for $1 \leq i \leq M$. To be an eigenvector of $\mathbf{S}_p$, then

$$\mathbf{S}_p \mathbf{v}_i = \lambda_i \mathbf{v}_i \quad . \tag{13.13}$$

Substituting Eq. (13.7) into Eq. (13.13) yields

$$\sum_{k=1}^{M} P_k \mathbf{s}_k \mathbf{s}_k^H \mathbf{v}_i = \lambda_i \mathbf{v}_i \tag{13.14}$$

or

$$\mathbf{v}_i = \sum_{k=1}^{M} \left(\frac{P_k}{\lambda_i} \mathbf{s}_k^H \mathbf{v}_i \right) \mathbf{s}_k \tag{13.15}$$

for $1 \leq i \leq M$, which means

$$\beta_{ik} = \frac{P_k}{\lambda_i} \mathbf{s}_k^H \mathbf{v}_i \quad . \tag{13.16}$$

For the case $M = 1$, note that $\lambda_1 = pP$ and $\mathbf{v}_1 = \mathbf{s}_1 / \sqrt{p}$.

An alternative representation of the identity matrix in terms of the orthonormal eigenvectors is

$$\mathbf{I} = \sum_{i=1}^{p+1} \mathbf{v}_i \mathbf{v}_i^H \quad . \tag{13.17}$$

Substitution of Eqs. (13.11) and (13.17) into Eq. (13.6) yields the eigendecomposition of the autocorrelation matrix

$$\mathbf{R}_p = \sum_{i=1}^{M} \lambda_i \mathbf{v}_i \mathbf{v}_i^H + \rho_w \sum_{i=1}^{p+1} \mathbf{v}_i \mathbf{v}_i^H = \sum_{i=1}^{M} (\lambda_i + \rho_w) \mathbf{v}_i \mathbf{v}_i^H + \sum_{i=M+1}^{p+1} \rho_w \mathbf{v}_i \mathbf{v}_i^H. \tag{13.18}$$

Thus, the eigenvectors $\mathbf{v}_{M+1}, \ldots, \mathbf{v}_{p+1}$ span the noise subspace of $\mathbf{R}_p$, all with the identical eigenvalue ρ_w. The principal eigenvectors $\mathbf{v}_1, \ldots, \mathbf{v}_M$ span the signal subspace of both $\mathbf{R}_p$ and $\mathbf{S}_p$, with eigenvalues of $\lambda_1 + \rho_w, \ldots, \lambda_M + \rho_w$. The eigenvalues of the principal eigenvectors, though, are composed of powers of *both* signal and noise, so white noise does contribute to the eigenvalue *weighting* of the noise-free signal subspace eigenvectors.

The eigendecomposition (13.18) of the autocorrelation matrix can be exploited in two ways to generate improved spectral estimators, or more correctly, improved frequency estimators. *Retaining only the information in the signal subspace eigenvectors, that is, forming a lower-rank approximation to $\mathbf{R}_p$, effectively enhances the SNR* because of the omission of the contribution of power in the noise subspace components. This is the basis of *principal component* (signal subspace) *frequency estimators*, discussed in Sec. 13.5. Noting that the eigenvectors are orthogonal and that the principal eigenvectors span the same subspace of the signal vectors, then the *signal vectors are orthogonal to all the vectors in the noise subspace*, including any linear combination

$$\mathbf{s}_i^H \left(\sum_{k=M+1}^{p+1} \alpha_k \mathbf{v}_k \right) = 0 \tag{13.19}$$

for $1 \leq i \leq M$ (or $2M$ in the case of M real sinusoids). This property forms the basis of the *noise subspace frequency estimators*, discussed in Sec. 13.6.

In the special case $p = M$ (or $p = 2M$ in the case of M real sinusoids), the noise subspace will have a single eigenvector, $\mathbf{v}_{p+1}$, with eigenvalue ρ_w. The M signal vectors will be orthogonal to this eigenvector

$$\mathbf{s}_i^H \mathbf{v}_{p+1} = \sum_{k=1}^{M+1} v_{p+1}[k] \exp(-j2\pi f_i kT) = 0 \tag{13.20}$$

for $1 \leq i \leq M$. Thus, the roots of the polynomial

$$\sum_{k=0}^{M} v_{p+1}[k+1] z^{-k} \tag{13.21}$$

will all lie on the unit circle at angles $2\pi f_i T$ for $1 \leq i \leq M$. This is the central concept of the Pisarenko harmonic decomposition (PHD), discussed further in Sec. 13.6.

13.4 EIGENANALYSIS OF DATA MATRIX FOR EXPONENTIALS IN NOISE

The autocorrelation sequence normally is not known, so that the properties of Sec. 13.3 are mostly of theoretical, rather than practical, interest. The concepts, however, can be extended to the covariance and modified covariance data matrices that are a part of the exponential estimation techniques of the Prony method (see Chap. 11). It is shown in this section that the data matrices have eigendecomposition properties similar to the autocorrelation matrix. The principal eigenvectors of the data matrix predominantly span the signal subspace, and the singular values of these principal eigenvectors tend to be larger than the noise subspace singular values. Thus, the singular values determined by a SVD of the data matrix are the basis for the separation of the eigenvectors into a mostly signal subspace and a mostly noise subspace.

The Prony method was introduced in Chap. 11 as a technique for estimation of the parameters of a *damped exponential* model that approximates a given data sequence. Central to this method is the solution of a set of linear equations involving the autocorrelation-like matrix product $\mathbf{T}_p^H \mathbf{T}_p$, in which $\mathbf{T}_p$ is the order p data matrix of the covariance method of linear prediction

$$
\mathbf{T}_p = \begin{pmatrix} x[p+1] & \cdots & x[1] \\ \vdots & \ddots & \vdots \\ x[N] & \cdots & x[N-p] \end{pmatrix} \quad .
\tag{13.22}
$$

The modified Prony method, a variation of the Prony method for *undamped sinusoidal* modeling, involves the modified covariance data matrix

$$
\begin{pmatrix} \mathbf{T}_p \\ \mathbf{T}_p^* \mathbf{J} \end{pmatrix} \quad .
\tag{13.23}
$$

The discussion which follows will focus on matrix $\mathbf{T}_p$, but the conclusions will also be valid for the modified covariance data matrix.

Consider the noiseless complex exponential signal sequence

$$
x[n] = \sum_{k=1}^{M} h_k z_k^n \quad ,
\tag{13.24}
$$

in which $z_k = \exp([\alpha_k + j2\pi f_k]T)$ and $h_k = A_k \exp(j\phi_k)$. Note that damped exponentials are permitted as valid signals. Matrix $\mathbf{T}_p$ formed from the $x[n]$ of Eq. (13.22) will have rank M as long as the selected order p is within the range $M \le p \le N - M$ (for the modified covariance matrix, the range is $M \le p \le [N-M]/2$). The data matrix $\mathbf{T}_p$ can be decomposed [Kumaresan, 1983] as

$$
\mathbf{T}_p = \mathbf{BC} \quad ,
\tag{13.25}
$$

in which $\mathbf{B}$, an $(N-p) \times M$ matrix, and $\mathbf{C}$, an $M \times p$ matrix, are

$$
\mathbf{B} = \begin{pmatrix} h_1 z_1^p & \cdots & h_M z_M^p \\ h_1 z_1^{p+1} & \cdots & h_M z_M^{p+1} \\ \vdots & & \vdots \\ h_1 z_1^N & \cdots & h_M z_M^N \end{pmatrix} , \quad \mathbf{C} = \begin{pmatrix} 1 & z_1^{-1} & \cdots & z_1^{-(p-1)} \\ 1 & z_2^{-1} & \cdots & z_2^{-(p-1)} \\ \vdots & \vdots & & \vdots \\ 1 & z_M^{-1} & \cdots & z_M^{-(p-1)} \end{pmatrix} .
\tag{13.26}
$$

Using Eq. (13.25), then

$$\mathbf{T}_p^H \mathbf{T}_p = \mathbf{C}^H \mathbf{B}^H \mathbf{B} \mathbf{C} \quad . \tag{13.27}$$

The related $M \times M$ matrix $\mathbf{B}^H \mathbf{B} \mathbf{C} \mathbf{C}^H$ is positive definite because both $\mathbf{B}$ and $\mathbf{C}$ have full rank M. If λ_i for $1 \leq i \leq M$ designates the eigenvalues and $\mathbf{w}_i$ for $1 \leq i \leq M$ designates the eigenvectors, then

$$(\mathbf{B}^H \mathbf{B} \mathbf{C} \mathbf{C}^H) \mathbf{w}_i = \lambda_i \mathbf{w}_i \tag{13.28}$$

for $1 \leq i \leq M$. Premultiply Eq. (13.28) by matrix $\mathbf{C}^H$ to yield

$$\mathbf{C}^H \mathbf{B}^H \mathbf{B} \mathbf{C} \mathbf{C}^H \mathbf{w}_i = \lambda_i \mathbf{C}^H \mathbf{w}_i \quad . \tag{13.29}$$

Define the vector

$$\mathbf{v}_i = \mathbf{C}^H \mathbf{w}_i \tag{13.30}$$

and substitute Eq. (13.30) into Eq. (13.29), leading to the result

$$\mathbf{T}_p^H \mathbf{T}_p \mathbf{v}_i = \lambda_i \mathbf{v}_i \tag{13.31}$$

for $1 \leq i \leq M$. The M nonzero eigenvalues of the $p \times p$ matrix $\mathbf{T}_p^H \mathbf{T}_p$ are, therefore, identical to the eigenvalues of the matrix $\mathbf{B}^H \mathbf{B} \mathbf{C} \mathbf{C}^H$. The remaining $p-M$ eigenvalues of $\mathbf{T}_p^H \mathbf{T}_p$ are zero because $\mathbf{T}_p^H \mathbf{T}_p$ is of rank M. The corresponding eigenvectors of the nonzero eigenvalues are given by Eq. (13.30). Thus, any principal eigenvector of $\mathbf{T}_p^H \mathbf{T}_p$ will be a linear combination of the columns of $\mathbf{C}^H$, which is composed of signal vectors as shown in Eq. (13.26). It can also be shown that any principal eigenvector of $\mathbf{T}_p \mathbf{T}_p^H$ is a linear combination of the columns of $\mathbf{B}$, which is also composed of signal vectors. The matrix $\mathbf{T}_p$ will have M nonzero singular values, as these are simply the square roots of the eigenvalues. The eigenvectors of the zero eigenvalues of $\mathbf{T}_p^H \mathbf{T}_p$ or $\mathbf{T}_p \mathbf{T}_p^H$ are orthogonal to the M signal subspace, or principal, eigenvectors associated with the nonzero eigenvalues in the signal subspace.

If the data has noise, the properties are not exactly true, but they tend to be approximately true. Thus, the M principal singular values of a $\mathbf{T}_p$ matrix composed of noisy samples tend to be larger than the $p - M$ smallest singular values (which were exactly zero in the noiseless case). The M eigenvectors corresponding to the M principal eigenvalues of either $\mathbf{T}_p^H \mathbf{T}_p$ or $\mathbf{T}_p \mathbf{T}_p^H$ have fewer noise contributions than the noise subspace eigenvectors corresponding to the $p - M$ smallest singular values. These statements have some justification as a result of the analysis provided in Sec. 13.3.

13.5 SIGNAL SUBSPACE FREQUENCY ESTIMATORS

It has been shown that retention of the signal subspace, or principal, eigenvectors effectively improves the SNR for processes consisting of exponentials in white noise by eliminating much of the noise contribution to an autocorrelation matrix or a data matrix. A class of signal subspace frequency estimators may be formed from any of the PSD estimators of Chaps. 5–12 by simply replacing the autocorrelation matrix or data matrix by its reduced rank approximation in terms of the principal eigenvectors.

Consider the correlogram method PSD estimator, the minimum variance PSD estimator, and the Yule-Walker autoregressive PSD estimator. The correlogram and MV methods reply on the known or estimated autocorrelation matrix $\mathbf{R}_p$ for the definition of the spectral estimate

$$P_{\text{CORR}}(f) = T\mathbf{e}^H(f)\mathbf{R}_p\mathbf{e}(f) \tag{13.32}$$

$$P_{\text{MV}}(f) = T\left[\mathbf{e}^H(f)\mathbf{R}_p^{-1}\mathbf{e}(f)\right]^{-1}, \tag{13.33}$$

while the autoregressive (AR) method depends on the autocorrelation matrix to obtain the AR parameters

$$\begin{pmatrix} 1 \\ \mathbf{a}_p \end{pmatrix} = \mathbf{R}_p^{-1}\begin{pmatrix} \rho_p \\ \mathbf{0}_p \end{pmatrix}, \tag{13.34}$$

where the vectors and matrix have the following definitions

$$\mathbf{R}_p = \begin{pmatrix} r_{xx}[0] & \cdots & r_{xx}^*[p] \\ \vdots & \ddots & \vdots \\ r_{xx}[p] & \cdots & r_{xx}[0] \end{pmatrix}$$

$$\mathbf{e}(f) = \begin{pmatrix} 1 \\ \exp(j2\pi fT) \\ \vdots \\ \exp(j2\pi fpT) \end{pmatrix}, \qquad \mathbf{a}_p = \begin{pmatrix} a[1] \\ a[2] \\ \vdots \\ a[p] \end{pmatrix}. \tag{13.35}$$

If the orthonormal eigendecomposition of $\mathbf{R}_p$ is

$$\mathbf{R}_p = \sum_{k=1}^{p} \lambda_k \mathbf{v}_k \mathbf{v}_k^H, \tag{13.36}$$

in which the eigenvalues are ranked in decreasing magnitude $\lambda_1 \geq \lambda_2 \geq \ldots \lambda_p$, and there are estimated to be M principal components ($M \leq p$), then the reduced rank principal eigenvector approximations to $\mathbf{R}_p$ and $\mathbf{R}_p^{-1}$,

$$\hat{\mathbf{R}}_p = \sum_{k=1}^{M} \lambda_k \mathbf{v}_k \mathbf{v}_k^H, \qquad \hat{\mathbf{R}}_p^{-1} = \sum_{k=1}^{M} \frac{1}{\lambda_k} \mathbf{v}_k \mathbf{v}_k^H, \tag{13.37}$$

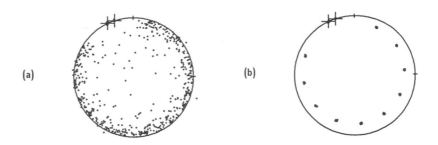

(a)   (b)

Figure 13.4   Location of zeros of modified covariance method for 50 independent data sets. Complex sinusoidals were located at fractional frequencies
of .32 and .3 in white noise of 10-dB SNR. Each realization is 25 samples.
(a) Order $p = 12$. (b) SVD of order $p = 12$ data matrix using two principal
eigenvectors.

may be used in lieu of $\mathbf{R}_p$ and $\mathbf{R}_p^{-1}$ in Eqs. (13.32), (13.33), and (13.34) to create spectral estimators with reduced noise contribution due to the omission of the
noise subspace eigenvectors. Owsley [1976, 1985a] originally proposed the signal
subspace, or principal components, approach to estimation of the classic correlogram method for linear array beamforming, the equivalent of temporal spectral
estimation. Johnson [1982] and Owsley [1985b] promoted the signal subspace improvements of the MV method.

The linear prediction algorithms of Chaps. 8 and 11 depend upon autocorrelation-like data matrix products, such as $\mathbf{T}_p^H \mathbf{T}_p$ as described by Eq. (13.22). The
eigenvectors and eigenvalues of $\mathbf{T}_p^H \mathbf{T}_p$ are obtained by forming the singular value
decomposition of rectangular Toeplitz data matrix $\mathbf{T}_p$, as described by Eq. (3.96).
The singular values will be the positive square roots of the eigenvalues of $\mathbf{T}_p^H \mathbf{T}_p$.
A reduced rank approximation of $\mathbf{T}_p$ may be formed by omitting the eigenvectors
associated with the small singular values, retaining only the principal eigenvectors
and their associated singular values. An application of this approach has been
demonstrated for the Prony method (Sec. 11.9). Tufts and Kumaresan [1982] have
promoted this approach to frequency estimation. They found experimentally that
the covariance data matrix $\mathbf{T}_p$ was best for damped exponentials in noise, while the
modified covariance data matrix of Eq. (13.23) was best for estimates of undamped
sinusoids in noise [Kumaresan, 1982]. This is not surprising, as the modified covariance matrix was also a central feature of the modified Prony method for sinusoidal
estimation. Figure 13.4 illustrates the improvement in effective SNR for a reduced
rank modified covariance data matrix based on 25 samples of the two-component
complex sinusoidal process

$$x[n] = \exp(j2\pi[.32]n + \pi/4) + \exp(j2\pi[.3]n) + w[n] \qquad \text{for} \quad n = 0 \text{ to } 24 \quad (13.38)$$

of 10-dB signal-to-noise ratio. This approach was shown by Tufts and Kumaresan to approach the exact maximum likelihood performance, distinguishing pairs of close sinusoidals at low SNRs where linear prediction techniques were unable to distinguish two frequencies accurately.

13.6 NOISE SUBSPACE FREQUENCY ESTIMATORS

All estimators in this class rely on the property that the noise subspace eigenvectors of the autocorrelation matrix or the data matrix are orthogonal to the signal eigenvectors, or any linear combination of the signal eigenvectors. The data matrices most often of interest are the ones associated with the covariance and modified covariance methods of linear prediction, as discussed in Chap. 8.

13.6.1 Pisarenko Harmonic Decomposition (PHD)

The Pisarenko harmonic decomposition (PHD) method was one of the earliest procedures for spectral estimation by eigenanalysis [Pisarenko, 1973]. The PHD assumes that the process consists of M complex sinusoids in additive complex white noise and derives the sinusoidal frequencies, sinusoidal powers, and white noise variance from the *known autocorrelation sequence* $r_{xx}[0]$ to $r_{xx}[M]$. If the process consists of M real sinusoids in additive real white noise, then the ACS must be known for lags 0 to $2M$. It was shown in Sec. 13.3 that the autocorrelation matrix $\mathbf{R}_{M+1}$ formed from the ACS will have, in the complex case, a single noise subspace eigenvector $\mathbf{v}_{M+1}$ with associated eigenvalue ρ_w, corresponding to the white noise variance. This eigenvalue is also the minimum eigenvalue of matrix $\mathbf{R}_{M+1}$. This can be expressed as

$$\mathbf{R}_{M+1}\mathbf{v}_{M+1} = \rho_w \mathbf{v}_{M+1} \quad . \tag{13.39}$$

Given $\mathbf{R}_{M+1}$, subroutine MINEIGVAL in Chap. 3 will solve for the minimum eigenvalue (the noise variance) and its associated eigenvector. This algorithm accounts for the conjugate symmetry of the eigenvector. Once found, the sinusoid frequencies may be determined by factoring the eigenfilter polynomial, Eq. (13.21). The roots are guaranteed to be on the unit circle.

Once the frequencies have been determined from the polynomial factoring, the sinusoidal powers can be determined from the autocorrelation sequence $r_{xx}[1]$, ..., $r_{xx}[M]$ and Eq. (13.1) [Marple, 1976]. In matrix form, this is

$$
\begin{Bmatrix}
\exp(j2\pi f_1 T) & \exp(j2\pi f_2 T) & \cdots & \exp(j2\pi f_M T) \\
\exp(j2\pi f_1 2T) & \exp(j2\pi f_2 2T) & \cdots & \exp(j2\pi f_M 2T) \\
\vdots & \vdots & & \vdots \\
\exp(j2\pi f_1 MT) & \exp(j2\pi f_2 MT) & \cdots & \exp(j2\pi f_M MT)
\end{Bmatrix}
\begin{Bmatrix}
P_1 \\ P_2 \\ \vdots \\ P_M
\end{Bmatrix}
=
\begin{Bmatrix}
r_{xx}[1] \\ r_{xx}[2] \\ \vdots \\ r_{xx}[M]
\end{Bmatrix}
$$
$$\tag{13.40}$$

which may be solved for the vector of unknown sinusoid powers $P_1, \ldots, P_M$ using standard linear equation solution routines for complex elements. In practice, one must estimate the ACS from the data samples. The biased autocorrelation estimate must be used to ensure a positive-definite matrix. Determining the order (number of sinusoids) M to use for the PHD method is difficult. Because the noise variance eigenvalues theoretically repeat when the order is larger than the number of sinusoids (see Eq. (13.18)], a check for repeating eigenvalues of a very large order autocorrelation matrix would seem to be one method of order selection. In practice, however, use of estimated autocorrelation sequences do not usually generate repeated eigenvalues. Thus, the performance of the PHD with short data sequences tends to be poor. Some statistical properties of the PHD have been described by Sakai [1984].

An adaptive variant of Pisarenko's method has been proposed by Thompson [1979] for tracking narrowband signals in broadband noise. Its performance has been studied in depth by Larimore [1983]. It is a time-sequential PHD-type algorithm that, in contrast to the block-data PHD algorithm just presented, updates the estimate of the eigenvector (associated with the minimum eigenvalue) on a sample-by-sample basis. The algorithm is a constrained gradient search version of the LMS algorithm presented in Chap. 9,

$$\mathbf{v}'[k+1] = \mathbf{v}[k] - 2\mu e_k[k+1]\mathbf{x}[k]$$

$$\mathbf{v}[k+1] = \frac{\mathbf{v}'[k+1]}{(\mathbf{v}'[k+1])^H(\mathbf{v}'[k+1])} \tag{13.41}$$

$$e_k[k+1] = x[k+1] + \sum_{n=1}^{M} v[n]x[k+1-n] \quad .$$

When converged, $\mathbf{v}$ is a unity norm vector in the order $p = 2M$ subspace associated with the minimum eigenvalue. Experience with this time-recursive algorithm has indicated that convergence may be nonmonotonic and require long windows of data to isolate spectral lines.

13.6.2 Frequency Estimator Functions

Frequency estimator functions can be devised, based on noise subspace principles, to yield spectrum-like plots with sharp peaks. The $p - M$ noise subspace eigenvectors $\mathbf{v}_{M+1}, \ldots, \mathbf{v}_p$ of an autocorrelation matrix, covariance data matrix, or modified covariance data matrix of p total eigenvectors and M principal eigenvectors will theoretically be orthogonal to the sinusoidal signal vectors, so that linear combinations with arbitrary weighting α_k such as

$$\sum_{k=M+1}^{p} \alpha_k \left| \mathbf{e}^H(f)\mathbf{v}_k \right|^2 = \mathbf{e}^H(f) \left(\sum_{k=M+1}^{p} \alpha_k \mathbf{v}_k \mathbf{v}_k^H \right) \mathbf{e}(f) \quad , \tag{13.42}$$

where $\mathbf{e}(f)$ is the complex sinusoid vector

$$\mathbf{e}(f) = \begin{pmatrix} 1 \\ \exp(j2\pi fT) \\ \vdots \\ \exp(j2\pi fMT) \end{pmatrix} \quad , \tag{13.43}$$

will be zero whenever $\mathbf{e}(f_i) = \mathbf{s}_i$, one of the sinusoidal signal vectors. This means that the frequency estimator function

$$\frac{1}{\displaystyle\sum_{k=M+1}^{p} \alpha_k \left| \mathbf{e}^H(f)\mathbf{v}_k \right|^2} \tag{13.44}$$

will theoretically have infinite value whenever evaluated at $f = f_i$, one of the sinusoidal signal frequencies. In practice, estimation errors will cause the function of Eq. (13.44) to be finite, but with very sharp peaks at the sinusoidal frequencies. Frequency estimators such as Eq. (13.44) are, of course, not true PSD estimators, but are pseudo spectral estimators useful for estimation of sinusoidal or narrowband spectral component frequencies with a resolution somewhat higher than that of autoregressive spectral estimation techniques.

Two specific frequency estimators have been proposed in the literature. Selecting $\alpha_k = 1$ for all k yields the multiple signal classification (MUSIC) algorithm [Schmidt, 1981, 1986] frequency estimator

$$P_{\text{MUSIC}}(f) = \frac{1}{\mathbf{e}^H(f) \left(\displaystyle\sum_{k=M+1}^{p} \mathbf{v}_k \mathbf{v}_k^H \right) \mathbf{e}(f)} \quad , \tag{13.45}$$

based strictly on the noise subspace eigenvectors with uniform weighting. Choosing $\alpha_k = 1/\lambda_k$ yields the eigenvector (EV) algorithm [Johnson, 1982] frequency estimator

$$P_{\text{EV}}(f) = \frac{1}{\mathbf{e}^H(f) \left(\displaystyle\sum_{k=M+1}^{p} \frac{1}{\lambda_k} \mathbf{v}_k \mathbf{v}_k^H \right) \mathbf{e}(f)} \quad , \tag{13.46}$$

which weights each noise subspace eigenvector by the inverse of its associated eigenvalue.

Johnson and DeGraaf [1982] have indicated that the EV method produces fewer spurious peaks than MUSIC for a given choice of order p due to the use of inverse eigenvalue weighting. They also claim that the EV method tends to shape the noise spectrum better than MUSIC. The ultimate performance of any frequency estimator, though, will be a function of how well the selection of signal and noise subspaces is made. Examination of the relative magnitudes of the eigenvalues (singular values) of the autocorrelation matrix (data matrix) eigendecomposition (SVD) will be the key tool for deciding the separation of the eigenvectors into two subspaces. Asymptotic performance analyses for the frequency estimator algorithms as a function of SNR, order, and frequency resolution may be found in Kaveh and Barabell [1986], Wang and Kaveh [1986], and Spielman et al. [1986]. The sensitivity of these techniques to colored noise, rather than white noise, has yet to be quantified. However, the fundamental limitation to performance in practice is how well the signal and noise eigenvalues can be separated from the noise-only eigenvalues.

Appendix 13.A contains subroutine EIGENFREQ. This program uses the modified covariance data matrix for the evaluation of either the MUSIC or EV methods, whichever is selected. Interesting applications of these techniques for spatial processing may be found in Evans et al. [1982] and Gabriel [1986].

13.7 ORDER SELECTION

The simple idea of separating eigenvectors into signal and noise subspaces based upon an examination of either the eigenvalues of the autocorrelation matrix or the singular values of the data matrix does not work well in practice, especially with short sample records. The AIC order-selection criterion first introduced in Chap. 8 has been extended by Wax and Kailath [1985] to handle the subspace separation problem. Assuming $\lambda_1 > \lambda_2 > \ldots > \lambda_p$ are the eigenvalues of the sample autocorrelation matrix $\hat{\mathbf{R}}_p$ and assuming $m < p$, where m is the number of sinusoidal signals actually present in the data, and N data samples, then

$$
\text{AIC}[m] = (p - m) \ln \left(\frac{\dfrac{1}{p-m} \displaystyle\sum_{i=m+1}^{p} \lambda_i}{\displaystyle\prod_{i=m+1}^{p} \lambda_i^{-(p-m)}} \right) + m(2p - m) \quad .
\tag{13.47}
$$

The number of sinusoids in the signal subspace is determined by selecting the minimum value of $\text{AIC}[m]$. Wax and Kailath [1986] have reported some preliminary results from use of the criterion of (13.47).

REFERENCES

Evans, J. E., J. R. Johnson, and D. F. Sun, Applications of Advanced Signal Processing Techniques to Angle of Arrival Estimation of ATC Navigation and Surveillance Systems, *MIT Lincoln Laboratory Technical Report 582*, June 1982.

Gabriel, W. F., Using Spectral Estimation Techniques in Adaptive Processing Antenna Systems, *IEEE Trans. Antennas Propag.*, vol. AP-34, pp. 291–300, March 1986.

Johnson, D. H., The Application of Spectral Estimation Methods to Bearing Estimation Problems, *Proc. IEEE*, vol. 70, pp. 1018–1028, September 1982.

Johnson, D. H., and S. R. DeGraaf, Improving the Resolution of Bearing in Passive Sonar Arrays by Eigenvalue Analysis, *IEEE Trans. Acoust. Speech Signal Process.*, vol. ASSP-30, pp. 638–647, August 1982.

Kaveh, M., and A. J. Barabell, The Statistical Performance of the MUSIC and the Minimum-Norm Algorithms for Resolving Plane Waves in Noise, *IEEE Trans. Acoust. Speech Signal Process.*, vol. ASSP-34, pp. 331–341, April 1986.

Kumaresan, R., Estimating the Parameters of Exponentially Damped or Undamped Sinusoidal Signals in Noise, Ph.D. dissertation, Department of Electrical Engineering, University of Rhode Island, Kingston, R. I., 1982.

Kumaresan, R., On the Zeros of the Linear Prediction Error Filter for Deterministic Signals, *IEEE Trans. Acoust. Speech Signal Process.*, vol. ASSP-31, pp. 217–220, February 1983.

Larimore, M. G., Adaption Convergence of Spectral Estimation Based on Pisarenko Harmonic Retrieval, *IEEE Trans. Acoust. Speech Signal Process.*, vol. ASSP-31, pp. 955–962, August 1983.

Marple, S. L. Jr., Conventional Fourier, Autoregressive, and Special ARMA Methods of Spectrum Analysis, Engineer's dissertation, Department of Electrical Engineering, Stanford University, Stanford, Calif., December 1976.

Noble, B., and J. W. Daniel, Applied Linear Algebra, 2nd ed., Prentice-Hall, Inc., Englewood Cliffs, N. J., 1977.

Owsley, N. L., A Recent Trend in Adaptive Signal Processing for Sensor Arrays: Constrained Adaptation, in *Signal Processing*, J. W. R. Griffiths et al., eds., Academic Press, Inc., New York, 1976.

Owsley, N. L., Sonar Array Processing, Chapter 3 in *Array Signal Processing*, S. Haykin, ed., Prentice-Hall, Inc., Englewood Cliffs, N. J., 1985a.

Owsley, N. L., High-Resolution Spectrum Analysis by Dominant-Mode Enhancement, Chapter 4 in *VLSI and Modern Signal Processing*, S. Y. Kung, H. J. Whitehouse, and T. Kailath, eds., Prentice-Hall, Inc., Englewood Cliffs, N.J., 1985b.

Pisarenko, V. F., The Retrieval of Harmonics from a Covariance Function, *Geophys. J. R. Astron. Soc.*, vol. 33, pp. 347–366, 1973.

Sakai, H., Statistical Analysis of Pisarenko's Method for Sinusoidal Frequency Estimation, *IEEE Trans. Acoust. Speech Signal Process.*, vol. ASSP-32, pp. 95–101, February 1984.

Schmidt, R. O., A Signal Subspace Approach to Multiple Emitter Location and Spectral Estimation, Ph.D. dissertation, Department of Electrical Engineering, Stanford University, Stanford, Calif., November 1981.

Schmidt, R. O., Multiple Emitter Location and Signal Parameter Estimation, *IEEE Trans. Antennas Propag.*, vol. AP-34, pp. 276–280, March 1986.

Spielman, D., A. Paulraj, and T. Kailath, Performance Analysis of the Music Algorithm, *Proceedings of the 1986 IEEE International Conference on Acoustics, Speech, and Signal Processing*, Tokyo, Japan, pp. 1909–1912, April 1986.

Thompson, P. A., An Adaptive Spectral Analysis Technique for Unbiased Frequency Estimation in the Presence of White Noise, *Proceddings of 13th Asilomar Conference on Circuits, Systems, and Computers*, pp. 529–533, November 1979.

Tufts, D. W., and R. Kumaresan, Estimation of Frequencies of Multiple Sinusoids: Making Linear Prediction Perform like Maximum Likelihood, *Proc. IEEE*, vol. 70, pp. 975–989, September 1982.

Wang, H., and M. Kaveh, Performance of Narrowband Signal-Subspace Processing, *Proceedings of the 1986 IEEE International Conference on Acoustics, Speech, and Signal Processing*, Tokyo, Japan, pp. 589–592, April 1986.

Wax, M., and T. Kailath, Detection of Signals by Information Theoretic Criteria, *IEEE Trans. Acoust. Speech Signal Process.*, vol. ASSP-33, pp. 387–392, April 1985.

PROBLEMS

1. Using the case of M noiseless complex sinusoids $x[n] = \sum_{i=1}^{M} \sin(2\pi f_i nT)$ and an order $p = M$, prove that the zeros of the polynomial formed from the prediction error filter of the modified covariance data matrix (11.23) will be on the unit circle at the sinusoid frequencies.

2. Show for AR of Eq. (13.34) that the signal subspace version is

$$\mathbf{a}_p = -\sum_{k=1}^{M} (\alpha_k/\lambda_k)\mathbf{v}_k$$

where $\alpha_k = \mathbf{v}_k^H \mathbf{r}_p$ is the inner product of the eigenvector $\mathbf{v}_k$ with $\mathbf{r}_p = [R_{xx}[1] \quad \cdots \quad r_{xx}[p]]^T$.

3. Prove that $\hat{\rho}_w = r[0] - \sum \hat{P}_i$. This can be used as a numerical check on the eigenvalue given by subroutine MINEIGVAL.

4. Show how the MUSIC frequency estimator can be expressed in terms of the signal subspace, rather than the noise subspace, eigenvectors. Use Eq. (13.17) to prove this.

APPENDIX 13.A
PROGRAM TO COMPUTE THE EIGENVECTOR METHOD AND MUSIC METHOD FREQUENCY ESTIMATORS

This subroutine will compute either the MUSIC (METHOD = 0) or the EV (METHOD = 1) noise subspace frequency estimator of Sec. 13.6.2, based on an SVD of the modified covariance data matrix [see Eq. (13.23)]

$$\begin{pmatrix} x[p] & \cdots & x[1] \\ \vdots & & \vdots \\ x[N-1] & \cdots & x[N-p] \\ x^*[2] & \cdots & x^*[p] \\ \vdots & & \vdots \\ x^*[N-p+1] & \cdots & x^*[N] \end{pmatrix}.$$

Based on selecting METHOD $= 1$, N $= 64$, IP $= 15$, and NSIG $= 11$, the subroutine will produce the following selected values of PSD when used with the test sequence of Appendix II

```
PSD(1)    = 0.110867E-02
PSD(1000) = 0.351216E+01
PSD(2000) = 0.124425E+00
PSD(3000) = 0.821904E+01
PSD(4000) = 0.966779E-03
PSD(4096) = 0.110536E-02  .
```

```
      SUBROUTINE EIGENFREQ (METHOD,N,IP,NSIG,X,PSD,ISTAT)
C
C   Input Parameters:
C
C     METHOD - Set to 0 for MUSIC method, 1 for EV method (integer)
C     N      - Number of data samples (integer)
C     IP     - Dimension of data matrix (integer)
C     NSIG   - Assumed number of "signal" space vectors (integer)
C     X      - Array of complex data samples
C
C   Output Parameters:
C
C     PSD    - Array of real frequency estimator values
C     ISTAT  - Status indicator (integer):
C                   0 for normal exit
C                   1 if NSIG > IP-1 or NSIG < 0
C
C   Notes:
C
C     External array X must be dimensioned .GE. N  and array PSD must be
C     dimensioned .GE. NPSD in calling program.  Internal array FB must
C     be dimensioned .GE.  2*(N-IP) x IP , array U  must be dimensioned
C     .GE. 2*(N-IP) x 2*(N-IP), array V must be dimensioned .GE. IP x IP,
C     and array S must be dimensioned .GE. IP or 2*(N-IP) , whichever is
C     greater.
C
      PARAMETER NPSD=4096   ! Must be a power of 2 (dim. of W,Z matrices)
      PARAMETER MAXU=100    ! Maximum dimension of U matrix
      PARAMETER MAXV=50     ! Maximum dimension of V,S matrix
      COMPLEX X(1),FB(MAXU,MAXV),U(MAXU,MAXU),V(MAXV,MAXV)
      COMPLEX W(NPSD),Z(NPSD)
      REAL PSD(1),S(MAXV)
      PI2=8.*ATAN(1.)
      ISTAT=0
      IF (NSIG .LT. IP .AND. NSIG .GE. 0)  GO TO 5
      ISTAT=1
      RETURN
5     NP=N-IP
      DO 20 I=1,NP
        DO 10 K=1,IP
          FB(I,K)=X(I-K+IP)
10        FB(I+NP,K)=CONJG(X(I+K))
20      CONTINUE
      NP2=2*NP
      CALL CSVD (FB,MAXU,MAXV,NP2,IP,0,IP,IP,S,U,V)
```

```
C    AI or Expert Knowledge to choose "signal" singular values, or input
C    NSIG at this point
     CALL PREFFT (NPSD,0,NEXP,W)
     DO 30 K=1,NPSD
30     PSD(K)=0.
     DO 70 I=NSIG+1,IP
       DO 40 K=1,IP
40       Z(K)=V(K,I)
       DO 50 K=IP+1,NPSD
50       Z(K)=(0.,0.)
       CALL FFT (NPSD,0,1.,NEXP,W,Z)
       DO 60 K=1,NPSD
         TEMP=REAL(Z(K))**2+AIMAG(Z(K))**2
         IF (METHOD .EQ. 0)  PSD(K)=PSD(K)+TEMP
60       IF (METHOD .NE. 0)  PSD(K)=PSD(K)+TEMP/S(I)
70     CONTINUE
     DO 80 K=1,NPSD
80     PSD(K)=1./PSD(K)
     RETURN
     END
```

14

SUMMARY OF
SPECTRAL ESTIMATORS

The unifying approach employed in Chaps. 5–13 has been to view each spectral estimation technique in the context of fitting data to an assumed model. The primary motivation for many of the alternative spectral estimators has been the unsatisfactory performance of classical spectral estimators, especially where the reciprocal of the data sequence duration is of the same order as the desired resolution. However, if the data set is sufficiently large and statistically stationary, then classical spectral estimators as discussed in Chap. 5 will be the most robust. The classical methods have been the most well characterized estimators of all the methods included in this text; the only assumption they make is that the data is wide-sense stationary. The nonclassical methods require additional assumptions. The variations in performance among the various spectral estimation methods may often be attributed to how well the underlying assumed model matches the process under analysis. When the model is an accurate representation of the data, spectral estimates can be obtained with performance exceeding that of the classical spectral estimators (e.g., the periodogram). If the model is accurate, but a poor spectral estimator of the parameters is used, poor (increased variance) spectral estimates will result. Unfortunately, few algorithms have been thoroughly analyzed for statistical performance with finite data records. Most comparisons among competing algorithms have been based on limited computer simulations. Different models may yield similar results, but one model may require fewer model parameters and therefore be more efficient than the other models in its representation of the observed process. Differences in performance are also found among algorithms that estimate the parameters of a common model, as was illustrated by the AR PSD estimates of Chap. 8.

The general spectral estimation problem is that of estimation of the power spectral density or, equivalently, the autocorrelation function of a random process. Because the PSD is formally determined by an infinite number of autocorrelation function values, the task of estimating the PSD based on a finite data set is inherently an ill-defined problem. At best, one could only hope to estimate a finite number of lags of the autocorrelation function. The classical spectral estimators of Chap. 5 attempt to estimate only the most significant lags from 0 to some maximum M. The resulting PSD estimator may be severely biased if the true PSD exhibits strong autocorrelation values for lags greater than M. In an attempt to reduce this spectral estimator problem to one which is more manageable, various models for the PSD were proposed in Chaps. 6–14. The class of time-series models that yielded rational PSD functions (AR, MA, ARMA) are typical. The models are parameterized by a finite, and hopefully small, set of coefficients. The incorporation of a model leads to the replacement of the general spectral estimation problem by a parameter estimation problem. Less biased spectral estimators of higher resolution will result to the extent that the model is an accurate representation of the process.

Table 14.1 provides a synopsis of key spectral estimation methods presented throughout Chaps. 5–13. Some PSD estimation methods have more than one parameter estimation algorithm listed. Quadratic matrix forms have been used in this book to concisely describe the structural form of the PSD function. Many of the methods involve a minimization problem on some data matrix to yield a solution for the model parameters; this data matrix is indicated on the table. Some constant scaling terms have been omitted to better highlight the similarities and differences among the various methods. Exact PSD and parameter normal equations may be found in the reference section indicated by Table 14.1. Approximate computational complexity for each method is summarized. Only the highest-order terms of the polynomial representing the computational count are shown. The computational complexities shown assume use of the computer programs listed in the table.

The $p \times 1$ data vector $\mathbf{x}$, $(p+1) \times 1$ parameter vector $\mathbf{a}$, a $p \times 1$ parameter vector $\mathbf{b}$, and a $(p+1) \times 1$ complex sinusoid vector $\mathbf{e}(f)$ used in Table 14.1 are defined as

$$\mathbf{x} = \mathbf{x}_p[n] = \begin{pmatrix} x[n] \\ x[n-1] \\ \vdots \\ x[n-p] \end{pmatrix}, \quad \mathbf{a} = \begin{pmatrix} 1 \\ a_p[1] \\ \vdots \\ a_p[p] \end{pmatrix}, \tag{14.1}$$

$$\mathbf{b} = \begin{pmatrix} 1 \\ b_p[1] \\ \vdots \\ b_p[p] \end{pmatrix}, \quad \mathbf{e}(f) = \begin{pmatrix} 1 \\ \exp(j2\pi fT) \\ \vdots \\ \exp(j2\pi[p-1]fT) \end{pmatrix}.$$

Table 14.1 Summary of Spectral Estimation Methods

Class	Model	Method	Key Text Section	Program Appendix [1]	Spectrum Quad. Form [2]	Data Matrix [3]	Relative Complexity [4]	Resol./Var. Control [5]
Classical	None [6]	Periodogram	5.7	—/5.C	$|e^H(f)x|^2$	—	$N\log_2 N$	Window
	None	Correlogram	5.6	—/5.B	$e^H(f)R_A e(f)$	X_1	$N\log_2 N$	Window
Parametric	Autoregressive	Yule-Walker(YW)	8.3	8.A/6.A	$|e^H(f)a|^{-2}$	X_1	N^2	AR order
		Burg	8.4.2	8.B/6.A		—	N^2	
		Covariance	8.5.1	8.C/6.A		X_2	N^2	
		Modified Covar.	8.5.2	8.D/6.A		X_3	N^2	
		Adaptive LMS	9.3	9.B/6.A		—	N [7]	
		Adaptive RLS	9.4.2	9.C/6.A		X_4	N [7]	
	Moving Average	High-Order AR	10.3	10.A/6.A	$|e^H(f)b|^2$	X_1	N^2	MA order
	Autoregressive-Moving Average	Modified YW	10.4	10.B/6.A	$\dfrac{|e^H(f)b|^2}{|e^H(f)a|^2}$	X_1	N^2	AR, MA orders
	Damped Sines	Prony	11.5	11.C/11.E	$|\mathrm{DTFT}[\sum h_k z^k]|^2$	X_2	N^2	No. Sines
	Undamped Sines	Modified Prony	11.6	11.C/—	Line Spectrum	X_3	N^2	No. Sines
	Sines+Noise	Pisarenko	13.6.1	3.F/—	Line Spectrum	X_1	N^3	No. Sines
Non Parametric	None	Min. Variance	12.4	—/12.A	$[e^H(f)R_A^{-1}e(f)]^{-1}$	X_1	N^2	Dimen. R_A
	None	MUSIC Eigen.	13.6.2	—/13.A	$[e^H(f)R_M e(f)]^{-1}$	X_3	N^3	Sing.Values
	None	EV Eigenanalysis	13.6.2	—/13.A	$[e^H(f)R_E e(f)]^{-1}$	X_3	N^3	Sing.Values

[1] Parameter estimation program/Spectrum evaluation program.
[2] See the text for vector and matrix definitions.
[3] See the text for data matrix definitions.
[4] The relative complexity is rough order-of-magnitude comparisons between spectral techniques. See the appropriate text section for detailed computational complexity analysis.
[5] The key parameter that affects the resolution vs. PSD variance trade-off is given in this column.
[6] The periodogram does have an interpretation as a sinusoidal model with preselected harmonic frequencies (see Chap. 11 Problems).
[7] Computation count per time update.

The Toeplitz autocorrelation data matrix $\mathbf{X}_1$, Toeplitz covariance data matrix $\mathbf{X}_2$, modified covariance data matrix $\mathbf{X}_3$, and prewindowed data matrix $\mathbf{X}_4$ were defined in Chap. 8 as

$$
\mathbf{X}_1 = \begin{pmatrix} x[1] & \cdots & 0 \\ \vdots & \ddots & \vdots \\ x[p+1] & \cdots & x[1] \\ \vdots & & \vdots \\ x[N] & \cdots & x[N-p] \\ \vdots & \ddots & \vdots \\ 0 & \cdots & x[N] \end{pmatrix}, \quad
\mathbf{X}_2 = \begin{pmatrix} x[p+1] & \cdots & x[1] \\ \vdots & \ddots & \vdots \\ x[N-p] & & x[p+1] \\ \vdots & \ddots & \vdots \\ x[N] & \cdots & x[N-p] \end{pmatrix},
$$

$$(14.2)$$

and

$$
\mathbf{X}_3 = \begin{pmatrix} \mathbf{X}_2 \\ \mathbf{X}_2^* \mathbf{J} \end{pmatrix}, \quad
\mathbf{X}_4 = \begin{pmatrix} x[1] & \cdots & 0 \\ \vdots & \ddots & \vdots \\ x[p+1] & \cdots & x[1] \\ \vdots & & \vdots \\ x[N] & \cdots & x[N-p] \end{pmatrix},
$$

and the $(p+1) \times (p+1)$ Toeplitz autocorrelation matrix $\mathbf{R}_A$ as

$$
\mathbf{R}_A = \mathcal{E}\{\mathbf{x}_p^*[n]\mathbf{x}_p^T[n]\} = \begin{pmatrix} r_{xx}[0] & \cdots & r_{xx}^*[p] \\ \vdots & \ddots & \vdots \\ r_{xx}[p] & \cdots & r_{xx}[0] \end{pmatrix}. \tag{14.3}
$$

The matrices $\mathbf{R}_M$ and $\mathbf{R}_E$ represent the reduced rank approximation to $\mathbf{R}_A$ for the MUSIC and EV eigenanalysis methods, respectively (see Chap. 13 for exact definitions). Many of the spectral estimation methods in Table 14.1 perform either a constrained minimization or an unconstrained minimization of a quadratic form involving the data matrices $\mathbf{X}_1$ to $\mathbf{X}_4$ or the autocorrelation matrix $\mathbf{R}_A$ to obtain the model parameters. The spectral estimates produced from the 64-sample test sequence of Appendix II by each method listed in Table 14.1 have been illustrated in the Summary section of each of the earlier chapters.

The research literature often attempts to classify the spectral estimation methods of Table 14.1 into data "adaptive" and "nonadaptive" categories. These terms were used to distinguish the classical spectral estimation techniques from the newer techniques, such as autoregressive spectral analysis. However, it has been shown that all spectral estimation methods fit, or "adapt," the model parameters in some manner to the data. The Prony method, for example, makes amplitude, phase, damping, and frequency estimates for an exponential model. A periodogram computed with the DTFS makes only amplitude and phase estimates, because the frequencies of the sinusoidal model have been preselected at harmonic intervals.

The *only* appropriate use for the term "adaptive" is for those time-sequential updating algorithms that track time variations in the model parameters, such as the methods in Chap. 9.

In some situations, data must be preprocessed prior to spectral estimation in order to remove significant signal components that could adversely effect the quality of the spectral estimate if not removed. Signal components that are candidates for removal include large means (DC), linear and higher-order polynomial trends, and strong tones (sinusoidal signals). Dominant tones or a high DC level will produce significant sidelobes in periodogram and correlogram method PSD estimates that can mask the presence of weak signal components close in frequency to the strong components. Polynomial trends are nonstationary in character and have been shown to have significant bias effects on the low-frequency end of AR spectral estimates [Kane and Trivedi, 1979]. Removing strong signal components and trends helps to reduce the dynamic range of spectral values, and may therefore be regarded as roughly *prewhitening* the spectrum. Data with bad or missing sample points can use linear prediction techniques of Chap. 8 to first replace these points before spectral estimation is performed [Nuttall, 1976; Bowling and Lai, 1979].

Polynomial trends up to Mth order may be removed with a FIR rejection filter of length $M + 1$

$$y[n] = \sum_{k=0}^{M} h[k]x[n-k] \quad .$$ (14.4)

Denoting the trend as

$$x[n] = \sum_{i=0}^{M} b[i](nT)^i,$$ (14.5)

where T is the sample interval, then in order to have

$$y[n] = \sum_{i=0}^{M} b[i] \sum_{k=0}^{M} h[k](nT - kT)^i = 0 \quad ,$$ (14.6)

the following equations must be satisfied

$$\sum_{k=0}^{M} (k)^i h[k] = 0$$ (14.7)

for $i = 0$ to $i = M$. This forms a set of $M + 1$ equations for the $M + 1$ unknown filter coefficients. Tones may also be removed by a symmetric FIR filter with linear phase.

Trend and tone rejection filters must be used with care. Not only are the trends and tones removed, but also components of the spectrum that are close to the rejection regions of the filter response [the Fourier transform of Eq. (14.4)]. This tends to be the low-frequency region of the spectrum. Removing the sample

Figure 14.1 Effect of incorrect mean removal. (a) Samples from part of a sinusoidal cycle. (b) AR PSD estimate by modified covariance method with sample mean removed. (b) AR PSD estimate by modified covariance method with sample mean not removed.

mean must also be used cautiously. Because of the zero-mean assumption made in the statistical development of many spectral estimators, one may be tempted to always remove the sample mean

$$\bar{x} = \frac{1}{N} \sum_{i=1}^{N} x[n] \qquad (14.8)$$

from the data. To see the impact such action may have, consider the example depicted in Fig. 14.1. A short sample sequence of a portion of sinusoidal cycle produces the sharp peak in the modified covariance AR spectral estimate shown in Fig. 14.1(c). When the sample mean is removed from the data, the modified covariance AR PSD estimate of the modified data, shown in Fig. 14.1(b), now indicates, erroneously, the presence of a DC component. This is a case where mean removal introduces artifacts into the spectrum, rather than improving it. Complete removal of the sample mean is also undesirable when the spectrum may have a random process with finite *power spectral density* at zero frequency, such as white noise, even though there is no finite *power* at zero frequency (zero mean). The sample mean should also not be removed from data composed of transient signals. As a rule of thumb, sample mean and trends should only be removed in situations in which they are physically expected or in which they are clearly dominant in the data.

REFERENCES

Bowling, S. B., and S. Lai, The Use of Linear Prediction for the Interpolation and Extrapolation of Missing Data Prior to Spectral Analysis, *Proceedings of the Rome Air Development Center Workshop on Spectrum Estimation*, pp. 39–50, October 1979.

Kane, R. P., and N. B. Trivedi, Effects of Linear Trend and Mean Value on Maximum Entropy Spectral Analysis, *Institute de Pesquisas Espaciais, Report INPE-1568-RPE/069*, Sao Jose dos Compos, Brasil, 1979 (available as NTIS N79-33949).

Nuttall, A. H., Spectral Analysis of a Univariate Process with Bad Data Points, via Maximum Entropy and Linear Predictive Techniques, *Naval Underwater Systems Center Technical Report TR-5303*, New London, Conn., March 1976.

15

MULTICHANNEL SPECTRAL ESTIMATION

15.1 INTRODUCTION

The discussion to this point in the book has been concerned with spectral estimation of a single stationary sample sequence. The next two chapters will extend these one-dimensional, single-variable spectral estimators to the multichannel case (vector functions of a scalar variable) and the two-dimensional case (scalar functions of a vector variable). This chapter extends the concepts developed earlier in the text to the simultaneous processing of samples from multiple data channels. Such arrays of signals are quite common in phased array radar, sonar, and seismic measurements, to name a few applications. Thus, each section of this chapter will parallel the development presented in Chaps. 5–13. Multichannel linear system theory, multichannel random process theory, multichannel parametric models, multichannel autoregressive PSD, multichannel linear prediction, and multichannel minimum variance spectral estimation are covered. Due to the interest in high-resolution spectral estimation for short data sequences, a significant part of this chapter is devoted to multichannel autoregressive PSD estimation. For additional background material on multichannel time series analysis, consult the text by Robinson [1983].

15.2 SUMMARY

The goal of multichannel spectral analysis of m channels of data is the estimation of the Hermitian power spectral density (PSD) matrix

$$\mathbf{P}(f) = \begin{pmatrix} P_{11}(f) & \cdots & P_{1m}(f) \\ \vdots & \ddots & \vdots \\ P_{m1}(f) & \cdots & P_{mm}(f) \end{pmatrix} \quad ,$$

which is formally defined by Eq. (15.19). The PSD matrix consists of autospectral terms P_{ii}, for $i = 1$ to m, and cross spectral terms P_{ij}, for $i \neq j$, from all possible channel pairings. Figure 15.1 is a flowchart of three possible multichannel estimation approaches for which computer programs have been provided in this text. Multichannel PSD analysis by the classical periodogram approach is covered in Sec. 15.5. Program MCPERIOD in Appendix 15.A is an implementation of one of the classical multichannel PSD estimators. Multichannel autoregressive (AR) PSD estimation is discussed extensively in Secs. 15.7–15.12. Two AR algorithms by Vieira-Morf and Nuttall-Strand have been jointly implemented in a single computer program MCAR that yields estimates of the autoregressive parameter matrices, from which an AR PSD matrix may be computed by subroutine MCARPSD. The multichannel minimum variance method is described in Sec. 15.13, where a step-by-step procedure is provided for implementation. The cross spectral terms from these various estimators are most conveniently interpreted in terms of the coherence function [see Eqs. (15.15)–(15.17)].

● ACQUIRE DATA M channels N samples/channel T seconds/sample		
MULTICHANNEL PERIODOGRAM	MULTICHANNEL AUTOREGRESSIVE PSD	MULTICHANNEL MINIMUM VARIANCE PSD
● SELECT SEGMENT PARAMETERS NSAMP samples/segment NSHIFT sample shift/segment ● COMPUTE MULTICHANNEL PERIODOGRAM (Subroutine MCPERIOD, Appendix 15.A)	● SELECT INPUT PARAMETERS Order IP Algorithm METHOD ● ESTIMATE MULTICHANNEL AR PARAMETERS (Subroutine MCAR, Appendix 15.B) ● COMPUTE MULTICHANNEL AR PSD (Subroutine MCARPSD, Appendix 15.D)	● SELECT ORDER ● COMPUTE MULTICHANNEL MINIMUM VARIANCE PSD (Subroutine MCMINVAR, Section 15.13)

Figure 15.1 Flowchart of three approaches to multichannel PSD estimation.

15.3 MULTICHANNEL LINEAR SYSTEMS THEORY

Let $\mathbf{x}[n]$ denote a vector of samples from an m-channel process at sample index n,

$$\mathbf{x}[n] = \begin{pmatrix} x_1[n] \\ \vdots \\ x_m[n] \end{pmatrix} . \tag{15.1}$$

If $\mathbf{x}[n]$ represents the input $m \times 1$ vector of m channels and $\mathbf{y}[n]$ represents the output $m \times 1$ vector of m channels, then the linear shift-invariant system convolution that relates $\mathbf{x}[n]$ to $\mathbf{y}[n]$ is given by

$$\mathbf{y}[n] = \sum_{k=-\infty}^{\infty} \mathbf{H}[n-k]\mathbf{x}[k] = \mathbf{H}[n] \star \mathbf{x}[n] \quad , \tag{15.2}$$

where the $m \times m$ *multichannel impulse response matrix* is given by

$$\mathbf{H}[k] = \begin{pmatrix} h_{1,1}[k] & \cdots & h_{1,m}[k] \\ h_{2,1}[k] & \cdots & h_{2,m}[k] \\ \vdots & & \vdots \\ h_{m,1}[k] & \cdots & h_{m,m}[k] \end{pmatrix} .$$

An individual output channel $y_i[n]$ would, therefore, have the convolution function

$$y_i[n] = \sum_{j=1}^{m} \sum_{k=-\infty}^{\infty} h_{ij}[n-k]x_j[k] \quad .$$

The *multichannel z-transform matrix* of a matrix sequence $\mathbf{H}[k]$ is defined as

$$\mathbf{H}(z) = \sum_{k=-\infty}^{\infty} \mathbf{H}[k]z^{-k} = Z\{\mathbf{H}[k]\} \quad , \tag{15.3}$$

where z is a complex scalar. In this case, $\mathbf{H}(z)$ is the *multichannel system response function*. The z-transform of the signal vector $\mathbf{x}[k]$ is defined as

$$\mathbf{X}(z) = \sum_{k=-\infty}^{\infty} \mathbf{x}[k]z^{-k} \quad . \tag{15.4}$$

The *multichannel discrete-time Fourier transform* (DTFT) *matrix* $\mathbf{H}(f)$ is defined as

$$\mathbf{H}(f) = T\,\mathbf{H}(z)\Big|_{z=\exp(j2\pi fT)} = T \sum_{k=-\infty}^{\infty} \mathbf{H}[k]\exp(-j2\pi fkT) \tag{15.5}$$

and the multichannel DTFT vector $\mathbf{X}(f)$ is defined as

$$\mathbf{X}(f) = T \sum_{k=-\infty}^{\infty} \mathbf{x}[k] \exp(-j2\pi fkT) \quad . \tag{15.6}$$

The multichannel convolution theorem relates the z-transform of the matrix and vectors in the convolution of Eq. (15.2) as

$$\mathbf{Y}(z) = \mathbf{H}(z)\mathbf{X}(z) \quad . \tag{15.7}$$

A causal m-channel linear system described by the constant coefficient matrix difference equation

$$\sum_{k=0}^{p} \mathbf{A}[k]\mathbf{y}[m-k] = \sum_{k=0}^{q} \mathbf{C}[k]\mathbf{x}[n-k] \quad , \tag{15.8}$$

in which $\mathbf{A}[k]$ and $\mathbf{C}[k]$ are $m \times m$ coefficient matrices, has the z-transform (assuming zero initial conditions)

$$\mathbf{A}(z)\mathbf{Y}(z) = \mathbf{C}(z)\mathbf{X}(z)$$

or

$$\mathbf{Y}(z) = \mathbf{A}^{-1}(z)\mathbf{C}(z)\mathbf{X}(z) \quad . \tag{15.9}$$

15.4   MULTICHANNEL RANDOM PROCESS THEORY

Elementary concepts of two-channel random process theory for wide-sense stationary processes were developed in Chap. 3. The cross correlation between the single-channel processes $x[n]$ and $y[n]$ was defined there as

$$r_{xy}[k] = \mathcal{E}\left\{x[n+k]y^*[n]\right\} \tag{15.10}$$

with the property that $r_{xy}[k] = r_{yx}^*[-k]$. The two-channel cross power spectral density was shown to be simply the discrete-time Fourier transform of the cross correlation function

$$P_{xy}(f) = T \sum_{k=-\infty}^{\infty} r_{xy}[k] \exp(-j2\pi fkT) \quad . \tag{15.11}$$

This function is, in general, complex and has the complex conjugate symmetry

$$P_{xy}(f) = P_{yx}^*(-f) \quad . \tag{15.12}$$

It is straightforward to show (see the Problems) that the cross spectrum is less than or equal to the geometric mean of the x and y process autospectra,

$$|P_{xy}(f)|^2 \leq P_{xx}(f)P_{yy}(f) \quad . \tag{15.13}$$

The Hermitian matrix

$$\begin{pmatrix} P_{xx}(f) & P_{xy}(f) \\ P_{yx}(f) & P_{yy}(f) \end{pmatrix} \tag{15.14}$$

is called the *coherence matrix*. Due to property (15.13), this 2×2 matrix must have a nonnegative determinant for all frequencies. The complex dimensionless expression

$$\Phi_{xy}(f) = \frac{P_{xy}(f)}{\sqrt{P_{xx}(f)}\sqrt{P_{yy}(f)}} \tag{15.15}$$

is termed the *coherence function*. Related functions are the *magnitude squared coherence* (MSC)

$$\mathrm{MSC}(f) = |\Phi_{xy}(f)|^2 = \frac{|P_{xy}(f)|^2}{P_{xx}(f)P_{yy}(f)} \tag{15.16}$$

and the *coherence phase spectrum* (or simply the "phase" spectrum)

$$\theta(f) = tan^{-1}\big[\mathrm{Im}\{\Phi_{xy}(f)\}/\mathrm{Re}\{\Phi_{xy}(f)\}\big] \quad . \tag{15.17}$$

Note that the MSC must lie between 0 (for frequencies where there is no coherence between channels) and 1 (for frequencies where the channels are perfectly coherent to within some fixed phase relationship). Thus, the MSC may be used to measure, as a function of frequency, the similarity between a pair of signals. Its primary use is the detection of a common signal on two different channels. The coherence phase represents the phase lag or lead of channel x with respect to channel y as a function of frequency.

To generalize the scalar auto/cross correlation and scalar auto/cross power spectral density functions to the multichannel case, define the *multichannel correlation sequence* (MCS) at lag k of the stationary m-channel data vector $\mathbf{x}[n]$ as

$$\mathbf{R_{xx}}[k] = \mathcal{E}\{\mathbf{x}[n+k]\mathbf{x}^H[n]\} = \begin{pmatrix} r_{11}[k] & r_{12}[k] & \ldots & r_{1m}[k] \\ r_{21}[k] & r_{22}[k] & \ldots & r_{2m}[k] \\ \vdots & \vdots & \ddots & \vdots \\ r_{m1}[k] & r_{m2}[k] & \ldots & r_{mm}[k] \end{pmatrix}, \tag{15.18}$$

which forms a correlation matrix whose on-diagonal terms are single-channel autocorrelations and whose off-diagonal terms are two-channel cross correlations. Although $r_{ij}[k] \neq r_{ji}^*[k]$, the property $r_{ij}[k] = r_{ji}^*[-k]$ does hold for $i \neq j$; $\mathbf{R_{xx}}[k]$ will, therefore, *not* have a Hermitian symmetry property, i.e., $\mathbf{R_{xx}}[k] \neq \mathbf{R_{xx}}^H[k]$, but will have, instead, the property $\mathbf{R_{xx}}[k] = \mathbf{R_{xx}}^H[-k]$. An analogous definition may be provided for the multichannel covariance function, using the vector of channel means. If the multichannel process $\mathbf{x}[n]$ has zero mean in all channels, then the multichannel covariance matrix is equal to the multichannel correlation matrix.

The $m \times m$ discrete-time Fourier transform matrix of the multichannel correlation matrix

$$\mathbf{P_{xx}}(f) = T \sum_{k=-\infty}^{\infty} \mathbf{R_{xx}}[k] \exp(-j2\pi f kT)$$

$$= \begin{pmatrix} P_{11}(f) & P_{12}(f) & \cdots & P_{1m}(f) \\ P_{21}(f) & P_{22}(f) & \cdots & P_{2m}(f) \\ \vdots & \vdots & \ddots & \vdots \\ P_{m1}(f) & P_{m2}(f) & \cdots & P_{mm}(f) \end{pmatrix} \qquad (15.19)$$

is defined to be the *multichannel power spectral density* (PSD) *matrix* of the multichannel random process. It has on-diagonal elements that are the single-channel autospectral densities and off-diagonal elements that are the two-channel cross spectral densities. Note that $\mathbf{P_{xx}}(f)$ is Hermitian, that is, $\mathbf{P_{xx}}(f) = \mathbf{P_{xx}}^H(f)$, and positive semidefinite. This means that every principal minor matrix of $\mathbf{P_{xx}}(f)$ has a nonnegative determinant and, therefore, all coherencies of channel pairs have values bounded between 0 and 1 in magnitude. For example, the two-channel PSD matrix

$$\det \begin{pmatrix} P_{11}(f) & P_{12}(f) \\ P_{21}(f) & P_{22}(f) \end{pmatrix} \geq 0$$

implies

$$0 \leq \frac{|P_{21}(f)|^2}{P_{11}(f)P_{22}(f)} \leq 1 \quad .$$

Similar statements may be made for higher-order determinants, implying the existence of multiple coherence functions, such as $\Phi_{ijk}(f)$, with the property

$$0 \leq |\Phi_{ijk}(f)| \leq 1 \quad .$$

A zero-mean multichannel random process of special interest is multichannel white noise $\mathbf{w}[n]$, which has a multichannel MCS of

$$\mathbf{R_{ww}}[k] = \begin{cases} \mathbf{P}_w & \text{if } k = 0 \\ \mathbf{0} & \text{otherwise} \end{cases} \quad , \qquad (15.20)$$

in which $\mathbf{P}_w$ is an $m \times m$ Hermitian matrix. The white noise in each channel is correlated with itself and correlated with the white noise in the other channels only at lag $k = 0$. The multichannel PSD of the multichannel white noise process is, therefore,

$$\mathbf{P_{ww}}(f) = T\mathbf{P}_w \quad . \qquad (15.21)$$

Using arguments similar to that in Sec. 4.3, it is simple to show (see the Problems) that the relationship between the correlation matrix $\mathbf{R_{yy}}[m]$, the output correlation matrix of a multichannel filter with impulse response matrix sequence $\mathbf{H}[m]$, and $\mathbf{R_{xx}}[m]$, the correlation matrix of the multichannel input process, is

$$\mathbf{R_{yy}}[m] = \mathbf{H}[m] \star \mathbf{R_{xx}}[m] \star \mathbf{H}^H[-m] \quad . \tag{15.22}$$

The multichannel z-transform of Eq. (15.22) is then

$$\mathbf{P_{yy}}(z) = \mathbf{H}(z)\mathbf{P_{xx}}(z)\mathbf{H}^H(1/z^*) \quad . \tag{15.23}$$

The $m \times m$ matrix PSD between the input and output process of a multichannel linear filter, based on definitions (15.5) and (15.19), is

$$\mathbf{P_{yy}}(f) = \mathbf{H}(f)\mathbf{P_{xx}}(f)\mathbf{H}^H(f) \quad , \tag{15.24}$$

in which

$$\mathbf{H}(f) = \sum_{k=-\infty}^{\infty} \mathbf{H}[k] \exp(-j2\pi f kT) \quad .$$

Note that $\mathbf{H}(f)$ is not formally a multichannel DTFT because it lacks the scaling factor T.

15.5 MULTICHANNEL CLASSICAL SPECTRAL ESTIMATORS

A discussion of classical methods of autospectral and cross spectral estimation has been presented in Chap. 5 for both the periodogram and the correlogram methods of PSD estimation. The reader may refer to that chapter for algorithms that will compute autospectral estimates of individual channels and cross spectral estimates of channel pairs, which may then be used to fill in the entries of the PSD matrix (15.19). Program MCPERIOD in Appendix 15.A computes the PSD matrix using the periodogram method.

The multichannel periodogram and correlogram methods for PSD estimation can be expressed more eloquently in multichannel matrix notation. The *multichannel averaged periodogram*, based on averaging K segments, has the form

$$\hat{\mathbf{P}}_{\text{PER}}(f) = \frac{1}{K}\left[\frac{1}{NT}\sum_{k=1}^{K}\mathbf{X}_k(f)\mathbf{X}_k^H(f)\right] \quad , \tag{15.25}$$

in which

$$\mathbf{X}_k(f) = T\sum_{n=0}^{N-1}\mathbf{x}_k[n]\exp(-j2\pi f nT)$$

is an $m \times 1$ vector DTFT made from N samples of the m-channel sample vector $\mathbf{x}_k[n]$ taken from the kth segment. Averaging is not only important for purposes of statistical smoothing of the periodogram , it is also important for minimizing the bias in the coherence estimate. Consider the extreme situation of a two-channel case without segment averaging (only a single segment). The auto- and cross-periodogram estimates made from N samples of channel x_1 and channel x_2 will then have the form

$$\hat{P}_{11}(f) = \frac{1}{NT} X_1(f) X_1^*(f)$$

$$\hat{P}_{22}(f) = \frac{1}{NT} X_2(f) X_2^*(f)$$

$$\hat{P}_{12}(f) = \frac{1}{NT} X_1(f) X_2^*(f) \quad ,$$

where

$$X_1(f) = T \sum_{n=0}^{N-1} x_1[n] \exp(-j2\pi f n T)$$

$$X_2(f) = T \sum_{n=0}^{N-1} x_2[n] \exp(-j2\pi f n T) \quad .$$

The magnitude squared coherence estimate will then be unity because

$$\text{MSC}(f) = \frac{\hat{P}_{12}(f)\hat{P}_{12}^*(f)}{\hat{P}_{11}(f)\hat{P}_{22}(f)} = \frac{\left[X_1(f)X_2^*(f)\right]\left[X_1^*(f)X_2(f)\right]}{\left[X_1(f)X_1^*(f)\right]\left[X_2(f)X_2^*(f)\right]} = 1 \qquad (15.26)$$

for all f, independent of the values of the data. This case illustrates an extreme situation of the effect of bias that is always present in coherence estimates made from periodogram spectral estimates.

The biased multichannel correlation matrix estimate for lag k can be expressed for $k > 0$, as

$$\check{\mathbf{R}}_{\mathbf{xx}}[k] = \frac{1}{N} \sum_{n=0}^{N-k-1} \mathbf{x}[n+k]\mathbf{x}^H[n] \quad , \qquad (15.27)$$

in which the multichannel data vector $\mathbf{x}[n]$ was defined in (15.1). Assuming lags from 0 to $\pm p$ are estimated, the multichannel correlogram method will yield the PSD estimate

$$\hat{\mathbf{P}}_{\text{CORR}}(f) = T \sum_{k=-p}^{p} \check{\mathbf{R}}_{\mathbf{xx}}[k] \exp(-j2\pi f k T) \quad . \qquad (15.28)$$

Expression (15.28) can be succinctly expressed as

$$\hat{\mathbf{P}}_{\text{CORR}}(f) = T\underline{\mathbf{e}}_p(f)\check{\underline{\mathbf{R}}}_p\underline{\mathbf{e}}_p^H(f) \quad , \qquad (15.29)$$

in which the block-Toeplitz correlation matrix of block dimension $(p+1) \times (p+1)$ is defined as

$$
\check{\underline{\mathbf{R}}}_p = \begin{pmatrix}
\check{\mathbf{R}}_{\mathbf{xx}}[0] & \check{\mathbf{R}}_{\mathbf{xx}}[1] & \cdots & \check{\mathbf{R}}_{\mathbf{xx}}[p] \\
\check{\mathbf{R}}_{\mathbf{xx}}[-1] & \check{\mathbf{R}}_{\mathbf{xx}}[0] & \cdots & \check{\mathbf{R}}_{\mathbf{xx}}[p-1] \\
\vdots & \vdots & \ddots & \vdots \\
\check{\mathbf{R}}_{\mathbf{xx}}[-p] & \check{\mathbf{R}}_{\mathbf{xx}}[-p+1] & \cdots & \check{\mathbf{R}}_{\mathbf{xx}}[0]
\end{pmatrix} \tag{15.30}
$$

and the complex sinusoid block *row* vector $\underline{\mathbf{e}}_p(f)$ of $p+1$ block elements is defined as

$$
\underline{\mathbf{e}}_p(f) = \begin{pmatrix} \mathbf{I}_m & \exp(j2\pi fT)\mathbf{I}_m & \cdots & \exp(j2\pi fpT)\mathbf{I}_m \end{pmatrix} \quad . \tag{15.31}
$$

Note that each element of block vector $\underline{\mathbf{e}}_p(f)$ is an $m \times m$ identity matrix $\mathbf{I}_m$ scaled by an appropriate complex sinusoidal value.

Schemes have been devised to utilize classical autospectral estimation algorithms to estimate cross spectral densities. If successful, this would alleviate the need to develop cross spectral estimates and the need for full multichannel algorithms. For example, forming the new complex data processes

$$
w[n] = x[n] + jy[n]
$$
$$
z[n] = x[n] + y[n]
$$

from the original data processes $x[n]$ and $y[n]$, and computing the autospectra $P_{xx}(f), P_{yy}(f), P_{ww}(f), P_{zz}(f)$, it may easily be shown that the real and imaginary parts of the cross spectral density between channels x and y are given by

$$
\operatorname{Re}\{P_{xy}(f)\} = \frac{1}{2}\left[P_{zz}(f) - P_{xx}(f) - P_{yy}(f)\right]
$$
$$
\operatorname{Im}\{P_{xy}(f)\} = \frac{1}{2}\left[P_{ww}(f) - P_{xx}(f) - P_{yy}(f)\right] \quad . \tag{15.32}
$$

This method of cross spectral estimation can yield values of the magnitude squared coherence, computed from the $\hat{P}_{xy}$ given by Eq. (15.32), that are *greater* than unity. This is obviously undesirable for detecting coherent components between channels, and therefore this approach should not be considered.

15.6 MULTICHANNEL ARMA, AR, AND MA PROCESSES

In analogy with the single-channel definition, the m-channel ARMA is defined as the vector recursion

$$
\mathbf{x}[n] = -\sum_{k=1}^{p} \mathbf{A}[k]\mathbf{x}[n-k] + \sum_{k=0}^{q} \mathbf{C}[k]\mathbf{u}[n-k] \quad , \tag{15.33}
$$

in which the $\mathbf{A}[k]$ are the $m \times m$ autoregressive parameter matrices, the $\mathbf{C}[k]$ are the $m \times m$ moving average parameter matrices, and $\mathbf{u}[k]$ is an $m \times 1$ vector representing the input driving noise process, assumed to be a wide-sense stationary multichannel process. The z-transform relating input and output was shown in Eq. (15.9) to be

$$\mathbf{X}(z) = \mathbf{A}^{-1}(z)\mathbf{C}(z)\mathbf{U}(z) \quad , \tag{15.34}$$

for which

$$\begin{aligned} \mathbf{A}(z) &= \mathbf{I} + \sum_{k=1}^{p} \mathbf{A}[k]z^{-k} \\ \mathbf{C}(z) &= \mathbf{I} + \sum_{k=1}^{q} \mathbf{C}[k]z^{-k} \quad . \end{aligned} \tag{15.35}$$

This means that the matrix transfer function from input to output is

$$\mathbf{H}(z) = \mathbf{A}^{-1}(z)\mathbf{C}(z) \quad . \tag{15.36}$$

The z-transform of the output correlation sequence is obtained by substituting (15.36) into (15.23), yielding

$$\mathbf{P_{xx}}(z) = \mathbf{A}^{-1}(z)\mathbf{C}(z)\mathbf{P_{uu}}(z)\mathbf{C}^{H}(1/z^{*})\mathbf{A}^{-H}(1/z^{*}) \quad , \tag{15.37}$$

where $^{-H}$ denotes the Hermitian transpose of the inverse. If the assumption is made that the multichannel input process is a white noise process with constant covariance matrix $\boldsymbol{P_w}$, then the output process has a multichannel ARMA PSD function, derived from (15.37), of

$$\mathbf{P}_{\mathrm{ARMA}}(f) = T\mathbf{A}^{-1}(f)\mathbf{C}(f)\boldsymbol{P_w}\mathbf{C}^{H}(f)\mathbf{A}^{-H}(f) \quad , \tag{15.38}$$

defined for $|f| \leq 1/2T$, in which

$$\mathbf{A}(f) = \mathbf{A}(\exp[j2\pi fT]) = \mathbf{I} + \sum_{k=1}^{p} \mathbf{A}[k]\exp(-j2\pi fkT)$$

and

$$\mathbf{C}(f) = \mathbf{C}(\exp[j2\pi fT]) = \mathbf{I} + \sum_{k=1}^{q} \mathbf{C}[k]\exp(-j2\pi fkT).$$

An alternative expression for the multichannel ARMA PSD function is

$$\mathbf{P}_{\mathrm{ARMA}}(f) = T\,[\underline{\mathbf{a}}_p\underline{\mathbf{e}}_p^{H}(f)]^{-1}[\underline{\mathbf{c}}_q\underline{\mathbf{e}}_q^{H}(f)]\boldsymbol{P_w}[\underline{\mathbf{e}}_q(f)\underline{\mathbf{c}}_q^{H}][\underline{\mathbf{e}}_p(f)\underline{\mathbf{a}}_p^{H}]^{-1}, \tag{15.39}$$

in which the block *row* vectors $\underline{\mathbf{a}}_p$, with $p + 1$ block elements, and $\underline{\mathbf{c}}_q$, with $q + 1$ block elements, are defined as

$$\underline{\mathbf{a}}_p = \begin{pmatrix} \mathbf{I} & \mathbf{A}[1] & \cdots & \mathbf{A}[p] \end{pmatrix}$$
$$\underline{\mathbf{c}}_q = \begin{pmatrix} \mathbf{I} & \mathbf{C}[1] & \cdots & \mathbf{C}[q] \end{pmatrix} \quad , \tag{15.40}$$

and $\underline{\mathbf{e}}_p(f)$ and $\underline{\mathbf{e}}_q(f)$ are complex sinusoid block row vectors, defined by Eq. (15.31).

A multichannel AR(p) process

$$\mathbf{x}[n] = -\sum_{k=1}^{p} \mathbf{A}[k]\mathbf{x}[n - k] + \mathbf{u}[n] \tag{15.41}$$

has the z-transform

$$\mathbf{P}_{\mathrm{AR}}(z) = \mathbf{A}^{-1}(z)\mathbf{P}_w\mathbf{A}^{-H}(1/z^*) \tag{15.42}$$

and, therefore, has the multichannel PSD function

$$\mathbf{P}_{\mathrm{AR}}(f) = T\,[\underline{\mathbf{a}}_p\underline{\mathbf{e}}_p^H(f)]^{-1}\mathbf{P}_w[\underline{\mathbf{e}}_p(f)\underline{\mathbf{a}}_p^H]^{-1} \quad . \tag{15.43}$$

A multichannel MA(q) process

$$\mathbf{x}[n] = \sum_{k=1}^{q} \mathbf{C}[k]\mathbf{u}[n - k] + \mathbf{u}[n] \tag{15.44}$$

has the z-transform

$$\mathbf{P}_{\mathrm{MA}}(z) = \mathbf{C}(z)\mathbf{P}_w\mathbf{C}^H(1/z^*) \tag{15.45}$$

and, therefore, has the multichannel PSD function

$$\mathbf{P}_{\mathrm{MA}}(f) = T\,[\underline{\mathbf{c}}_q\underline{\mathbf{e}}_q^H(f)]\mathbf{P}_w[\underline{\mathbf{e}}_q(f)\underline{\mathbf{c}}_q^H] \quad . \tag{15.46}$$

Although a multichannel process may be a vector autoregression, it does not follow that each channel is individually an autoregressive process [Nuttall, 1976a, 1976b]. Consider the two-channel first-order vector autoregression

$$\mathbf{x}[n] = -\mathbf{A}[1]\mathbf{x}[n - 1] + \mathbf{u}[n] \quad , \tag{15.47}$$

in which the input process is uncorrelated from channel to channel and the variance for each channel is unity ($\mathbf{P}_w = \mathbf{I}$), and

$$\mathbf{A}[1] = \begin{pmatrix} a & b \\ c & d \end{pmatrix} \quad ,$$

containing complex elements a, b, c, and d. The two-channel AR z-transform for this case is

$$\mathbf{P}_{AR}(z) = \mathbf{A}^{-1}(z)\mathbf{A}^{-H}(1/z^*) \quad , \tag{15.48}$$

in which

$$\mathbf{A}(z) = (\mathbf{I} - \mathbf{A}[1]z^{-1}) = \begin{pmatrix} 1 - z^{-1}a & -z^{-1}b \\ -z^{-1}c & 1 - z^{-1}d \end{pmatrix} \quad .$$

Substituting for $\mathbf{A}(z)$ in (15.42) yields the expression

$$\mathbf{P}_{AR}(z) =$$

$$\frac{1}{D(z)D(1/z)} \begin{pmatrix} 1 + |b|^2 + |d|^2 + z^{-1}d + zd^* & -(a^*b + c^*d + z^{-1}b + zc^*) \\ -(ab^* + cd^* + z^{-1}c + zb^*) & 1 + |a|^2 + |c|^2 + z^{-1}a + za^* \end{pmatrix} \tag{15.49}$$

in which the polynomial $D(z)$ is

$$D(z) = \left(1 - z^{-1}(a + d) + z^{-2}(ad - bc)\right) \quad . \tag{15.50}$$

Inspection of denominator $D(z)$ reveals that each of the elements of matrix $\mathbf{P}_{AR}(z)$ has *four* poles and *three* zeros in the finite z-plane. Thus, the autospectra of each channel are representative of a *single-channel* ARMA(4,3) process, even though the multichannel problem is a *first-order vector autoregression* with independent white excitation inputs. Generally, an m-channel autoregression of order p with independent white excitation driving each channel will have autospectra and cross spectra with $m^2 p$ poles and $(m^2 - 1)p$ zeros in the finite z-plane (of which p zeros occur at the origin), in contrast to the single-channel autoregression, which only has $2p$ poles. This case illustrates that an autospectrum of a multichannel autoregression has more degrees of freedom than an autospectrum of a single-channel autoregression.

15.7   MULTICHANNEL YULE-WALKER EQUATIONS

The focus in the next five sections will be on the multichannel autoregressive spectral estimate. Multichannel ARMA and MA have received only limited attention in the literature. For those interested, the Yule-Walker equations for a multichannel ARMA is presented as a problem exercise. Recent references to multichannel ARMA include Lee et al. [1982], Friedlander [1982], and Friedlander and Porat [1986].

The stationary m-channel autoregressive process may be expressed as the block vector inner product

$$\mathbf{e}_p^f[n] = \underline{\mathbf{a}}_p \underline{\mathbf{x}}_p[n] \tag{15.51}$$

for which the block *row* vector of multichannel AR matrix coefficients was defined
in (15.40) as

$$\underline{\mathbf{a}}_p = \left(\mathbf{I} \quad \mathbf{A}_p[1] \quad \cdots \quad \mathbf{A}_p[p] \right) \quad , \tag{15.52}$$

$\mathbf{I}$ is an $m \times m$ identity matrix, and the block *column* vector of multichannel data
vectors is

$$\underline{\mathbf{x}}_p[n] = \begin{pmatrix} \mathbf{x}[n] \\ \vdots \\ \mathbf{x}[n-p] \end{pmatrix} \quad . \tag{15.53}$$

A superscript ^{f} has been added in Eq. (15.51) to distinguish $\mathbf{e}_p^f[n]$ as not only the
autoregressive driving sequence (previously written as $\mathbf{u}[n]$), but also as the forward
linear prediction error. In order to establish a relationship between the AR matrix
coefficients and the matrix correlation sequence for lags 0 to p, postmultiply both
sides of (15.51) by $\underline{\mathbf{x}}_p^H[n]$ and take the expectation,

$$\mathcal{E}\left\{\mathbf{e}^f[n]\underline{\mathbf{x}}_p^H[n]\right\} = \mathcal{E}\left\{\underline{\mathbf{a}}_p\underline{\mathbf{x}}_p[n]\underline{\mathbf{x}}_p^H[n]\right\} = \underline{\mathbf{a}}_p\mathcal{E}\left\{\underline{\mathbf{x}}_p[n]\underline{\mathbf{x}}_p^H[n]\right\} \quad . \tag{15.54}$$

Define the block matrix $\underline{\mathbf{R}}_p$ of $(p+1) \times (p+1)$ block entries $\mathbf{R}_{\mathbf{xx}}[k]$ (each of which
is dimension $m \times m$) as

$$\begin{aligned}
\underline{\mathbf{R}}_p &= \mathcal{E}\left\{\underline{\mathbf{x}}_p[n]\underline{\mathbf{x}}_p^H[n]\right\} \\
&= \begin{pmatrix} \mathcal{E}\left\{\mathbf{x}[n]\mathbf{x}^H[n]\right\} & \cdots & \mathcal{E}\left\{\mathbf{x}[n]\mathbf{x}^H[n-p]\right\} \\ \vdots & & \vdots \\ \mathcal{E}\left\{\mathbf{x}[n-p]\mathbf{x}^H[n]\right\} & \cdots & \mathcal{E}\left\{\mathbf{x}[n-p]\mathbf{x}^H[n-p]\right\} \end{pmatrix} \\
&= \begin{pmatrix} \mathbf{R}_{\mathbf{xx}}[0] & \mathbf{R}_{\mathbf{xx}}[1] & \cdots & \mathbf{R}_{\mathbf{xx}}[p] \\ \mathbf{R}_{\mathbf{xx}}[-1] & \mathbf{R}_{\mathbf{xx}}[0] & \cdots & \mathbf{R}_{\mathbf{xx}}[p-1] \\ \vdots & \vdots & \ddots & \vdots \\ \mathbf{R}_{\mathbf{xx}}[-p] & \mathbf{R}_{\mathbf{xx}}[-p+1] & \cdots & \mathbf{R}_{\mathbf{xx}}[0] \end{pmatrix} \quad .
\end{aligned} \tag{15.55}$$

The matrix $\underline{\mathbf{R}}_p$ has both a *Hermitian* and a *block-Toeplitz* structure. Individual
matrix elements of $\underline{\mathbf{R}}_p$ are *not*, in general, Hermitian ($\mathbf{R}_{\mathbf{xx}}[k] \neq \mathbf{R}_{\mathbf{xx}}^H[k]$), although
$\mathbf{R}_{\mathbf{xx}}[-k] = \mathbf{R}_{\mathbf{xx}}^H[k]$. The $(p+1) \times 1$ block vector $\mathcal{E}\left\{\mathbf{e}^f[n]\underline{\mathbf{x}}_p^H[n]\right\}$ may be simplified
to

$$\begin{aligned}
\mathcal{E}\left\{\mathbf{e}^f[n]\underline{\mathbf{x}}_p^H[n]\right\} &= \mathcal{E}\left\{\mathbf{e}^f[n]\left(\mathbf{e}^{f\,H}[n] - \sum_{k=1}^p \mathbf{x}^H[n-k]\mathbf{A}_p^H[k]\right)\right\} \\
&= \left(P_p^f \quad \mathbf{0} \quad \cdots \quad \mathbf{0} \right) \quad ,
\end{aligned} \tag{15.56}$$

in which $\mathbf{0}$ are $m \times m$ all-zero matrices and $P_p^f = \mathcal{E}\left\{\mathbf{e}^f[n]\mathbf{e}^{f\,H}[n]\right\} = P_w$ is the
covariance matrix of the AR driving noise. The last equality in Eq. (15.56) follows
from the property that the driving noise process is uncorrelated with past values

of the AR process, $\mathcal{E}\{e^f[n]\mathbf{x}^H[n-k]\} = \mathbf{0}$ for $k < n$. Equation (15.54) may be rewritten with this result as

$$\underline{\mathbf{a}}_p\mathbf{R}_p = \left(P_p^f \quad \mathbf{0} \quad \cdots \quad \mathbf{0} \right) \quad . \tag{15.57}$$

This is the multichannel version of the Yule-Walker normal equations for both a multichannel AR(p) and a multichannel forward linear prediction filter of order p.

The multichannel autoregressive process created by the *backward* filter process at time index $n-1$ is

$$e_p^b[n-1] = \mathbf{x}[n-p-1] + \sum_{k=1}^{p}\mathbf{B}[k]\mathbf{x}[n-p-1+k] = \underline{\mathbf{b}}_p\underline{\mathbf{x}}_p[n-1] \quad , \tag{15.58}$$

for which the block *row* vector of backward multichannel AR matrix coefficients is

$$\underline{\mathbf{b}}_p = \left(\mathbf{B}_p[p] \quad \cdots \quad \mathbf{B}_p[1] \quad \mathbf{I} \right) \quad . \tag{15.59}$$

The corresponding multichannel Yule-Walker equations for the backward coefficients of a stationary multichannel process are found by constructing

$$\mathcal{E}\{e_p^b[n-1]\underline{\mathbf{x}}_p^H[n-1]\} = \mathcal{E}\{\underline{\mathbf{b}}_p\underline{\mathbf{x}}_p[n-1]\underline{\mathbf{x}}_p^H[n-1]\}$$

to yield

$$\underline{\mathbf{b}}_p\mathbf{R}_p = \left(\mathbf{0} \quad \cdots \quad \mathbf{0} \quad P_p^b \right) \quad , \tag{15.60}$$

for which $P_p^b = \mathcal{E}\{e^b[n-1]e^{bH}[n-1]\}$ is the covariance of the driving noise process for the backward AR process. P_p^b will, in general, be different than P_p^f for multichannel processes. In the single-channel case, they were identical. The Hermitian Toeplitz structure of the correlation matrix in the single-channel case was sufficient to guarantee the conjugate relationship $a_p[k] = b_p^*[k]$ between the forward and backward AR parameters shown in Sec. 3.8.1. In the multichannel case, though, the elements of the block correlation matrix $\mathbf{R}_p$ lack the Hermitian property needed to produce a similar property between elements of $\underline{\mathbf{a}}_p$ and $\underline{\mathbf{b}}_p$. The multichannel AR(p) process also has the spectral density z-transform given in terms of the backward filter coefficients

$$\mathbf{P}_{\mathrm{AR}}(z) = \mathbf{B}^{-1}(z)P_p^b\mathbf{B}^{-H}(1/z^*) \quad , \tag{15.61}$$

for which $\mathbf{B}(z)$ is the matrix polynomial

$$\mathbf{B}(z) = z^{-p}\mathbf{I} + \sum_{k=1}^{p}\mathbf{B}[k]z^{-p+k} = z^{-p}\left(\mathbf{I} + \sum_{k=1}^{p}\mathbf{B}[k]z^k\right) \quad . \tag{15.62}$$

The transforms for $\mathbf{P}_{AR}(z)$ given by Eqs. (15.42) and (15.62) must be equivalent for a stationary multichannel process and, therefore, either expression may be used to obtain the multichannel AR PSD.

15.8   MULTICHANNEL LEVINSON ALGORITHM

A fast algorithm for the simultaneous solution of Yule-Walker equations (15.57) and (15.60) was apparently first developed by Wiggins and Robinson [1965]. It is structured along the same lines as the single-channel Levinson algorithm presented in Sec. 3.8.1. The block-Toeplitz multichannel correlation matrix $\underline{\mathbf{R}}_{p+1}$ may be partitioned in two ways,

$$\underline{\mathbf{R}}_{p+1} = \begin{pmatrix} \underline{\mathbf{R}}_p & \underline{\mathbf{s}}_{p+1}^H \\ \underline{\mathbf{s}}_{p+1} & \mathbf{R}_{xx}[0] \end{pmatrix} = \begin{pmatrix} \mathbf{R}_{xx}[0] & \underline{\mathbf{r}}_{p+1} \\ \underline{\mathbf{r}}_{p+1}^H & \underline{\mathbf{R}}_p \end{pmatrix} , \qquad (15.63)$$

for which the block *row* vectors $\underline{\mathbf{r}}_{p+1}$ and $\underline{\mathbf{s}}_{p+1}$ are defined as

$$\begin{aligned} \underline{\mathbf{r}}_{p+1} &= \begin{pmatrix} \mathbf{R}_{xx}[1] & \cdots & \mathbf{R}_{xx}[p+1] \end{pmatrix} \\ \underline{\mathbf{s}}_{p+1} &= \begin{pmatrix} \mathbf{R}_{xx}[-(p+1)] & \cdots & \mathbf{R}_{xx}[-1] \end{pmatrix} . \end{aligned} \qquad (15.64)$$

These partitions may then be used to construct the following relationship

$$\begin{pmatrix} \underline{\mathbf{a}}_p & \mathbf{0} \end{pmatrix} \underline{\mathbf{R}}_{p+1} = \begin{pmatrix} P_p^f & \mathbf{0} & \cdots & \mathbf{0} & \Delta_{p+1} \end{pmatrix} \qquad (15.65)$$

$$\begin{pmatrix} \mathbf{0} & \underline{\mathbf{b}}_p \end{pmatrix} \underline{\mathbf{R}}_{p+1} = \begin{pmatrix} \nabla_{p+1} & \mathbf{0} & \cdots & \mathbf{0} & P_p^b \end{pmatrix} , \qquad (15.66)$$

for which the $m \times m$ matrices Δ_{p+1} and ∇_{p+1} are defined as

$$\Delta_{p+1} = \mathbf{R}_{xx}[p+1] + \sum_{k=1}^{p} \mathbf{A}_p[k]\mathbf{R}_{xx}[p+1-k] = \underline{\mathbf{a}}_p \underline{\mathbf{s}}_{p+1}^H \qquad (15.67)$$

$$\nabla_{p+1} = \mathbf{R}_{xx}[-p-1] + \sum_{k=1}^{p} \mathbf{B}_p[k]\mathbf{R}_{xx}[k-p-1] = \underline{\mathbf{b}}_p \underline{\mathbf{r}}_{p+1}^H . \qquad (15.68)$$

The order update recursion for the forward and backward autoregressive coefficient matrices take the form

$$\underline{\mathbf{a}}_{p+1} = \begin{pmatrix} \underline{\mathbf{a}}_p & \mathbf{0} \end{pmatrix} + \mathbf{A}_{p+1}[p+1] \begin{pmatrix} \mathbf{0} & \underline{\mathbf{b}}_p \end{pmatrix} \qquad (15.69)$$

$$\underline{\mathbf{b}}_{p+1} = \begin{pmatrix} \mathbf{0} & \underline{\mathbf{b}}_p \end{pmatrix} + \mathbf{B}_{p+1}[p+1] \begin{pmatrix} \underline{\mathbf{a}}_p & \mathbf{0} \end{pmatrix} . \qquad (15.70)$$

On a matrix element-by-matrix element basis, the linear prediction filter matrix coefficients then obey the recursions

$$\mathbf{A}_{p+1}[k] = \mathbf{A}_p[k] + \mathbf{A}_{p+1}[p+1]\mathbf{B}_p[p+1-k] \tag{15.71}$$
$$\mathbf{B}_{p+1}[k] = \mathbf{B}_p[k] + \mathbf{B}_{p+1}[p+1]\mathbf{A}_p[p+1-k] \tag{15.72}$$

for $k = 1$ to $k = p$. In the multichannel case, there are two distinct reflection coefficient matrices given by

$$\mathbf{A}_{p+1}[p+1] = -\boldsymbol{\Delta}_{p+1}\left(\boldsymbol{P}_p{}^b\right)^{-1} \tag{15.73}$$
$$\mathbf{B}_{p+1}[p+1] = -\boldsymbol{\nabla}_{p+1}\left(\boldsymbol{P}_p{}^f\right)^{-1} \quad . \tag{15.74}$$

This is in contrast to the single-channel case, for which there was only a single reflection coefficient, due to the property $b_p[p] = a_p^*[p]$ (Sec. 3.8.1). The validity of Eqs. (15.69) and (15.70) may be checked by postmultiplying each side of these equations by $\underline{\mathbf{R}}_{p+1}$ and using Eqs. (15.65), (15.66), (15.73), and (15.74). A by-product of this check is the order update for the noise prediction error covariance matrices,

$$P_{p+1}^f = P_p{}^f + \mathbf{A}_{p+1}[p+1]\boldsymbol{\nabla}_{p+1} = \left(\mathbf{I} - \mathbf{A}_{p+1}[p+1]\mathbf{B}_{p+1}[p+1]\right)P_p{}^f \tag{15.75}$$
$$P_{p+1}^b = P_p{}^b + \mathbf{B}_{p+1}[p+1]\boldsymbol{\Delta}_{p+1} = \left(\mathbf{I} - \mathbf{B}_{p+1}[p+1]\mathbf{A}_{p+1}[p+1]\right)P_p{}^b . \tag{15.76}$$

Using the matrix identity

$$\begin{pmatrix} \underline{\mathbf{a}}_p & \mathbf{0} \end{pmatrix} \underline{\mathbf{R}}_{p+1} \begin{pmatrix} \mathbf{0} \\ \underline{\mathbf{b}}_p^H \end{pmatrix} = \begin{pmatrix} \mathbf{0} & \underline{\mathbf{b}}_p \end{pmatrix} \underline{\mathbf{R}}_{p+1} \begin{pmatrix} \underline{\mathbf{a}}_p^H \\ \mathbf{0} \end{pmatrix} \quad , \tag{15.77}$$

the following lemma may be derived

$$\boldsymbol{\nabla}_{p+1} = \boldsymbol{\Delta}_{p+1}^H \quad . \tag{15.78}$$

The $m \times m$ matrix $\boldsymbol{\Delta}_{p+1}$ is simply the cross correlation between the forward and backward linear prediction residuals at one unit of delay (lag),

$$\boldsymbol{\Delta}_{p+1} = \mathcal{E}\left\{\mathbf{e}_p^f[n]\mathbf{e}_p^{b\,H}[n-1]\right\} = P_p{}^{fb} \quad . \tag{15.79}$$

The proof of this relationship is left to the problem set.

A definition for a normalized cross correlation, or *normalized partial correlation*, comparable to the single-channel reflection coefficient defined by Eq. (7.22), is

$$\boldsymbol{\Lambda}_{p+1} = \left(P_p^{f\,1/2}\right)^{-1}\left(P_p{}^{fb}\right)\left(P_p^{b\,1/2}\right)^{-H}$$
$$= \left(\mathcal{E}\{\mathbf{e}_p^f[n]\mathbf{e}_p^{f\,H}[n]\}^{1/2}\right)^{-1}\left(\mathcal{E}\{\mathbf{e}_p^f[n]\mathbf{e}_p^{b\,H}[n-1]\}\right)\left(\mathcal{E}\{\mathbf{e}_p^b[n-1]\mathbf{e}_p^{b\,H}[n-1]\}^{1/2}\right)^{-H}.$$
$$\tag{15.80}$$

In the multichannel case, the partial correlation coefficient matrix and the reflection coefficient matrices are *not* identical, unlike the single-channel case, for which they are the same. The superscript $^{-H}$ denotes the conjugate transpose of the inverse, i.e., the order of application is the inverse first, followed by the conjugate transpose. The superscript $^{1/2}$ denotes the lower triangular matrix obtained by the Cholesky decomposition of the Hermitian matrix to which the operation is applied. Therefore, if $\mathbf{M}$ is a Hermitian matrix, then

$$\mathbf{M} = \left(\mathbf{M}^{1/2}\right)\left(\mathbf{M}^{1/2}\right)^{H} \quad . \tag{15.81}$$

The forward and backward reflection coefficients of Eqs. (15.73) and (15.74) may be expressed in terms of $\mathbf{\Lambda}_{p+1}$ as

$$\mathbf{A}_{p+1}[p+1] = -\left(P_p^{f\,1/2}\right)\mathbf{\Lambda}_{p+1}\left(P_p^{b\,1/2}\right)^{-1} \tag{15.82}$$

$$\mathbf{B}_{p+1}[p+1] = -\left(P_p^{b\,1/2}\right)\mathbf{\Lambda}_{p+1}^{H}\left(P_p^{f\,1/2}\right)^{-1} \quad . \tag{15.83}$$

The multichannel normalized correlation $\mathbf{\Lambda}_p$ provides a unique parameterization sequence for the multichannel algorithm, just as the reflection coefficient $a_p[p]$ provided a unique parameterization of the single-channel AR process. It has been shown [Morf et al., 1978b], based on the nonnegative definite correlation $\mathbf{R}_p$, that the singular values of $\mathbf{\Lambda}_{p+1}\mathbf{\Lambda}_{p+1}^{H}$ are within the unit circle. This is the multichannel extension to the requirement that single-channel reflection coefficients have magnitudes less than unity.

Equations (15.67), (15.69), (15.70), (15.73), (15.74), (15.75), and (15.76) constitute the multichannel extension of the Levinson algorithm. Equations (15.80) and (15.83) may be used in lieu of Eqs. (15.73) and (15.74). The recursive-in-order nature of the algorithm requires that $\mathbf{R}_q$ be strictly positive definite and nonsingular at any order from $q = 1$ to $q = p$. This will be true as long as $\det|P_q^{f}| > 0$ and $\det|P_q^{b}| > 0$ at each order. The initial conditions $P_0^{f} = P_0^{b} = \mathbf{R}_{\mathbf{xx}}[0]$, required to commence the Levinson recursion, are obtained by inspection of Eqs. (15.65) and (15.66).

A useful relationship between the order p multichannel linear prediction errors and the order $p + 1$ linear prediction errors may be obtained by postmultiplying both Eqs. (15.69) and (15.70) by $\underline{\mathbf{x}}_{p+1}[n]$ to yield

$$\mathbf{e}_{p+1}^{f}[n] = \mathbf{e}_p^{f}[n] + \mathbf{A}_{p+1}[p+1]\mathbf{e}_p^{b}[n-1] \tag{15.84}$$

$$\mathbf{e}_{p+1}^{b}[n] = \mathbf{e}_p^{b}[n-1] + \mathbf{B}_{p+1}[p+1]\mathbf{e}_p^{f}[n] \quad . \tag{15.85}$$

15.9   MULTICHANNEL BLOCK-TOEPLITZ MATRIX INVERSE

The multichannel Levinson algorithm serves as the basis for methods that describe the complete inverse of the Hermitian block-Toeplitz correlation matrix of

Eq. (15.55). Akaike [1973] and Watson [1973] were two of the first to publish algorithms for such a block inverse. A form of the Hermitian block-Toeplitz inverse that will be especially useful in this chapter is

$$\underline{\mathbf{R}}_p^{-1} = \underline{\mathbf{A}}_p^H \underline{\mathbf{P}}_p^f \underline{\mathbf{A}}_p - \underline{\mathbf{B}}_p^H \underline{\mathbf{P}}_p^b \underline{\mathbf{B}}_p \tag{15.86}$$

in which

$$\underline{\mathbf{A}}_p = \begin{pmatrix} \mathbf{I} & \mathbf{A}_p[1] & \cdots & \mathbf{A}_p[p] \\ \mathbf{0} & \ddots & \ddots & \vdots \\ \vdots & \ddots & \ddots & \mathbf{A}_p[1] \\ \mathbf{0} & \cdots & \mathbf{0} & \mathbf{I} \end{pmatrix}, \quad \underline{\mathbf{P}}_p^f = \begin{pmatrix} (P_p^f)^{-1} & \mathbf{0} & \cdots & \mathbf{0} \\ \mathbf{0} & (P_p^f)^{-1} & \ddots & \vdots \\ \vdots & \ddots & \ddots & \mathbf{0} \\ \mathbf{0} & \cdots & \mathbf{0} & (P_p^f)^{-1} \end{pmatrix},$$

$$\underline{\mathbf{B}}_p = \begin{pmatrix} \mathbf{0} & \mathbf{B}_p[p] & \cdots & \mathbf{B}_p[1] \\ \mathbf{0} & \ddots & \ddots & \vdots \\ \vdots & \ddots & \ddots & \mathbf{B}_p[p] \\ \mathbf{0} & \cdots & \mathbf{0} & \mathbf{0} \end{pmatrix}, \quad \underline{\mathbf{P}}_p^b = \begin{pmatrix} (P_p^b)^{-1} & \mathbf{0} & \cdots & \mathbf{0} \\ \mathbf{0} & (P_p^b)^{-1} & \ddots & \vdots \\ \vdots & \ddots & \ddots & \mathbf{0} \\ \mathbf{0} & \cdots & \mathbf{0} & (P_p^b)^{-1} \end{pmatrix}.$$

This result may be derived using the approach of Sec. 3.8.1 (see also Friedlander et al., 1979].

15.10 MULTICHANNEL AUTOREGRESSIVE SPECTRAL ESTIMATION

Algorithms that directly estimate the parameters of a multichannel AR process from the data are patterned after algorithms that have been developed for the single-channel AR process in Chap. 8. Algorithms based on correlation function estimation, partial correlation estimation, and least squares linear prediction are covered in this section.

15.10.1 Correlation Function Estimation Method

The most obvious approach to AR PSD estimation from the r-channel sample data is to use correlation function estimates in lieu of the unknown correlation function. One estimate based on the N vector samples $\mathbf{x}[1]$ to $\mathbf{x}[N]$ is the biased matrix lag product sum

$$\hat{\mathbf{R}}_{\mathbf{xx}}[m] = \frac{1}{N} \sum_{m=1}^{N-m} \mathbf{x}[n+m]\mathbf{x}^H[n] \quad , \tag{15.87}$$

defined for $0 \le m \le N-1$. The autocorrelation terms for negative lags are obtained by the property $\hat{\mathbf{R}}_{\mathbf{xx}}[-m] = \hat{\mathbf{R}}_{\mathbf{xx}}^H[m]$. Subroutine CORRELATION can be used to calculate the individual autocorrelation and cross correlation elements of matrix $\mathbf{R}_{\mathbf{xx}}[m]$. The use of biased correlation estimates will guarantee that $\underline{\mathbf{R}}_p$ will be positive semidefinite. Combining the correlation estimates with the multichannel Levinson algorithm will yield the estimates of the AR coefficient matrices, which can then be used in Eq. (15.43) to obtain the AR PSD. This procedure will be termed the *multichannel Yule-Walker algorithm.*

15.10.2 Partial Correlation Estimation: Vieira-Morf Method

Only the residual cross correlation $\boldsymbol{\Delta}_p$ or, equivalently, the partial correlation $\boldsymbol{\Lambda}_p$ depend on the correlation function $\mathbf{R_{xx}}[m]$. Replacing these with estimates based on the available data would permit the remainder of the Levinson recursion to be incorporated into an AR parameter estimation algorithm. Algorithms that parallel the geometric and harmonic algorithms of Chap. 8 for the estimation of the reflection coefficients have been developed.

The multichannel version of the geometric algorithm was proposed by Vieira and Morf [see Morf et al., 1978a]. They proposed to estimate the partial correlation as

$$\hat{\boldsymbol{\Lambda}}_{p+1} = \left(\hat{\boldsymbol{P}}_p^{f\,1/2}\right)^{-1}\left(\hat{\boldsymbol{P}}_p^{fb}\right)\left(\hat{\boldsymbol{P}}_p^{b\,1/2}\right)^{-H} \tag{15.88}$$

based on estimates of the residual variance matrices $\boldsymbol{P}_p^f$, $\boldsymbol{P}_p^b$, and covariance matrix $\boldsymbol{P}_p^{fb}$

$$\hat{\boldsymbol{P}}_p^f = \frac{1}{N}\sum_{n=p+2}^{N} \mathbf{e}_p^f[n]\mathbf{e}_p^{f\,H}[n]$$

$$\hat{\boldsymbol{P}}_p^b = \frac{1}{N}\sum_{n=p+2}^{N} \mathbf{e}_p^b[n-1]\mathbf{e}_p^{b\,H}[n-1] \tag{15.89}$$

$$\hat{\boldsymbol{P}}_p^{fb} = \frac{1}{N}\sum_{n=p+2}^{N} \mathbf{e}_p^f[n]\mathbf{e}_p^{b\,H}[n-1] \quad .$$

Note that the factor $1/N$ is canceled when computing $\hat{\boldsymbol{\Lambda}}_{p+1}$.

The residuals $\mathbf{e}_p^f[n]$ and $\mathbf{e}_p^b[n]$ for $p+1 \leq n \leq N$ are updated at each order using recursions provided by Eqs. (15.84) and (15.85). With these modifications to estimate $\hat{\boldsymbol{\Lambda}}_{p+1}$, the multichannel Levinson algorithm can proceed as in the known correlation case. This includes the order updates (15.75) and (15.76) for $\boldsymbol{P}_p^f$ and $\boldsymbol{P}_p^b$; the estimates $\hat{\boldsymbol{P}}_p^f$ and $\hat{\boldsymbol{P}}_p^b$ are used *strictly* for estimating $\hat{\boldsymbol{\Lambda}}_{p+1}$.

The Vieira-Morf geometric algorithm is initialized by setting

$$\boldsymbol{P}_0^f = \boldsymbol{P}_0^b = \frac{1}{N}\sum_{n=1}^{N} \mathbf{x}[n]\mathbf{x}^H[n] \tag{15.90}$$

and

$$\mathbf{e}_0^f[n] = \mathbf{e}_0^b[n] = \mathbf{x}[n] \tag{15.91}$$

for $1 \leq n \leq N$. This multichannel algorithm reduces to the geometric mean algorithm for a single channel, because $P_p{}^f = P_p{}^b = \rho$ in this case. Appendix 15.B provides program MCAR which implements the Vieira-Morf algorithm. Appendix 15.C contains program MCARPSD to evaluate the resulting multichannel AR power spectral density.

15.10.3 Partial Correlation Estimation: Nuttall-Strand Method

A multichannel version of the harmonic mean algorithm was independently proposed by Nuttall [1976a,b] and Strand [1977]. They elected to directly estimate the cross correlation coefficient $\mathbf{\Lambda}_p$ from the data, rather than to estimate the normalized partial correlation $\mathbf{\Delta}_p$. The estimate is given by that matrix $\mathbf{\Delta}_p$ which minimizes the trace of a weighted average (arithmetic mean) of the *estimated* forward and backward linear prediction residuals covariance matrices

$$\text{tr}\left\{ \mathbf{V}_{p-1}\hat{P}_p{}^f + \mathbf{W}_{p-1}\hat{P}_p{}^b \right\} \tag{15.92}$$

subject to the three constraints

$$\mathbf{e}_p^f[n] = \mathbf{e}_{p-1}^f[n] - \mathbf{\Delta}_p(P_p{}^b)^{-1}\mathbf{e}_{p-1}^b[n-1] \tag{15.93}$$

$$\mathbf{e}_p^b[n] = \mathbf{e}_p^b[n-1] - \mathbf{\Delta}_p^H(P_p{}^f)^{-1}\mathbf{e}_{p-1}^f[n] \tag{15.94}$$

$$\mathbf{A}_p[p]P_p{}^f = \left(\mathbf{B}_p[p]P_p{}^b\right)^H \quad . \tag{15.95}$$

The estimates $\hat{P}_p{}^f$ and $\hat{P}_p{}^b$ were defined previously by Eq. (15.89). Matrices $\mathbf{V}_p$ and $\mathbf{W}_p$ are arbitrary positive-definite weighting matrices to be selected. Constraints (15.93) and (15.94) follow directly from Eqs. (15.69), (15.70), (15.73), and (15.74). The linear matrix constraint (15.95) follows directly from Eqs. (15.73), (15.74), and (15.78). This last constraint demonstrates that the reflection coefficient matrices cannot be specified independently. These constraints jointly force the solution for $\mathbf{\Delta}_p$ to obey as many properties of the multichannel Levinson algorithm as possible. The weighting matrices must be carefully selected so that the resulting solution for $\mathbf{\Delta}_p$ will yield a stable correlation sequence (guaranteed if $\mathbf{\Lambda}_p$ has singular values less than or equal to unity) and a positive-definite multichannel spectral estimate.

Nuttall [1977] has made an extensive examination of weighting matrices and has determined that the inverse matrices

$$\mathbf{V}_p = \left(P_p{}^f\right)^{-1} \tag{15.96}$$

$$\mathbf{W}_p = \left(P_p{}^b\right)^{-1} \tag{15.97}$$

will yield the desired stability property. The AR parameter estimates are stable if both $\det[\mathbf{A}_p(z)]$ and $\det[z^{-p}\mathbf{B}_p(1/z)]$ possess all of their zeros within the unit z-plane circle. Stability ensures that the forward and backward correlation extrapolations are damped extensions, i.e., the terms grow smaller rather than increase in magnitude [Nuttall, 1977]. It is desirable not to have the channels with larger errors to receive the most emphasis. The weightings of Eqs. (15.96) and (15.97) seem intuitive in that they weight each channel proportional to its inverse squared error. If these weightings are selected, then a minimization of Eq. (15.92) produces the matrix expression

$$\hat{P}_p^f \left(P_p^f\right)^{-1} \hat{\Delta}_{p+1} + \hat{\Delta}_{p+1} \left(P_p^b\right)^{-1} \hat{P}_p^b = -2\hat{P}_p^{fb} \quad , \tag{15.98}$$

which contains a mixture of the error covariance matrices P_p^f and P_p^b from the Levinson recursion and the error covariance matrix *estimates* $\hat{P}_p^f$, $\hat{P}_p^b$, and $\hat{P}_p^{fb}$. In the single-channel case, each element of Eq. (15.98) reduces to a scalar and the error covariances are identical, i.e., $P_p^f = P_p^b$. Noting that $\mathbf{A}_{p+1}[p+1] = \hat{\Delta}_{p+1} P_p^f$, the solution for $\mathbf{A}_{p+1}[p+1]$ in the single-channel case reduces to the harmonic mean relationship

$$\mathbf{A}_{p+1}[p+1] = \frac{-2\hat{P}_p^{fb}}{\hat{P}_p^f + \hat{P}_p^b} \quad . \tag{15.99}$$

Thus, the single-channel case of the Nuttall-Strand multichannel algorithm is identical to the Burg algorithm of Sec. 8.4.

Equation (15.98) is a special case of a bilinear matrix equation

$$\mathbf{AX} + \mathbf{XB} = \mathbf{C} \quad , \tag{15.100}$$

in which $\mathbf{A}$, $\mathbf{B}$, $\mathbf{C}$, and $\mathbf{X}$ are $m \times m$ matrices. Solutions that obtain a unique matrix $\mathbf{X}$ have been provided by several authors. Nuttall [1976b] selected the solution

$$\mathbf{X} = \mathbf{PQ}^{-1}$$

$$\mathbf{P} = \sum_{k=0}^{m-1} (-1)^k \mathbf{A}_k \mathbf{CB}^{m-1-k}$$

$$\mathbf{Q} = \sum_{k=0}^{m} (-1)^k a_k \mathbf{B}^{m-k} \tag{15.101}$$

$$a_k = -\frac{1}{k} \text{tr}\left(\mathbf{A}\mathbf{A}_{k-1}\right) \quad 1 \le k \le m$$

$$\mathbf{A}_k = \mathbf{A}\mathbf{A}_{k-1} + a_k \mathbf{I} \quad 1 \le k \le m \quad ,$$

in which $a_0 = 1$ and $\mathbf{A}_0 = \mathbf{I}$. The matrices $\mathbf{P}$ and $\mathbf{Q}$ may be simplified for the two-channel case [Nuttall, 1981] to

$$\mathbf{P} = \mathbf{CB} - \left(\mathbf{A} - \text{tr}(\mathbf{A})\mathbf{I}\right)\mathbf{C} \tag{15.102}$$

$$\mathbf{Q} = \left(\text{tr}\,\mathbf{A} + \text{tr}\,\mathbf{B}\right)\mathbf{B} + \left(\det\mathbf{A} - \det\mathbf{B}\right)\mathbf{I} \quad . \tag{15.103}$$

The Nuttall-Strand algorithm is initialized by setting P_0^f, P_0^b, $e_0^f[n]$, and $e_0^b[n]$ to the values given by Eqs. (15.90) and (15.91). Appendix 15.B provides program MCAR to compute this algorithm. If the parameters in this program are set to METHOD = 2 and NUMCHS = 1, then the program will provide a solution identical to that given by program BURG in Appendix 8.B.

15.10.4 Covariance Linear Prediction Method

Algorithms based on multichannel extensions of the single-channel least squares linear prediction algorithms of Sec. 8.5 follow in a straightforward manner. The multichannel forward linear prediction error

$$e_p^f[n] = \mathbf{x}[n] + \sum_{k=1}^p \mathbf{A}_p[k]\mathbf{x}[n-k] = \underline{\mathbf{a}}_p \underline{\mathbf{x}}_p[n] \tag{15.104}$$

and the backward linear prediction error

$$e_p^b[n] = \mathbf{x}[n-p] + \sum_{k=1}^p \mathbf{B}_p[k]\mathbf{x}[n-p+k] = \underline{\mathbf{b}}_p \underline{\mathbf{x}}_p[n] \tag{15.105}$$

may be defined for time indices from $n = 1$ to $n = N + p$ if the assumption that $\mathbf{x}[n] = \mathbf{0}$ outside the available data range (assumed to be $n = 1$ to $n = N$) is made. The Hermitian, nonnegative-definite squared forward and backward linear prediction error matrices

$$P_p^f = \sum_{n=p+1}^N e_p^f[n]\left(e_p^f[n]\right)^H = \sum_{n=p+1}^N \underline{\mathbf{a}}_p \underline{\mathbf{x}}_p[n]\underline{\mathbf{x}}_p^H[n]\underline{\mathbf{a}}_p^H = \underline{\mathbf{a}}_p \underline{\mathbf{R}}_p \underline{\mathbf{a}}_p^H \tag{15.106}$$

$$P_p^b = \sum_{n=p+1}^N e_p^b[n]\left(e_p^b[n]\right)^H = \underline{\mathbf{b}}_p \underline{\mathbf{R}}_p \underline{\mathbf{b}}_p^H \tag{15.107}$$

and the $(p+1) \times (p+1)$ Hermitian block data matrix

$$\underline{\mathbf{R}}_p = \sum_{n=p+1}^N \underline{\mathbf{x}}_p[n]\underline{\mathbf{x}}_p^H[n] \tag{15.108}$$

will be formed, however, by summing only over the range from $n = p+1$ to $n = N$. This uses only the available data and corresponds to the multichannel "covariance" case of linear prediction. It uses only valid errors of nonwindowed multichannel data. The "autocorrelation" and prewindowed cases of linear prediction with index ranges of $1 \le n \le N + p$ and $1 \le n \le N$, respectively, could also be used, but the covariance case yields the best results for short data sequences.

Some multichannel matrix algebra to separately minimize scalars $\text{tr } \boldsymbol{P}_p{}^f = \sum (\mathbf{e}_p^f)^H \mathbf{e}_p^f$ and $\text{tr } \boldsymbol{P}_p{}^b = \sum (\mathbf{e}_p^b)^H \mathbf{e}_p^b$ leads to the following pair of multichannel linear prediction normal equations

$$\underline{\mathbf{a}}_p \underline{\mathbf{R}}_p = \begin{pmatrix} \boldsymbol{P}_p{}^f & \mathbf{0} & \cdots & \mathbf{0} \end{pmatrix} \tag{15.109}$$

$$\underline{\mathbf{b}}_p \underline{\mathbf{R}}_p = \begin{pmatrix} \mathbf{0} & \cdots & \mathbf{0} & \boldsymbol{P}_p{}^b \end{pmatrix} \quad . \tag{15.110}$$

Note that $\underline{\mathbf{R}}_p$ must be positive definite (nonsingular) in order to obtain the solutions. The matrix $\underline{\mathbf{R}}_p$ may be expressed as

$$\underline{\mathbf{R}}_p = \begin{pmatrix} \mathbf{R_{xx}}[0,0] & \cdots & \mathbf{R_{xx}}[0,p] \\ \vdots & & \vdots \\ \mathbf{R_{xx}}[p,0] & \cdots & \mathbf{R_{xx}}[p,p] \end{pmatrix} \quad , \tag{15.111}$$

which has entries

$$\mathbf{R_{xx}}[i,j] = \sum_{n=p+1}^{N} \mathbf{x}[n-i]\mathbf{x}^H[n-j] \quad . \tag{15.112}$$

Even though $\underline{\mathbf{R}}_p$ is not block Toeplitz, a fast algorithm that solves Eqs. (15.109) and (15.110) has been developed by the author along similar lines as the single-channel covariance algorithm in Chap. 8. As in the single-channel case, the multichannel PSD formed from the forward linear prediction coefficient matrices will yield a PSD estimate different from that formed from the backward coefficient matrices, due to the separate unconstrained minimizations of the traces of the forward and backward squared errors that lead to $\underline{\mathbf{R}}_p$ not having a block-Toeplitz structure. This is not consistent with the stationary assumption of the underlying model. However, the spectral estimates will still be similar. The stability of the multichannel linear prediction filters is, as with the single-channel case, not guaranteed, i.e., a stable correlation function is not guaranteed.

15.10.5 Multichannel AR Spectral Evaluation

The AR spectral estimate is completed by evaluating the multichannel PSD. The forward autoregressive coefficient spectral density (15.43) or the backward autoregressive coefficient spectral density (15.61) as a function of frequency f

$$\mathbf{P}_{\text{AR}}(f) = T[\mathbf{A}(f)]^{-1} \boldsymbol{P}_p{}^f [\mathbf{A}(f)]^{-H} \tag{15.113}$$

$$\mathbf{P}_{\text{AR}}(f) = T[\mathbf{B}(f)]^{-1} \boldsymbol{P}_p{}^b [\mathbf{B}(f)]^{-H} \quad , \tag{15.114}$$

for which

$$\mathbf{A}(f) = \mathbf{I} + \sum_{k=1}^{p} \mathbf{A}[k] \exp(-j2\pi f kT) \tag{15.115}$$

$$\mathbf{B}(f) = \exp(-j2\pi f pT) \left[\mathbf{I} + \sum_{k=1}^{p} \mathbf{B}[k] \exp(j2\pi f kT) \right] \quad . \tag{15.116}$$

Computer program MCARPSD will evaluate either (15.113) or (15.114) if given the frequency.

15.11   AUTOREGRESSIVE ORDER SELECTION

An aid in the determination of the order of the multichannel AR model is the multichannel version of the Akaike AIC criterion [Jones, 1974; Nuttall, 1976b], which has the form

$$\text{AIC}[p] = N \ln(\det \boldsymbol{P}_p{}^f) + 2m^2 p = M \ln(\det \boldsymbol{P}_p{}^b) + 2m^2 p \quad . \tag{15.117}$$

The order to choose is the one for which $\text{AIC}[p]$ is a minimum. A suggested upper bound for the order is $3\sqrt{N}/m$ [Nuttall, 1976b], where m is the number of channels and N is the number of data points per channel. In general, the order selection procedure for multichannel AR analysis has not been researched in depth, so that the $\text{AIC}[p]$ must be used only as a guideline for the approximate order.

15.12   EXPERIMENTAL COMPARISON OF MULTICHANNEL AUTOGRESSIVE PSD ESTIMATORS

Analytical characterization of the performance of the various multichannel AR PSD estimators is mathematically intractable, so one must resort to experimental approaches to yield empirical characterizations. Two types of two-channel data sets are employed here to characterize performance. One is an actual first-order two-channel autoregression. The second is a two-channel process with tones embedded in a colored noise process similar to the test case of Appendix II.

In the first test, a first-order ($p = 1$) two-channel autoregressive process was used to generate data ensembles. Data were generated according to the recursion

$$\mathbf{x}[n] = -\mathbf{A}[1]\mathbf{x}[n-1] + \mathbf{w}[n] \quad , \tag{15.118}$$

in which the autoregressive coefficient matrix is

$$\mathbf{A}[1] = \begin{pmatrix} -.85 & +.75 \\ -.65 & -.55 \end{pmatrix} \tag{15.119}$$

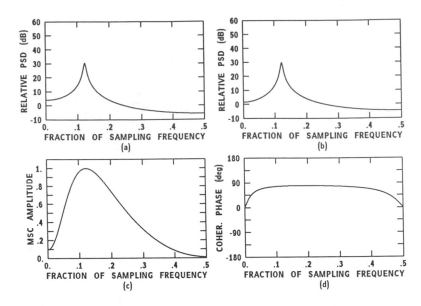

Figure 15.2   True spectra of AR(1) test case. (a) Channel 1 autospectrum. (b) Channel 2 autospectrum. (c) Magnitude squared coherence. (d) Phase of coherence.

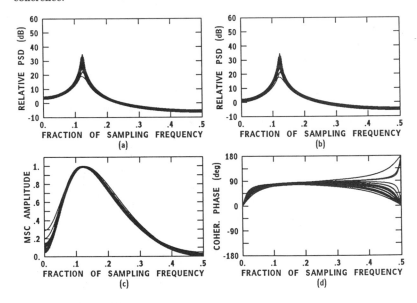

Figure 15.3   Nuttall-Strand algorithm AR(1) estimate. (a) Channel 1 autospectrum. (b) Channel 2 autospectrum. (c) Magnitude squared coherence. (d) Phase of coherence.

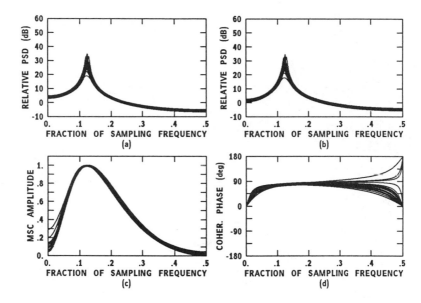

Figure 15.4   Vieira-Morf algorithm AR(1) estimate.   (a) Channel 1 autospectrum. (b) Channel 2 autospectrum. (c) Magnitude squared coherence. (d) Phase of coherence.

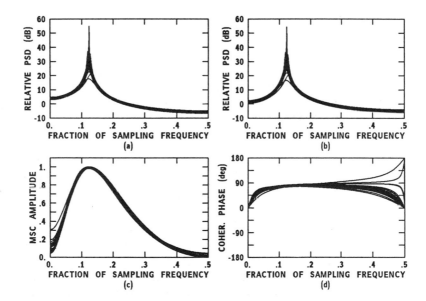

Figure 15.5   Covariance algorithm AR(1) estimate (forward coefficients). (a) Channel 1 autospectrum. (b) Channel 2 autospectrum. (c) Magnitude squared coherence. (d) Phase of coherence.

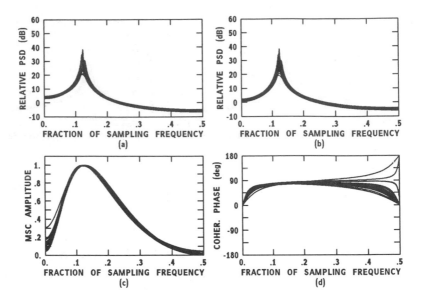

Figure 15.6   Covariance algorithm AR(1) estimate (backward coefficients).
(a) Channel 1 autospectrum. (b) Channel 2 autospectrum. (c) Magnitude
squared coherence. (d) Phase of coherence.

and $\mathbf{w}[n]$ is a white two-channel process, uncorrelated between channels and of unit
variance in each channel. Even though this is a first-order autoregressive process,
the autospectra of each channel will have four poles and three zeros. Figure 15.2
depicts the true autospectra and coherence for this process. The autospectra for
each of the two channels and the MSC will have peaks at a fraction of sampling
frequency of .12295. The phase of the complex coherence (cross spectrum) is $90°$
at this peak frequency and $0°$ at frequencies .0 and .5 . The peak magnitude of
the squared coherence is .999013 at this peak frequency. Twenty sequences, each
of 100 sample points, were processed by each of the three AR algorithms, with
the order p restricted to be unity. The 20 spectral estimates were overlapped, as
shown in Figs. 15.3–15.6. The autospectra were plotted with respect to the same
reference value of 1500. Of the four set of plots, the Nuttall-Strand and backward
linear prediction algorithms had the least variance in PSD amplitude, while the
Vieira-Morf and forward linear prediction algorithms had the least variance of the
spectral peak in frequency. Otherwise, all four methods yielded very similar spectral
estimates.

The next test consisted of data sequences with three sinusoids in a colored
noise process. In channel 1, sinusoids with fractions of the sampling frequency of
.1, .2, and .24 were used. The respective amplitudes were .1, 1., and 1., while
the respective initial phases were $0°$, $90°$, and $235°$. The colored noise process,
which had most of its power above the frequencies of the sinusoids, was generated
by passing white noise of .05 variance through a digital filter with a raised-cosine

Figure 15.7 Nuttall-Strand algorithm AR(12) estimate for 64 samples. (a) Channel 1 autospectrum. (b) Channel 2 autospectrum. (c) Magnitude squared coherence. (d) Phase of coherence.

Figure 15.8 Vieira-Morf algorithm AR(12) estimate for 64 samples. (a) Channel 1 autospectrum. (b) Channel 2 autospectrum. (c) Magnitude squared coherence. (d) Phase of coherence.

Figure 15.9   Covariance algorithm AR(12) estimate for 64 samples (forward coefficients). (a) Channel 1 autospectrum. (b) Channel 2 autospectrum. (c) Magnitude squared coherence. (d) Phase of coherence.

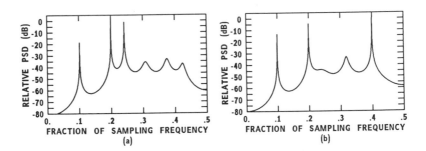

Figure 15.10   Burg single-channel algorithm AR(12) estimate for 64 samples. (a) Channel 1 autospectrum. (b) Channel 2 autospectrum.

spectral response between .2 and .5, identical to the process used for the test sequence in Appendix II. In channel 2, sinusoids of fractional frequencies .1, .2, .4, amplitudes of .1, 1., 1., and initial phases of 0°, 210°, 25° were generated. A colored noise process similar to channel 1, but independently generated, was added to the sinusoids. Note that the sinusoidal components at fractional frequencies .1 and .2 are common to both channels. A data sequence of 64 points was generated for each channel. Figures 15.7–15.9 depict the autospectra, coherence magnitude, and coherence phase for order $p = 12$ estimates by the three autoregressive methods. Note that in all plots, some energy of the .24 fractional frequency sinusoid, which

Figure 15.11 Nuttall-Strand algorithm AR(12) estimate for 500 samples.
(a) Channel 1 autospectrum. (b) Channel 2 autospectrum. (c) Magnitude
squared coherence. (d) Phase of coherence.

should be present only in channel 1, has coupled into the autospectral estimate
for channel 2 and, conversely, the .4 fractional frequency sinusoid, which should
be present only in channel 2, has coupled into the autospectral estimate for channel 1. The MSC plots also show spikes at the tone frequencies .24 and .4, where,
ideally, the coherence should be zero. This "feed-across" artifact is an undesirable effect; however, it is common to all the methods presented in this chapter and
seems unavoidable whenever processing short data sequences with multichannel AR
algorithms [see also Fougere, 1981]. If the data sequences from each channel are processed separately by the single-channel AR methods, such as the Burg algorithm,
the autospectra do not give a false tonal indication, as illustrated in Fig. 15.10. By
increasing the data sequence length to 500 samples, there is an improvement in the
feed-across effect in the multichannel autospectra, as shown in Fig. 15.11, although
the coherence still has sharp spikes near unity. Thus it seems that the attractive
high-resolution properties of the single-channel linear prediction spectrum analysis
when processing short data records do not extend to the multichannel case without
problems. The coupling effect is even more pronounced for more than two channels. Although the cross spectral PSD entries are for two channels, the data from
all channels contributes to the individual two-channel cross spectral estimates. The
feed-across effect leads to false indications of narrowband components, especially
when processing short data sequences. A detailed analysis [Marple and Nuttall,
1983] of the cause of the feed-across effect has shown it is due to inexact pole-zero
cancellation in the multichannel PSD estimate. This example emphasizes the need

to confirm details seen in the autospectra generated by a multichannel algorithm with independent single-channel autospectral estimates.

The spectral line-splitting phenomenon observed in single-channel linear prediction spectrum analysis has also been observed under similar tone conditions in some multichannel algorithms, particularly the Nuttall-Strand and Vieira-Morf algorithms. It has not been observed in the multichannel covariance algorithm.

15.13 MULTICHANNEL MINIMUM VARIANCE SPECTRAL ESTIMATION

Similar arguments as those used in Chap. 12 could be used here to develop a multichannel minimum variance spectral estimator, in which the estimator represents the variance at the output of an m-channel finite impulse response filter with filter coefficients constrained to pass a sinusoid at a given frequency without distortion and to attenuate all other spectral components. The resultant multichannel MV PSD estimator will be found to have the form [Lacoss, 1977]

$$\hat{\mathbf{P}}_{\mathrm{MV}}(f) = T\left[\underline{\mathbf{e}}_p(f)\underline{\mathbf{R}}_p^{-1}\underline{\mathbf{e}}_p^H(f)\right]^{-1} \quad , \tag{15.120}$$

in which the block complex sinusoid vector $\underline{\mathbf{e}}_p(f)$ is defined in (15.31) and $\underline{\mathbf{R}}_p^{-1}$ is the inverse of the block-Toeplitz matrix defined in (15.55).

One could use an estimate $\hat{\mathbf{R}}_p$ of the block correlation matrix, such as that of (15.87), and then evaluate Eq. (15.120) over a range of frequencies, yielding the MV PSD estimate. However, an alternative approach based on a relation of the correlation matrix inverse to the multichannel autoregressive parameters can greatly reduce the computational effort needed to evaluate multichannel MV PSD function (15.120). It can be shown (see the Problems) that an equivalent representation of the multichannel MV PSD is

$$\hat{\mathbf{P}}_{\mathrm{MV}}(f) = T\left[\sum_{k=-p}^{p} \boldsymbol{\Psi}[k]\exp(-j2\pi fkT)\right]^{-1} \quad , \tag{15.121}$$

in which the set of $p \times p$ matrices $\boldsymbol{\Psi}[k]$ are calculated as the correlation of the multichannel AR parameter matrices as follows

$$\boldsymbol{\Psi}[k] = \begin{cases} \displaystyle\sum_{i=0}^{p-k}\left\{(p+1-k-i)\mathbf{A}_p^H[k+i](\mathbf{P}_p{}^f)^{-1}\mathbf{A}_p[i]\right. \\ \qquad\qquad\qquad \left. -i\,\mathbf{B}_p^H[k+i](\mathbf{P}_p{}^b)^{-1}\mathbf{B}_p[i]\right\} & \text{for } 0 \le k \le p \\ \boldsymbol{\Psi}^H[-k] & \text{for } -1 \le k \le -p \end{cases}$$
$$\tag{15.122}$$

Figure 15.12   (a) Periodogram of unfiltered St. Louis monthly mean temperatures. (b) Temperature data after filtering and decimation by a factor of six.

A program called MCMINVAR could be assembled to compute the multichannel minimum variance spectral estimate in three steps: (1) Compute the multichannel AR parameter matrices $\mathbf{A}[k]$ and $\mathbf{B}[k]$ using subroutine MCAR; (2) Correlate [Eq. (15.122)] the AR matrix parameters to produce the $\mathbf{\Psi}[k]$ matrix sequence; (3) Generate the MV PSD estimate using an FFT program to evaluate Eq. (15.121).

15.14   TWO-CHANNEL SPECTRAL ANALYSIS OF SUNSPOT NUMBERS AND AIR TEMPERATURE

Using two-channel spectral analysis, correlative effects have been shown by analysis to exist between sunspot numbers and variations in terrestrial phenomena, such as sea level (tides), surface air temperature, earth rotation interval, air pressure, magnetic declination, and drought/flood cycles [Currie, 1981, 1984]. The possible relationship between sunspot numbers and surface air temperature at one terrestrial location will be investigated here. Appendix III lists the monthly mean temperature in °C of the American city of St. Louis for the years 1845 through 1978. This data was provided courtesy of Dr. R. Currie, who collected and performed an exhaustive analysis of worldwide temperature records. A preliminary periodogram analysis of the 1608 monthly temperature samples is shown in Fig. 15.12(a). The periodogram was computed by averaging the sample periodograms of six segments of 400 samples each with 200 samples of overlap between segments (8 samples were not used). A large DC component and a 1-cycle per year component, due to the seasonal variation of the temperature, are clearly indicated. A weak seasonal harmonic at 2 cycles per year is also just detectable. These dominant components must be eliminated before a two-channel analysis with the filtered sunspot numbers can be performed. Low-pass filtering, sample rate decimation by a factor of 6, and high-pass filtering yielded the filtered temperature data plotted in Fig. 15.12(b). The linear-phase filter responses are shown in Fig. 15.13. Both filters were designed with the Parks-McClellan method. The low-pass filter is 25 samples in duration. It filters out the 1- and 2-cycle per year seasonal periods. The high-pass filter is 37 samples in duration. It attentuates the DC component by 60.45 dB. A total of 227 filtered temperature samples is generated at the rate of two samples per year, from July 1855 to July 1968.

Figure 15.13   Frequency response of temperature data filters. (a) 25-term linear-phase low-pass filter. (b) 37-term linear-phase high-pass filter.

The result of a two-channel periodogram analysis of the 227 samples of filtered temperature and sunspot data is shown in Fig. 15.14. The autospectra are the usual single-channel periodograms. Five Hamming windowed segments of 75 samples each with 38 samples of overlap were used. The magnitude squared coherence and coherence phase were computed as described by Eqs. (15.9) and (15.10), using a cross spectral periodogram of the same five segments. No significant features are apparent in the temperature spectrum of Fig. 15.14(b). The two peaks near the low-frequency end of Fig. 15.14(c) are located at .077 and .253 cycle per year (12.96 and 3.95 years per cycle) and have coherencies of .73 and .83, respectively. Thus, it would appear that periodogram analysis does not indicate a strong correlation between sunspot and temperature data.

The result of a two-channel autoregressive analysis by the Nuttall-Strand algorithm is shown in Fig. 15.15. Order 25 was selected. Similar results were obtained with the Vieira-Morf and covariance algorithms. Both autospectra have peaks at the identical frequency of .0942 cycle per year (10.61 years per cycle). The MSC indicates peaks at .0938 and .2471 cycle per year (10.67 and 4.05 years per cycle) with coherences of .70 and .64, respectively. It seems possible, therefore, that there is a correlation between the dominant sunspot cycle and a component in the temperature data. The coherence phase at .0938 cycle per year is -186.5 degrees, which means the modulated component in the temperature data lags the sunspot cycle by 5.52 years. A single-channel AR(25) analysis by the Burg algorithm, shown in Fig. 15.16, serves as a check on the two-channel AR analysis. The sharp peak seen

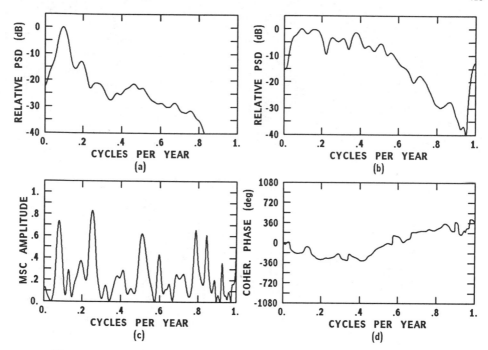

Figure 15.14   Two-channel periodogram analysis of sunspot and temperature data. (a) Autospectrum of filtered sunspot data. (b) Autospectrum of filtered temperature data. (c) Magnitude squared coherence. (d) Phase of coherence (unwrapped).

in Fig. 15.15(b) does not appear in the single-channel spectrum of Fig. 15.16(b). This suggests that the correlative peaks at .0938 cycle per year may be an artifact of the two-channel AR analysis.

REFERENCES

Akaike, H., Block Toeplitz Matrix Inversion, *SIAM J. Appl. Math.*, vol. 24, pp. 334–341, March 1973.

Currie, R. G., Solar Cycle Signal in Air Temperature in North America: Amplitude, Gradient, Phase, and Distribution, *J. Atmos. Sci.*, vol. 38, pp. 808–818, April 1981.

Currie, R. G., Periodic (18.6-Years) and Cyclic (11-Year) Induced Drought and Flood in Western North America, *J. Geophys. Res.*, vol. 89, pp. 7215–7230, August 1984.

Fougere, P. F., Spontaneous Line Splitting in Multichannel Maximum Entropy Power Spectra, *Proceedings of First ASSP Workshop on Spectral Estimation*, McMaster University, Hamilton, Ontario, Canada, pp. 1.6.1–1.6.3, August 1981.

Friedlander, B., Lattice Methods for Spectral Estimation, *Proc. IEEE*, vol. 70, pp. 990–1017, September 1982.

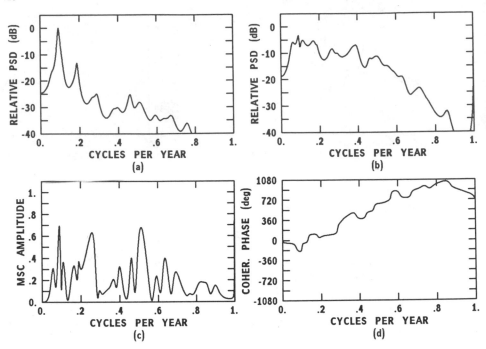

Figure 15.15   Two-channel Nuttall-Strand AR(25) analysis of sunspot and temperature data. (a) Autospectrum of filtered sunspot data. (b) Autospectrum of filtered temperature data. (c) Magnitude squared coherence. (d) Phase of coherence (unwrapped).

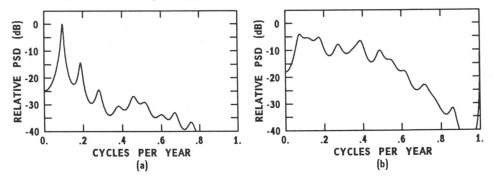

Figure 15.16   Single-channel Burg AR(25) analysis. (a) Autospectrum of filtered sunspot data. (b) Autospectrum of filtered temperature data.

Friedlander, B., M. Morf, T. Kailath, and L. Ljung, New Inversion Formulas for Matrices Classified in Terms of Their Distance from Toeplitz Matrices, *Linear Algebra and Its Applications*, vol. 27, pp. 31–60, 1979.

Friedlander, B., and B. Porat, Multichannel ARMA Spectral Estimation by the Modified Yule-Walker Method, *Signal Process.*, vol. 10, pp. 49–59, 1986.

Jones, R. H., Identification and Autoregressive Spectrum Estimation, *IEEE Trans. Autom. Control*, vol. AC-19, pp. 894–897, December 1974.

Lacoss, R. T., Autoregressive and Maximum Likelihood Spectral Analysis Techniques, in *Aspects of Signal Processing*, part 2, G. Tucconi, ed., pp. 591–615, Reidel, Boston, Mass., 1977.

Lee, D., B. Friedlander, and M. Morf, Recursive Ladder Forms for ARMA Modeling, *IEEE Trans. Autom. Control*, vol. AC-27, pp. 753–764, August 1982.

Marple, S. L., Jr. and A. H. Nuttall, Experimental Comparison of Three Multichannel Linear Prediction Spectral Estimators, *IEE Proc.*, vol. 130, Part F, pp. 218–229, April 1983.

Morf, M., A. Vieira, D. T. Lee, and T. Kailath, Recursive Multichannel Maximum Entropy Spectral Estimation, *IEEE Trans. Geosci. Electron.*, vol. GE-16, pp. 85–94, April 1978a.

Morf, M., A. Vieira, D. T. Lee, and T. Kailath, Covariance Characterization by Partial Autocorrelation Matrices, *Ann. Stat.*, vol. 6, pp. 643–648, May 1978b.

Nuttall, A. H., FORTRAN Program for Multivariate Linear Predictive Spectral Analysis, Employing Forward and Backward Averaging, *Naval Underwater Systems Center Technical Report 5419*, New London, Conn., May 1976a.

Nuttall, A. H., Multivariate Linear Predictive Spectral Analysis Employing Weighted Forward and Backward Averaging: A Generalization of Burg's Algorithm, *Naval Underwater Systems Center Technical Report 5501*, New London, Conn., October 1976b.

Nuttall, A. H., Positive Definite Spectral Estimate and Stable Correlation Recursion for Multivariate Linear Predictive Spectral Analysis, *Naval Underwater Systmes Center Technical Report 5729*, New London, Conn., November 1977.

Nuttall, A. H., Two-Channel Linear-Predictive Spectral Analysis: Program for the HP 9845 Desk Calculator, *Naval Underwater Systems Center Technical Report 6533*, New London, Conn., October 1981.

Robinson, E. A., *Multichannel Time Series Analysis with Digital Computer Programs*, 2nd ed., Goose Pond Press, Houston, Tex., 1983.

Strand, O. N., Multichannel Complex Maximum Entropy (Autoregressive) Spectral Analysis, *IEEE Trans. Autom. Control*, vol. AC-22, pp. 634–640, August 1977.

Watson, G. A., An Algorithm for the Inversion of Block Matrices of Toeplitz Form, *J. Assoc. Comput. Mach.*, vol. 20, pp. 409–415, July 1973.

Whittle, P., On the Fitting of Multivariate Autoregressions, and the Approximate Canonical Factorization of a Spectral Density Matrix, *Biometrika*, vol. 50, pp. 129–134, 1963.

Wiggins, R. A., and E. A. Robinson, Recursive Solution to the Multichannel Filtering Problem, *J. Geophys. Res.*, vol. 70, pp. 1885–1891, April 1965.

PROBLEMS

1. Prove Eq. (15.79), i.e., show that

$$\Delta_{p+1} = \mathcal{E}\{\mathbf{e}_p^f[n]\mathbf{e}_p^{b\,H}[n-1]\}\quad.$$

2. Show that the residual covariance matrices $P_p{}^f$ and $P_p{}^b$ satisfy the order update relationships

$$P_p{}^f = P_{p-1}^f - \left[(P_{p-1}^f)^{1/2}\mathbf{\Lambda}_p\right]\left[(P_{p-1}^f)^{1/2}\mathbf{\Lambda}_p\right]^H$$

$$P_p{}^b = P_{p-1}^b - \left[(P_{p-1}^b)^{1/2}\mathbf{\Lambda}_p^H\right]\left[(P_{p-1}^b)^{1/2}\mathbf{\Lambda}_p^H\right]^H$$

3. Show for the multichannel case that a one-to-one correspondence exists between $\{\mathbf{R_{xx}}[0], \mathbf{R_{xx}}[1], \ldots, \mathbf{R_{xx}}[p]\}$ and the set $\{\mathbf{R_{xx}}[0], \mathbf{\Lambda}_1, \ldots, \mathbf{\Lambda}_p\}$. Either sequence constitutes a parameterization of the autoregression sequence $\{P_p^f, \mathbf{A}_p[1], \ldots, \mathbf{A}_p[p]\}$.

4. Define the normalized residuals

$$\tilde{\mathbf{e}}_p^f[n] = (\hat{P}_{p-1}^f{}^{1/2})^{-1}\mathbf{e}_p^f[n] = \tilde{\mathbf{e}}_{p-1}^f - \mathbf{\Lambda}_p\tilde{\mathbf{e}}_{p-1}^b$$

$$\tilde{\mathbf{e}}_p^b[n] = (\hat{P}_{p-1}^b{}^{1/2})^{-1}\mathbf{e}_p^b[n] = \tilde{\mathbf{e}}_{p-1}^b - \mathbf{\Lambda}_p^H\tilde{\mathbf{e}}_{p-1}^f$$

that use the previous error covariance as normalizing weights. Show that minimizing the arithmetic mean of the weighted residuals

$$\text{tr}\left[\sum_{n=p+1}^{N} \tilde{\mathbf{e}}_p^f[n]\tilde{\mathbf{e}}_p^{f\,H}[n] + \tilde{\mathbf{e}}_p^b[n]\tilde{\mathbf{e}}_p^{b\,H}[n]\right]$$

with respect to $\mathbf{\Lambda}_{p+1}$ yields the normalized partial correlation of Eq. (15.88).

5. Prove that Eqs. (15.121) and (15.122) form a valid alternative expression for the multichannel minimum variance spectral estimate. Hint: use the concepts in Sec. 12.4 and relationship (15.86) for the inverse of a block-Toeplitz matrix.

6. In the multichannel Levinson algorithm, $\mathbf{B}_p[p] \neq \mathbf{A}_p^H[p]$. However, show that

$$\det \mathbf{B}_p[p] = \det \mathbf{A}_p^H[p]$$

does hold. Also show that

$$\text{tr } \mathbf{A}_p[1] = \text{tr } \mathbf{B}_p^H[1]$$

and that

$$\det \mathbf{R}_p = \prod_{n=1}^{p} \det P_n{}^f = \prod_{n=1}^{p} \det P_n{}^b.$$

7. Develop the fast algorithm to solve the multichannel covariance linear prediction normal equations. Use the same concepts as employed with the single-channel covariance algorithm in Appendix 8.C.

8. Show that the selection of $\mathbf{V}_p = \mathbf{W}_p = \mathbf{I}$ in the Nuttall-Strand algorithm does not guarantee a stable correlation sequence or a positive-definite spectral estimate.

9. Develop a two-channel substitute for subroutine MCARPSD of Appendix 15.C that uses FFTs in order to be more computationally efficient in the computation of polynomials $\mathbf{A}(f)$ and $\mathbf{B}(f)$.

10. Analytically determine the pole and zero locations of the two-channel example of Eq. (15.118). Find an analytic expression for the MSC. Show that it has four poles and four zeros in the finite z-plane. What is its maximum value?

11. Prove that filtering the X and Y channels with the same filter will yield the same MSC for input and output.

12. Determine the computational operation count of the two algorithms in subroutine MCAR as a function of number of channels, number of data points, and order. How does the Nuttall-Strand algorithm compare with the operation count provided for subroutine BURG in Chap. 8?

13. Prove Eq. (15.13).

14. Why is the matrix of Eq. (15.11) not Hermitian, except for $\mathbf{R}_{xx}[0]$?

15. Prove Eqs. (15.22) and (15.23).

16. Using principles from Chap. 6, show that the multichannel Yule-Walker equations for a multichannel ARMA(p, q) are

$$\mathbf{R}_{xx}[m] = \begin{cases} -\sum_{k=1}^{p} \mathbf{A}[k]\mathbf{R}_{xx}[m-k] + \sum_{k=m}^{q} \mathbf{B}[k]\mathbf{P}_w\mathbf{H}^H[k-m] & \text{for } 0 \leq m \leq q \\ -\sum_{k=1}^{p} \mathbf{A}[k]\mathbf{R}_{xx}[m-k] & \text{for } m > q \end{cases} .$$

What is the block-matrix structure of the modified Yule-Walker equations for the multichannel ARMA case?

17. Develop computer program MCMINVAR as outlined in Sec. 15.13.

APPENDIX 15.A
PROGRAM FOR MULTICHANNEL PERIODOGRAM

The multichannel periodogram spectral estimator is developed in Sec. 15.5.

```
      SUBROUTINE MCPERIOD (N,NSHIFT,NSAMP,T,PSD)
C
C   This program computes a multichannel periodogram PSD matrix
C
C   Input Parameters:
C
C     N      - Number of sample points per channel (integer)
C     NSHIFT - Number of samples shifted between segments
C     NSAMP  - Number of samples per segment (must be even)
C     T      - Sample interval in seconds
C     X      - Complex array of channel data samples
C
C   Output Parameters:
C
C     PSD    - Complex array of NPSD power spectral density
C              matrices of dimension NUMCHS x NUMCHS covering
C              the frequency range m/(NPSD*T) for m=-NPSD/2
C              to NPSD/2-1.  Note that NPSD must be a power of 2.
C
C   Notes:
C     Array dimensions are controlled by PARAMETER statements below.
C     External subroutines used: PERIODOGRAM, PREFFT, FFT
C
      PARAMETER NUMCHS=2      ! Number of channels
      PARAMETER NPSD=4096     ! Number of frequencies to evaluate PSD
```

```
      PARAMETER MAXPTS=500    ! Maximum number of data pts per channel
      COMPLEX X(NUMCHS,MAXPTS),PSD(NUMCHS,NUMCHS,NPSD),P(NPSD)
      DO 30 K=1,NUMCHS
        DO 20 J=K,NUMCHS
          CALL PERIODOGRAM (N,NSHIFT,NSAMP,T,X(K,1),X(J,1),NSEG,P)
          DO 10 I=1,NPSD
            PSD(J,K,I)=P(I)
10          PSD(K,J,I)=CONJG(P(I))
20        CONTINUE
30      CONTINUE
      RETURN
      END
```

APPENDIX 15.B
PROGRAM FOR MULTICHANNEL AUTOREGRESSIVE ESTIMATION BY
NUTTALL-STRAND OR VIEIRA-MORF ALGORITHMS

The two multichannel autoregressive spectral estimators are described in Sec. 15.10. One simple test case is to select NUMCHS = 1 and METHOD = 2 and to use the 64-point test sequence in Appendix II. The results in array A should be identical to the results in array A of subroutine BURG.

```
      SUBROUTINE MCAR (METHOD,N,IP,X,PF,A,PB,B,ISTAT)
C
C   Computes the multichannel autoregressive matrix coefficients using
C   either the Vieira-Morf algorithm   (a generalization of the single-
C   channel geometric method) or the Nuttall-Strand algorithm (a gener-
C   alization of the single-channel harmonic method).
C
C   Input Parameters:
C
C     METHOD - Integer variable; if 1, then the Vieira-Morf algorithm
C              is selected; if 2, the Nuttall-Strand algorithm is used
C     N      - Number of sample points per channel (integer)
C     IP     - Order of autoregressive model (integer)
C     X      - Complex array of NUMCHS channel data samples
C
C   Output Parameters:
C
C     PF     - Complex NUMCHS x NUMCHS forward linear prediction error
C              covariance
C     A      - Complex array of forward linear prediction matrix
C              coefficients
C     PB     - Complex backward linear prediction error covariance array
C     B      - Complex array of backward linear prediction matrix
C              coefficients
C     ISTAT  - Integer status indicator at time of subroutine exit
C              0 - Normal exit with no errors detected
C              1 - Processing of more than two channels was requested
C                  of subroutines BILINEAR, INVERT, SQROOT
C              2 - Singular matrix encountered by subroutine SQROOT
C              3 - IP exceeds the maximum order permitted; redimension
```

```
C                      appropriate subroutine arrays
C
C     Notes:  Array dimensions controlled by the PARAMETER statements below.
C             Supporting subroutines are provided in Appendix 15.D.
C
      PARAMETER NUMCHS=2            ! Number of channels
      PARAMETER MAXORDER=32        ! Maximum permitted model order
      PARAMETER MAXPTS=500         ! Maximum number of data points
      COMPLEX X(NUMCHS,MAXPTS),PF(NUMCHS,NUMCHS),PB(NUMCHS,NUMCHS)
      COMPLEX A(NUMCHS,NUMCHS,MAXORDER),B(NUMCHS,NUMCHS,MAXORDER)
      COMPLEX PFHAT(NUMCHS,NUMCHS),PBHAT(NUMCHS,NUMCHS),S
      COMPLEX PFBHAT(NUMCHS,NUMCHS),RHO(NUMCHS,NUMCHS),COL1(NUMCHS)
      COMPLEX EF(NUMCHS,MAXPTS),EB(NUMCHS,MAXPTS),TEMP1(NUMCHS,NUMCHS)
      COMPLEX TEMP2(NUMCHS,NUMCHS),TEMP3(NUMCHS,NUMCHS),COL2(NUMCHS)
      COMPLEX TEMP4(NUMCHS,NUMCHS),TEMP5(NUMCHS,NUMCHS),COL3(NUMCHS)
C
C     ** Initialization **
C
      ISTAT=0
      IF (IP .LE. MAXORDER)  GO TO 5
      ISTAT=3
      RETURN
5     CALL ZERO (NUMCHS,NUMCHS,PF)
      DO 10 K=1,N
        CALL ASSIGN (NUMCHS,1,X(1,K),EF(1,K))          ! Eq. (15.91)
        CALL ASSIGN (NUMCHS,1,X(1,K),EB(1,K))          ! Eq. (15.91)
        CALL OUTPROD (NUMCHS,X(1,K),X(1,K),TEMP1)
10      CALL ADD (NUMCHS,NUMCHS,PF,TEMP1,PF)
      S=CMPLX(1./FLOAT(N),0.)
      CALL SCALE (NUMCHS,NUMCHS,S,PF,PF)               ! Eq. (15.90)
      CALL ASSIGN (NUMCHS,NUMCHS,PF,PB)                ! Eq. (15.90)
C
      M=0
C
C     ** Main Loop **
C
100      CONTINUE
C
C     Update the estimated error covariances            ! Eq. (15.89)
C
      CALL ZERO (NUMCHS,NUMCHS,PFHAT)
      CALL ZERO (NUMCHS,NUMCHS,PBHAT)
      CALL ZERO (NUMCHS,NUMCHS,PFBHAT)
      DO 20 K=M+2,N
        CALL ASSIGN (NUMCHS,1,EF(1,K),COL1)
        CALL ASSIGN (NUMCHS,1,EB(1,K-1),COL2)
        CALL OUTPROD (NUMCHS,COL1,COL1,TEMP1)
        CALL ADD (NUMCHS,NUMCHS,PFHAT,TEMP1,PFHAT)
        CALL OUTPROD (NUMCHS,COL2,COL2,TEMP1)
        CALL ADD (NUMCHS,NUMCHS,PBHAT,TEMP1,PBHAT)
        CALL OUTPROD (NUMCHS,COL1,COL2,TEMP1)
20      CALL ADD (NUMCHS,NUMCHS,PFBHAT,TEMP1,PFBHAT)
C
      M=M+1
      IF (METHOD .EQ. 2)  GO TO 30
C
C     Compute estimated normalized partial correlation matrix
C          Eq. (15.88)  (Vieira-Morf algorithm only)
```

```
C
      CALL SQROOT (NUMCHS,PFHAT,TEMP1,ISTAT)
      IF (ISTAT .NE. 0)  RETURN
      CALL INVERT (NUMCHS,TEMP1,TEMP3,ISTAT)
      IF (ISTAT .NE. 0)  RETURN
      CALL SQROOT (NUMCHS,PBHAT,TEMP1,ISTAT)
      CALL INVERT (NUMCHS,TEMP1,TEMP2,ISTAT)
      IF (ISTAT .NE. 0)  RETURN
      CALL XPOSE (NUMCHS,TEMP2,TEMP4)
      CALL MULT (NUMCHS,NUMCHS,TEMP3,PFBHAT,TEMP1)
      CALL MULT (NUMCHS,NUMCHS,TEMP1,TEMP4,RHO)
C
C  Update forward and backward reflection coefficients
C    Eqs. (15.82),(15.83)  (Vieira-Morf algorithm only)
C
      CALL SQROOT (NUMCHS,PF,TEMP3,ISTAT)
      CALL SQROOT (NUMCHS,PB,TEMP4,ISTAT)
      CALL MULT (NUMCHS,NUMCHS,TEMP3,RHO,TEMP1)
      CALL XPOSE (NUMCHS,RHO,TEMP5)
      CALL MULT (NUMCHS,NUMCHS,TEMP4,TEMP5,TEMP2)
      CALL INVERT (NUMCHS,TEMP4,TEMP5,ISTAT)
      IF (ISTAT .NE. 0)  RETURN
      CALL MULT (NUMCHS,NUMCHS,TEMP1,TEMP5,A(1,1,M))
      CALL INVERT (NUMCHS,TEMP3,TEMP5,ISTAT)
      IF (ISTAT .NE. 0)  RETURN
      CALL MULT (NUMCHS,NUMCHS,TEMP2,TEMP5,B(1,1,M))
      GO TO 35
C
C  Compute estimated partial correlation matrix - Eq. (15.98)
C          (Nuttall-Strand algorithm only)
C
30    CALL INVERT (NUMCHS,PF,TEMP1,ISTAT)
      IF (ISTAT .NE. 0)  RETURN
      CALL MULT (NUMCHS,NUMCHS,PFHAT,TEMP1,TEMP2)
      CALL INVERT (NUMCHS,PB,TEMP3,ISTAT)
      IF (ISTAT .NE. 0)  RETURN
      CALL MULT (NUMCHS,NUMCHS,TEMP3,PBHAT,TEMP4)
      S=(2.,0.)
      CALL SCALE (NUMCHS,NUMCHS,S,PFBHAT,TEMP5)
      CALL BILINEAR (NUMCHS,TEMP2,TEMP4,TEMP5,RHO,ISTAT)
      IF (ISTAT .NE. 0)  RETURN
C
C  Update the forward and backward reflection coefficients
C  Eqs. (15.73),(15.74),(15.78) (Nuttall-Strand algorithm only)
C
      CALL MULT (NUMCHS,NUMCHS,RHO,TEMP3,A(1,1,M))
      CALL XPOSE (NUMCHS,RHO,TEMP2)
      CALL MULT (NUMCHS,NUMCHS,TEMP2,TEMP1,B(1,1,M))
35    S=(-1.,0.)
      CALL SCALE (NUMCHS,NUMCHS,S,A(1,1,M),A(1,1,M))
      CALL SCALE (NUMCHS,NUMCHS,S,B(1,1,M),B(1,1,M))
C
C  Update forward and backward error covariances - Eqs. (15.75),(15.76)
C
      CALL MULT (NUMCHS,NUMCHS,A(1,1,M),B(1,1,M),TEMP1)
      CALL MULT (NUMCHS,NUMCHS,TEMP1,PF,TEMP2)
      CALL SUB (NUMCHS,NUMCHS,PF,TEMP2,PF)
      CALL MULT (NUMCHS,NUMCHS,B(1,1,M),A(1,1,M),TEMP1)
```

```
           CALL MULT (NUMCHS,NUMCHS,TEMP1,PB,TEMP2)
           CALL SUB (NUMCHS,NUMCHS,PB,TEMP2,PB)
C
C    Update forward and backward predictor coefficients - Eqs.(15.84),(15.85)
C
           IF (M .EQ. 1)  GO TO 50
           DO 40 K=1,M-1
           MK=M-K
           CALL ASSIGN (NUMCHS,NUMCHS,A(1,1,K),TEMP1)
           CALL ASSIGN (NUMCHS,NUMCHS,B(1,1,MK),TEMP2)
           CALL MULT (NUMCHS,NUMCHS,A(1,1,M),TEMP2,TEMP3)
           CALL ADD (NUMCHS,NUMCHS,TEMP1,TEMP3,A(1,1,K))
           CALL MULT (NUMCHS,NUMCHS,B(1,1,M),TEMP1,TEMP3)
40         CALL ADD (NUMCHS,NUMCHS,TEMP2,TEMP3,B(1,1,MK))
C
C    Check for proper order
C
50         IF (M .EQ. IP)  RETURN
C
C    Update the residuals
C
           DO 60 K=N,M+1,-1
           CALL ASSIGN (NUMCHS,1,EF(1,K),COL1)
           CALL ASSIGN (NUMCHS,1,EB(1,K-1),COL2)
           CALL MULT (NUMCHS,1,A(1,1,M),COL2,COL3)
           CALL ADD (NUMCHS,1,COL1,COL3,EF(1,K))
           CALL MULT (NUMCHS,1,B(1,1,M),COL1,COL3)
60         CALL ADD (NUMCHS,1,COL2,COL3,EB(1,K))
           GO TO 100
           END
```

APPENDIX 15.C
PROGRAM TO COMPUTE MULTICHANNEL AUTOREGRESSIVE PSD

If the forward autogressive coefficients from MCAR are used, the call to this subroutine takes the form

CALL MCARPSD (IP,F,PF,A,PSD,ISTAT) .

If the backward autoregresssive coefficients from MCAR arc uscd, thc call to this subroutine takes the form

CALL MCARPSD (IP,−F,PB,B,PSD,ISTAT) .

The minus sign on F is necessary to yield identical PSD results as obtained with the forward coefficients. Conjugating the entries of array B would have the equivalent effect of negating the frequency input to the subroutine.

```
      SUBROUTINE MCARPSD (IP,F,P,A,PSD,ISTAT)
C
C    This subroutine computes the multichannel power spectral density
```

```
C   matrix at a given frequency F
C
C   Input Parameters:
C
C     IP    - Order of autoregressive model (integer)
C     F     - Fraction of sampling frequency (ranges from -.5 to .5)
C     P     - Complex array of driving noise covariance
C     A     - Complex arrays of autoregressive matrix coefficients
C
C   Output Parameters:
C
C     PSD   - Complex arrays of power spectral density values
C     ISTAT - Integer status indicator at time of subroutine exit
C             0 for normal exit
C             1 if nonsingular matrix encountered by INVERT
C
C   Notes:  Array dimensions are controlled by the PARAMETER statements
C           below.  Supporting subroutines are provided in Appendix 18.D.
C
      PARAMETER NUMCHS=2              ! Number of channels
      PARAMETER MAXORDER=32          ! Maximum permitted model order
      PARAMETER TWOPI=6.283185
      COMPLEX P(NUMCHS,NUMCHS),A(NUMCHS,NUMCHS,MAXORDER)
      COMPLEX PSD(NUMCHS,NUMCHS),R(NUMCHS,NUMCHS),S(NUMCHS,NUMCHS)
      COMPLEX T(NUMCHS,NUMCHS),TEMP
      ISTAT=0
      ARG=-TWOPI*F
      CALL IDENT (NUMCHS,T)
      DO 10 K=1,IP
         TEMP=CEXP(CMPLX(0.,ARG*FLOAT(K)))
         CALL SCALE (NUMCHS,NUMCHS,TEMP,A(1,1,K),R)
 10      CALL ADD (NUMCHS,NUMCHS,T,R,T)
      CALL INVERT (NUMCHS,T,R,ISTAT)
      IF (ISTAT .NE. 0)  RETURN
      CALL XPOSE (NUMCHS,R,S)
      CALL MULT (NUMCHS,NUMCHS,R,P,T)
      CALL MULT (NUMCHS,NUMCHS,T,S,PSD)
      RETURN
      END
```

APPENDIX 15.D
SUPPORTING SUBROUTINES FOR SUBROUTINES MCAR and MCARPSD

The following utility subroutines support the AR parameter estimation subroutine MCAR and the multichannel AR PSD generation subroutine MCARPSD. All routines are applicable to any number of channels, except subroutines BILINEAR, INVERT, and SQROOT. These latter three subroutines will work only for cases of one or two channels. An error indication is returned if more than two channels are requested. The reader may substitute more complex versions of BILINEAR, INVERT, and SQROOT to handle more than two channels.

```
      SUBROUTINE ADD (M,N,A,B,C)
C   Adds M x N matrices A and B with result in matrix C
      COMPLEX A(M,N),B(M,N),C(M,N)
      DO 10 J=1,N
      DO 10 I=1,M
10       C(I,J)=A(I,J)+B(I,J)
      RETURN
      END



      SUBROUTINE ASSIGN (M,N,A,B)
C   Assigns contents of M x N matrix A to matrix B
      COMPLEX A(M,N),B(M,N)
      DO 10 J=1,N
      DO 10 I=1,M
10       B(I,J)=A(I,J)
      RETURN
      END



      SUBROUTINE BILINEAR (M,A,B,C,X,ISTAT)
C   Solves the bilinear equation AX + XB = C for M=1,2 cases only
      COMPLEX A(M,M),B(M,M),C(M,M),X(M,M),TEMP(2,2)
      REAL C1,C2
      IF (M .EQ. 1)  GO TO 10
      IF (M .EQ. 2)  GO TO 20
      ISTAT=1
      RETURN
10    X(1,1)=C(1,1)/(A(1,1)+B(1,1))
      RETURN
20    C1=REAL(A(1,1)+A(2,2)+B(1,1)+B(2,2))
      C2=REAL(A(1,1)*A(2,2)-A(1,2)*A(2,1)-B(1,1)*B(2,2)+B(1,2)*B(2,1))
      CALL MULT (M,M,C,B,TEMP)
      X(1,1)=A(2,2)
      X(1,2)=-A(1,2)
      X(2,1)=-A(2,1)
      X(2,2)=A(1,1)
      CALL MULT (M,M,X,C,A)
      CALL ADD (M,M,TEMP,A,TEMP)
      B(1,1)=C1*B(1,1)+C2
      B(2,2)=C1*B(2,2)+C2
      B(1,2)=C1*B(1,2)
      B(2,1)=C1*B(2,1)
      CALL INVERT (M,B,A,ISTAT)
      IF (ISTAT .NE. 0)  RETURN
      CALL MULT (M,M,TEMP,A,X)
      RETURN
      END



      SUBROUTINE IDENT (M,A)
C   Returns identity matrix in A
      COMPLEX A(M,M)
      DO 10 J=1,M
      DO 10 I=1,M
        A(I,J)=(0.,0.)
        IF (I .EQ. J)  A(I,J)=(1.,0.)
10       CONTINUE
```

```
      RETURN
      END


      SUBROUTINE INVERT (M,A,B,ISTAT)
C   Inverts matrix A with result in matrix B for M=1,2 cases only
      COMPLEX A(M,M),B(M,M),DET,T
      IF (M .EQ. 1)  GO TO 10
      IF (M .EQ. 2)  GO TO 20
      ISTAT=1
      RETURN
10    B(1,1)=1./A(1,1)
      RETURN
20    DET=A(1,1)*A(2,2)-A(1,2)*A(2,1)
      IF (CABS(DET) .NE. 0.)  GO TO 30
      ISTAT=2
      RETURN
30    T=1./DET
      B(1,1)=A(2,2)*T
      B(1,2)=-A(1,2)*T
      B(2,1)=-A(2,1)*T
      B(2,2)=A(1,1)*T
      RETURN
      END


      SUBROUTINE MULT (M,N,A,B,C)
C   Multiplies M x M matrix A with M x N matrix B
C   with result in M x N matrix C
      COMPLEX A(M,M),B(M,N),C(M,N),S
      DO 10 J=1,N
      DO 10 I=1,M
        S=(0.,0.)
        DO 20 K=1,M
20        S=S+A(I,K)*B(K,J)
10      C(I,J)=S
      RETURN
      END


      SUBROUTINE OUTPROD (M,X,Y,A)
C   Computes outer product of vectors X and Y with
C   result in matrix A
      COMPLEX X(M),Y(M),A(M,M)
      DO 10 J=1,M
      DO 10 I=1,M
10      A(I,J)=X(I)*CONJG(Y(J))
      RETURN
      END


      SUBROUTINE SCALE (M,N,S,A,B)
C   Scales a M x N matrix A by scalar S with result in matrix B
      COMPLEX S,A(M,N),B(M,N)
      DO 10 J=1,N
      DO 10 I=1,M
10      B(I,J)=S*A(I,J)
      RETURN
```

```
      END


      SUBROUTINE SQROOT (M,A,B,ISTAT)
C   Computes lower triangular "square root" matrix of Hermitian
C   matrix A with result in matrix B for M=1,2 cases only
      COMPLEX A(M,M),B(M,M)
      REAL C
      IF (M .LE. 2)  GO TO 10
      ISTAT=1
      RETURN
10    C=SQRT(REAL(A(1,1)))
      B(1,1)=CMPLX(C,0.)
      IF (M .EQ. 1)  RETURN
      B(2,1)=A(2,1)/C
      B(1,2)=0.
      C=REAL(A(2,2)-A(1,2)*A(2,1)/A(1,1))
      B(2,2)=CMPLX(SQRT(C),0.)
      RETURN
      END


      SUBROUTINE SUB (M,N,A,B,C)
C   Subtracts M x N matrix B from matrix A with result in matrix C
      COMPLEX A(M,N),B(M,N),C(M,N)
      DO 10 J=1,N
      DO 10 I=1,M
10     C(I,J)=A(I,J)-B(I,J)
      RETURN
      END


      SUBROUTINE XPOSE (M,A,B)
C   Complex conjugate transpose of matrix A placed in matrix B
      COMPLEX A(M,M),B(M,M)
      DO 10 J=1,M
      DO 10 I=1,M
10     B(I,J)=CONJG(A(J,I))
      RETURN
      END


      SUBROUTINE ZERO (M,N,A)
C   Places zeros in M x N matrix A
      COMPLEX A(M,N)
      DO 10 J=1,N
      DO 10 I=1,M
10     A(I,J)=(0.,0.)
      RETURN
      END
```

16

TWO-DIMENSIONAL SPECTRAL ESTIMATION

16.1 INTRODUCTION

The high-resolution performance of the one-dimensional (1-D) spectral estimators of Chaps. 5–13 has led many researchers to expect similar performance for two-dimensional (2-D) and higher-dimensional extensions of these spectral estimators, where these extensions exist. Two-dimensional spectral analysis can be used for space-space data arrays (e.g., image processing), space-time data arrays (e.g., sonar, seismic, and synthetic aperture radar processing), or even time-time data arrays (e.g., analysis of radar pulse repetition interval vs. arrival time). Difficulties extending the 1-D techniques to 2-D are often encountered due to differences in the 1-D and 2-D linear systems theory, particularly the inability to factor a 2-D polynomial into polynomials of lower degress. The 1-D concept of isolated poles, zeros, and roots thus cannot be extended, in general, to the 2-D case. Two-dimensional systems have many more degrees of freedom than 1-D systems. The computational burden imposed by some of the advanced 2-D spectral estimation methods have limited their testing and application to small 2-D data sets with simple signal scenarios, such as a few sinusoids in spatially white noise. These two reasons explain why 2-D spectral estimation continues to be an active area of research. Only the 2-D periodogram, 2-D hybrid methods, and 2-D minimum variance method have

	ACQUIRE DATA N1 x N2 samples T1 x T2 samples/second	
TWO-DIMENSIONAL PERIODOGRAM	TWO-DIMENSIONAL AUTOREGRESSIVE PSD	TWO-DIMENSIONAL MINIMUM VARIANCE PSD
• COMPUTE TWO- DIMENSIONAL PERIODOGRAM (Subroutine TDPERIOD, Appendix 16.A)	• SELECT ORDERS IP1, IP2 • ESTIMATE TWO- DIMENSIONAL AR PARAMETERS (Subroutine TDAR, Appendix 16.C) • COMPUTE TWO- DIMENSIONAL AR PSD (Subroutine TDARPSD, Appendix 16.D)	• SELECT ORDERS IP1, IP2 • COMPUTE TWO- DIMENSIONAL MINIMUM VARIANCE PSD (Subroutine TDMINVAR, Section 16.9)

Figure 16.1   Flowchart of three approaches to 2-D spectral estimation.

seen practical application to extensive 2-D data sets, primarily due to the fact that these methods do not depend on 2-D polynomial factorization.

A single chapter can only briefly highlight 2-D spectral estimation techniques. Although the mathematics in this chapter could be expressed for multidimensional spectral analysis, the greatest interest currently is 2-D spectral analysis. It is for this reason that this chapter focuses only on the the 2-D case. The issues and mathematical details caused by the significant theoretical differences between 1-D and 2-D spectral techniques require an entire book unto itself. The reader is invited to consult resources, such as the text by Dudgeon and Mersereau [1984] or the tutorial paper by McClellan [1982], for additional details and references on multidimensional digital signal processing and spectral estimation. The developments in this chapter will roughly parallel the topical sequence of Chaps. 2–13 on 1-D techniques.

16.2   SUMMARY

It is assumed that 2-D signals are obtained by sampling over a rectangular grid for both mathematical convenience and ease of presentation. This is the way 2-D discrete signals are usually obtained in practice. Limitations of space permit only two 2-D spectrum analysis programs to be included in this chapter: the 2-D classic periodogram spectral estimator and the 2-D quarter-plane autoregressive spectral estimator. Figure 16.1 is a flowchart of the steps needed to produce spectra from the two programs and the 2-D minimum variance technique. Examples of 2-D spectra

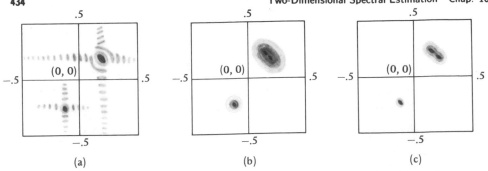

Figure 16.2 Illustration of three 2-D spectral estimates based on known 2-D autocorrelation sequence of three complex 2-D sinusoids in white noise. (a) 2-D correlogram method. (b) 2-D minimum variance. (c) 2-D autoregressive.

are shown in Fig. 16.2. The three methods selected show the possible resolution improvements over classical 2-D spectral estimators.

Following a review of 2-D linear system, Fourier transform, and random process theory in Secs. 16.3 and 16.4, five techniques of 2-D spectral estimation are covered in the remaining sections. Section 16.5 discusses classical 2-D spectral estimators. Section 16.6 demonstrates how the separability of the 2-D exponential may be used to develop a modified classical spectral estimator that is a standard FFT in one dimension and a high-resolution 1-D spectral estimator in the other dimension. This permits all of the 1-D techniques previously developed to be used in a hybrid 2-D spectral method. This approach is especially useful in time-space data, where there is often a wealth of time data and a paucity of space data. Section 16.7 is a lengthy discourse on 2-D autoregressive spectral estimation. Section 16.8 summarizes the 2-D maximum entropy PSD estimator, which is not identical to the 2-D AR spectral estimator. Finally, Sec. 16.9 highlights the 2-D minimum variance spectral estimator.

Only very limited experimental results have been reported in the literature regarding 2-D spectral estimators, so performance comparisons are difficult to make. The high complexity of computations, even with fast algorithms, have limited application of 2-D PSD estimators to small data sets with only a few 2-D parameters.

16.3 TWO-DIMENSIONAL LINEAR SYSTEMS AND TRANSFORM THEORY

A *discrete 2-D signal* is any function $x[m, n]$ that is a 2-D sequence, or *array*, of real or complex numbers defined for the ordered pair of integers m and n over $-\infty < m, n < \infty$. The discrete 2-D signal may represent a sampled 2-D continuous function $x(t_1, t_2)$, in which t_1 and t_2 range over a continuum of values. Although many different 2-D sampling grids of the continuous function $x(t_1, t_2)$ are possible, only the rectangular grid

$$x[m, n] = x(mT_1, nT_2) \tag{16.1}$$

is considered in this chapter. The sampling intervals along each dimension, denoted as T_1 and T_2, may be in units of time or space. The range of m and n indices over which the 2-D sequence is nonzero is called the *region of support*. A typical finite data record is assumed in this chapter to have a rectangular region of support, $0 \leq m \leq M - 1$ and $0 \leq n \leq N - 1$, as this is the most common situation found in practice.

The 2-D *unit impulse* (sample) *function* has the definition

$$\delta[m, n] = \delta[m]\delta[n] = \begin{cases} 1 & \text{for } m = n = 0 \\ 0 & \text{otherwise.} \end{cases} \tag{16.2}$$

The 2-D *discrete convolution sum* for a 2-D linear shift invariant system is

$$y[m, n] = \sum_{i=-\infty}^{\infty} \sum_{j=-\infty}^{\infty} h[m - i, n - j]x[i, j] = h[m, n] \star x[m, n] \tag{16.3}$$

for input $x[i, j]$ and output $y[m, n]$. The 2-D sequence $h[m, n]$, defined over an infinite range in both dimensions, is the *2-D system impulse response sequence*, obtained as the output sequence when the input is $x[i, j] = \delta[i, j]$. As in the 1-D case, a 2-D linear shift-invariant system is said to be *stable* if its output sequence remains bounded for all bounded input sequences. The stability of 2-D systems is significantly more difficult to test than 1-D stability.

A 1-D linear system was characterized as causal if its output $y[n]$ was based on a convolution sum involving only the current and past inputs $x[k]$ to the system

$$y[n] = \sum_{k=-\infty}^{n} h[n - k]x[k] \tag{16.4}$$

for n, $n + 1$, $n + 2$, and so forth. The 1-D discrete impulse response sequence is nonzero only for $h[0]$, $h[1]$, ..., $h[\infty]$. This made physical sense when the signals were functions of time. Causality is not inherent, however, for 2-D signals in which one or both dimensions of the signal are functions of space rather than time. One region of support for the 2-D discrete impulse response sequences that has been adopted as a convention for a "causal" 2-D system is the *nonsymmetric half plane* (NSHP), as illustrated in Fig. 16.3(a). This definition of 2-D causality assumes that the output sequence $y[m, n]$ is calculated in a manner analogous to that of a raster on a television: scan line by line top to bottom, moving left to right on each line. If the output $y[m, n]$ is visualized as position n on line m, then the output is generated recursively by first computing $y[m, -\infty]$ to $y[m, \infty]$, followed by incrementing line

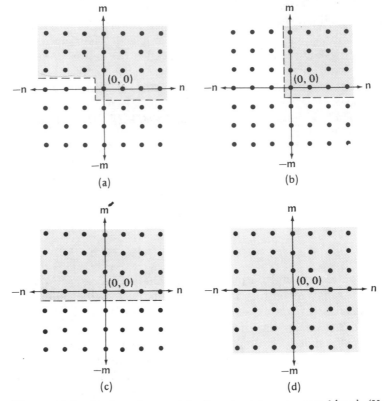

Figure 16.3   Regions of support for discrete system sequence h[m,n]. (Non-zero in shaded area). (a) Causal (NSHP). (b) Causal (QP). (c) Semicausal (SHP). (d) Noncausal (FP).

index m. Note that both input and output sequences may have support over the infinite *full plane* (FP), even though the impulse response has NSHP support.

A special case region of support for causal 2-D systems confines the 2-D impulse response to the *quarter plane* (QP), as illustrated by Fig. 16.3(b). The QP case will be the region of support of most interest for purposes of 2-D spectral analysis. Two other regions of support for the 2-D discrete impulse response are illustrated in Fig. 16.3(c) and (d). The semicausal region of support covers the *symmetric half plane* (SHP). It is causal in one dimension and noncausal in the other dimension. The noncausal region of support is simply the entire *full plane* (FP), as assumed by Eq. (16.3).

A 2-D recursive difference equation relating the input to the output of a 2-D system is

$$\sum_i \sum_j a[i,j]x[m-i,n-j] = \sum_i \sum_j b[i,j]u[m-i,n-j] \quad . \qquad (16.5)$$

The assumption $a[0,0] = 1$ can be made with no loss in generality, so that Eq. (16.5) can be rewritten as

$$x[m,n] = -\sum_i \sum_j a[i,j]x[m-i,n-j] + \sum_i \sum_j b[i,j]u[m-i,n-j] \quad . \quad (16.6)$$

The range of the various summations denote the *order* of the 2-D difference equation. The order of array $a[i,j]$, for example, would be $p_1 \times p_2$ if its region of support were the rectangular QP covering $0 \le i \le p_1$ and $0 \le j \le p_2$. Selecting a NSHP region of support for both array $a[i,j]$ and array $b[i,j]$ and the appropriate initial conditions for $x[i,j]$ can be shown [Dudgeon and Mersereau, 1984] to create a causal 2-D output sequence, i.e., the discrete impulse response describing Eq. (16.3) also has a NSHP region of support (see the Problems) and can, therefore, be computed recursively in the raster fashion previously described.

Exponentials of the form $x[m,n] = z_1^m z_2^n$ are eigenfunctions of 2-D linear shift-invariant systems because the output response $y[m,n]$ to $z_1^m z_2^n$ as an input to the convolution of Eq. (16.3) yields

$$y[m,n] = H(z_1,z_2)z_1^m z_2^n \quad , \quad (16.7)$$

in which

$$H(z_1,z_2) = \sum_{i=-\infty}^{\infty} \sum_{j=-\infty}^{\infty} h[i,j]z_1^{-i}z_2^{-j} = Z\{h[i,j]\} \quad (16.8)$$

is the *discrete 2-D system response function*, or the *discrete 2-D transfer function* of the 2-D discrete impulse response sequence, defined in the region of z_1 and z_2 such that Eq. (16.8) converges. Equation (16.8) is also the general definition of the *2-D z-transform* for any 2-D sequence $h[i,j]$. The 2-D system function of the recursive difference equation (16.5) is easily shown to be the ratio of 2-D polynomials given by

$$H(z_1,z_2) = \frac{B(z_1,z_2)}{A(z_1,z_2)} \quad , \quad (16.9)$$

in which $A(z_1,z_2)$ and $B(z_1,z_2)$ are the z-transforms of the $a[i,j]$ and $b[i,j]$ arrays

$$A(z_1,z_2) = \sum_i \sum_j a[i,j]z_1^{-i}z_2^{-j} \quad (16.10)$$

$$B(z_1,z_2) = \sum_i \sum_j b[i,j]z_1^{-i}z_2^{-j} \quad (16.11)$$

over summation ranges determined by the respective regions of support. A causal 1-D rational system function involved summation ranges of *only* positive index values. The 2-D system function (16.9) for the "causal" NSHP will involve one summation in both (16.10) and (16.11) to use only positive index values and the other summation to have both positive and negative index values. It is said that

$H(z_1, z_2)$ has a 2-D "zero" at (z_1, z_2) if $B(z_1, z_2) = 0$ and $A(z_1, z_2) \neq 0$. It is said that $H(z_1, z_2)$ has a 2-D "pole" at (z_1, z_2) if $A(z_1, z_2) = 0$ and $B(z_1, z_2) \neq 0$. Poles and zeros of 2-D rational system functions are quite different from their 1-D counterparts. Roots of 1-D polynomials occur at isolated points in the z-plane, whereas roots of 2-D polynomials are generally continuous contours, rather than isolated points. Consider the simple 2-D polynomial

$$A(z_1, z_2) = 1 - az_1^{-1}z_2^{-1} \quad , \tag{16.12}$$

which is zero wherever $z_1 z_2 = a$. This is a continuous surface in a 2-D complex z-space. The inability to factor 2-D polynomials into isolated poles and zeros (i.e., first-order polynomials) makes stability testing in 2-D very difficult.

A continuous 2-D signal $x(t_1, t_2)$ has a *2-D continuous-time Fourier transform* (2-D CTFT)

$$X_{\text{CTFT}}(f_1, f_2) = \int_{-\infty}^{\infty} \int_{-\infty}^{\infty} x(t_1, t_2) \exp(-j2\pi[f_1 t_1 + f_2 t_2]) \, dt_1 \, dt_2 \tag{16.13}$$

under similar conditions cited for the 1-D CTFT in Chap. 2. If the continuous signal is sampled at intervals of T_1 along the dimension of variable t_1 and T_2 along the dimension of variable t_2, creating the sampled sequence $x[m, n] = x(mT_1, nT_2)$, then the *2-D discrete-time Fourier transform* (2-D DTFT) is given by

$$X_{\text{DTFT}}(f_1, f_2) = T_1 T_2 X(z_1, z_2) \Big|_{\substack{z_1 = \exp(j2\pi f_1 T_1) \\ z_2 = \exp(j2\pi f_2 T_2)}} \tag{16.14}$$

$$= T_1 T_2 \sum_{m=-\infty}^{\infty} \sum_{n=-\infty}^{\infty} x[m, n] \exp(-j2\pi[f_1 mT_1 + f_2 nT_2]) . \tag{16.15}$$

If the continuous 2-D signal is temporally/spatially bandlimited, such that

$$X_{\text{CTFT}}(f_1, f_2) = 0 \tag{16.16}$$

outside the rectangular region $|f_1| \leq 1/2T_1$ and $|f_2| \leq 1/2T_2$, then

$$X_{\text{DTFT}}(f_1, f_2) = X_{\text{CTFT}}(f_1, f_2) \tag{16.17}$$

only over the region of support $|f_1| \leq 1/2T_1$ and $|f_2| \leq 1/2T_2$. The DTFT is periodic, $X_{\text{DTFT}}(f_1 + \alpha/2T_1, f_2 + \beta/2T_2) = X_{\text{DTFT}}(f_1, f_2)$, for any integers α and β. The original continuous 2-D signal may be recovered from the sampled 2-D sequence in this case by the 2-D interpolation function

$$x(t_1, t_2) = \sum_{m=-\infty}^{\infty} \sum_{n=-\infty}^{\infty} x[m, n] \operatorname{sinc}[(t_1 - mT_1)/T_1] \operatorname{sinc}[(t_2 - nT_2)/T_2], \tag{16.18}$$

a consequence of the 2-D sampling theorem.

The squared magnitude of the 2-D discrete-time Fourier transform may be interpreted as the *2-D energy spectral density*

$$S(f_1, f_2) = \left| X_{\mathrm{DTFT}}(f_1, f_2) \right|^2 \tag{16.19}$$

due to the *2-D energy theorem* relationship

$$
\begin{aligned}
\mathrm{Energy} &= T_1 T_2 \sum_{m=-\infty}^{\infty} \sum_{n=-\infty}^{\infty} \left| x[m,n] \right|^2 \\
&= \int_{-1/2T_1}^{1/2T_1} \int_{-1/2T_2}^{1/2T_2} \left| X_{\mathrm{DTFT}}(f_1, f_2) \right|^2 \, df_1 \, df_2 \quad .
\end{aligned}
\tag{16.20}
$$

The subscript DTFT will be omitted for convenience in later references to this transform in this chapter.

Assume that a discrete 2-D sequence is periodic with period M in one dimension and period N in the other dimension, that is,

$$x[m + \alpha M, n + \beta N] = x[m,n] \tag{16.21}$$

for any integers α and β, so that the sequence is completely specified by the MN values in the QP region $0 \le m \le M-1$ and $0 \le n \le N-1$. The *2-D discrete-time Fourier series*

$$X_{\mathrm{DTFS}}[k,l] = T_1 T_2 \sum_{m=0}^{M-1} \sum_{n=0}^{N-1} x[m,n] \exp(-j2\pi[mk/M + nl/N]) \tag{16.22}$$

may be defined for this periodic sequence. The DTFS is itself periodic with periods of M and N in the respective dimensions. The 2-D DTFS would require $M^2 N^2$ complex operations (multiplies and adds) in order to compute all MN transform values. The one-dimensional FFT of Appendix 2.C may be used to reduce this computational burden to approximately $(MN \log_2 MN)/2$ complex operations. This is achieved by taking advantage of the separability of the exponential argument in Eq. (16.22) to first compute the intermediate array, which has been transformed in one dimension,

$$X_{\mathrm{INT}}[m,l] = T_2 \sum_{n=0}^{N-1} x[m,n] \exp(-j2\pi nl/N) \quad , \tag{16.23}$$

followed by the completion of the computation of the DTFS from the intermediate array by transforming along the other dimension

$$X_{\mathrm{DTFS}}[k,l] = T_1 \sum_{m=0}^{M-1} X_{\mathrm{INT}}[m,l] \exp(-j2\pi mk/M) \quad . \tag{16.24}$$

This forms a row-column decomposition of the 2-D DTFS into two sets of 1-D DTFS operations, which may be evaluated as a series of N one-dimensional FFTs of the *columns* of the original data array, followed by a series of M FFTs of the *rows* of the intermediate array.

16.4 TWO-DIMENSIONAL RANDOM PROCESS THEORY

The concept of a 2-D power spectral density (PSD) requires, as in the 1-D case, that the 2-D array $x[m, n]$ of samples from a 2-D random process be wide-sense stationary. Such 2-D random processes are said to form *homogeneous* sequences because the 2-D mean of the process is independent of the location on the 2-D plane and the 2-D autocorrelation sequence (ACS) is a function only of the differential distance between two points in the 2-D plane. The discrete 2-D mean, autocorrelation sequence, autocovariance sequence, and cross correlation sequence for homogeneous random processes are, respectively,

$$\bar{x} = \mathcal{E}\{x[m, n]\} = \text{a constant}$$
$$r_{xx}[k, l] = \mathcal{E}\{x[m + k, n + l]x^*[m, n]\}$$
$$c_{xx}[k, l] = \mathcal{E}\{(x[m + k, n + l] - \bar{x})(x^*[m, n] - \bar{x}^*)\} = r_{xx}[k, l] - |\bar{x}|^2 \qquad (16.25)$$
$$r_{yx}[k, l] = \mathcal{E}\{y[m + k, n + l]x^*[m, n]\} \quad .$$

It will generally be assumed that the mean is zero, so that the 2-D autocorrelation and autocovariance sequences are equivalent. The autocorrelation $r_{xx}[0, 0]$ is real and positive (see the Problems). The 2-D ACS may be shown [Dudgeon and Mersereau, 1984] to form a positive-semidefinite sequence, that is,

$$\sum_i \sum_j \sum_k \sum_l a[i, j]a^*[k, l]r_{xx}[i - k, j - l] \geq 0$$

for all $a[i, j]$ sequences. The positive-definite property will assure that the 2-D DTFT of the 2-D ACS will be nonnegative and that correlation matrices formed from the 2-D ACS are invertible.

The *2-D power spectral density* (PSD) $P_{xx}(f_1, f_2)$ is defined, in a similar manner as that of the 1-D PSD definition (4.33), as the 2-D discrete-time Fourier transform of the 2-D autocorrelation sequence

$$P_{xx}(f_1, f_2) = T_1 T_2 \sum_{m=-\infty}^{\infty} \sum_{n=-\infty}^{\infty} r_{xx}[m, n] \exp(-j2\pi[f_1 m T_1 + f_2 n T_2]) \qquad (16.26)$$

over the interval $|f_1| \leq 1/2T_1$ and $|f_2| \leq 1/2T_2$. Equation (16.26) is the 2-D version of the Wiener-Khintchine theorem. It may be shown (see the Problems) that the 2-D PSD is real and positive.

The assumption of ergodicity in the 2-D autocorrelation sequence justifies the use of the time average

$$r_{xx}[m,n] = \lim_{\substack{N\to\infty \\ M\to\infty}} \frac{1}{2M+1}\frac{1}{2N+1} \sum_{i=-M}^{M} \sum_{j=-N}^{N} x[i+m, j+n]x^*[i,j] \qquad (16.27)$$

of a single realization of the 2-D random process to yield the 2-D ACS. Using a similar approach as that used in Chap. 4, it can be shown that an equivalent representation of the 2-D PSD function is

$$P_{xx}(f_1, f_2)$$

$$= \lim_{\substack{N\to\infty \\ M\to\infty}} \mathcal{E} \left\{ \frac{T_1}{2M+1}\frac{T_2}{2N+1} \left| \sum_{m=-M}^{M} \sum_{n=-N}^{N} x[m,n]\exp(-j2\pi[f_1 m T_1 + f_2 n T_2]) \right|^2 \right\}.$$

$$(16.28)$$

An important 2-D random process is the 2-D white noise sequence $w[m,n]$, which is defined to have the 2-D ACS

$$r_{ww}[k,l] = \rho_w \delta[k,l] \quad , \qquad (16.29)$$

that is, a process that is uncorrelated with itself everywhere except at lag $[0,0]$. The PSD for the 2-D white noise process is simply $P_{ww}(f_1, f_2) = T_1 T_2 \rho_w$.

If $y[m,n]$ is the 2-D random process response resulting from passing stationary 2-D random process $x[m,n]$ through the linear system of (16.3), then the output ACS $r_{yy}[k,l]$ and input ACS $r_{xx}[k,l]$ are related by

$$r_{yy}[k,l] = h[k,l] \star h^*[-k,-l] \star r_{xx}[k,l] \quad . \qquad (16.30)$$

If the 2-D z-transform of the 2-D ACS $r_{xx}[k,l]$ is

$$P_{xx}(z_1, z_2) = \sum_{k=-\infty}^{\infty} \sum_{l=-\infty}^{\infty} r_{xx}[k,l] z_1^{-k} z_2^{-l} \quad ,$$

and if $P_{yy}(z_1, z_2)$ is the similar z-transform of $r_{yy}[k,l]$, then the z-transform of (16.30) will relate $P_{xx}(z_1, z_2)$ and $P_{yy}(z_1, z_2)$ as follows

$$P_{yy}(z_1, z_2) = H(z_1, z_2)H^*(1/z_1^*, 1/z_2^*)P_{xx}(z_1, z_2) \quad , \qquad (16.31)$$

in which $H(z_1, z_2)$ is the z-transform (16.8) of the system response function. The 2-D power spectral density relationship between input and output processes is, therefore,

$$P_{yy}(f_1, f_2) = T_1 T_2 \left. P_{yy}(z_1, z_2) \right|_{\substack{z_1 = \exp(j2\pi f_1 T_1) \\ z_2 = \exp(j2\pi f_2 T_2)}} = \left| H(f_1, f_2) \right|^2 P_{xx}(f_1, f_2) \quad . \quad (16.32)$$

If the input process is white with ACS given by Eq. (16.29) and the filter has a 2-D transfer function given by the rational function (16.9) of 2-D polynomials, then the output process is that of a *2-D autoregressive-moving average process* (2-D ARMA) with PSD of

$$P_{\text{ARMA}}(f_1, f_2) = T_1 T_2 \rho_w \left| \frac{B(f_1, f_2)}{A(f_1, f_2)} \right|^2 , \qquad (16.33)$$

in which

$$A(f_1, f_2) = \sum_m \sum_n a[m, n] \exp(-j2\pi[f_1 m T_1 + f_2 n T_2])$$

$$B(f_1, f_2) = \sum_m \sum_n b[m, n] \exp(-j2\pi[f_1 m T_1 + f_2 n T_2])$$

are defined over some arbitrary region of support. If $B(f_1, f_2) = 1$, then the PSD represents a *2-D autoregressive process* (2-D AR). If $A(f_1, f_2) = 1$, then the PSD represents a *2-D moving average process* (2-D MA). Two-dimensional processes also permit different process representations in each dimension. If the numerator, for example, is strictly a function of f_1, i.e., $B(f_1, f_2) = B(f_1)$, then the 2-D process is ARMA in the dimension corresponding to f_1 and AR in the dimension corresponding to f_2.

16.5   CLASSICAL 2-D SPECTRAL ESTIMATION

The two-dimensional versions of the classical spectral estimators follow simply from the one-dimensional forms of the periodogram and correlogram methods. It will be convenient for presentation purposes to assume that the data has a quarter-plane region of support, that is, MN data samples $x[m, n]$ are available over the rectangular region $0 \leq m \leq M - 1$ and $0 \leq n \leq N - 1$. Other nonrectangular regions of support are possible, but are not considered here because they are not often encountered in practice.

The unbiased 2-D autocorrelation estimate at lag $[k, l]$ is given by

$$\hat{r}_{xx}[k, l] = \qquad (16.34)$$

$$\begin{cases} \dfrac{1}{(M-k)(N-l)} \displaystyle\sum_{m=0}^{M-1-k} \sum_{n=0}^{N-1-l} x[m+k, n+l] x^*[m, n] & \text{for } k \geq 0, l \geq 0 \\[2ex] \dfrac{1}{(M-k)(N-l)} \displaystyle\sum_{m=0}^{M-1-k} \sum_{n=-l}^{N-1} x[m+k, n+l] x^*[m, n] & \text{for } k \geq 0, l < 0 \\[2ex] \hat{r}_{xx}^*[-k, -l] & \text{for } k \leq 0, \text{any } l \end{cases}$$

over a lag range of $|k| \leq p_1$ and $|l| \leq p_2$. The maximum lag values are limited to $p_1 \leq M - 1$ and $p_2 \leq N - 1$. The biased 2-D ACS $\check{r}_{xx}[k, l]$ may by computed by simply substituting MN for the divisor $(M - k)(N - l)$ in Eq. (16.34).

The correlogram method PSD estimator for 2-D data samples is

$$\hat{P}_{\text{CORR}}(f_1, f_2) = T_1 T_2 \sum_{k=-p_1}^{p_1} \sum_{l=-p_2}^{p_2} w[k, l]\hat{r}[k, l] \exp(-j2\pi[f_1 kT_1 + f_2 lT_2]), \quad (16.35)$$

where $w[k, l]$ is a lag window sequence used, as in the 1-D case, to trade off resolution, sidelobe bias, and estimator variance. There is not much in the literature on 2-D window functions for spectral estimation. Two-dimensional windows are often constructed as the product of 1-D windows, such as the 2-D Hamming window

$$w[k, l] = [.54 + .46 \cos(\pi k/p_1)][.54 + .46 \cos(\pi l/p_2)]$$

for $|k| \leq p_1$ and $|l| \leq p_2$. Huang [1972] has studied 2-D windows with circular, rather than rectangular, symmetry. If the biased ACS $\check{r}_{xx}[k, l]$ is used (i.e., set $w[k, l]$ to a triangular window), then an alternative matrix-vector product expression for the correlogram method PSD is

$$\hat{P}_{\text{CORR}}(f_1, f_2) = T_1 T_2 \, \underline{e}^H(f_1, f_2)\underline{\check{R}} \, \underline{e}(f_1, f_2) \quad , \quad (16.36)$$

in which the block-Toeplitz autocorrelation matrix of block dimension $(p_1 + 1) \times (p_1 + 1)$

$$\underline{\check{R}} = \begin{pmatrix} \check{R}[0] & \check{R}[1] & \cdots & \check{R}[p_1] \\ \check{R}[-1] & \check{R}[0] & \cdots & \check{R}[p_1 - 1] \\ \vdots & \vdots & \ddots & \vdots \\ \check{R}[-p_1] & \check{R}[-p_1 + 1] & \cdots & \check{R}[0] \end{pmatrix} \quad (16.37)$$

has Toeplitz matrix elements of dimension $(p_2 + 1) \times (p_2 + 1)$

$$\check{R}[k] = \begin{pmatrix} \check{r}_{xx}[k, 0] & \check{r}_{xx}[k, 1] & \cdots & \check{r}_{xx}[k, p_2] \\ \check{r}_{xx}[k, -1] & \check{r}_{xx}[k, 0] & \cdots & \check{r}_{xx}[k, p_2 - 1] \\ \vdots & \vdots & \ddots & \vdots \\ \check{r}_{xx}[k, -p_2] & \check{r}_{xx}[k, -p_2 + 1] & \cdots & \check{r}_{xx}[k, 0] \end{pmatrix} \quad . \quad (16.38)$$

The 2-D complex sinusoid block vector $\underline{e}(f_1, f_2)$ is defined as

$$\underline{e}(f_1, f_2) = \begin{pmatrix} e_0(f_1, f_2) \\ e_1(f_1, f_2) \\ \vdots \\ e_{p_1}(f_1, f_2) \end{pmatrix}, \quad e_k(f_1, f_2) = \exp(j2\pi f_1 kT_1)\begin{pmatrix} 1 \\ \exp(j2\pi f_2 T_2) \\ \vdots \\ \exp(j2\pi f_2 p_2 T_2) \end{pmatrix}. \quad (16.39)$$

Note that vectors $e_k(f_1, f_2)$ each have $(p_2 + 1)$ elements.

The 2-D periodogram follows the form of the 1-D periodogram,

$$\hat{P}_{\text{PER}}(f_1, f_2) = \frac{T_1 T_2}{MN} \left| \sum_{m=0}^{M-1} \sum_{n=0}^{N-1} w[m,n]x[m,n] \exp(-j2\pi[f_1 m T_1 + f_2 n T_2]) \right|^2 ,$$

(16.40)

in which $w[m,n]$ is an appropriate data window. The variance of the 2-D periodogram estimator may be reduced by sectioning the data into smaller 2-D arrays, which may be overlapped, taking the 2-D periodogram of each subarray, and averaging the subarray periodograms. Data sequences from space-time arrays are often so limited along the spatial domain that subarray averaging can only be performed along the time dimension; the loss in spectral resolution by averaging subarrays along the spatial dimension usually cannot be tolerated. If the individual subarrays are statistically independent, the variance will be reduced by the number of subarrays averaged. If they are not independent, then the variance reduction will be less. Appendix 16.A contains subroutine TDPERIOD, which computes the 2-D periodogram using the 1-D FFT algorithm.

The statistical performance of the 2-D classical estimators appears to be similar to that of the 1-D classical spectral estimators, although analytical results are not readily available. The resolution in each dimension depends upon the data extent in each dimension and will be different, in general, if $MT_1 \neq NT_2$. The 1-D resolution analyzed in Chap. 5 basically holds in the 2-D case for spectral components aligned along one of the two frequency dimensions.

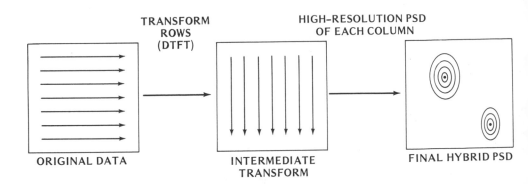

Figure 16.4   Hybrid 2-D spectral estimation.

16.6 MODIFIED CLASSICAL 2-D SPECTRAL ESTIMATORS

The 2-D discrete-time Fourier transform (DTFT) used to compute the periodogram was shown in Sec. 16.3 to be computable as a sequence of 1-D DTFTs of the columns followed by a sequence of 1-D DTFTs of the rows. A *hybrid 2-D spectral estimator* may be devised by substituting any of the 1-D high-resolution spectral techniques presented in Chaps. 6–13 for the row DTFTs, as illustrated in Fig. 16.4. The intermediate array generated by the column DTFTs will be composed of complex-valued transform values, so the complex form of the high-resolution techniques must be used. The intent of the hybrid scheme is to improve the resolution in the dimension where the data record may be limited as often occurs with space-time data arrays, where the spatial resolution can be inadequate due to a small number of spatial sensors relative to the larger number of time samples available from each sensor. Mathematically, the two steps of the hybrid approach to 2-D spectral estimation are

$$X_{\mathrm{INT}}[m, f_2] = T_2 \sum_{n=0}^{N-1} x[m, n] \exp(-j2\pi f_2 n T_2) \qquad (16.41)$$

$$\hat{P}_{\mathrm{HYBRID}}(f_1, f_2) = \text{High-resolution 1-D PSD of } X_{\mathrm{INT}}[m, f_2] \qquad (16.42)$$

at each frequency f_2 computed in Eq. (16.41). Joyce [1979] describes one such hybrid 2-D spectral estimator based on the 1-D FFT and the 1-D complex Burg algorithm. Hybrid schemes tend to work best when the signal-to-noise ratio is fairly high in the limited-record dimension.

Another approach that seeks to improve the resolution of the classical 2-D spectral estimators is the use of linear prediction techniques to extrapolate the original 2-D data array to an enlarged data array. The enlarged data array is then processed in the usual fashion by either of the two classical spectral estimators. Frost [1980], Frey [1982], Pendrel [1979], and Ulrych and Walker [1981] have examined 2-D quarter-plane linear prediction procedures for simultaneous extension of the data array in both dimensions. The data extrapolation procedure appears to provide limited resolution improvement of perhaps up to a factor of 2 in high signal-to-noise scenarios.

16.7 TWO-DIMENSIONAL AUTOREGRESSIVE SPECTRAL ESTIMATION

Parametric models of 2-D random processes are used, as in the 1-D case, with the expectation of improved spectral estimation performance over that achievable with the classical 2-D periodogram and correlogram methods. The 2-D autoregressive (AR) model has received the greatest attention in the literature and will, therefore, be the only parametric 2-D model considered in this chapter. Two-dimensional moving average spectral estimation has not, to this author's knowledge, been studied in the literature. One method of 2-D autoregressive–moving average spectral estimation has been proposed by Cadzow and Ogino [1981].

16.7.1 The 2-D Autoregressive Process

A 2-D autoregressive sequence $x[m,n]$ is generated by driving a 2-D linear shift-invariant filter with a 2-D white noise sequence $w[m,n]$,

$$x[i,j] = -\sum_m \sum_n a[m,n]x[i-m,j-n] + w[i,j] \quad , \tag{16.43}$$

in which the range of the indices m and n depends on the assumed region of support for the AR parameter array. The corresponding 2-D AR power spectral density was shown in Sec. 16.4 to have the form

$$P_{\mathrm{AR}}(f_1,f_2) = \frac{T_1 T_2 \rho_w}{\left| 1 + \sum_m \sum_n a[m,n]\exp(-j2\pi[f_1 mT_1 + f_2 nT_2]) \right|^2} \tag{16.44}$$

in which ρ_w is the 2-D white noise variance.

A primary issue with 2-D AR modeling is the choice of a region of support [Marzetta, 1980]. Only causal 2-D AR processes will be examined here, although the constraint of a stable and causal autoregressive process does not necessarily produce a better 2-D spectral estimate than would be produced by a semicausal or noncausal autoregressive process. Even with the assumption of causality, the 2-D AR process is not unique. Both NSHP and QP support regions may be defined. An upper-half-plane NSHP autoregressive parameter array $a_U[m,n]$ and a lower-half-plane NSHP autoregressive parameter array $a_L[m,n]$ may be defined as

$$a[m,n] = \begin{cases} a_U[m,n] & -p_1 \le m \le p_1 \text{ if } 1 \le n \le p_2,\ 1 \le m \le p_1 \text{ if } n = 0 \\ a_L[m,n] & -p_1 \le m \le p_1 \text{ if } -p_2 \le n \le -1,\ -p_1 \le m \le -1 \text{ if } n = 0 \end{cases} \tag{16.45}$$

for positive integers p_1 and p_2. The total number of NSHP AR parameters is, therefore, $2p_1 p_2 + p_1 + p_2$. Figure 16.5 illustrates the region of support for these two NSHP autoregressive arrays. First-, second-, third-, and fourth-quadrant QP autoregressive parameter arrays $a_1[m,n]$, $a_2[m,n]$, $a_3[m,n]$, and $a_4[m,n]$ may be defined as

$$a[m,n] = \begin{cases} a_1[m,n] & 0 \le m \le p_1 \text{ if } 1 \le n \le p_2,\ 1 \le m \le p_1 \text{ if } n = 0 \\ a_2[m,n] & -p_1 \le m \le 0 \text{ if } 1 \le n \le p_2,\ -p_1 \le m \le -1 \text{ if } n = 0 \\ a_3[m,n] & -p_1 \le m \le 0 \text{ if } -p_2 \le n \le -1,\ -p_1 \le m \le -1 \text{ if } n = 0 \\ a_4[m,n] & 0 \le m \le p_1 \text{ if } -p_2 \le n \le -1,\ 1 \le m \le p_1 \text{ if } n = 0 \end{cases} \tag{16.46}$$

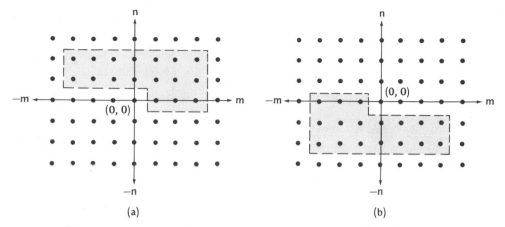

Figure 16.5   Typical NSHP regions of support for the 2-D autoregressive parameter array for $p_1 = 3$ and $p_2 = 2$. (a) Upper half NSHP. (b) Lower half NSHP.

The total number of QP AR parameters in any of the four quadrant cases is $p_1 p_2 + p_1 + p_2$. Figure 16.6 illustrates the region of support for these four QP autoregressive arrays.

16.7.2 Two-Dimensional Linear Prediction

A 2-D linear prediction estimate of the array sample $x[m, n]$ will take the form

$$\hat{x}[m, n] = -\sum_i \sum_j \alpha[i, j] x[m - i, n - j] \quad , \tag{16.47}$$

in which $\alpha[i, j]$ is a 2-D linear prediction coefficient. If the causal region of support for the linear prediction coefficient array is selected, then the 2-D linear prediction coefficients that minimize the variance of the error $x[m, n] - \hat{x}[m, n]$,

$$\rho_{\text{LP}} = \mathcal{E}\left\{ |x[m, n] - \hat{x}[m, n]|^2 \right\} \quad ,$$

will yield a linear prediction error that is a 2-D white process. This is analogous to the whitening filter interpretation of the 1-D linear prediction error filter examined in Chap. 7. The normal equations that yield the 2-D linear prediction coefficients from the 2-D ACS are identical to the 2-D Yule-Walker equations for a causal 2-D AR process, to be described in Sec. 16.7.3. Reflection coefficients in 2-D, not covered here, are discussed by Marzetta [1980].

The use of 2-D linear prediction filters with semicausal or noncausal regions of support have also been studied for use in 2-D spectral estimation by Pendrel [1979], Jain [1981], Jain and Ranganath [1981], and Nikias et al. [1984]. The semicausal 2-D linear prediction spectral estimator seems to have slightly better peak location

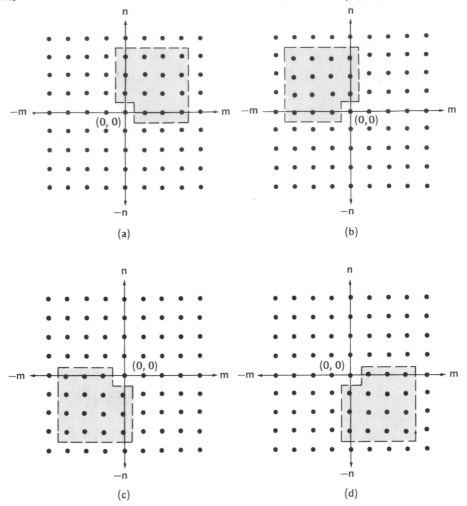

Figure 16.6 Typical QP regions of support for the 2-D autoregressive parameter arrays for $p_1 = p_2 = 3$. (a) First quadrant. (b) Second quadrant. (c) Third quadrant. (d) Fourth quadrant.

accuracy than either the NSHP or QP causal 2-D linear prediction spectral estimators [Jain, 1981]. It can be shown [Jain, 1981] that the semicausal linear prediction error variance has a spectral density that is white in the causal dimension and moving average in the noncausal dimension, yielding a spectral density expressed as a z-transform of the form

$$P_{\text{SCLP}}(z_1, z_2) = \frac{\rho_{\text{LP}} \left[1 + \sum \alpha[i, 0] z_1^{-i} \right]}{A(z_1, z_2) A^*(1/z_1^*, 1/z_2^*)} \quad , \tag{16.48}$$

where $\mathsf{A}(z_1, z_2)$ is defined as $\mathsf{A}(z_1, z_2) = 1 + \sum \sum a[i,j] z_1^{-i} z_2^{-j}$. This is no longer a 2-D AR but represents a 2-D ARMA. Similarly, it can be shown that the noncausal linear prediction error variance has a spectral density that is a moving average process in both dimensions, yielding a spectral density, also expressed as a z-transform, of the form

$$\mathsf{P}_{\mathrm{NCLP}}(z_1, z_2) = \frac{\rho_{\mathrm{LP}}}{\mathsf{A}(z_1, z_2)} \quad , \tag{16.49}$$

in which the $\mathsf{A}^*(1/z_1^*, 1/z_2^*)$ term appears in both the numerator and denominator, thereby canceling. The semicausal and noncausal linear prediction spectral estimators do not guarantee a non-negative power spectral density when the model parameters are estimated from finite length data records, whereas the causal linear prediction spectral estimators are guaranteed to always be nonnegative.

16.7.3 Two-Dimensional Yule–Walker Equations

The 2-D Yule-Walker equations for a causal 2-D AR process are obtained by multiplying Eq. (16.39) by $x^*[m - k, n - l]$ and taking the expectation, yielding

$$\sum_i \sum_j a[i,j] r_{xx}[k - i, l - j] = \begin{cases} \rho_w & \text{for } [k, l] = [0, 0] \\ 0 & \text{otherwise} \end{cases} .$$

The summation ranges can be selected to be any one of the six support regions of Eq. (16.45) or (16.46). The relationship between the 2-D AR parameters and the 2-D ACS is, therefore, through a set of linear equations.

The 2-D AR process with QP region of support has received, by far, the most attention in the literature. A key reason is the close relationship between the 2-D AR process and the multichannel AR process described in Chap. 15. This close relationship will provide a means of devising a 2-D Levinson-like algorithm, based on the multichannel Levinson algorithm, to solve the 2-D Yule-Walker equations for the 2-D AR parameter array.

The 2-D Yule-Walker equations for the QP support regions can be arranged, or ordered, into at least two convenient block-matrix forms by ordering the 2-D AR parameters either by rows or by columns. The row-ordered 2-D AR Yule-Walker equations for the first-quadrant region of support can be succinctly expressed as

$$\underline{\mathbf{R}}^r \underline{\mathbf{a}}_1^r = \underline{\rho}_1^r \quad , \tag{16.50}$$

in which the block matrix

$$\underline{\mathbf{R}}^r = \begin{pmatrix} \mathbf{R}^r[0] & \mathbf{R}^r[1] & \cdots & \mathbf{R}^r[p_1] \\ \mathbf{R}^r[-1] & \mathbf{R}^r[0] & \cdots & \mathbf{R}^r[p_1 - 1] \\ \vdots & \vdots & \ddots & \vdots \\ \mathbf{R}^r[-p_1] & \mathbf{R}^r[-p_1 + 1] & \cdots & \mathbf{R}^r[0] \end{pmatrix} \tag{16.51}$$

is defined in terms of the matrix elements

$$
\mathbf{R}^r[i] = \begin{pmatrix} r_{xx}[i,0] & r_{xx}[i,1] & \cdots & r_{xx}[i,p_2] \\ r_{xx}[i,-1] & r_{xx}[i,0] & \cdots & r_{xx}[i,p_2-1] \\ \vdots & \vdots & \ddots & \vdots \\ r_{xx}[i,-p_2] & r_{xx}[i,-p_2+1] & \cdots & r_{xx}[i,0] \end{pmatrix} , \qquad (16.52)
$$

and the block vectors

$$
\underline{\mathbf{a}}_1^r = \begin{pmatrix} \mathbf{a}_1^r[0] \\ \mathbf{a}_1^r[1] \\ \vdots \\ \mathbf{a}_1^r[p_1] \end{pmatrix} , \qquad \underline{\boldsymbol{\rho}}_1^r = \begin{pmatrix} \boldsymbol{\rho}_1^r \\ \mathbf{0} \\ \vdots \\ \mathbf{0} \end{pmatrix}
$$

are defined in terms of the vector elements

$$
\mathbf{a}_1^r[i] = \begin{pmatrix} a_1[i,0] \\ a_1[i,1] \\ \vdots \\ a_1[i,p_2] \end{pmatrix} , \qquad \boldsymbol{\rho}_1^r = \begin{pmatrix} \rho_w \\ 0 \\ \vdots \\ 0 \end{pmatrix} . \qquad (16.53)
$$

Each bold $\mathbf{0}$ is a column vector of $p_2 + 1$ zeros and, by definition, $a_1[0,0] = 1$. The block Toeplitz matrix $\underline{\mathbf{R}}^r$ is composed of $(p_1 + 1) \times (p_1 + 1)$ autocorrelation matrices $\mathbf{R}^r[i]$, which are themselves Toeplitz. Matrix $\underline{\mathbf{R}}^r$ is, therefore, said to be *doubly Toeplitz* or *Toeplitz-block Toeplitz*. A superscript r is used to remind the reader that row ordering has been used. Each matrix $\mathbf{R}^r[i]$ has dimension $(p_2 + 1) \times (p_2 + 1)$. The block vector $\underline{\mathbf{a}}_1^r$ of $p_2 + 1$ autoregressive parameters, which has a subscript 1 to designate this as a set of first-quadrant AR parameters, is composed of $p_1 + 1$ vectors $\mathbf{a}_1^r[i]$, each of dimension $p_2 + 1$. The block vector $\underline{\boldsymbol{\rho}}_1^r$ has all zero entries, except for the top entry, which is the noise variance ρ_w.

The column-ordered 2-D AR Yule-Walker equations for the first-quadrant region of support has the form

$$
\underline{\mathbf{R}}^c \underline{\mathbf{a}}_1^c = \underline{\boldsymbol{\rho}}_1^c \quad , \qquad (16.54)
$$

in which the block matrix

$$
\underline{\mathbf{R}}^c = \begin{pmatrix} \mathbf{R}^c[0] & \mathbf{R}^c[1] & \cdots & \mathbf{R}^c[p_2] \\ \mathbf{R}^c[-1] & \mathbf{R}^c[0] & \cdots & \mathbf{R}^c[p_2-1] \\ \vdots & \vdots & \ddots & \vdots \\ \mathbf{R}^c[-p_2] & \mathbf{R}^c[-p_2+1] & \cdots & \mathbf{R}^c[0] \end{pmatrix} \qquad (16.55)
$$

is defined in terms of the matrix elements

$$\mathbf{R}^c[j] = \begin{pmatrix} r_{xx}[0,j] & r_{xx}[1,j] & \cdots & r_{xx}[p_1,j] \\ r_{xx}[-1,j] & r_{xx}[0,j] & \cdots & r_{xx}[p_1-1,j] \\ \vdots & \vdots & \ddots & \vdots \\ r_{xx}[-p_1,j] & r_{xx}[-p_1+1,j] & \cdots & r_{xx}[0,j] \end{pmatrix}, \qquad (16.56)$$

and the block vectors

$$\underline{\mathbf{a}}_1^c = \begin{pmatrix} \mathbf{a}_1^c[0] \\ \mathbf{a}_1^c[1] \\ \cdots \\ \mathbf{a}_1^c[p_2] \end{pmatrix}, \qquad \underline{\rho}_1^c = \begin{pmatrix} \rho_1^c \\ 0 \\ \vdots \\ 0 \end{pmatrix}$$

are defined in terms of the vector elements

$$\mathbf{a}_1^c[j] = \begin{pmatrix} a_1[0,j] \\ a_1[1,j] \\ \vdots \\ a_1[p_1,j] \end{pmatrix}, \qquad \rho_1^c = \begin{pmatrix} \rho_w \\ 0 \\ \vdots \\ 0 \end{pmatrix}. \qquad (16.57)$$

In this case, $\underline{\mathbf{R}}^c$ has block matrix dimension $(p_2+1) \times (p_2+1)$, both $\underline{\mathbf{a}}_1^c$ and $\underline{\rho}_1^c$ have block vector dimension (p_2+1), $\mathbf{R}^c[j]$ has matrix dimension $(p_1+1) \times (p_1+1)$, both $\mathbf{a}_1^c[j]$ and ρ_1^c have vector dimension (p_1+1), and $\mathbf{0}$ is a column vector of p_1+1 zeros.

The 2-D Yule-Walker equations for the second-, third-, and fourth-quadrant support regions may also be succinctly expressed in terms of either the row-ordered block matrix $\underline{\mathbf{R}}^r$ or the column-ordered block matrix $\underline{\mathbf{R}}^c$. The row-ordered forms, for example, are

$$\underline{\mathbf{R}}^r \underline{\mathbf{a}}_2^r = \underline{\rho}_2^r \qquad (16.58)$$

$$\underline{\mathbf{R}}^r \underline{\mathbf{a}}_3^r = \underline{\rho}_3^r \qquad (16.59)$$

$$\underline{\mathbf{R}}^r \underline{\mathbf{a}}_4^r = \underline{\rho}_4^r \quad , \qquad (16.60)$$

in which

$$\underline{\mathbf{a}}_2^r = \begin{pmatrix} \mathbf{a}_2^r[0] \\ \mathbf{a}_2^r[1] \\ \vdots \\ \mathbf{a}_2^r[p_1] \end{pmatrix}, \quad \mathbf{a}_2^r[i] = \begin{pmatrix} a_2[i,p_2] \\ \vdots \\ a_2[i,1] \\ a_2[i,0] \end{pmatrix}, \quad \underline{\rho}_2^r = \begin{pmatrix} \rho_2^r \\ 0 \\ \vdots \\ 0 \end{pmatrix}, \quad \rho_2^r = \begin{pmatrix} 0 \\ \vdots \\ 0 \\ \rho_w \end{pmatrix}$$

and

$$\underline{\mathbf{a}}_3^r = \begin{pmatrix} \mathbf{a}_3^r[p_1] \\ \vdots \\ \mathbf{a}_3^r[1] \\ \mathbf{a}_3^r[0] \end{pmatrix}, \quad \mathbf{a}_3^r[i] = \begin{pmatrix} a_3[i,p_2] \\ \vdots \\ a_3[i,1] \\ a_3[i,0] \end{pmatrix}, \quad \underline{\rho}_3^r = \begin{pmatrix} 0 \\ \vdots \\ 0 \\ \rho_3^r \end{pmatrix}, \quad \rho_3^r = \begin{pmatrix} 0 \\ \vdots \\ 0 \\ \rho_w \end{pmatrix}$$

and

$$
\underline{\mathbf{a}}_4^r = \begin{pmatrix} \mathbf{a}_4^r[p_1] \\ \vdots \\ \mathbf{a}_4^r[1] \\ \mathbf{a}_4^r[0] \end{pmatrix} , \quad \mathbf{a}_4^r[i] = \begin{pmatrix} a_4[i,0] \\ a_4[i,1] \\ \vdots \\ a_4[i,p_2] \end{pmatrix} , \quad \underline{\rho}_4^r = \begin{pmatrix} \mathbf{0} \\ \vdots \\ \mathbf{0} \\ \rho_4^r \end{pmatrix} , \quad \rho_4^r = \begin{pmatrix} \rho_w \\ 0 \\ \vdots \\ 0 \end{pmatrix} .
$$

The autocorrelation matrices $\mathbf{R}^r[i]$ are not Hermitian, but they do satisfy the relationship $\mathbf{R}^r[-i] = (\mathbf{R}^r[i])^H$. This is sufficient, however, to make the block matrix $\underline{\mathbf{R}}^r$ Hermitian, that is, $\underline{\mathbf{R}}^r = (\underline{\mathbf{R}}^r)^H$. Matrix $\underline{\mathbf{R}}^r$ also has the property

$$
\mathbf{J}\underline{\mathbf{R}}^r\mathbf{J} = (\underline{\mathbf{R}}^r)^* \quad , \tag{16.61}
$$

in which $\mathbf{J}$ is a $(p_1+1)(p_2+1) \times (p_1+1)(p_2+1)$ reflection matrix. This property follows from the Hermitian and Toeplitz properties of $\underline{\mathbf{R}}^r$. Noting that $\mathbf{J}\mathbf{J} = \mathbf{I}$, where $\mathbf{I}$ is the identity matrix, then Eqs. (16.59) and (16.60) may be expressed as

$$
\mathbf{J}(\underline{\mathbf{R}}^r)^*\mathbf{J}\mathbf{J}\underline{\mathbf{a}}_3^r = \mathbf{J}\underline{\rho}_3^r \tag{16.62}
$$

$$
\mathbf{J}(\underline{\mathbf{R}}^r)^*\mathbf{J}\mathbf{J}\underline{\mathbf{a}}_4^r = \mathbf{J}\underline{\rho}_4^r \quad . \tag{16.63}
$$

Observing that $\mathbf{J}\underline{\rho}_3^r = \underline{\rho}_1^r$ and $\mathbf{J}\underline{\rho}_4^r = \underline{\rho}_2^r$ and using property (16.61), then Eqs. (16.62) and (16.63) become

$$
\underline{\mathbf{R}}^r(\mathbf{J}\underline{\mathbf{a}}_3^r)^* = (\underline{\rho}_1^r)^* = \underline{\rho}_1^r \tag{16.64}
$$

$$
\underline{\mathbf{R}}^r(\mathbf{J}\underline{\mathbf{a}}_4^r)^* = (\underline{\rho}_2^r)^* = \underline{\rho}_2^r \quad , \tag{16.65}
$$

which uses the fact that $\rho_w = \rho_w^*$ because the variance ρ_w is real. Comparing Eq. (16.64) with (16.58) and Eq. (16.65) with (16.59), it can be concluded that

$$
\underline{\mathbf{a}}_1^r = (\mathbf{J}\underline{\mathbf{a}}_3^r)^* \tag{16.66}
$$

$$
\underline{\mathbf{a}}_2^r = (\mathbf{J}\underline{\mathbf{a}}_4^r)^* \quad , \tag{16.67}
$$

that is, the third quadrant AR parameters are the complex conjugates of the first-quadrant AR parameters,

$$
a_3[m,n] = a_1^*[m,n] \quad , \tag{16.68}
$$

and the fourth-quadrant AR parameters are the complex conjugates of the second-quadrant AR parameters,

$$
a_4[m,n] = a_2^*[m,n] \quad . \tag{16.69}
$$

Equations (16.68) and (16.69) are similar to the conjugate relationship of the forward and backward linear prediction coefficients found in 1-D AR analysis.

A unique relationship was shown in Chap. 7 to exist between a sequence of $p+1$ ACS lags and the sequence of p 1-D autoregressive parameters and the noise variance ρ_w. Given one sequence, the other sequence could be uniquely determined. This one-to-one mapping is often described as the *autocorrelation matching property* of 1-D autoregressive analysis. This autocorrelation matching property is lost for 2-D AR process. An examination of the normal equations (16.54) and (16.58)–(16.60) will reveal that $2p_1p_2 - p_1 - p_2$ unique 2-D ACS terms are required to solve for the $p_1p_2 + p_1 + p_2$ 2-D AR parameters and the variance ρ_w. There are, therefore, insufficient AR parameters to uniquely determine the ACS terms. This implies that no one-to-one relationship can exist between these two alternative representations of a 2-D AR process. Inverse transforming the 2-D power spectral density function, Eq. (16.44), will generate a 2-D autocorrelation sequence that generally will not match the ACS values used to compute the 2-D AR parameters from the 2-D Yule-Walker equations. They will, however, tend to *approximate* the original ACS values. It should also be pointed out that a positive-definite $\underline{\mathbf{R}}^r$ matrix will guarantee a unique solution of the 2-D Yule-Walker equations, but it will not necessarily guarantee a stable AR model. The autocorrelation matching issue will be central to the 2-D maximum entropy method of Sec. 16.8.

16.7.4   Solving the 2-D Quarter-Plane Yule-Walker Equations

A fast algorithm for solving the 2-D QP Yule-Walker equations can be derived by developing a relationship with the multichannel Yule-Walker equations of Chap. 15, which have the multichannel Levinson algorithm for their solution [Therrien, 1981]. The procedure permits computation of the AR parameters for all four quarter planes simultaneously. The algorithm provided here is a row-ordered 2-D Levinson algorithm in which column order p_2 is fixed and the solution for row order p_1 is obtained recursively, starting from order 1. A companion column-ordered 2-D Levinson algorithm can also be developed by simply exchanging the roles of p_1 and p_2. There can be computational advantages to selecting one ordering over another, especially if $p_1 \gg p_2$ or $p_2 \gg p_1$, even though the orderings will lead to the same solution. Other 2-D Levinson algorithms are also possible [Justice, 1977], such as one that operates recursively on both dimensions simultaneously or one that operates alternately on each dimension.

The multichannel Yule-Walker equations for a (p_2+1)-channel AR process of order p_1, in which the channels are numbered from 0 to p_2, was shown [Eq. (15.57)] to have the form

$$
\begin{pmatrix}
\mathbf{R_{xx}}[0] & \mathbf{R_{xx}}[1] & \cdots & \mathbf{R_{xx}}[p_1] \\
\mathbf{R_{xx}}[-1] & \mathbf{R_{xx}}[0] & \cdots & \mathbf{R_{xx}}[p_1-1] \\
\vdots & \vdots & \ddots & \vdots \\
\mathbf{R_{xx}}[-p_1] & \mathbf{R_{xx}}[-p_1+1] & \cdots & \mathbf{R_{xx}}[0]
\end{pmatrix}
\begin{pmatrix}
\mathbf{I} \\
\mathbf{A}_{p_1}^H[1] \\
\vdots \\
\mathbf{A}_{p_1}^H[p_1]
\end{pmatrix}
=
\begin{pmatrix}
\mathbf{P}_{p_1}^f \\
\mathbf{0} \\
\vdots \\
\mathbf{0}
\end{pmatrix}
$$

$$(16.70)$$

for the forward multichannel AR parameters, and

$$
\begin{pmatrix}
\mathbf{R_{xx}}[0] & \cdots & \mathbf{R_{xx}}[p_1-1] & \mathbf{R_{xx}}[p_1] \\
\vdots & \ddots & \vdots & \vdots \\
\mathbf{R_{xx}}[-p_1+1] & \cdots & \mathbf{R_{xx}}[0] & \mathbf{R_{xx}}[1] \\
\mathbf{R_{xx}}[-p_1] & \cdots & \mathbf{R_{xx}}[-1] & \mathbf{R_{xx}}[0]
\end{pmatrix}
\begin{pmatrix}
\mathbf{B}_{p_1}^H[p_1] \\
\vdots \\
\mathbf{B}_{p_1}^H[1] \\
\mathbf{I}
\end{pmatrix}
=
\begin{pmatrix}
\mathbf{0} \\
\vdots \\
\mathbf{0} \\
\mathbf{P}_{p_1}^b
\end{pmatrix}
\qquad (16.71)
$$

for the backward multichannel AR parameters, in which

$$
\mathbf{R_{xx}}[k] =
\begin{pmatrix}
r_{00}[k] & \cdots & r_{0p_2}[k] \\
\vdots & & \vdots \\
r_{p_20}[k] & \cdots & r_{p_2p_2}[k]
\end{pmatrix}
= \mathbf{R_{xx}}^H[-k]
\qquad (16.72)
$$

is the multichannel correlation matrix at lag k. The correlation matrix displayed in Eqs. (16.70) and (16.71) is Hermitian and has a block Toeplitz structure. These properties were also characteristic of the 2-D QP Yule-Walker equations, which suggests that the solutions of the 2-D Yule-Walker equations and the multichannel Yule-Walker equations are related. Comparing Eq. (16.54) with Eq. (16.70), a one-to-one correspondence between $\underline{\mathbf{R}}_{p_1}$ and $\underline{\mathbf{R}}^r$ can be made by associating the multichannel crosscorrelation $r_{ij}[k]$ with the 2-D autocorrelation $r_{xx}[k,l]$ as follows

$$
r_{ij}[k] = r_{xx}[k, i-j]
\qquad (16.73)
$$

for $0 \le i, j \le p_2$. If one now compares Eq. (16.54) with Eq. (16.70), then it is clear that if

$$
\rho_1^r = \mathbf{R}_{p_1}^f \mathbf{a}_1^r[0] \quad ,
\qquad (16.74)
$$

then it follows that

$$
\mathbf{a}_1^r[k] = \mathbf{A}_{p_1}^H[k]\mathbf{a}_1^r[0]
\qquad (16.75)
$$

for $1 \le k \le p_1$. Thus, *the multichannel Levinson algorithm can be used to compute a solution of the 2-D Yule-Walker equations* by first solving for matrices $\mathbf{P}_{p_1}^f$ and $\mathbf{A}_{p_1}[k]$ for $k = 1$ to p_1, and then using Eqs. (16.74) and (16.75) to yield the 2-D autoregressive parameters and variance.

The second-quadrant 2-D AR parameters may similarly be computed from the multichannel solution using

$$
\rho_2^r = \mathbf{P}_{p_1}^f \mathbf{a}_2^r[0]
\qquad (16.76)
$$

and

$$
\mathbf{a}_2^r[k] = \mathbf{A}_{p_1}^H[k]\mathbf{a}_2^r[0]
\qquad (16.77)
$$

for $1 \le k \le p_1$.

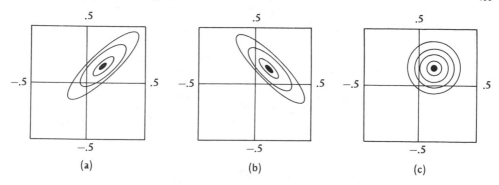

Figure 16.7   Illustration of the bias in the QP AR spectral estimator for a single sinusoid in white noise. (a) First-quadrant 2-D AR PSD estimate. (b)Second-quadrant 2-D AR PSD estimate. (c) Combined 2-D AR PSD estimate.

The Toeplitz structure of the 2-D autocorrelation matrices $\mathbf{R_{xx}}[k]$ can be exploited to further reduce the computational complexity of the multichannel Levinson algorithm. It can be shown (see the Problems) that the doubly Toeplitz structure will force the relationship

$$\mathbf{B}_{p_1}[k] = \mathbf{A}_{p_1}^{H}[k] \tag{16.78}$$

for $1 \leq k \leq p_1$ and the relationship

$$P_{p_1}^{f} = P_{p_1}^{b} \tag{16.79}$$

to be true, although these do not hold in the general multichannel case. These relationships will simplify the multichannel Levinson algorithm when applied to the 2-D case as follows,

$$\mathbf{\Delta}_{p_1+1} = \left(\mathbf{I} \quad \mathbf{A}_{p_1}[1] \quad \cdots \quad \mathbf{A}_{p_1}[p_1] \right) \begin{pmatrix} \mathbf{R_{xx}}[p_1+1] \\ \mathbf{R_{xx}}[p_1] \\ \vdots \\ \mathbf{R_{xx}}[1] \end{pmatrix} \tag{16.80}$$

$$\mathbf{A}_{p_1+1}[p_1+1] = -\mathbf{\Delta}_{p_1+1}(P_{p_1}^{f})^{-1} \tag{16.81}$$

$$\mathbf{A}_{p_1+1}[k] = \mathbf{A}_{p_1}[k] + \mathbf{A}_{p_1+1}[p_1+1]\mathbf{A}_{p_1}^{H}[p_1-k] \quad \text{for } 1 \leq k \leq p_1 \tag{16.82}$$

$$P_{p_1+1}^{f} = (\mathbf{I} - \mathbf{A}_{p_1+1}[p_1+1]\mathbf{A}_{p_1+1}^{H}[p_1+1])P_{p_1}^{f} \tag{16.83}$$

with initial condition $P_0^{f} = \mathbf{R_{xx}}[0]$. This reduces the computational burden of the general multichannel Levinson by approximately one-half [Kalouptsidis et al., 1984; Wax and Kailath, 1983]. Appendix 16.B contains subroutine TDAR that solves for the 2-D first- and second-quadrant AR parameters, given the 2-D ACS samples.

16.7.5 A Modified Quarter-Plane AR Spectral Estimator

The 2-D first-quadrant autoregressive spectral estimator

$$
\hat{P}_{AR1}(f_1, f_2) = \frac{T_1 T_2 \hat{\rho}_w}{\left| \displaystyle\sum_{m=0}^{p_1} \sum_{n=0}^{p_2} \hat{a}_1[m,n] \exp(-j2\pi[f_1 m T_1 + f_2 n T_2]) \right|^2}
$$

$$
= \frac{T_1 T_2 \hat{\rho}_w}{\left| \underline{e}(f_1, f_2) \underline{\hat{a}}_1^r \right|^2} \quad,
$$

(16.84)

for which $\underline{e}(f_1, f_2)$ is the 2-D complex sinusoid block vector of Eq. (16.39) and $\underline{a}_1^r$ is the first-quadrant autoregressive parameter vector estimate of (16.53) (note that $\hat{a}_1[0,0] = 1$ by definition), and the 2-D second-quadrant autoregressive spectral estimator

$$
\hat{P}_{AR2}(f_1, f_2) = \frac{T_1 T_2 \hat{\rho}_w}{\left| \displaystyle\sum_{m=-p_1}^{0} \sum_{n=0}^{p_2} \hat{a}_2[m,n] \exp(-j2\pi[f_1 m T_1 + f_2 n T_2]) \right|^2} \quad,
$$

(16.85)

in which $\hat{a}_2[0,0] = 1$, will yield asymmetrically biased spectral estimates, as illustrated in Fig. 16.7 for the case of a known 2-D ACS for a single sinusoid in white noise. The spectral responses are seen to have opposing elliptical skews. Jackson and Chien [1979] suggested that a combined QP AR estimator $\hat{P}_{ARC}(f_1, f_2)$ be formed as

$$
\frac{1}{\hat{P}_{ARC}(f_1, f_2)} = \frac{1}{\hat{P}_{AR1}(f_1, f_2)} + \frac{1}{\hat{P}_{AR2}(f_1, f_2)} \quad.
$$

(16.86)

The combined QP estimator will yield the circular response shown in Fig. 16.7(c). Jackson and Chien also found in practice that less spurious peaks were likely to be introduced into the spectral estimate when using the combined estimator because the first- and second-quadrant estimators are not likely to be zero at the same place unless there is actually a signal component existing at that location in the 2-D frequency plane. Note that the fast algorithm of Appendix 16.B simultaneously provides the AR parameter vector solution for both the quadrants needed to evaluate Eq. (16.86).

16.7.6 Estimating 2-D Autoregressive Parameters from Data

The algorithmic techniques employed in Chap. 8 for 1-D AR parameter estimation may be extended to the 2-D case. The data can be used to estimate a set of 2-D ACS values over a finite support region, and the 2-D Yule-Walker equations then solved for the desired QP or NSHP autoregressive parameter array. Least squares

2-D linear prediction algorithms based on the covariance and modified covariance techniques of Chap. 8 may also be used [Nikias et al., 1984; Nikias and Raghuveer, 1985; Ulrych and Walker, 1981]. Assuming data samples $x[m, n]$ over a rectangular region of support $1 \leq m \leq M$ and $1 \leq n \leq N$, then the total squared error E_1 of the first-quadrant linear predictor is

$$E_1 = \frac{1}{2NM} \sum_{m=p_1+1}^{M} \sum_{n=p_2+1}^{N} \left| \sum_{i=0}^{p_1} \sum_{j=0}^{p_2} a_1[i,j]x[m-i, n-j] \right|^2 , \qquad (16.87)$$

in which $a_1[0,0] = 1$ is assumed. This may be minimized to yield a set of 2-D covariance linear prediction equations in terms of the linear prediction parameters $a_1[i, j]$. A modified covariance linear prediction normal equation set may also be formulated (see the Problems) by minimizing the sum of the first- and third-quadrant squared errors, $E_1 + E_3$, subject to the complex conjugate relationship (16.68) that relates the first- and third-quadrant 2-D AR parameters.

16.8   TWO-DIMENSIONAL MAXIMUM ENTROPY SPECTRAL ESTIMATION

The 2-D maximum entropy method PSD estimator $P_{\text{MEM}}(f_1, f_2)$ maximizes the 2-D entropy rate

$$h = \int_{-1/2T_1}^{1/2T_1} \int_{-1/2T_2}^{1/2T_2} \ln P_{\text{MEM}}(f_1, f_2) \, df_1 \, df_2 , \qquad (16.88)$$

subject to the constraints that it match the known 2-D ACS values

$$r_{xx}[k, l] = \int_{-1/2T_1}^{1/2T_1} \int_{-1/2T_2}^{1/2T_2} P_{\text{MEM}}(f_1, f_2) \exp(j2\pi[f_1 kT_1 + f_2 lT_2]) \, df_1 \, df_2. \quad (16.89)$$

Unlike the parametric 2-D spectral estimators such as the QP AR estimator, the MEM PSD does not require that the known lags of the 2-D ACS have a uniform support grid; arbitrary lags can be used as the constraints. The optimum maximum entropy spectrum in 1-D was shown in Chap. 7 to be the inverse of a positive polynomial that could be factored as the squared magnitude of a finite-order polynomial. The lack of a factorization theorem for 2-D polynomials means that the inverse polynomial of the 2-D maximum entropy PSD cannot be factored, requiring nonlinear means of solution to find the 2-D maximum entropy PSD, which is not always guaranteed to exist given any arbitrary set of 2-D ACS values. It has been shown in Sec. 16.7.3 that the 2-D AR process will not possess the ACS matching property that existed with 1-D AR processes. Thus, *2-D MEM and 2-D AR do not yield identical spectral estimators*, in contrast to the 1-D case for which they were identical.

If the known ACS lags fall on a uniform quarter-plane support grid, then the MEM solution can be shown [Jain and Ranganath, 1981] to have the form

$$P_{\text{MEM}}(f_1, f_2) = \frac{1}{\displaystyle\sum_{k=-p_1}^{p_1} \sum_{l=-p_2}^{p_2} \alpha[k,l] \exp(-j2\pi[f_1 k T_1 + f_2 l T_2])} \quad , \quad (16.90)$$

whenever it exists. This is the same form as the noncausal 2-D linear prediction spectral estimator. It is not generally possible to factor the denominator into two conjugate polynomials similar to Eq. (16.48). No closed-form solution for the $\alpha[k,l]$ has been found, but techniques have been devised that compute $P_{\text{MEM}}(f_1, f_2)$ directly from the known 2-D ACS values without the need to solve for the $\alpha[k,l]$ parameters. These techniques require either iterative algorithms which have trouble converging, or nonlinear optimizations which are guaranteed to converges but which are computationally intensive [Lim and Malik, 1981; Malik and Lim, 1982; Wernecke, 1977; Lang, 1981; Lang and McClellan, 1982; Lang and Marzetta, 1984; Sharma and Chellappa, 1985].

Equation (16.90) implies an extension of the 2-D ACS. The AR parameters in 1-D were used to extrapolate the 1-D ACS function while maintaining the positive-definite property of the extended autocorrelation sequence. Given a finite, positive-definite 1-D ACS, it is always possible to extrapolate to a valid 1-D ACS. In 2-D, however, a finite 2-D positive-definite 2-D ACS cannot always be extrapolated to a valid 2-D ACS (i.e., it may not be *extendible*) [Dickinson, 1980]. It is true, though, that as long as $P_{\text{MEM}}(f_1, f_2) > 0$ for all f_1 and f_2, then the inverse DTFT of Eq. (16.90) will always generate a valid positive-definite 2-D ACS [Lang and McClellan, 1983; Nikias and Venetsamopoulos, 1985]. Whether a better spectral estimator than 2-D AR can be obtained by constraining the estimator to match the available ACS values has not yet been satisfactorily confirmed by the limited experiments performed to date, especially when using estimated ACS values rather than exactly known ACS values.

16.9 TWO-DIMENSIONAL MINIMUM VARIANCE SPECTRAL ESTIMATION

The 2-D minimum variance spectral (MV) estimator was originally developed as a frequency-wavenumber spectral estimator by Capon [1969]. The extension of the 1-D minimum variance spectral estimator to 2-D requires a mathematical development that very closely parallels the development of Chap. 12 and Sec. 15.13, based on the idea of using a 2-D finite impulse response filter to pass a 2-D complex sinusoid of a certain frequency while simultaneously minimizing the power out of the filter. Unlike the parametric methods of 2-D PSD analysis, the 2-D MV PSD is not constrained to use uniformly-sampled ACS values. If the first QP grid of ACS lags is known, however, then the 2-D minimum variance spectral estimator will have the form

$$P_{MV}(f_1, f_2) = \frac{T_1 T_2}{\underline{e}^H(f_1, f_2)(\underline{\mathbf{R}}^r)^{-1}\underline{e}(f_1, f_2)} \quad , \tag{16.91}$$

in which $\underline{e}(f_1, f_2)$ is the complex sinusoid block vector of Eq. (16.39) and $(\underline{\mathbf{R}}^r)^{-1}$ is the inverse of the doubly-Toeplitz block autocorrelation matrix of Eq. (16.51). Other variations of Eq. (16.91) will depend on the selected region of support. Dowla and Lim [1984] have shown that the 2-D first-quadrant MV PSD and the 2-D first-quadrant AR PSD have a comparable relationship as that of Eq. (12.18). This means that the first-quadrant MV PSD suffers from the same bias as that of the 2-D first-quadrant AR PSD. Defining a combined MV PSD that uses both the first- and second-quadrant MV PSD estimators

$$\frac{1}{\hat{P}_{MVC}(f_1, f_2)} = \frac{1}{\hat{P}_{MV1}(f_1, f_2)} + \frac{1}{\hat{P}_{MV2}(f_1, f_2)} \tag{16.92}$$

will alleviate this bias.

The inverse of $\underline{\mathbf{R}}^r$ may be obtained simply by use of the inversion formula (15.86) with a further reduction in computation possible by using properties (16.78) and (16.79), due to the doubly-Toeplitz property of $\underline{\mathbf{R}}^r$. Comparable expressions to Eqs. (12.24) and (12.25) may then be developed for the 2-D MV PSD (see the Problems).

Dudgeon and Mersereau [1984] have reported some problems with the 2-D minimum variance spectral estimator when the data is insufficient to yield good autocorrelation estimates to be used in the matrix inversion of $\underline{\mathbf{R}}^r$. Nikias et al. [1984] have reported that better results in processing ECG medical sensor data were obtained with 2-D MV than with either the 2-D periodogram or the 2-D AR.

REFERENCES

Cadzow, J. A., and K. Ogino, Two-Dimensional Spectral Estimation, *IEEE Trans. Acoust. Speech Signal Process.*, vol. ASSP-29, pp. 396–401, June 1981.

Capon, J., High Resolution Frequency-Wavenumber Spectrum Analysis, *Proc. IEEE*, vol. 57, pp. 1408–1418, August 1969.

Dickinson, B. W., Two-Dimensional Markov Spectrum Estimates Need Not Exist, *IEEE Trans. Inf. Theory*, vol. IT-26, pp. 120–121, January 1980.

Dowla, F. U., and J. S. Lim, Relationship between Maximum Likelihood Method and Autoregressive Modeling in Multidimensional Power Spectrum Estimation, *IEEE Trans. Acoust. Speech Signal Process.*, vol. ASSP-32, pp. 1083 1087, October 1984.

Dudgeon, D. E., and R. M. Mersereau, *Multidimensional Digital Signal Processing*, Prentice-Hall, Inc., Englewood Cliffs, N. J., 1984.

Frey, E. J., Two-Dimensional Spectral Estimation: Comparison of Current Techniques, M. S. thesis, University of Colorado, Boulder, Colo., April 1982.

Frost, O. L. III, High-Resolution 2-D Spectral Analysis at Low SNR, *Proceedings of the 1980 IEEE International Conference on Acoustics, Speech, and Signal Processing*, Denver, Colo., pp. 580–583, April 1980.

Huang, T. S., Two-Dimensional Windows, *IEEE Trans. Audio Electroacoust.*, vol. AU-20, pp. 88–90, March 1972.

Jackson, L. B., and H. C. Chien, Frequency and Bearing Estimation by Two-Dimensional Linear Prediction, *Proceedings of the 1979 IEEE International Conference on Acoustics, Speech, and Signal Processing*, Washington, D.C., pp. 665–668, April 1979.

Jain, A. K., Advances in Mathematical Models for Image Processing, *Proc. IEEE*, vol. 69, pp. 502–528, May 1981.

Jain, A. K., and S. Ranganath, High Resolution Spectrum Estimation in Two Dimensions, *Proceedings of the First ASSP Workshop on Spectrum Estimation*, Hamilton, Ontario, Canada, pp. 3.4.1–3.4.5, August 1981.

Joyce, L. S., A Separable 2-D Autoregressive Spectral Estimation Algorithm, *Proceedings of the 1979 IEEE International Conference on Acoustics, Speech, and Signal Processing*, Washington, D.C., pp. 677-680, April 1979.

Justice, J. H., A Levinson-Type Algorithm for Two-Dimensional Wiener Filtering Using Bivariate Szego Polynomials, *Proc. IEEE*, vol. 65, pp. 882–886, June 1977.

Kalouptsidis, N., G. Carayannis, and D. Manolakis, Fast Algorithms for Block Toeplitz Matrices with Toeplitz Entries, *Signal Process.*, vol. 6, pp. 77–81, January 1984.

Lang, S. W., and T. L. Marzetta, Image Spectral Estimation, Chapter 4 in *Digital Image Processing Techniques*, M. P. Ekstrom, ed., Academic Press, Inc., Orlando, Fla., 1984.

Lang, S. W., and J. H. McClellan, Multidimensional MEM Spectral Estimation, *IEEE Trans. Acoust. Speech Signal Process.*, vol. ASSP-30, pp. 880–887, December 1982.

Lang, S. W., and J. H. McClellan, Spectral Estimation for Sensor Arrays, *IEEE Trans. Acoust. Speech Signal Process.*, vol. ASSP-31, pp. 349–358, April 1983.

Lim, J. S., and N. A. Malik, A New Algorithm for Two-Dimensional Maximum Entropy Power Spectrum Estimation, *IEEE Trans. Acoust. Speech Signal Process.*, vol. ASSP-29, pp. 401–413, June 1981.

Malik, N. A., and J. S. Lim, Properties of Two-Dimensional Maximum Entropy Power Spectrum Estimates, *IEEE Trans. Acoust. Speech Signal Process.*, vol. ASSP-30, pp. 788–797, October 1982.

Marzetta, T. L., Two-Dimensional Linear Prediction: Autocorrelation Arrays, Minimum-Phase Prediction Error Filters, and Reflection Coefficient Arrays, *IEEE Trans. Acoust. Speech Signal Process.*, vol. ASSP-28, pp. 725–733, December 1980.

McClellan, J. H., Multidimensional Spectral Estimation, *Proc. IEEE*, vol. 70, pp. 1029–1039, September 1982.

Nikias, C. L., and M. R. Raghuveer, Multi-Dimensional Parametric Spectral Estimation, *Signal Process.*, vol. 9, pp. 191–205, October 1985.

Nikias, C. L., P. D. Scott, and J. H. Siegel, Computer Based Two-Dimensional Spectral Estimation for the Detection of Prearrhythmic States after Hypothermic Myocardial Preservation, *Comput. Biol. Med.*, vol. 14, pp. 159–178, 1984.

Nikias, C. L., and A. N. Venetsanopoulos, Sufficient Condition for Extendibility and Two-Dimensional Power Spectrum Estimation, *Proceedings of the 1985 IEEE International Conference on Acoustics, Speech, and Signal Processing*, Tampa, Fla., pp. 792–795, March 1985.

Pendrel, J. V., The Maximum Entropy Principle in Two Dimensional Spectral Analysis, Ph.D. dissertation, York University, Ontario, Canada, November 1979.

Sharma, G., and R. Chellappa, A Model-Based Approach for Estimation of Two-Dimensional Maximum Entropy Power Sectra, *IEEE Trans. Inform. Theory*, vol. IT-31, pp. 90–99, January 1985.

Therrien, C. W., Relations between 2-D and Multichannel Linear Prediction, *IEEE Trans. Acoust. Speech Signal Process.*, vol. ASSP-29, pp. 454–456, June 1981.

Ulrych, T. J., and C. J. Walker, High Resolution Two-Dimensional Power Spectral Estimation, in *Applied Time Series II*, D. F. Findley, ed., Academic Press, Inc., New York, pp. 71–99, 1981.

Wax, M., and T. Kailath, Efficient Inversion of Toeplitz-Block Toeplitz Matrix, *IEEE Trans. Acoust. Speech Signal Process.*, vol. ASSP-31, pp. 1218–1221, October 1983.

Wernecke, S. J., Two-Dimensional Maximum Entropy Reconstruction of Radio Brightness, *Radio Sci.*, vol. 12, pp. 831–844, September-October 1977.

PROBLEMS

1. A separable 2-D sequence is one that can be expressed as the product of two independent sequences, $x[m, n] = x_1[m]x_2[n]$. Prove that the 2-D convolution of a separable sequence is also separable.

2. Prove that the 2-D DTFS is a 2-D periodic function.

3. Show that the frequency response function for a rectangular impulse function

$$h[m, n] = \begin{cases} 1 & \text{for } |m| \leq a/2 \quad , \quad |n| \leq b/2 \\ 0 & \text{otherwise} \end{cases}$$

is

$$H(f_1, f_2) = \text{sinc}(f_1/a)\text{sinc}(f_2/b)/ab.$$

4. Prove that the 2-D autocorrelation term $r_{xx}[0, 0]$ is real and positive, and satisfies

$$r_{xx}[0, 0] \geq |r_{xx}[m, n]|$$

for all m and n. Furthermore, show that the 2-D autocorrelation is Hermitian symmetric, $r_{xx}^*[m, n] = r_{xx}[-m, -n]$.

5. Show that the 2-D PSD as defined by Eq. (16.26) is real and positive. Also show that $P(f_1, f_2) = P(-f_1, -f_2)$ if the 2-D ACS is real.

6. Suppose the following samples of a 2-D ACS are known:

$$r_{xx}[0,0] = 1$$
$$r_{xx}[1,0] = r_{xx}[-1,0] = \alpha$$
$$r_{xx}[0,1] = r_{xx}[0,-1] = \beta$$
$$r_{xx}[1,1] = r_{xx}[1,-1] = r_{xx}[-1,1] = r_{xx}[-1,-1] = 0 \quad ,$$

where α and β are real-valued parameters. Compute and plot the 2-D correlogram method PSD estimate.

7. Using the same 2-D ACS values of Problem 6, form the 4×4 autocorrelation matrix of Eq. (16.51) and analytically determine its inverse. Form the minimum variance spectral estimator, Eq. (16.91), and plot the PSD.

8. Using the same 2-D ACS values of Problem 6 and the autocorrelation matrix of Problem 7, analytically determine the first- and second-quadrant QP autoregressive parameters. Compute and plot the first-quadrant, second-quadrant, and combined-quadrant AR PSD estimates [Eqs. (16.84), (16.85), and (16.86)].

9. Explain why it requires more 2-D ACS samples than unknown 2-D AR parameters, in contrast to the 1-D case, in which the number of ACS samples was one more than the number of 1-D AR parameters.

10. Write the matrix expression for the Yule-Walker equations of the causal NSHP region of support [Jain and Ranganath, 1981].

11. Develop the normal equations for the 2-D modified covariance method of 2-D linear prediction for a first-quadrant linear prediction region of support.

12. Show that the 2-D minimum variance spectral estimator can be expressed in the form

$$\hat{P}_{MV}(f_1, f_2) = \frac{T_1 T_2}{\sum_{k=-p}^{p} \sum_{l=-q}^{q} \alpha[k,l] \exp(-j2\pi[f_1 kT_1 + f_2 lT_2])} .$$

What is the relationship of the coefficients $\alpha[k,l]$ to the elements of the inverse autocorrelation matrix?

13. Derive a 2-D version of Eq. (4.53) for the 2-D block autocorrelation matrix of M 2-D complex sinusoids in 2-D white noise. What would be the 2-D form of the MUSIC frequency estimator of Chap. 13 that would be suggested by this block autocorrelation matrix?

14. Prove the relationships of Eqs. (16.78) and (16.79).

15. Finish program TDAR of Appendix 16.B in the two areas indicated in the listing.

APPENDIX 16.A
PROGRAM TO COMPUTE THE 2-D PERIODOGRAM

```
      SUBROUTINE TDPERIOD (N1,N2,T1,T2,X,PSD)
C
C   This subroutine computes the two-dimensional periodogram
C
C   Input Parameters:
```

```
C
C     N1    - Number of column samples
C     N2    - Number of row samples
C     T1    - Sample interval in column direction
C     T2    - Sample interval in row direction
C     X     - Complex two-dimensional array of N1 x N2 data samples
C
C   Output Parameters:
C
C     PSD   - Real two-dimensional array of NPSD1 x NPSD2 power
C             spectral density values
C
      PARAMETER NPSD1=512      ! Number of PSD values in column direction
      PARAMETER NPSD2=512      ! Number of PSD values in row direction
      PARAMETER N2MAX=16       ! Maximum expected size for N2
      COMPLEX X(N1,N2),Z1(NPSD1),Z2(NPSD2),TEMP(NPSD1,N2MAX)
      COMPLEX W1(NPSD1),W2(NPSD2)
      REAL PSD(NPSD1,NPSD2)
C
      SCALE=T1*T2/FLOAT(N1*N2)
      CALL PREFFT (NPSD1,0,NEXP1,W1)
      CALL PREFFT (NPSD2,0,NEXP2,W2)
C  Compute the column transforms
      DO 100 K=1,N2
         DO 110 J=1,N1
110         Z1(J)=X(J,K)
         DO 120 J=N1+1,NPSD1
120         Z1(J)=(0.,0.)
         CALL FFT (NPSD1,0,1.,NEXP1,W1,Z1)
         DO 130 J=1,NPSD1
130         TEMP(J,K)=Z1(J)
100      CONTINUE
C  Compute the row transforms and squared magnitude to yield PSD
      DO 200 K=1,NPSD1
         DO 210 J=1,N2
210         Z2(J)=TEMP(K,J)
         DO 220 J=N2+1,NPSD2
220         Z2(J)=(0.,0.)
         CALL FFT (NPSD2,0,1.,NEXP2,W2,Z2)
         DO 230 J=1,NPSD2
230         PSD(K,J)=(REAL(Z2(J))**2+AIMAG(Z2(J))**2)*SCALE
200      CONTINUE
      RETURN
      END
```

APPENDIX 16.B
PROGRAM TO COMPUTE THE FIRST-QUADRANT AND SECOND-QUADRANT 2-D AUTOREGRESSIVE PARAMETERS

```
      SUBROUTINE TDAR (IP1,IP2,R,RHO,A1,A2,ISTAT)
C
C   Computes the two-dimensional QP autoregressive parameter arrays given
C   the two-dimensional autocorrelation array using a modified multichannel
```

```
C    Levinson algorithm.  Only the first- and second-quadrant AR arrays are
C    provided, as the third- and fourth-quadrant AR arrays may be obtained as
C    complex conjugates of the first- and second-quadrant arrays,
C    respectively.
C
C    Input Parameters:
C
C       IP1  - Number of rows in the autoregressive array
C       IP2  - Number of columns in the autoregressive array
C       R    - Complex three-dimensional array of block
C                 autocorrelation matrices
C
C    Output Parameters:
C
C       RHO  - White noise variance driving the 2-D AR process
C       A1   - Complex two-dimensional array of first-quadrant
C                 autoregressive parameters
C       A2   - Complex two-dimensional array of second-quadrant
C                 autoregressive parameters
C       ISTAT- Integer status indicator
C
C    Notes:  This subroutine uses the subroutine package in the
C            multichannel chapter, Appendix 15.D.  Elements of
C            arrays A1 and A2 indexed as [0,0] to [IP1,IP2] in
C            the text are indexed as [1,1] to [IP1+1, IP2+1] in
C            this subroutine.  Arrays A, PF, DELTA, TEMP1, and
C            TEMP2 must have storage allocated in a COMMON.
C
      COMPLEX R(IP2+1,IP2+1,IP1+1),A1(IP1+1,IP2+1),A2(IP1+1,IP2+1)
      COMPLEX A(IP2+1,IP2+1,IP1),PF(IP2+1,IP2+1),DELTA(IP2+1,IP2+1)
      COMPLEX TEMP1(IP2+1,IP2+1),TEMP2(IP2+1,IP2+1),S
C
C    Initialization
C
      ISTAT=0
      J=IP2+1
      CALL ASSIGN (J,J,R(1,1,1),PF)
      M=0
C
C    Main Loop
C
100   CONTINUE
      M=M+1
C    Compute partial correlation matrix, Eq. (16.80)
      CALL ASSIGN (J,J,R(1,1,M+1),DELTA)
      DO 10 K=1,M
         CALL MULT (J,J,A(1,1,K),R(1,1,M-K),TEMP1)
10       CALL ADD (J,J,TEMP1,DELTA,DELTA)
C    Compute the multichannel reflection matrix, Eq. (16.81)
      CALL INVERT (J,PF,TEMP1,ISTAT)
      CALL MULT (J,J,DELTA,TEMP1,TEMP2)
      S=(-1.,0.)
      CALL SCALE (J,J,S,TEMP2,A(1,1,M))
C    Update the multichannel error covariance matrix, Eq. (16.83)
      CALL XPOSE (J,A(1,1,M),TEMP1)
      CALL MULT (J,J,A(1,1,M),TEMP1,TEMP2)
      CALL IDENT (J,TEMP1)
      CALL SUB (J,J,TEMP1,TEMP2,TEMP1)
```

```
        CALL MULT (J,J,TEMP1,PF,TEMP2)
        CALL ASSIGN (J,J,TEMP2,PF)
C   Update the multichannel prediction coefficient matrices, Eq. (16.82)
        IF (M .EQ. 1)  GO TO 40
        DO 30 K=1,(M-1)/2
          MK=M-K
          CALL ASSIGN (J,J,A(1,1,K),TEMP1)
          CALL ASSIGN (J,J,A(1,1,MK),TEMP2)
          CALL XPOSE (J,TEMP2,TEMP3)
          CALL MULT (J,J,A(1,1,M),TEMP3,TEMP4)
          CALL ADD (J,J,TEMP1,TEMP4,A(1,1,K))
          IF (K .EQ. MK)  GO TO 30
          CALL XPOSE (J,TEMP1,TEMP3)
          CALL MULT (J,J,A(1,1,M),TEMP3,TEMP4)
          CALL ADD (J,J,TEMP2,TEMP4,A(1,1,MK))
30        CONTINUE
C
C   Check for order
C
40      IF (M .LT. IP1)  GO TO 100
C
C   Compute the first-quadrant 2-D AR parameter array
C***********************************************************************
C   Set up a subroutine that calls CHOLESKY to solve for RHO and A1[1,2] to
C   A1[1,IP1+1] here.  Element A1[1,1]=1 by definition. This is Eq. (16.74).
C***********************************************************************
        DO 50 K=1,IP1
          CALL XPOSE (J,J,A(1,1,K),TEMP1)
50        CALL MULT (J,1,TEMP1,A1(1,1),A1(K+1,1))        ! Eq. (16.75)
C
C   Compute the second-quadrant 2-D AR parameter array
C***********************************************************************
C   Set up a subroutine that calls CHOLESKY to solve for RHO (should be
C   identical to the RHO computed for the first quadrant) and A[1,2] to
C   A2[1,IP1+1] here. Element A2[1,1]=1 by definition. This is Eq. (16.76).
C***********************************************************************
        DO 60 K=1,IP1
          CALL XPOSE (J,J,A(1,1,K),TEMP1)
60        CALL MULT (J,1,TEMP1,A2(1,1),A2(K+1,1))        ! Eq. (16.77)
        RETURN
        END
```

APPENDIX 16.C
PROGRAM TO COMPUTE THE FIRST-QUADRANT 2-D AUTOREGRESSIVE SPECTRUM

```
        SUBROUTINE TDARPSD (IP1,IP2,RHO,T1,T2,A1,PSD)
C
C   This subroutine computes the first-quadrant autoregressive PSD
C   given the first-quadrant AR parameters.
C
C   Input Parameters:
C
```

```
C     IP1 - Number of rows in the autoregressive array
C     IP2 - Number of columns in the autoregressive array
C     RHO - White noise variance of AR driving process
C     T1  - Lag sample interval in the row dimension
C     T2  - Lag sample interval in the column dimension
C     A1  - Complex two-dimensional array of first-quadrant
C           autoregressive parameters
C
C  Output Parameters:
C
C     PSD - Real two-dimensional array of NPSD1 by NPSD2
C           autoregressive power spectral density values
C
C  Notes:
C     Uses subroutine TDPERIOD in Appendix 16.A.
C
      PARAMETER NPSD1=512      ! Number of PSD values in row dimension
      PARAMETER NPSD2=512      ! Number of PSD values in column dimension
      COMPLEX A1(IP1+1,IP2+1)
      REAL PSD(NPSD1,NPSD2)
C
      CALL TDPERIOD (IP1+1,IP2+1,1.,1.,A1,PSD)
      DO 10 J=1,NPSD1
        DO 10 K=1,NPSD2
10        PSD(J,K)=T1*T2*RHO/PSD(J,K)
      RETURN
      END
```

17

EPILOGUE

I was attacking the problem which . . . used the method that seemed best at the moment; but experience may suggest better methods.

George Udny Yule, 1927

Digital spectral estimation continues to be an active area of research for better spectral estimation methods and faster computational algorithms. As experience finds shortcomings in old and newly introduced techniques, especially with spectral estimation of short data records, improvements will be improvised and new ideas tried. Some of the so-called "modern" spectral estimators are beginning to mature into useful signal processing tools, as evidenced by the increase in journal and conference papers on applications to actual data sets. The autoregressive spectral estimator is one such method finding much utility in industry. Let us now pose two questions. Where are we going in spectral estimation research? Where should we be going?

The topic areas of greatest interest to the digital signal processing research community are ARMA spectral estimation, eigenanalysis methods, and multidimensional spectral estimation. Eigenanalysis methods, in particular, are receiving extensive attention for spectral analysis of spatial data records from arrays of sensors due to the ability of these methods to perform high-resolution beamforming. Development of fast computational algorithms will continue to be of great interest in order to reduce the computational burden of calculating some of the "modern" methods, making them amenable to real-time implementation. The architecture of some of these fast algorithms is now influencing the design of VLSI signal processing chips. Extension of the parametric methods to third- and higher-order statistics is just beginning, generating new spectral quantities such as the bispectrum and the trispectrum.

An area receiving little attention at present is the testing of the current PSD estimation methods for robustness of performance with a larger class of signals. The classic one, two, or three sinusoids in white noise test sequence continues to predominate spectral estimation research. Characterizing the performance is also needed. Much of the research of the last two decades has focused on spectral analysis of narrowband signals. More effort needs to be directed towards spectral analysis of wideband signals and signals buried deeper in noise. More research into multi-dimensional spectral analysis is needed in order to produce practical algorithms for large data array applications and to characterize the performance for signals other than sinusoids.

I

APPENDIX
SUNSPOT NUMBERS

The international relative sunspot numbers R_I were provided by courtesy of Dr. Paul Fougere of the U.S. Air Force Geophysics Lab. Additional information on sunspot numbers may be found in Waldmeir [1961] and Chernosky and Hogan [1958]. Recent sunspot activity is published monthly in the journal *Sky and Telescope*. The values of R_I were originally reported by the Federal Observatory in Zurich, Switzerland. Starting in 1980, they have been reported by the Sunspot Index Data Center in Brussels, Belgium. Only the R_I numbers since 1835 should be considered as reliable values; numbers prior to 1835 are of lesser measurement quality and should be used with care.

REFERENCES

Chernosky, E. J., and M. P. Hogan, The Zurich Sunspot Number and Its Variations for 1700–1957, *J. Geophys. Res.*, vol. 63, pp. 775–788, December 1958.

Waldmeir, M., *The Sunspot Activity in the Years 1610–1960*, Schulthess and Co., Zurich, 1961.

MONTHLY RELATIVE SUNSPOT NUMBERS

YEAR	JAN	FEB	MAR	APR	MAY	JUN	JUL	AUG	SEP	OCT	NOV	DEC
1700	6.0	6.0	6.0	6.0	6.0	6.0	6.0	6.0	6.0	6.0	6.0	6.0
1701	11.0	11.0	11.0	11.0	11.0	11.0	11.0	11.0	11.0	11.0	11.0	11.0
1702	17.0	17.0	17.0	17.0	17.0	17.0	17.0	17.0	17.0	17.0	17.0	17.0
1703	23.0	23.0	23.0	23.0	23.0	23.0	23.0	23.0	23.0	23.0	23.0	23.0
1704	35.0	35.0	35.0	35.0	35.0	35.0	35.0	35.0	35.0	35.0	35.0	35.0
1705	54.0	54.0	54.0	54.0	54.0	54.0	54.0	54.0	54.0	54.0	54.0	54.0
1706	29.0	29.0	29.0	29.0	29.0	29.0	29.0	29.0	29.0	29.0	29.0	29.0
1707	21.0	21.0	21.0	21.0	21.0	21.0	21.0	21.0	21.0	21.0	21.0	21.0
1708	11.0	11.0	11.0	11.0	11.0	11.0	11.0	11.0	11.0	11.0	11.0	11.0
1709	8.0	8.0	8.0	8.0	8.0	8.0	8.0	8.0	8.0	8.0	8.0	8.0
1710	3.0	3.0	3.0	3.0	3.0	3.0	3.0	3.0	3.0	3.0	3.0	3.0
1711	0.0	0.0	0.0	0.0	0.0	0.0	0.0	0.0	0.0	0.0	0.0	0.0
1712	0.0	0.0	0.0	0.0	0.0	0.0	0.0	0.0	0.0	0.0	0.0	0.0
1713	2.0	2.0	2.0	2.0	2.0	2.0	2.0	2.0	2.0	2.0	2.0	2.0
1714	11.0	11.0	11.0	11.0	11.0	11.0	11.0	11.0	11.0	11.0	11.0	11.0
1715	27.0	27.0	27.0	27.0	27.0	27.0	27.0	27.0	27.0	27.0	27.0	27.0
1716	44.0	44.0	44.0	44.0	44.0	44.0	44.0	44.0	44.0	44.0	44.0	44.0
1717	58.0	58.0	58.0	58.0	58.0	58.0	58.0	58.0	58.0	58.0	58.0	58.0
1718	56.0	56.0	56.0	56.0	56.0	56.0	56.0	56.0	56.0	56.0	56.0	56.0
1719	38.0	38.0	38.0	38.0	38.0	38.0	38.0	38.0	38.0	38.0	38.0	38.0
1720	28.0	28.0	28.0	28.0	28.0	28.0	28.0	28.0	28.0	28.0	28.0	28.0
1721	26.0	26.0	26.0	26.0	26.0	26.0	26.0	26.0	26.0	26.0	26.0	26.0
1722	22.0	22.0	22.0	22.0	22.0	22.0	22.0	22.0	22.0	22.0	22.0	22.0
1723	11.0	11.0	11.0	11.0	11.0	11.0	11.0	11.0	11.0	11.0	11.0	11.0
1724	22.0	22.0	22.0	22.0	22.0	22.0	22.0	22.0	22.0	22.0	22.0	22.0
1725	38.0	38.0	38.0	38.0	38.0	38.0	38.0	38.0	38.0	38.0	38.0	38.0
1726	74.0	74.0	74.0	74.0	74.0	74.0	74.0	74.0	74.0	74.0	74.0	74.0
1727	113.0	113.0	113.0	113.0	113.0	113.0	113.0	113.0	113.0	113.0	113.0	113.0
1728	98.0	98.0	98.0	98.0	98.0	98.0	98.0	98.0	98.0	98.0	98.0	98.0
1729	67.0	67.0	67.0	67.0	67.0	67.0	67.0	67.0	67.0	67.0	67.0	67.0
1730	44.0	44.0	44.0	44.0	44.0	44.0	44.0	44.0	44.0	44.0	44.0	44.0
1731	28.0	28.0	28.0	28.0	28.0	28.0	28.0	28.0	28.0	28.0	28.0	28.0
1732	11.0	11.0	11.0	11.0	11.0	11.0	11.0	11.0	11.0	11.0	11.0	11.0
1733	6.0	6.0	6.0	6.0	6.0	6.0	6.0	6.0	6.0	6.0	6.0	6.0
1734	17.0	17.0	17.0	17.0	17.0	17.0	17.0	17.0	17.0	17.0	17.0	17.0
1735	33.0	33.0	33.0	33.0	33.0	33.0	33.0	33.0	33.0	33.0	33.0	33.0
1736	64.0	64.0	64.0	64.0	64.0	64.0	64.0	64.0	64.0	64.0	64.0	64.0
1737	77.0	77.0	77.0	77.0	77.0	77.0	77.0	77.0	77.0	77.0	77.0	77.0
1738	106.0	106.0	106.0	106.0	106.0	106.0	106.0	106.0	106.0	106.0	106.0	106.0
1739	96.0	96.0	96.0	96.0	96.0	96.0	96.0	96.0	96.0	96.0	96.0	96.0
1740	67.0	67.0	67.0	67.0	67.0	67.0	67.0	67.0	67.0	67.0	67.0	67.0
1741	39.0	39.0	39.0	39.0	39.0	39.0	39.0	39.0	39.0	39.0	39.0	39.0
1742	20.0	20.0	20.0	20.0	20.0	20.0	20.0	20.0	20.0	20.0	20.0	20.0
1743	16.0	16.0	16.0	16.0	16.0	16.0	16.0	16.0	16.0	16.0	16.0	16.0
1744	6.0	6.0	6.0	6.0	6.0	6.0	6.0	6.0	6.0	6.0	6.0	6.0
1745	11.0	11.0	11.0	11.0	11.0	11.0	11.0	11.0	11.0	11.0	11.0	11.0
1746	22.0	22.0	22.0	22.0	22.0	22.0	22.0	22.0	22.0	22.0	22.0	22.0
1747	39.0	39.0	39.0	39.0	39.0	39.0	39.0	39.0	39.0	39.0	39.0	39.0
1748	56.0	56.0	56.0	56.0	56.0	56.0	56.0	56.0	56.0	56.0	56.0	56.0
1749	58.0	62.6	70.0	55.7	85.0	83.5	94.8	66.3	75.9	75.5	158.6	85.2

MONTHLY RELATIVE SUNSPOT NUMBERS

YEAR	JAN	FEB	MAR	APR	MAY	JUN	JUL	AUG	SEP	OCT	NOV	DEC
1750	73.3	75.9	89.2	88.3	90.0	100.0	85.4	103.0	91.2	65.7	63.3	75.4
1751	70.0	43.5	45.3	56.4	60.7	50.7	66.3	59.8	23.5	23.2	28.5	44.0
1752	35.0	50.0	71.0	59.3	59.7	39.6	78.4	29.3	27.1	46.6	37.6	40.0
1753	44.0	32.0	45.7	38.0	36.0	31.7	22.0	39.0	28.0	25.0	20.0	6.7
1754	0.0	3.0	1.7	13.7	20.7	26.7	18.8	12.3	8.2	24.1	13.2	4.2
1755	10.2	11.2	6.8	6.5	0.0	0.0	8.6	3.2	17.8	23.7	6.8	20.0
1756	12.5	7.1	5.4	9.4	12.5	12.9	3.6	6.4	11.8	14.3	17.0	9.4
1757	14.1	21.2	26.2	30.0	38.1	12.8	25.0	51.3	39.7	32.5	64.7	33.5
1758	37.6	52.0	49.0	72.3	46.4	45.0	44.0	38.7	62.5	37.7	43.0	43.0
1759	48.3	44.0	46.8	47.0	49.0	50.0	51.0	71.3	77.2	59.7	46.3	57.0
1760	67.3	59.5	74.7	58.3	72.0	48.3	66.0	75.6	61.3	50.6	59.7	61.0
1761	70.0	91.0	80.7	71.7	107.2	99.3	94.1	91.1	100.7	88.7	89.7	46.0
1762	43.8	72.8	45.7	60.2	39.9	77.1	33.8	67.7	68.5	69.3	77.8	77.2
1763	56.5	31.9	34.2	32.9	32.7	35.8	54.2	26.5	68.1	46.3	60.9	61.4
1764	59.7	59.7	40.2	34.4	44.3	30.0	30.0	30.0	28.2	28.0	26.0	25.7
1765	24.0	26.0	25.0	22.0	20.2	20.0	27.0	29.7	16.0	14.0	14.0	13.0
1766	12.0	11.0	36.6	6.0	26.8	3.0	3.3	4.0	4.3	5.0	5.7	19.2
1767	27.4	30.0	43.0	32.9	29.8	33.3	21.9	40.8	42.7	44.1	54.7	53.3
1768	53.5	66.1	46.3	42.7	77.7	77.4	52.6	66.8	74.8	77.8	90.6	111.8
1769	73.9	64.2	64.3	96.7	73.6	94.4	118.6	120.3	148.8	158.2	148.1	112.0
1770	104.0	142.5	80.1	51.0	70.1	83.3	109.8	126.3	104.4	103.6	132.2	102.3
1771	36.0	46.2	46.7	64.9	152.7	119.5	67.7	58.5	101.4	90.0	99.7	95.7
1772	100.9	90.8	31.1	92.2	38.0	57.0	77.3	56.2	50.5	78.6	61.3	64.0
1773	54.6	29.0	51.2	32.9	41.1	28.4	27.7	12.7	29.3	26.3	40.9	43.2
1774	46.8	65.4	55.7	43.8	51.3	28.5	17.5	6.6	7.9	14.0	17.7	12.2
1775	4.4	0.0	11.6	11.2	3.9	12.3	1.0	7.9	3.2	5.6	15.1	7.9
1776	21.7	11.6	6.3	21.8	11.2	19.0	1.0	24.2	16.0	30.0	35.0	40.0
1777	45.0	36.5	39.0	95.5	80.3	80.7	95.0	112.0	116.2	106.5	146.0	157.3
1778	177.3	109.3	134.0	145.0	238.9	171.6	153.0	140.0	171.7	156.3	150.3	105.0
1779	114.7	165.7	118.0	145.0	140.0	113.7	143.0	112.0	111.0	124.0	114.0	110.0
1780	70.0	98.0	98.0	95.0	107.2	88.0	86.0	86.0	93.7	77.0	60.0	58.7
1781	98.7	74.7	53.0	68.3	104.7	97.7	73.5	66.0	51.0	27.3	67.0	35.2
1782	54.0	37.5	37.0	41.0	54.3	38.0	37.0	44.0	34.0	23.2	31.5	30.0
1783	28.0	38.7	26.7	28.3	23.0	25.2	32.2	20.0	18.0	8.0	15.0	10.5
1784	13.0	8.0	11.0	10.0	6.0	9.0	6.0	10.0	10.0	8.0	17.0	14.0
1785	6.5	8.0	9.0	15.7	20.7	26.3	36.3	20.0	32.0	47.2	40.2	27.3
1786	37.2	47.6	47.7	85.4	92.3	59.0	83.0	89.7	111.5	112.3	116.0	112.7
1787	134.7	106.0	87.4	127.2	134.8	99.2	128.0	137.2	157.3	157.0	141.5	174.0
1788	138.0	129.2	143.3	108.5	113.0	154.2	141.5	136.0	141.0	142.0	94.7	129.5
1789	114.0	125.3	120.0	123.3	123.5	120.0	117.0	103.0	112.0	89.7	134.0	135.5
1790	103.0	127.5	96.3	94.0	93.0	91.0	69.3	87.0	77.3	84.3	82.0	74.0
1791	72.7	62.0	74.0	77.2	73.7	64.2	71.0	43.0	66.5	61.7	67.0	66.0
1792	58.0	64.0	63.0	75.7	62.0	61.0	45.8	60.0	59.0	59.0	57.0	56.0
1793	56.0	55.0	55.5	53.0	52.3	51.0	50.0	29.3	24.0	47.0	44.0	45.7
1794	45.0	44.0	38.0	28.4	55.7	41.5	41.0	40.0	11.1	28.5	67.4	51.4
1795	21.4	39.9	12.6	18.6	31.0	17.1	12.9	25.7	13.5	19.5	25.0	18.0
1796	22.0	23.8	15.7	31.7	21.0	6.7	26.9	1.5	18.4	11.0	8.4	5.1
1797	14.4	4.2	4.0	4.0	7.3	11.1	4.3	6.0	5.7	6.9	5.8	3.0
1798	2.0	4.0	12.4	1.1	0.0	0.0	0.0	3.0	2.4	1.5	12.5	9.9
1799	1.6	12.6	21.7	8.4	8.2	10.6	2.1	0.0	0.0	4.6	2.7	8.6

MONTHLY RELATIVE SUNSPOT NUMBERS

YEAR	JAN	FEB	MAR	APR	MAY	JUN	JUL	AUG	SEP	OCT	NOV	DEC
1800	6.9	9.3	13.9	0.0	5.0	23.7	21.0	19.5	11.5	12.3	10.5	40.1
1801	27.0	29.0	30.0	31.0	32.0	31.2	35.0	38.7	33.5	32.6	39.8	48.2
1802	47.8	47.0	40.8	42.0	44.0	46.0	48.0	50.0	51.8	38.5	34.5	50.0
1803	50.0	50.8	29.5	25.0	44.3	36.0	48.3	34.1	45.3	54.3	51.0	48.0
1804	45.3	48.3	48.0	50.6	33.4	34.8	29.8	43.1	53.0	62.3	61.0	60.0
1805	61.0	44.1	51.4	37.5	39.0	40.5	37.6	42.7	44.4	29.4	41.0	38.3
1806	39.0	29.6	32.7	27.7	26.4	25.6	30.0	26.3	24.0	27.0	25.0	24.0
1807	12.0	12.2	9.6	23.8	10.0	12.0	12.7	12.0	5.7	8.0	2.6	0.0
1808	0.0	4.5	0.0	12.3	13.5	13.5	6.7	8.0	11.7	4.7	10.5	12.3
1809	7.2	9.2	0.9	2.5	2.0	7.7	0.3	0.2	0.4	0.0	0.0	0.0
1810	0.0	0.0	0.0	0.0	0.0	0.0	0.0	0.0	0.0	0.0	0.0	0.0
1811	0.0	0.0	0.0	0.0	0.0	0.0	6.6	0.0	2.4	6.1	0.8	1.1
1812	11.3	1.9	0.7	0.0	1.0	1.3	0.5	15.6	5.2	3.9	7.9	10.1
1813	0.0	10.3	1.9	16.6	5.5	11.2	18.3	8.4	15.3	27.8	16.7	14.3
1814	22.2	12.0	5.7	23.8	5.8	14.9	18.5	2.3	8.1	19.3	14.5	20.1
1815	19.2	32.2	26.2	31.6	9.8	55.9	35.5	47.2	31.5	33.5	37.2	65.0
1816	26.3	68.8	73.7	58.8	44.3	43.6	38.8	23.2	47.8	56.4	38.1	29.9
1817	36.4	57.9	96.2	26.4	21.2	40.0	50.0	45.0	36.7	25.6	28.9	28.4
1818	34.9	22.4	29.7	34.5	53.1	36.4	28.0	31.5	26.1	31.7	10.9	25.8
1819	32.5	20.7	3.7	20.2	19.6	35.0	31.4	26.1	14.9	27.5	25.1	30.6
1820	19.2	26.6	4.5	19.4	29.3	10.8	20.6	25.9	5.2	9.0	7.9	9.7
1821	21.5	4.3	5.7	9.2	1.7	1.8	2.5	4.8	4.4	18.8	4.4	0.0
1822	0.0	0.9	16.1	13.5	1.5	5.6	7.9	2.1	0.0	0.4	0.0	0.0
1823	0.0	0.0	0.6	0.0	0.0	0.0	0.5	0.0	0.0	0.0	0.0	20.4
1824	21.6	10.8	0.0	19.4	2.8	0.0	0.0	1.4	20.5	25.2	0.0	0.8
1825	5.0	15.5	22.4	3.8	15.4	15.4	30.9	25.4	15.7	15.6	11.7	22.0
1826	17.7	18.2	36.7	24.0	32.4	37.1	52.5	39.6	18.9	50.6	39.5	68.1
1827	34.6	47.4	57.8	46.0	56.3	56.7	42.9	53.7	49.6	57.2	48.2	46.1
1828	52.8	64.4	65.0	61.1	89.1	98.0	54.3	76.4	50.4	34.7	57.0	46.9
1829	43.0	49.4	72.3	95.0	67.5	73.9	90.8	78.3	52.8	57.2	67.6	56.5
1830	52.2	72.1	84.6	107.1	66.3	65.1	43.9	50.7	62.1	84.4	81.2	82.1
1831	47.5	50.1	93.4	54.6	38.1	33.4	45.2	54.9	37.9	46.2	43.5	28.9
1832	30.9	55.5	55.1	26.9	41.3	26.7	13.9	8.9	8.2	21.1	14.3	27.5
1833	11.3	14.9	11.8	2.8	12.9	1.0	7.0	5.7	11.6	7.5	5.9	9.9
1834	4.9	18.1	3.9	1.4	8.8	7.8	8.7	4.0	11.5	24.8	30.5	34.5
1835	7.5	24.5	19.7	61.5	43.6	33.2	59.8	59.0	100.8	95.2	100.0	77.5
1836	88.6	107.6	98.1	142.9	111.4	124.7	116.7	107.8	95.1	137.4	120.9	206.2
1837	188.0	175.6	134.6	138.2	111.3	158.0	162.8	134.0	96.3	123.7	107.0	129.8
1838	144.9	84.8	140.8	126.6	137.6	94.5	108.2	78.8	73.6	90.8	77.4	79.8
1839	107.6	102.5	77.7	61.8	53.8	54.6	84.7	131.2	132.7	90.8	68.8	63.6
1840	81.2	87.7	55.5	65.9	69.2	48.5	60.7	57.8	74.0	49.8	54.3	53.7
1841	24.0	29.9	29.7	42.6	67.4	55.7	30.8	39.3	35.1	28.5	19.8	38.8
1842	20.4	22.1	21.7	26.9	24.9	20.5	12.6	26.5	18.5	38.1	40.5	17.6
1843	13.3	3.5	8.3	8.8	21.1	10.5	9.5	11.8	4.2	5.3	19.1	12.7
1844	9.4	14.7	13.6	20.8	12.0	3.7	21.2	23.9	6.9	21.5	10.7	21.6
1845	25.7	43.6	43.3	56.9	47.8	31.1	30.6	32.3	29.6	40.7	39.4	59.7
1846	38.7	51.0	63.9	69.2	59.9	65.1	46.5	54.8	107.1	55.9	60.4	65.5
1847	62.6	44.9	85.7	44.7	75.4	85.3	52.2	140.6	161.2	180.4	138.9	109.6
1848	159.1	111.8	108.9	107.1	102.2	123.8	139.2	132.5	100.3	132.4	114.6	159.9
1849	156.7	131.7	96.5	102.5	80.6	81.2	78.0	61.3	93.7	71.5	99.7	97.0

MONTHLY RELATIVE SUNSPOT NUMBERS

YEAR	JAN	FEB	MAR	APR	MAY	JUN	JUL	AUG	SEP	OCT	NOV	DEC
1850	78.0	89.4	82.6	44.1	61.6	70.0	39.1	61.6	86.2	71.0	54.8	60.0
1851	75.5	105.4	64.6	56.5	62.6	63.2	36.1	57.4	67.9	62.5	50.9	71.4
1852	68.4	67.5	61.2	65.4	54.9	46.9	42.0	39.7	37.5	67.3	54.3	45.4
1853	41.1	42.9	37.7	47.6	34.7	40.0	45.9	50.4	33.5	42.3	28.8	23.4
1854	15.4	20.0	20.7	26.4	24.0	21.1	18.7	15.8	22.4	12.7	28.2	21.4
1855	12.3	11.4	17.4	4.4	9.1	5.3	0.4	3.1	0.0	9.7	4.2	3.1
1856	0.5	4.9	0.4	6.5	0.0	5.0	4.6	5.9	4.4	4.5	7.7	7.2
1857	13.7	7.4	5.2	11.1	29.2	16.0	22.2	16.9	42.4	40.6	31.4	37.2
1858	39.0	34.9	57.5	38.3	41.4	44.5	56.7	55.3	80.1	91.2	51.9	66.9
1859	83.7	87.6	90.3	85.7	91.0	87.1	95.2	106.8	105.8	114.6	97.2	81.0
1860	81.5	88.0	98.9	71.4	107.1	108.6	116.7	100.3	92.2	90.1	97.9	95.6
1861	62.3	77.8	101.0	98.5	56.8	87.8	78.0	82.5	79.9	67.2	53.7	80.5
1862	63.1	64.5	43.6	53.7	64.4	84.0	73.4	62.5	66.6	42.0	50.6	40.9
1863	48.3	56.7	66.4	40.6	53.8	40.8	32.7	48.1	22.0	39.9	37.7	41.2
1864	57.7	47.1	66.3	35.8	40.6	57.8	54.7	54.8	28.5	33.9	57.6	28.6
1865	48.7	39.3	39.5	29.4	34.5	33.6	26.8	37.8	21.6	17.1	24.6	12.8
1866	31.6	38.4	24.6	17.6	12.9	16.5	9.3	12.7	7.3	14.1	9.0	1.5
1867	0.0	0.7	9.2	5.1	2.9	1.5	5.0	4.9	9.8	13.5	9.3	25.2
1868	15.6	15.8	26.5	36.6	26.7	31.1	28.6	34.4	43.8	61.7	59.1	67.6
1869	60.9	59.3	52.7	41.0	104.0	108.4	59.2	79.6	80.6	59.4	77.4	104.3
1870	77.3	114.9	159.4	160.0	176.0	135.6	132.4	153.8	136.0	146.4	147.5	130.0
1871	88.3	125.3	143.2	162.4	145.5	91.7	103.0	110.0	80.3	89.0	105.4	90.3
1872	79.5	120.1	88.4	102.1	107.6	109.9	105.5	92.9	114.6	103.5	112.0	83.9
1873	86.7	107.0	98.3	76.2	47.9	44.8	66.9	68.2	47.5	47.4	55.4	49.2
1874	60.8	64.2	46.4	32.0	44.6	38.2	67.8	61.3	28.0	34.3	28.9	29.3
1875	14.6	22.2	33.8	29.1	11.5	23.9	12.5	14.6	2.4	12.7	17.7	9.9
1876	14.3	15.0	31.2	2.3	5.1	1.6	15.2	8.8	9.9	14.3	9.9	8.2
1877	24.4	8.7	11.7	15.8	21.2	13.4	5.9	6.3	16.4	6.7	14.5	2.3
1878	3.3	6.0	7.8	0.1	5.8	6.4	0.1	0.0	5.3	1.1	4.1	0.5
1879	0.8	0.6	0.0	6.2	2.4	4.8	7.5	10.7	6.1	12.3	12.9	7.2
1880	24.0	27.5	19.5	19.3	23.5	34.1	21.9	48.1	66.0	43.0	30.7	29.6
1881	36.4	53.2	51.5	51.7	43.5	60.5	76.9	58.0	53.2	64.0	54.8	47.3
1882	45.0	69.3	67.5	95.8	64.1	45.2	45.4	40.4	57.7	59.2	84.4	41.8
1883	60.6	46.9	42.8	82.1	32.1	76.5	80.6	46.0	52.6	83.8	84.5	75.9
1884	91.5	86.9	86.8	76.1	66.5	51.2	53.1	55.8	61.9	47.8	36.6	47.2
1885	42.8	71.8	49.8	55.0	73.0	83.7	66.5	50.0	39.6	38.7	33.3	21.7
1886	29.9	25.9	57.3	43.7	30.7	27.1	30.3	16.9	21.4	8.6	0.3	12.4
1887	10.3	13.2	4.2	6.9	20.0	15.7	23.3	21.4	7.4	6.6	6.9	20.7
1888	12.7	7.1	7.8	5.1	7.0	7.1	3.1	2.8	8.8	2.1	10.7	6.7
1889	0.8	8.5	7.0	4.3	2.4	6.4	9.7	20.6	6.5	2.1	0.2	6.7
1890	5.3	0.6	5.1	1.6	4.8	1.3	11.6	8.5	17.2	11.2	9.6	7.8
1891	13.5	22.2	10.4	20.5	41.1	48.3	58.8	33.2	53.8	51.5	41.9	32.2
1892	69.1	75.6	49.9	69.6	79.6	76.3	76.8	101.4	62.8	70.5	65.4	78.6
1893	75.0	73.0	65.7	88.1	84.7	88.2	88.8	129.2	77.9	79.7	75.1	93.8
1894	83.2	84.6	52.3	81.6	101.2	98.9	106.0	70.3	65.9	75.5	56.6	60.0
1895	63.3	67.2	61.0	76.9	67.5	71.5	47.8	68.9	57.7	67.9	47.2	70.7
1896	29.0	57.4	52.0	43.8	27.7	49.0	45.0	27.2	61.3	28.4	38.0	42.6
1897	40.6	29.4	29.1	31.0	20.0	11.3	27.6	21.8	48.1	14.3	8.4	33.3
1898	30.2	36.4	38.3	14.5	25.8	22.3	9.0	31.4	34.8	34.4	30.9	12.6
1899	19.5	9.2	18.1	14.2	7.7	20.5	13.5	2.9	8.4	13.0	7.8	10.5

MONTHLY RELATIVE SUNSPOT NUMBERS

YEAR	JAN	FEB	MAR	APR	MAY	JUN	JUL	AUG	SEP	OCT	NOV	DEC
1900	9.4	13.6	8.6	16.0	15.2	12.1	8.3	4.3	8.3	12.9	4.5	0.3
1901	0.2	2.4	4.5	0.0	10.2	5.8	0.7	1.0	0.6	3.7	3.8	0.0
1902	5.2	0.0	12.4	0.0	2.8	1.4	0.9	2.3	7.6	16.3	10.3	1.1
1903	8.3	17.0	13.5	26.1	14.6	16.3	27.9	28.8	11.1	38.9	44.5	45.6
1904	31.6	24.5	37.2	43.0	39.5	41.9	50.6	58.2	30.1	54.2	38.0	54.6
1905	54.8	85.8	56.5	39.3	48.0	49.0	73.0	58.8	55.0	78.7	107.2	55.5
1906	45.5	31.3	64.5	55.3	57.7	63.2	103.3	47.7	56.1	17.8	38.9	64.7
1907	76.4	108.2	60.7	52.6	43.0	40.4	49.7	54.3	85.0	65.4	61.5	47.3
1908	39.2	33.9	28.7	57.6	40.8	48.1	39.5	90.5	86.9	32.3	45.5	39.5
1909	56.7	46.6	66.3	32.3	36.0	22.6	35.8	23.1	38.8	58.4	55.8	54.2
1910	26.4	31.5	21.4	8.4	22.2	12.3	14.1	11.5	26.2	38.3	4.9	5.8
1911	3.4	9.0	7.8	16.5	9.0	2.2	3.5	4.0	4.0	2.6	4.2	2.2
1912	0.3	0.0	4.9	4.5	4.4	4.1	3.0	0.3	9.5	4.6	1.1	6.4
1913	2.3	2.9	0.5	0.9	0.0	0.0	1.7	0.2	1.2	3.1	0.7	3.8
1914	2.8	2.6	3.1	17.3	5.2	11.4	5.4	7.7	12.7	8.2	16.4	22.3
1915	23.0	42.3	38.8	41.3	33.0	68.8	71.6	69.6	49.5	53.5	42.5	34.5
1916	45.3	55.4	67.0	71.8	74.5	67.7	53.5	35.2	45.1	50.7	65.6	53.0
1917	74.7	71.9	94.8	74.7	114.1	114.9	119.8	154.5	129.4	72.2	96.4	129.3
1918	96.0	65.3	72.2	80.5	76.7	59.4	107.6	101.7	79.9	85.0	83.4	59.2
1919	48.1	79.5	66.5	51.8	88.1	111.2	64.7	69.0	54.7	52.8	42.0	34.9
1920	51.1	53.9	70.2	14.8	33.3	38.7	27.5	19.2	36.3	49.6	27.2	29.9
1921	31.5	28.3	26.7	32.4	22.2	33.7	41.9	22.8	17.8	18.2	17.8	20.3
1922	11.8	26.4	54.7	11.0	8.0	5.8	10.9	6.5	4.7	6.2	7.4	17.5
1923	4.5	1.5	3.3	6.1	3.2	9.1	3.5	0.5	13.2	11.6	10.0	2.8
1924	0.5	5.1	1.8	11.3	20.8	24.0	28.1	19.3	25.1	25.6	22.5	16.5
1925	5.5	23.2	18.0	31.7	42.8	47.5	38.5	37.9	60.2	69.2	58.6	98.6
1926	71.8	70.0	62.5	38.5	64.3	73.5	52.3	61.6	60.8	71.5	60.5	79.4
1927	81.6	93.0	69.6	93.5	79.1	59.1	54.9	53.8	68.4	63.1	67.2	45.2
1928	83.5	73.5	85.4	80.6	76.9	91.4	98.0	83.8	89.7	61.4	50.3	59.0
1929	68.9	64.1	50.2	52.8	58.2	71.9	70.2	65.8	34.4	54.0	81.1	108.0
1930	65.3	49.2	35.0	38.2	36.8	28.8	21.9	24.9	32.1	34.4	35.6	25.8
1931	14.6	43.1	30.0	31.2	24.6	15.3	17.4	13.0	19.0	10.0	18.7	17.8
1932	12.1	10.6	11.2	11.2	17.9	22.2	9.6	6.8	4.0	8.9	8.2	11.0
1933	12.3	22.2	10.1	2.9	3.2	5.2	2.8	0.2	5.1	3.0	0.6	0.3
1934	3.4	7.8	4.3	11.3	19.7	6.7	9.3	8.3	4.0	5.7	8.7	15.4
1935	18.9	20.5	23.1	12.2	27.3	45.7	33.9	30.1	42.1	53.2	64.2	61.5
1936	62.8	74.3	77.1	74.9	54.6	70.0	52.3	87.0	76.0	89.0	115.4	123.4
1937	132.5	128.5	83.9	109.3	116.7	130.3	145.1	137.7	100.7	124.9	74.4	88.8
1938	98.4	119.2	86.5	101.0	127.4	97.5	165.3	115.7	89.6	99.1	122.2	92.7
1939	80.3	77.4	64.6	109.1	118.3	101.0	97.6	105.8	112.6	88.1	68.1	42.1
1940	50.5	59.4	83.3	60.7	54.4	83.9	67.5	105.5	66.5	55.0	58.4	68.3
1941	45.6	44.5	46.4	32.8	29.5	59.8	66.9	60.0	65.9	46.3	38.3	33.7
1942	35.6	52.8	54.2	60.7	25.0	11.4	17.7	20.2	17.2	19.2	30.7	22.5
1943	12.4	28.9	27.4	26.1	14.1	7.6	13.2	19.4	10.0	7.8	10.2	18.8
1944	3.7	0.5	11.0	0.3	2.5	5.0	5.0	16.7	14.3	16.9	10.8	28.4
1945	18.5	12.7	21.5	32.0	30.6	36.2	42.6	25.9	34.9	68.8	46.0	27.4
1946	47.6	86.2	76.6	75.7	84.9	73.5	116.2	107.2	94.4	102.3	123.8	121.7
1947	115.7	133.4	129.8	149.8	201.3	163.9	157.9	188.8	169.4	163.6	128.0	116.5
1948	108.5	86.1	94.8	189.7	174.0	167.8	142.2	157.9	143.3	136.3	95.8	138.0
1949	119.1	182.3	157.5	147.0	106.2	121.7	125.8	123.8	145.3	131.6	143.5	117.6

MONTHLY RELATIVE SUNSPOT NUMBERS

YEAR	JAN	FEB	MAR	APR	MAY	JUN	JUL	AUG	SEP	OCT	NOV	DEC
1950	101.6	94.8	109.7	113.4	106.2	83.6	91.0	85.2	51.3	61.4	54.8	54.1
1951	59.9	59.9	55.9	92.9	108.5	100.6	61.5	61.0	83.1	51.6	52.4	45.8
1952	40.7	22.7	22.0	29.1	23.4	36.4	39.3	54.9	28.2	23.8	22.1	34.3
1953	26.5	3.9	10.0	27.8	12.5	21.8	8.6	23.5	19.3	8.2	1.6	2.5
1954	0.2	0.5	10.9	1.8	0.8	0.2	4.8	8.4	1.5	7.0	9.2	7.6
1955	23.1	20.8	4.9	11.3	28.9	31.7	26.7	40.7	42.7	58.5	89.2	76.9
1956	73.6	124.0	118.4	110.7	136.6	116.6	129.1	169.6	173.2	155.3	201.3	192.1
1957	165.0	130.2	157.4	175.2	164.6	200.7	187.2	158.0	235.8	253.8	210.9	239.4
1958	202.5	164.9	190.7	196.0	175.3	171.5	191.4	200.2	201.2	181.5	152.3	187.6
1959	217.4	143.1	185.7	163.3	172.0	168.7	149.6	199.6	145.2	111.4	124.0	125.0
1960	146.3	106.0	102.2	122.0	119.6	110.2	121.7	134.1	127.2	82.8	89.6	85.6
1961	57.9	46.1	53.0	61.4	51.0	77.4	70.2	55.8	63.6	37.7	32.6	39.9
1962	38.7	50.3	45.6	46.4	43.7	42.0	21.8	21.8	51.3	39.5	26.9	23.2
1963	19.8	24.4	17.1	29.3	43.0	35.9	19.6	33.2	38.8	35.3	23.4	14.9
1964	15.3	17.7	16.5	8.6	9.5	9.1	3.1	9.3	4.7	6.1	7.4	15.1
1965	17.5	14.2	11.7	6.8	24.1	15.9	11.9	8.9	16.8	20.1	15.8	17.0
1966	28.2	24.4	25.3	48.7	45.3	47.7	56.7	51.2	50.2	57.2	57.2	70.4
1967	110.9	93.6	111.8	69.5	86.5	67.3	91.5	107.2	76.8	88.2	94.3	126.4
1968	121.8	111.9	92.2	81.2	127.2	110.3	96.1	109.3	117.2	107.7	86.0	109.8
1969	104.3	120.5	135.8	106.8	120.0	106.0	96.8	98.0	91.3	95.7	93.5	97.9
1970	111.5	127.7	102.9	109.5	127.5	106.8	112.5	93.0	99.5	86.6	95.2	83.5
1971	91.3	79.0	60.7	71.8	57.5	49.8	81.0	61.4	50.2	51.7	63.2	82.2
1972	61.5	88.4	80.1	63.2	80.5	88.0	76.5	76.8	64.0	61.3	41.6	45.3
1973	43.4	42.9	46.0	57.7	42.4	39.5	23.1	25.6	59.3	30.7	23.9	23.3
1974	27.6	26.0	21.3	40.3	39.5	36.0	55.8	33.6	40.2	47.1	25.0	20.5
1975	18.9	11.5	11.5	5.1	9.0	11.4	28.2	39.7	13.9	9.1	19.4	7.8
1976	8.1	4.3	21.9	18.8	12.4	12.2	1.9	16.4	13.5	20.6	5.2	15.3
1977	16.4	23.1	8.7	12.9	18.6	38.5	21.4	30.1	44.0	43.8	29.1	43.2
1978	51.9	93.6	76.5	99.7	82.7	95.1	70.4	58.1	138.2	125.1	97.9	122.7
1979	166.6	137.5	138.0	101.5	134.4	149.5	159.4	142.2	188.4	186.2	183.3	176.3
1980	159.6	155.0	126.2	164.1	179.9	157.3	136.3	135.4	155.0	164.7	147.9	174.4
1981	114.0	141.3	135.5	156.4	127.5	90.9	143.8	158.7	167.3	162.4	137.5	150.1
1982	111.2	163.6	153.8	122.0	82.2	110.4	106.1	107.6	118.8	94.7	98.1	127.0
1983	84.3	51.0	66.5	80.7	99.2	91.1	82.2	71.8	50.3	55.8	33.3	33.4
1984	57.0	85.4	83.5	69.7	76.4	46.1	37.4	25.5	15.7	12.6	22.4	18.2

II

APPENDIX
COMPLEX TEST DATA

The complex-valued test data sequence consists of 64 samples of a synthetically generated process of four complex sinusoidals in colored noise. The data is listed as a complex pair of numbers. The first value is the real part and the second value is the imaginary part.

COMPLEX TEST DATA SEQUENCE

X(1) = (1.349839091. 2.011167288)
X(2) = (-2.117270231. 0.817693591)
X(3) = (-1.786421657,-1.291698933)
X(4) = (1.162236333,-1.482598066)
X(5) = (1.641072035. 0.372950256)
X(6) = (0.072213709. 1.828492761)
X(7) = (-1.564284801. 0.824533045)
X(8) = (-1.080565453,-1.869776845)
X(9) = (0.927129090,-1.743406534)
X(10) = (1.891979456. 0.972347319)
X(11) = (-0.105391249. 1.602209687)
X(12) = (-1.618367076. 0.637513280)
X(13) = (-0.945704579,-1.079569221)
X(14) = (1.135566235,-1.692269921)
X(15) = (1.855816245. 0.986030221)
X(16) = (-1.032083511. 1.414613724)
X(17) = (-1.571600199. 0.089229003)
X(18) = (-0.243143231,-1.444692016)
X(19) = (0.838980973,-0.985756695)
X(20) = (1.516003132. 0.928058863)
X(21) = (0.257979959. 1.170676708)
X(22) = (-2.057927608. 0.343388647)
X(23) = (-0.578682184,-1.441192508)
X(24) = (1.584011555,-1.011150956)
X(25) = (0.614114344. 1.508176208)
X(26) = (-0.710567117. 1.130144477)
X(27) = (-1.100205779,-0.584209621)
X(28) = (0.150702029,-1.217450142)
X(29) = (0.748856127,-0.804411888)
X(30) = (0.795235813. 1.114466429)
X(31) = (-0.071512341. 1.017092347)
X(32) = (-1.732939839,-0.283070654)

X(33) = (0.404945314,-0.781708360)
X(34) = (1.293794155,-0.352723092)
X(35) = (-0.119905084. 0.905150294)
X(36) = (-0.522588372. 0.437393665)
X(37) = (-0.974838495,-0.670074046)
X(38) = (0.275279552,-0.509659231)
X(39) = (0.854210198,-0.008278057)
X(40) = (0.289598197. 0.506233990)
X(41) = (-0.283553183. 0.250371397)
X(42) = (-0.359602571,-0.135261074)
X(43) = (0.102775671,-0.466086507)
X(44) = (-0.009722650. 0.030377999)
X(45) = (0.185930878. 0.808869600)
X(46) = (-0.243692726,-0.200126961)
X(47) = (-0.270986766,-0.460243553)
X(48) = (0.399368525. 0.249096692)
X(49) = (-0.250714004,-0.362990230)
X(50) = (0.419116348,-0.389185309)
X(51) = (-0.050458215. 0.702862442)
X(52) = (-0.395043731. 0.140808776)
X(53) = (0.746575892,-0.126762003)
X(54) = (-0.559076190. 0.523169816)
X(55) = (-0.344389260,-0.913451135)
X(56) = (0.733228028,-0.006237417)
X(57) = (-0.480273813. 0.509469569)
X(58) = (0.033316225. 0.087501869)
X(59) = (-0.321229130,-0.254548967)
X(60) = (-0.063007891,-0.499800682)
X(61) = (1.239739418,-0.013479125)
X(62) = (0.083303742. 0.673984587)
X(63) = (-0.762731433. 0.408971250)
X(64) = (-0.895898521,-0.364855707)

III

APPENDIX
TEMPERATURE DATA

This appendix is a table of the monthly mean St. Louis, Missouri, temperature in degrees Celsius for the years 1845 to 1978. The data is used for the multichannel spectral estimation techniques discussed in Chap. 15. The data was provided by courtesy of Dr. Robert G. Currie of State University of New York, Stonybrook, New York.

MONTHLY MEAN TEMPERATURE

YEAR	JAN	FEB	MAR	APR	MAY	JUN	JUL	AUG	SEP	OCT	NOV	DEC
1845	4.1	5.6	7.1	16.9	17.4	23.4	26.4	24.8	22.7	12.4	5.2	-3.6
1846	3.1	-1.4	7.9	13.8	20.7	21.7	27.1	25.6	22.8	12.7	6.8	3.5
1847	-3.6	1.4	4.2	14.3	17.2	22.4	25.9	23.4	20.2	12.6	6.7	0.4
1848	2.9	3.8	6.2	11.7	19.8	22.7	24.0	23.7	17.5	12.6	3.1	-0.4
1849	-2.9	-1.3	8.7	12.1	18.1	24.4	23.8	23.1	19.7	10.9	10.1	-1.7
1850	1.8	1.8	5.8	9.4	16.9	24.6	26.6	26.4	20.1	12.9	7.7	-0.7
1851	1.2	3.0	8.4	10.9	19.9	22.6	25.7	24.6	22.2	12.9	4.4	-1.3
1852	-2.4	2.7	8.4	11.2	19.3	22.2	25.8	23.1	19.9	16.0	3.6	1.2
1853	0.8	0.1	5.7	13.4	17.9	25.6	24.2	24.7	20.6	11.0	8.4	0.3
1854	-2.9	3.3	8.2	13.3	19.4	24.1	28.2	27.6	24.2	15.6	5.7	2.0
1855	0.1	-2.2	3.3	16.0	18.6	21.7	25.9	23.1	22.3	11.4	7.6	-0.7
1856	-7.6	-3.9	1.6	14.6	18.6	25.2	28.0	23.0	18.7	14.9	4.4	-1.5
1857	-7.2	5.3	4.1	6.7	16.2	22.1	26.0	24.5	21.6	12.4	3.8	4.6
1858	4.6	-2.8	8.7	14.1	17.4	24.3	27.5	25.7	21.6	14.6	3.0	3.3
1859	0.6	2.9	9.0	10.8	19.8	22.1	25.7	24.1	18.8	11.6	8.2	1.2
1860	0.4	2.7	9.2	14.2	21.1	23.0	27.1	25.7	19.8	15.1	5.6	-0.4
1861	0.2	4.7	6.9	14.2	17.4	24.2	24.9	25.1	20.2	13.9	7.8	4.2
1862	-1.3	3.3	6.7	12.3	20.2	22.8	26.2	26.1	21.6	13.5	5.3	5.1
1863	3.0	2.0	6.8	13.7	18.9	20.8	24.1	24.1	19.7	8.3	6.2	2.1
1864	-1.6	3.2	4.7	10.4	19.8	24.9	27.9	24.8	21.4	10.8	6.6	-1.1
1865	-2.0	3.2	7.9	13.2	19.4	25.2	24.0	24.4	24.3	14.3	8.8	-0.4
1866	0.3	0.7	5.7	15.6	17.8	23.2	27.3	23.7	17.4	14.3	7.7	0.9
1867	-3.4	4.3	0.9	13.2	15.6	25.2	25.8	26.1	21.9	14.3	9.1	2.1
1868	-3.4	1.5	10.1	10.4	18.9	23.3	28.6	23.7	17.7	12.9	6.9	-1.7
1869	3.7	2.8	3.7	12.3	17.9	21.9	25.1	26.3	19.5	8.8	4.5	0.6
1870	0.9	2.3	4.4	13.6	20.3	23.1	26.6	24.0	21.7	14.7	8.2	-0.6
1871	3.2	4.4	10.5	15.8	20.4	26.5	26.6	25.6	18.9	15.0	4.3	-2.1
1872	-2.1	0.1	3.2	14.1	19.7	24.7	26.2	26.4	21.0	14.1	3.6	-3.7
1873	-3.6	0.8	5.7	10.7	18.5	25.6	25.7	25.9	19.4	11.2	5.2	2.8
1874	1.7	2.2	6.5	8.8	20.8	26.3	27.8	26.0	21.4	14.6	6.7	3.0
1875	-4.6	-3.4	4.4	11.4	18.4	23.1	26.3	23.2	19.8	12.6	5.3	6.3
1876	5.2	4.8	4.3	14.2	19.7	23.0	26.6	25.6	19.6	13.3	4.9	-4.0
1877	-0.4	5.2	3.5	12.6	17.8	23.8	26.0	24.7	21.2	15.5	5.7	8.8
1878	2.1	5.0	12.2	16.4	17.7	23.0	27.9	26.4	20.8	13.8	8.4	-2.8
1879	-2.1	1.0	8.8	12.8	20.7	23.2	27.3	24.1	18.6	16.9	8.2	0.1
1880	7.6	3.9	6.1	14.2	21.1	23.2	26.2	25.3	19.3	12.7	-0.1	-2.8
1881	-5.8	5.3	3.6	10.5	21.8	24.1	27.5	28.4	24.3	16.2	6.5	4.8
1882	0.0	6.6	8.4	14.4	15.5	23.2	23.5	23.7	20.4	16.2	7.0	0.1
1883	-4.9	-0.4	3.6	13.4	16.8	22.4	24.8	23.0	19.7	13.2	98	4.1
1884	-3.5	1.9	6.4	12.1	18.3	22.9	25.4	23.9	23.6	17.2	8.4	0.4
1885	-3.4	-2.8	5.1	13.7	18.5	23.3	27.2	24.0	20.5	13.3	8.8	3.8
1886	-4.1	1.7	6.9	15.2	21.0	23.7	27.2	26.9	22.6	16.7	7.6	-1.3
1887	-0.7	4.7	7.7	16.1	17.2	25.4	29.0	26.6	21.4	12.6	7.1	-0.3
1888	-4.3	0.1	4.9	15.0	17.5	23.1	26.4	23.7	19.0	12.5	6.9	3.3
1889	1.4	-0.5	7.9	14.2	17.6	21.3	25.3	24.0	19.2	12.6	5.1	9.8
1890	3.9	4.4	3.7	13.8	17.6	26.2	26.4	23.6	18.1	13.8	9.1	3.0
1891	2.4	2.0	3.7	14.7	17.5	24.2	23.7	23.7	23.1	13.9	4.9	5.9
1892	-3.5	4.3	4.4	12.1	17.1	24.7	24.9	25.3	21.1	15.4	5.1	0.4
1893	-4.1	-0.8	6.3	13.5	17.7	23.9	26.7	24.4	22.3	14.5	6.6	2.3
1894	1.8	0.1	10.4	14.2	18.8	25.7	26.1	25.8	21.3	15.1	5.7	3.7

MONTHLY MEAN TEMPERATURE

YEAR	JAN	FEB	MAR	APR	MAY	JUN	JUL	AUG	SEP	OCT	NOV	DEC
1895	-3.3	-4.0	6.5	15.3	19.2	24.9	24.6	25.4	23.2	11.7	6.1	2.7
1896	1.6	2.5	4.6	18.1	22.7	23.2	26.0	26.2	19.9	13.7	7.7	4.8
1897	-0.9	2.5	7.9	13.2	17.4	23.9	26.9	24.8	25.0	18.8	7.7	0.3
1898	2.8	3.4	8.2	12.3	19.4	25.3	25.6	25.7	23.2	13.1	6.0	0.2
1899	0.2	-4.6	4.0	14.2	20.3	25.1	25.9	27.2	20.9	17.7	11.1	0.4
1900	2.9	-1.4	5.8	14.3	20.4	23.4	25.9	28.7	23.2	18.5	8.4	3.2
1901	2.8	-0.7	6.9	12.3	18.9	26.9	30.7	26.6	21.9	16.3	6.5	-1.1
1902	0.1	-3.3	8.0	12.8	22.1	23.3	26.7	24.6	18.9	16.5	11.7	1.0
1903	0.8	0.7	9.4	13.9	20.5	21.2	27.0	25.0	20.7	14.8	5.3	-1.3
1904	-2.4	-0.8	6.9	9.4	18.3	22.3	24.3	23.4	21.4	14.6	8.8	1 4
1905	-4.4	-4.9	9.7	13.1	19.5	24.4	24.0	25.2	21.3	13.3	7.9	1.7
1906	2.6	-0.1	0.7	15.3	19.4	22.3	24.6	25.5	22.8	13.6	6.4	2.4
1907	2.2	1.2	11.4	8.2	14.9	21.7	25.9	24.7	20.1	13.1	6.7	3.2
1908	1.0	1.1	9.7	13.2	19.3	22.8	25.3	25.2	22.8	14.1	9.1	3.7
1909	0.3	3.9	6.3	12.2	17.4	23.8	24.9	27.2	19.9	13.2	12.3	-3.2
1910	0.2	-1.7	13.9	13.1	15.9	22.3	24.8	23.9	21.1	15.7	5.4	0.0
1911	1.8	3.4	8.0	12.2	21.8	26.2	26.2	24.2	23.2	13.8	3.8	3.4
1912	-6.6	-2.4	1.8	13.8	20.1	21.2	25.9	24.4	21.3	15.7	8.4	3.6
1913	1.4	-0.2	5.4	13.2	19.6	25.7	27.0	28.2	20.8	13.2	11.2	5.0
1914	4.2	-2.7	6.2	13.4	20.7	27.2	28.3	25.9	20.7	15.7	10.0	-4.0
1915	-1.4	4.6	3.4	17.2	18.1	22.1	24.6	21.2	22.2	16.2	10.3	1.8
1916	1.1	0.3	7.0	12.3	19.9	21.8	28.9	25.8	19.9	14.8	9.4	0.8
1917	1.4	-1.1	7.9	11.9	15.8	22.8	25.9	23.9	20.3	10.3	8.6	-3.0
1918	-7.4	1.8	11.2	10.4	21.5	24.9	25.7	28.0	17.3	16.6	7.7	6.0
1919	3.1	2.4	8.2	14.0	17.2	25.1	27.4	24.9	22.9	15.7	6.9	-1.4
1920	-2.1	1.4	7.9	10.5	18.2	23.9	25.9	23.8	22.3	17.5	6.3	2.9
1921	3.9	5.4	12.0	14.3	20.2	25.7	28.3	25.2	23.3	15.1	8.3	3.6
1922	-1.1	2.3	7.7	14.4	20.7	25.6	25.9	26.1	23.0	16.5	9.2	2.5
1923	4.1	-1.1	5.0	12.6	17.8	23.9	26.9	25.4	20.3	12.4	8.7	6.8
1924	-3.1	1.8	4.1	14.5	15.2	22.9	23.8	25.6	18.1	17.8	8.5	-1.2
1925	0.4	4.7	9.0	16.8	17.3	25.7	26.0	25.6	24.9	9.4	6.2	0.3
1926	1.3	4.4	4.0	10.0	20.2	22.4	27.1	26.2	21.4	14.4	4.6	0.7
1927	-0.3	6.1	8.6	13.7	18.0	21.7	25.2	22.2	23.8	16.8	8.7	0.1
1928	1.4	2.9	7.6	11.2	19.2	20.2	26.5	25.2	19.4	16.5	7.6	3.6
1929	-2.6	-1.9	10.2	14.4	16.7	22.6	26.4	24.6	20.2	14.4	5.1	2.9
1930	-4.2	7.2	6.7	16.1	19.6	23.8	28.6	26.8	22.3	13.7	8.5	2.0
1931	3.1	5.2	4.6	13.9	17.1	26.3	27.8	25.0	24.7	16.9	12.5	7.2
1932	4.2	6.8	3.6	14.3	19.9	25.2	27.4	25.3	20.7	13.8	4.8	1.1
1933	6.3	1.6	6.9	12.9	19.5	27.5	27.2	25.3	25.0	13.8	7.6	4.4
1934	3.1	-0.5	4.7	13.7	21.7	28.0	30.6	26.6	19.0	17.1	10.1	0.7
1935	1.1	3.4	10.4	11.2	16.3	21.8	27.8	25.8	21.7	14.5	6.2	-1.1
1936	-3.8	-4.4	9.3	11.2	21.7	25.0	30.7	29.7	23.2	14.6	6.2	4.0
1937	-0.8	0.7	5.0	12.6	19.5	24.0	26.4	27.8	21.1	13.6	5.4	-0.1
1938	0.7	5.5	11.8	14.2	18.7	23.3	27.4	27.6	23.1	18.3	8.8	2.3
1939	4.6	1.2	8.8	11.6	20.6	24.4	26.9	24.6	24.7	16.7	7.3	4.0
1940	-8.3	0.9	6.2	12.4	17.7	24.4	26.7	25.7	21.9	18.4	6.6	4.3
1941	1.8	0.3	4.7	15.7	21.4	25.1	27.2	27.1	22.8	17.1	8.3	5.1
1942	0.2	0.9	8.1	15.4	18.6	23.8	26.9	24.8	20.7	15.3	9.3	0.6
1943	-0.1	4.2	4.6	12.7	17.9	25.2	27.6	27.1	19.4	14.6	6.3	0.2
1944	3.1	3.3	4.9	11.9	21.4	25.9	26.4	25.6	21.3	15.9	8.1	-1.7

MONTHLY MEAN TEMPERATURE

YEAR	JAN	FEB	MAR	APR	MAY	JUN	JUL	AUG	SEP	OCT	NOV	DEC
1945	-1.9	2.2	12.2	13.7	16.1	21.3	25.2	25.4	20.9	14.4	7.7	-2.0
1946	2.9	-2.1	2.7	13.1	17.7	22.8	24.9	29.7	22.2	19.3	5.2	3.7
1947	1.3	4.6	13.8	16.0	16.9	24.5	26.9	23.0	20.9	17.1	9.3	4.9
1948	-3.1	1.4	6.6	15.4	18.4	24.1	26.1	26.0	22.4	13.8	8.9	3.7
1949	0.6	2.7	6.7	12.3	20.6	25.3	27.0	25.5	18.4	15.9	9.4	4.9
1950	3.4	2.8	5.0	10.6	20.1	23.6	24.6	22.7	19.7	18.3	3.9	-1.4
1951	0.3	1.9	4.5	11.2	19.7	22.3	25.7	24.8	19.1	15.1	3.8	0.9
1952	2.2	4.3	5.8	12.7	18.8	28.4	27.4	24.8	21.1	12.1	7.8	2.8
1953	1.8	4.4	8.2	11.2	19.6	27.5	27.4	25.7	22.4	16.7	8.7	3.2
1954	0.4	6.6	5.6	16.7	16.4	26.3	29.4	26.7	23.7	14.9	7.7	2.6
1955	0.6	2.2	7.2	17.2	20.2	21.9	28.6	26.8	23.1	14.6	5.4	0.6
1956	-1.6	2.7	7.3	11.9	19.9	24.6	25.4	26.3	21.6	18.1	7.2	3.6
1957	-2.8	4.7	6.3	13.6	19.0	24.2	26.7	26.3	20.2	12.7	6.4	4.9
1958	-0.4	-3.7	3.3	13.2	18.9	21.9	24.7	25.3	20.6	15.1	9.4	-0.9
1959	-3.2	2.1	7.6	13.8	20.9	24.7	25.6	27.1	21.8	13.9	3.9	4.1
1960	0.8	-0.7	-0.9	14.9	17.1	23.3	24.6	26.2	23.4	15.0	8.1	-0.6
1961	-2.1	2.2	7.5	10.0	14.6	21.2	24.5	24.1	21.7	15.1	6.7	0.0
1962	-4.1	2.6	4.2	11.8	22.2	23.3	24.3	24.2	19.1	16.1	7.2	-0.4
1963	-5.9	-1.9	9.3	14.6	17.7	24.1	25.2	23.8	20.3	19.4	7.6	-5.4
1964	1.5	1.3	5.7	14.8	20.9	23.8	25.8	24.7	20.7	12.2	8.5	-0.1
1965	-0.1	1.0	1.4	14.7	21.4	23.9	24.9	24.3	20.6	13.6	9.2	5.4
1966	-3.9	0.1	8.2	10.9	16.5	23.2	28.3	23.4	18.7	12.3	8.4	1.6
1967	1.5	-0.4	9.1	14.7	16.0	23.3	23.8	22.4	19.2	14.1	5.6	1.6
1968	-0.1	-1.6	7.8	13.1	16.6	25.0	25.3	25.1	19.3	13.9	6.4	0.2
1969	-1.6	1.8	3.2	13.8	18.7	22.5	26.9	25.0	20.7	13.4	6.3	0.1
1970	-4.0	0.5	4.7	14.4	20.7	22.4	25.5	24.6	22.1	13.4	6.4	2.8
1971	-2.6	1.1	5.4	13.3	16.8	26.1	24.1	24.3	22.5	17.6	7.8	4.8
1972	-1.2	1.3	7.2	13.4	19.1	23.0	25.3	24.6	21.7	12.7	4.3	-0.9
1973	0.3	1.4	10.5	12.1	16.5	23.7	25.9	24.9	21.1	15.9	8.3	-1.1
1974	-1.2	2.3	8.9	14.2	18.3	20.8	26.6	23.6	16.8	14.3	6.7	1.1
1975	0.7	0.0	3.9	11.9	19.8	23.8	25.4	25.5	18.2	15.0	9.1	1.9
1976	-2.2	6.4	9.3	13.6	16.0	22.6	26.4	23.5	20.1	10.5	2.8	-1.9
1977	-9.4	-9.8	9.8	16.0	21.7	23.7	27.3	24.7	21.5	13.1	7.1	-0.8
1978	-6.9	-6.1	3.3	13.4	17.6	23.6	25.8	24.7	22.8	13.1	8.6	1.7

IV

APPENDIX
PROGRAM CONVERSION FOR
COMPLEX-TO-REAL CASE

FORTRAN programs provided in this text can generally be converted for real data processing, rather than complex data processing. The following six modifications will convert most programs:

Complex Program	Real Program
COMPLEX X(10),Y,etc.	REAL X(10),Y,etc.
REAL(Y)	Y
AIMAG(Y)	0. (or delete)
CONJG(Y)	Y
CABS(Y)	ABS(Y)
CABS(Y)**2	Y*Y

Alternatively, setting the imaginary part of the data array to zero and ignoring the imaginary portion of the output array(s) (which should be nearly, if not exactly, zero) will accomplish the identical results.

V

APPENDIX
LIST OF COMPUTER
PROGRAMS

The appendix where each computer program is located in shown in parentheses beside each program name.

PROGRAM NAME	FUNCTION
ARMA (10.B)	Estimate AR and MA parameters from data
ARMAPSD (6.A)	Compute PSD from ARMA, AR, or MA parameters
BURG (8.B)	Estimate AR parameters from data
CHOLESKY (3.A)	Solve Hermitian set of linear equations
CORRELATION (5.A)	Estimate autocorrelation or crosscorrelation
CORRELOGRAMPSD	Compute correlogram method PSD estimate (5.B)
COVAR (8.C)	Estimate AR parameters from data
CSVD (3.B)	Complex singular value decomposition
✓CPOLY (11.B)	Factor complex coefficient polynomial
EIGENFREQ (13.A)	Eigenanalysis spectrum by MUSIC or EV method
ESD (11.E)	Compute Prony energy spectral density
EXPARAMS (11.D)	Derive exponential parameters (Amp,Damp,Freq,Phase)
FASTRLS (9.C)	Fast recursive least squares adaptive AR
FFT (2.C)	Fast Fourier transform (forward and inverse)
HERMTOEP (3.E)	Solve Hermitian Toeplitz set of linear equations
LEVINSON (3.C)	Solve for AR parameters by Levinson algorithm
LMS (9.B)	Gradient least mean squares adaptive AR

PROGRAM NAME	FUNCTION
MA (10.A)	Estimate MA parameters from data
MCAR (15.B)	Estimate multichannel AR parameters from data
MCARPSD (15.C)	Compute multichannel PSD matrix from AR parameters
MCPERIOD (15.A)	Compute multichannel periodogram PSD matrix
MCSUPPORT (15.D)	Supporting subroutines for MCAR, MCARPSD
MINEIGVAL (3.F)	Toeplitz matrix minimum eigenvalue and eigenvector
MINVAR (12.A)	Compute minimum variance PSD estimate
MODCOVAR (8.D)	Estimate AR parameters from data
PERIODOGRAM (5.C)	Compute periodogram PSD estimate
PREFFT (2.C)	Set up exponential table for FFT
PRONY (11.C)	Estimate exponential/sinusoidal model for data
SHIFT (9.A)	Shift register for adaptive AR algorithms
SYMCOVAR (11.A)	Symmetric covariance algorithm for Prony
TOEPLITZ (3.D)	Solve Toeplitz set of linear equations
TDAR (16.B)	Estimate two-dimensional AR parameters
TDARPSD (16.C)	Compute two-dimensional AR PSD estimate
TDPERIOD (16.A)	Compute two-dimensional periodogram PSD
YULEWALKER (8.A)	Estimate AR parameters from data

INDEX